384

AN INTRODUCTION TO
MATHEMATICAL ANALYSIS

Revised Edition

By

FRANK LOXLEY GRIFFIN, Ph.D.

Professor of Mathematics, Reed College, Portland, Oregon

HOUGHTON MIFFLIN COMPANY

COPYRIGHT, 1936

The Riverside Press
CAMBRIDGE · MASSACHUSETTS
PRINTED IN THE U.S.A.

PREFACE TO ORIGINAL EDITION

UNDER the traditional plan of studying trigonometry, college algebra, analytic geometry, and calculus separately, a student can form no conception of the character and possibilities of modern mathematics, nor of the relations of its several branches as parts of a unified whole, until he has taken several successive courses. Nor can he, early enough, get the elementary working knowledge of mathematical analysis, *including integral calculus*, which is rapidly becoming indispensable for students of the natural and social sciences. Moreover, he must deal with complicated technique in each introductory course; and must study many topics apart from their uses in other subjects, thus missing their full significance and gaining little facility in drawing upon one subject for help in another.

To avoid these disadvantages of the separate-subject plan the unified course presented here has been evolved. This enables even those students who can take only one semester's work to get some idea of differential and integral calculus, trigonometry, and logarithms. And specialist students, as experience has shown, acquire an excellent command of mathematical tools by first getting a bird's-eye view of the field, and then proceeding to perfect their technique.

A regular course in calculus, following this, can proceed more rapidly than usual, include more advanced topics, and give a fine grasp: the principles and processes have become an old story. And the regular course in analytic geometry can be devoted to a genuine study of the geometrical properties of loci, since most of the type equations, basic formulas, and calculus methods are already familiar.

The materials presented here have been thoroughly tried out with the freshman classes in Reed College during the past nine years. Problems and methods which have proved unsatisfactory have been eliminated. Care has been taken to make the concepts tangible, relate them to the familiar ideas of daily life, exhibit practical applications, and develop the attitude of investigation. *E.g.*, in many "leading problems" — indicated in the text by bracketed numerals — students are asked to formulate for themselves methods not yet discussed.

The order of topics while unusual — especially in starting calculus before trigonometry — is a natural one.

We begin with graphical methods because they afford a simple and interesting means of introducing the function-concept and the big central problems — and also because they tend to develop at the very outset the self-reliant habit of attacking problems by "rough and ready" methods of approximation when no better methods are known.

Refining the graphical methods leads naturally to the calculus. After some work with this, the need for trigonometric functions is seen, and these are introduced. During the work on trigonometry, analytic geometry, etc., the continuity of the course is preserved by frequent problems which require calculus as well as these other subjects.

The intervals between the several parts of the calculus are thus a gain rather than a loss: they give the big principles a chance to emerge from the details. These principles are kept before the student during almost the entire year, notwithstanding the fact that systematic courses in trigonometry, analytic geometry, etc., are worked in.

There is, by the way, considerable analytics in the course besides what appears in Chapter VIII. (Cf. §§ 26–32, 40–41, 170–175, 244–247, 258, 268, 274–278, 296, 298, and the numerous plotting exercises in Chapters II–IV, VII, IX–XII.) But the idea of coordinates proper is not introduced until we are ready to use it in studying geometry. Up to that point the *function-concept* is the thing: we are interested simply in the *varying height of the graph*, and do not need the more subtle conception of a *relation* between the coordinates of every point along a curve — in other words, the idea of *implicit functions*.

The trigonometry also is continued for some time — the analytical portion being treated late, when needed. The transition to the general definitions when we are ready to study periodic variations is made smoothly.*

* There seems to be a widespread idea that by giving the general definitions of the functions at the outset all re-statements can be avoided. On the contrary, to adapt such definitions to the solution of triangles, re-statement in the form "(opposite side) ÷ (hypotenuse)," etc., is necessary, and the two statements must both be learned almost at the outset.

The natural difficulty in assimilating the many new ideas in the course is largely overcome by close correlation, and by the practice of assigning some review problem with advance work. This last, with frequent rapid oral quizzes reviewing recently studied material, enables us to work with each essential topic long enough to fix it clearly in mind, although proceeding rapidly. No effort is made to cover intricate points of technique or to discuss subtle niceties of logic. But we do insist upon clear ideas, grasp of the train of thought running through the course, and ability to use the processes accurately in simple cases.* Problem work in class is prominently featured.

Certain topics, *e.g.*, those treated in §§ 32, 72–73, 84, 101, 115–116, 118, 142–143, 151–154, 183, 219–221, 224, 241, 242, 281, 282, 284–286, 298–304, and Chapters XIV–XV, we have usually dealt with very briefly — but sufficiently to make them clear at the time and enable the student to pick them up again easily if he needs them later on. Still other topics, such as those of §§ 82, 155–156, 228, 275–276, 318, 320–324, are merely touched upon in lectures for the sake of extending the student's horizon and developing his imagination.

These latter topics coming mainly near the ends of chapters are mentioned without appreciably reducing the time spent upon essentials. *E.g.*, students work investment problems, in part, while studying the rest of Chapter XIII.

Any of the more advanced topics can of course be omitted if desired, and attention focused on drill work — for which an abundance of exercises is provided. Thus the presence of these topics in the text merely makes for flexibility.

The course as given at Reed College takes four hours a week through the year, the number of lessons devoted to the several chapters, when taken complete, having run about as follows: 14, 4, 14, 8, 11, 12, 11, 16, 5, 7, 10, 6, 6, 5, 4. A considerable shortening can be effected by omitting any of the chapters IX, XII–XV, or §§ 181–184, or any work on functions of functions, or many details in Chapter I.

---

* Thus we introduce, for example, the easy "short method" of setting up integrals — but only after the exact methods are familiar. And the relation of the various methods is constantly pointed out.

The course is adapted to students of widely differing prepara-tions. A knowledge of plane and solid geometry and of algebra through quadratics is the most suitable equipment; but a num-ber of students who had had only two years of secondary mathe-matics have carried the course very well. On the other hand, students who have already taken trigonometry and college algebra find in the present course very little that merely dupli-cates their former work.

The problems of the course have been collected largely from scientific, technical, and business sources. I am indebted to Miss Maurine Laber and to Miss Edna V. Johnston, alumnae of Reed College, for drawing most of the figures in Chapters I–V and VII–XIV, respectively. I am also under great obliga-tion to Professors C. S. Atchison, J. G. Hardy, W. R. Longley, and W. A. Wilson for reading the galley proofs and making valuable suggestions.

F. L. Griffin

PREFACE TO REVISED EDITION

EXPERIENCE with the earlier edition indicates that the major objectives of the course presented here are attainable, both for non-specialist students and for those who are to pursue mathematics further. In fact, the latter can under this unified plan cover in two years more advanced work than is customary under the plan of studying trigonometry, college algebra, analytic geometry, and calculus separately.*

Here, as in the earlier edition, the guiding principle in the arrangement of material, subject to the obvious requirement of orderly development, is to introduce topics *where most closely related*. This develops appreciation of interrelations, and facility in applying different subjects jointly. Also it gives the topics individually a more vital significance. The present edition, however, presents a reorganization which makes the arrangement much more *flexible*, so that even sweeping changes in order can be effected smoothly if needed.

> To illustrate: trigonometry is really something of a hybrid subject, dealing in part with triangle problems involving fixed dimensions, in part with periodic variation, cycles, etc., and in part with invariant relations between functions. It is here presented accordingly, but reorganized in such a way that instructors who so desire can without inconvenience treat all the trigonometry consecutively. If preferred, the elements of logarithms (§§132–150) can be covered in advance. Or, the trigonometry can be introduced near the beginning, after assigning §§ 1–9, 14, 23, 35.

Other major changes made in this edition are as follows: (1) Chapter I has been shortened. The discussion of formulas and varieties of functions has been moved to Chapter II and amplified. (2) The applications of trigonometry to force problems in Chapter V have been segregated. These will afford novel

---

* Cf. the author's *Mathematical Analysis, Higher Course*. For an indication of the research possibilities of undergraduates, starting with this foundation — and for the educational philosophy underlying this plan — see "The undergraduate mathematical curriculum of the liberal arts college," *The American Mathematical Monthly*, Feb., 1930, pp. 46–54. Cf. also an editorial, "The unity of mathematics," *The Scientific American*, Feb., 1924, pp. 84–85.

problems for students who have had some trigonometry previously, as will also the problems involving both calculus and trigonometry — indicated by a C, thus, 18 C. (3) An elementary treatment of determinants is given, with applications to analytic geometry and the latter has been expanded elsewhere. (4) Further statistical concepts and procedures are treated. (5) Numerous paragraphs which could be omitted without creating later difficulties are indicated by an S, thus, § 8 S. Some of these could be mentioned briefly as Supplementary Topics in lecture comment, while classes have further practice on essential topics. (6) A virtually new problem list has been provided; but the feature of "leading problems," indicated by bracketed numerals, has been retained. The range of applications has been made even broader than in the first edition. With few exceptions, answers are supplied for the odd-numbered exercises — available in a separate pamphlet.

I am under deep obligation to Professor A. A. Bennett who has read the manuscript critically and has offered numerous suggestions of great value. Professors L. D. Ames, R. C. Archibald, R. A. Johnson, and numerous other teachers and professional men have also given me many helpful ideas and comments, for which I am very grateful. I regret having been unable to adopt a number of thoughtful suggestions. My colleague, Professor Jessie M. Short, has kindly helped with the galley proofs, and has supplied some exercises for Chapter IX.

I also appreciate the continuing fine cooperation of the publishers.

F. L. GRIFFIN

CONTENTS

A PRELIMINARY WORD TO STUDENTS

I. "What It is All About." In scientific work and in daily affairs, we frequently observe that some two things seem to be *related* — that any change in the one produces some corresponding change in the other. Often it is important to ascertain *precisely how the one will change with the other.*

To illustrate: the speed of a locomotive depends in part on the amount of fuel consumed. Just how will the speed vary with the consumption of fuel? The blood-pressure in a healthy person is different at different ages. Just how should the pressure vary with the age? How should the price of corn vary with the size of the crop? Or the cost of a reservoir with the capacity? Or the speed of development of a photograph with the temperature of the developer? And so on.

Mathematical Analysis makes a systematic study of many different *modes of variation,* discovers exact relations between varying quantities, and devises suitable methods of making any necessary calculations. It has played a leading part in the modern development of the exact sciences and is being used extensively in other fields — the biological and social sciences, psychology and medicine, engineering, and business administration.

The subject is a large one, and could be studied for many years without exhausting it. But the introduction given by the present course will provide mathematical tools adequate for many kinds of scientific work. Also — what is desirable as part of a liberal education — it will give some idea of the nature and power of modern mathematics, and its important place in modern life and thought.

II. Some Suggestions as to Methods of Study. No subject can be mastered by merely receiving instruction. One must *study it actively* for himself. Where possible, try to react on each new question, and to devise some plan of your own for dealing with it.

Before studying each new lesson think over the recent work. Recall it clearly. Then, after reading the assignment, reflect

2 A PRELIMINARY WORD TO STUDENTS

upon this, too; formulate briefly in your own words just what each new process is, what it does, and why it is valid. This will save you much time in working the exercises. Study with care the examples solved in the text, as these often cover elusive points. Rework such examples for yourself, with the book laid aside: then compare.

Now and then run rapidly over in your mind an outline of the course to date, in order to see each major topic in perspective. Re-read occasionally the "summaries" of preceding chapters. Make free use of the Index, pp. 543–546, and of reference material in the Appendix.

Practice quizzing yourself. That is, think of questions which might come up in class, and see whether you can answer them. (In the first few lessons some ideas for such questions are listed, to indicate what is intended by this suggestion.) If any point is not clear, make a note of it, and ask about it or look it up soon. Note carefully the exact meaning of each new technical term that is introduced. In short, "get into the game," *actively*.

Some effort may be required for a thorough mastery of the course, but the final achievement will be well worth it.

CHAPTER I

FUNCTIONS AND GRAPHS

SOME FUNDAMENTAL PROBLEMS OF VARIATION

A. The Problem of Exhibiting Variation

§ 1. Graphs. One of the best ways of showing how a quantity varies is by means of a *graph*.

What graphs are, and how widely they are used, will be clear from the following typical examples. You will doubtless recall having seen many others in your general reading.

Fig. 1 is reproduced from an advertisement explaining low charges for transatlantic "cable letters" sent during certain hours. The height of the curve above the base line at any hour represents the rate at which messages are then being sent. Where the curve is high, much business is being dispatched; where low, little business. The fluctuations from hour to hour are portrayed far more vividly than by a statistical table.

Fig. 1.

Fig. 2 exhibits the growth of the native and foreign born populations in Portland (Ore.) from 1870 to 1910. It not only shows at a glance the comparative sizes of the two populations at any time, as represented by the heights of the two curves, but also gives an idea of the comparative rates of increase and reveals a peculiar fluctuation in the rate of increase of the foreign born.

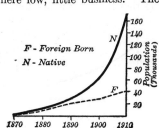

Fig. 2.

Besides showing how a quantity varies — and revealing peculiarities, as in Fig. 2 — a graph is often helpful in explaining some principle, or in studying some scientific law. Figs. 3–5 illustrate this.

Curves like those in Fig. 3 are used by economists to show how the laws of Supply and Demand together fix the selling price of a manufactured article — *e.g.*, ice-cream. Curve *S* shows how the *supply* increases with the price: *i.e.*, its height at any point shows how much would be made to sell at the price there represented. Curve *D* shows the *demand* — *i.e.*, the quantity that could be sold at each price. There is a price where demand equals supply: this is the natural selling price.

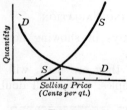

FIG. 3.

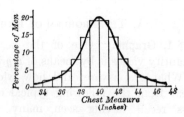

FIG. 4.

Diagrams like Fig. 4 are helpful in studying biological measurements. Here the height of each rectangle shows what percentage of soldiers in certain Scotch regiments had the chest measure indicated at the base of the rectangle. (*E.g.*, there were 18% whose measure was between 40 and 41 in.)

The height of the *curved* line shows the relative frequency with which any particular measure would be found in the long run. The fact that the curve is low toward either extreme means that the chest-measure of very few men departs widely from the average. The same is true of many other physical measurements; and probably also of mental ability.

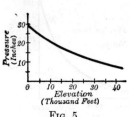

FIG. 5.

Fig. 5 shows how the atmospheric pressure decreases as the elevation above sea-level increases — under normal conditions. We see that, although the pressure continually falls, it decreases less rapidly at the greater altitudes.

Still more important: graphs are frequently used in making approximate calculations rapidly.

For example, a graph like Fig. 6 is used by a certain designer of large tanks. He can see at a glance the approximate cost of a proposed tank of any desired size, and can submit a bid at once. From other graphs he reads off the amounts of materials and labor needed.

The graphs are "ready-computers" which save many hours of tedious calculation.

The basic principle underlying all uses of graphs is this:

Points along the base line represent values of one quantity, while the varying height of the curve above the base line shows how some other quantity varies with the first.

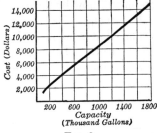

Fig. 6.

§ 2. **Function Defined.** Whenever one quantity, y, varies with another quantity, x, in some definite way, y is called a *function* of x. Thus the atmospheric pressure is a function of the elevation above sea-level; for the pressure varies with the elevation in some definite way, other things being equal. Fig. 5 shows *how* the pressure varies — in other words, shows *what sort of function* the pressure is.

We shall regard y as varying with x in a definite way — and hence as being a function of x — *if to every allowed value of x there corresponds a value of y according to a definite law or agreement.* Here y need not change continually: it may remain constant while x runs through a range of values.

Thus the postage on a letter is a function of the weight. For any weight up to 1 oz., the local postage is 2¢. For any weight from 1 oz. up to 2 oz., the postage is 4¢, jumping instantly from 2¢ to 4¢ as soon as the weight passes an exact ounce. And so on. This is a very peculiar type of function, whose graph consists of a series of horizontal lines, entirely separated.

The quantity x upon which y depends is called the *Independent Variable.* It is regarded as running freely through its values, represented horizontally in a graph, while y must take definite corresponding values, as shown by the height of the graph.

The primary use of a graph is to exhibit some quantity y as a function of some other quantity x. Thus Fig. 6 exhibits the cost of a tank as a function of the capacity.

The functions here considered are often called "one-valued," since to each x there corresponds only one value of y. Later, we shall need to study cases where there are two or more values of y for each x.

§ 3. How Graphs are Drawn. The process of drawing a graph will now be illustrated.

EXAMPLE. The amount of moisture, or weight of water vapor, that a cubic meter of air can hold depends upon the temperature. Table 1 shows the greatest amount possible at various temperatures from − 20° to + 40°, Centigrade. Plot a graph exhibiting the possible weight of vapor as a function of the temperature.

TABLE 1

TEMPERATURE (degrees)	WEIGHT (grams)	TEMPERATURE (degrees)	WEIGHT (grams)
− 20	1.0	15	12.8
− 15	1.5	20	17.2
− 10	2.3	25	22.9
− 5	3.4	30	30.1
0	4.9	35	39.3
5	6.8	40	50.9
10	9.3		

We first mark off on a horizontal line a series of points, equally spaced, and label them as in Fig. 7 to represent the temperatures shown in the table.

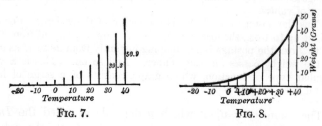

FIG. 7.   FIG. 8.

Now at 40° the weight is 50.9 gm. To show this we erect at the 40° point a vertical line-segment 50.9 units tall. (The unit may have any convenient size.) Similarly at the 35° point we erect a segment 39.3 units tall; and represent likewise all other weights given in the table.

These vertical line-segments or *"ordinates"* show roughly how the weight of vapor varies with the temperature in saturated air. The variation is shown better when we join the ends of the ordinates by a smooth curve, as in Fig. 8. This curve is the required graph.

If, at any point on the horizontal base line, representing any temperature from − 20° to 40°, we erect an ordinate, *its length up to the curve will represent the maximum weight of vapor which 1 cubic meter of air can hold at that temperature.*

Indeed, one use for the graph is just this: to ascertain by measuring ordinates how much vapor can be held by air at *other temperatures* than those given in the table.

For accuracy and convenience we use "graph paper," ruled in squares. (See Fig. 6, p. 5.)

Even a well-constructed graph, however, will not be perfect; and readings will show at least a small percentage of error. The results may, nevertheless, be entirely adequate for the particular engineering or scientific problem in hand.

§ 4. Suggestions as to Details. — Before plotting always examine the table carefully to decide upon suitable scales. The most convenient are those in which each space represents 1 unit, 10 units, or 100 units, etc. But if these would make the graph too large for the paper or too small for accurate readings, we let each space represent 2 or 20 units, etc., or $\frac{1}{2}$, 5, or 50 units, etc. In short, the essentials are: (1) a convenient number of units to each space; (2) as large a graph as possible.

Before marking off the chosen scales along the base line and some vertical line, note carefully which quantity is the *function*, to be exhibited vertically. Turning the paper afterward would make one of the scales increase in the wrong direction. The horizontal scale should always increase toward the right and the vertical scale upward. Never mind whether this makes the curve higher at the right or at the left. Run *negative values* toward the left or downward, respectively.

Make the graph *as smooth a curve as possible*: free from needless turns and abrupt changes of direction. Draw the curve lightly until it appears satisfactory. A help toward smooth drawing is to turn the paper so that your hand is on the inner or concave side of the curve.

Look for any hump or hollow in your curve, due to a value which does not fit in smoothly with the other values, and see whether you have plotted correctly.   Errors in plotting, and even errors in a table, can often be detected by merely looking carefully at the graph.

Until one has become skilled in drawing graphs free-hand, it is best not to use "French curves," compasses, and other drafting instruments.   In particular, avoid the ruler.   To make the graph a series of straight line-segments with different inclinations in successive intervals would imply abrupt changes in the growth of the quantity, quite unlike the smooth and gradual changes almost always produced by forces of nature.

Exceptions: In plotting statistics about the fluctuations of a quantity which we have no reason to suppose varies regularly, or where no meaning can be attached to ordinates erected between those given, we join the ends of the given ordinates by a series of straight lines.   The graph then merely "carries the eye."   Also, if the ends of the ordinates happen to lie exactly in a straight line, we of course use a ruler, and make the graph as straight as possible.

In plotting a graph we use in reality only the *ends* of the ordinates. In the first few exercises, however, it is desirable to draw the entire ordinates, as in Fig. 8, to fix in mind the important fact that the *varying height* is what we are really studying.

N.B. Before starting on the exercises below, try "quizzing yourself" on the foregoing ideas, as suggested on p. 2.   For instance, be clear about the following list of points.   Similar lists will be given a few more times.   After that, think up your own lists!

Points for Self-Quiz

General object of Mathematical Analysis; meaning of function, independent variable, ordinate; size and direction for scales; how to decide which quantity is to be plotted vertically; when straight lines should be used; three general ways in which graphs are utilized.

EXERCISES *

1. The distance (*D* mi.) of the horizon at sea varies with the height (*h* ft.) of the observer's eye above the water, as in Table 1. Plot *D* as a function of *h*, using scales of 5 mi. and 50 ft. How far can one see at a height of 360 ft.? How much farther at 270 ft. than at 70 ft.?

TABLE 1		TABLE 2		TABLE 3		TABLE 4		TABLE 5		TABLE 6	
h	*D*	*p*	*v*	*A*	*N*	*t*	*T*	*t*	*E*	*P*	*N*
0	0	20	525	20	4.7	0	78	1	1.0	2	100
10	3.9	25	420	30	6.0	.5	83	3	3.5	3	250
50	8.7	30	350	40	8.3	1.0	88	5	7.0	4	200
100	12.3	35	300	55	19.0	1.5	93	7	9.9	5	300
150	15.1	40	262	65	44.0	2.0	98	8	9.9	6	150
200	17.4	45	233	75	105.5	2.5	100	10	8.0	7	100
300	21.3	50	210	80	171.5	3.0	100	15	3.0	8	50
400	24.5	55	191			3.5	100	18	1.8	10	20

2. Under various pressures (*p* lb. per sq. in.) a volume of gas (*v* cu. in.) changed as in Table 2. Plot, using scales of 5 and 50 units. (Start the horizontal scale at 20; the vertical at 100 or 150.) What *p* gives *v* = 400?

3. Table 3 shows the number of days of illness during a year for an average person at various ages (*A* yr.). Plot, using scales of 10 yr. and 20 days, but starting at *A* = 20. Find *N* for age 48. Also the increase in *N* between the ages of 70 and 80.

4. As some water was heated, its temperature (*T*°, Centigrade) increased with the elapsed time as in Table 4. Plot. For what physical reason does this graph have an abrupt turn?

5. A nerve when stimulated shows a measurable electromotive force (*E*). In a frog's nerve this varied with the elapsed time (*t* ten-thousandths sec.) as in Table 5. Plot. Find *E* at *t* = 12. When was *E* = 9?

6. Table 6 shows the number of rooms (*N*) in a hotel listed at various rates ($*P* per day). Exhibit this distribution graphically. (Note the remark about exceptions to smooth plotting. § 4.)

7. In running a waterwheel the power obtained (*p* horsepower) varied with the velocity (*v* revolutions per min.) as in Table 7. Find graphically: (*A*) The value of *p* at *v* = 2200. (*B*) What velocity yields the maximum power? How much power?

---

* Use graph paper. The most convenient is that having 10 small spaces to 1 large space. Label graphs and scales plainly, and list your answers clearly in one place.

TABLE 7		TABLE 8			TABLE 9		TABLE 10		TABLE 11	
v	p	A	N	V	A	I	A	E	t	P
1200	.94	20	3690	120	20	77	10	48.7	0	1000
1500	1.06	30	2830	680	30	136	20	42.2	5	957
1800	1.15	40	2130	1860	40	164	30	35.3	10	923
2100	1.15	50	1575	3510	50	177	40	28.2	15	896
2400	1.07	60	1150	4780	60	181	50	20.9	20	875
2700	.94	70	875	5590	70	181	60	14.1	25	859
3000	.75	80	735	6060	80	178	70	8.5	30	846
3300	.51	90	676	6340	90	173	80	4.4	35	836
3600	.31	100	650	6520	100	166				

8. In a forest the number (N) of living trees per acre and the total volume (V cu. ft.) per acre, without bark, varied with the age (A yr.) as in Table 8. Plot N and V over the same base line.

9. In a good stand of fir trees the annual increase in volume (I cu. ft.) per acre varied with the age (A yr.) as in Table 9. Plot. What I at $A = 35$? When was I greatest, and how large then?

10. The number of years that an average person at any given age will live is the *expectancy* for that age. This is shown in Table 10 for various ages (A yr.). Plot E as a function of A. How much does a man's expectancy decrease between the ages of 18 and 38? When is E half as great as at age 10?

11. Table 11 shows the price ($\$P$) of a $1000 4% bond, if bought t yr. before maturity, to yield 5% on the investment. Plot. What is P if $t = 28$? For what t would $P = 900$?

12. Find some graph in the Encyclopedia Britannica, or another outside source, and state what quantity it exhibits as a function of what other.

13. Which quantity would you plot vertically if given a table showing the erosive power of a jet of water, striking at different speeds? The speed of water in a jet, at different distances from the nozzle?

14. To practice using the Index, pp. 543–46, locate the pages on which the following are defined: "acceleration," "reciprocal," "slope."

B. THE RATE PROBLEM

§ 5. The Idea of a Rate. In studying a varying quantity or function we often need to know how fast it is increasing or decreasing — in other words, the *rate* at which it is changing.

The general idea of a rate is, of course, *the amount of change in the function per unit change in the independent variable.* Graphically this is represented by the distance the **graph of** the function rises or falls per horizontal unit. Thus a rate is shown by the *steepness* of the graph, and not by the height at any point.

If the graph is a straight line, rising by a fixed amount in each and every horizontal unit, the function must be increasing at a constant rate.

Thus in Fig. 9, representing the growing value of a certain investment, the value increases at the constant rate of $200 per year. (How can this be seen?)

Conversely, if the rate is constant, the graph must be straight, as it must rise by a fixed amount in each unit, or in any specified part of a unit.

Most quantities, however, change at a varying rate. In such cases we distinguish between the *average rate* of change during some *interval*, and the *instantaneous rate* at some particular *instant*.

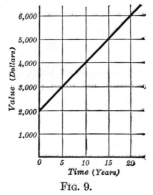

FIG. 9.

For instance, if the volume of a balloon increased by 1200 cu. ft. in six hours, it increased at the average rate of 200 cu. ft. per hr. But it may have been increasing more or less rapidly than this at any particular instant — or even decreasing part of the time.

The distinction, and the relation, between the two kinds of rates will be discussed more fully as we proceed. Both kinds can be found approximately from a graph.

§ 6. **Average Rates Found Graphically.** To find from a graph the average rate of increase of a varying quantity or function in any interval, we merely read off the *amount* of increase during the interval, and divide by the length of the interval or change in the independent variable. Similarly for a rate of decrease.

EXAMPLE. Find the average rate at which the weight of vapor in saturated air increases with the temperature between 18° and 28°.

The graph in Fig. 10 (without using the tangent line) shows that the weight increases by 11.8 gm. during this 10° interval.   Hence the average rate is 1.18 gm. per deg.

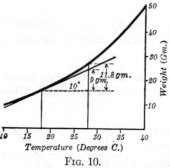

FIG. 10.

§ 7. Instantaneous Rates Found Graphically.   A straight line tangent to a graph at any point will forever rise at the same rate as the graph was rising at the point of tangency.*

Hence, when we wish to find how fast a given function was increasing at a certain *instant* or *point,* rather than its average rate of increase during some *interval,* we need merely draw a tangent to the graph at the point in question, and find the required instantaneous rate from it, using any convenient interval.

E.g., from the tangent line in Fig. 10 we see that if the weight continued to increase at the same rate as at 18°, it would increase by 9 gm. while the temperature rose 10°.   Hence the instantaneous rate at 18° is .9 gm. per deg.

To draw a tangent line accurately by the eye, however, requires great care.   The ruler should have the direction of the curve at the point of tangency and should run along the curve closely in both directions near by.

In solving rate problems the respective increases should be clearly labeled on the graph, as in Fig. 10.   Also the answer should name the *units* — as grams per degree, etc.

Rate units are often written as if they were fractions.   Thus grams per degree is abbreviated *gm./deg.,* indicating that this rate is found by dividing some number of grams by some number of degrees.

Remark.   Two specially important rates are the *speed* and the *acceleration* of a moving object.   The rate of motion, or rate at which distance is traveled, is called the "speed."   And *the rate at which the speed is changing* is commonly called the

---

* This intuitive conception will be justified logically in § 46.

"acceleration."* An object may be moving with very high speed and yet have no acceleration whatever. A common unit for acceleration is *feet per sec. gained per sec.*, or, symbolically, ft./sec.²

§ 8 S. Small Intervals. It is sometimes necessary to find the change in a quantity, in an interval far too short for the increase to be read from the graph with accuracy. *E.g.*, we might desire to know the increase in the weight (W gm.) in Fig. 10 between the temperatures $T = 17.99$ and $T = 18.01$ deg.

We may reason as follows: The average rate of increase during this short interval must be nearly the same as the instantaneous rate at $T = 18°$. By § 7 the instantaneous rate at 18° is .9 *grams per degree.* Hence, while T rises from 17.99° to 18.01° (a rise of .02 deg.), W will increase by about .9 × .02, or .018 (gm.).

N.B. Do not confuse the amount of increase with the *rate*. A function may increase very little in a short interval and yet be increasing very *fast* — just as a train may run only an inch in a small fraction of a second and yet be running at a very high speed.

Points for Self-Quiz

Meaning of rate, speed, acceleration; how to find graphically an average rate, an instantaneous rate, or the minute changes occurring in small intervals; how rate units are written; relation of a straight graph to rate questions.

EXERCISES

1. Table 1 shows the number of bacteria (N million) in a culture, t hr. after first observing them. Plot. Judging by the steepness of the graph, when was N increasing most rapidly? At what average rate was N increasing from $t = 4$ to $t = 4.5$? How fast at $t = 3$?

2. The temperature of an object ($T°$) fell as in Table 2 after various intervals (t min.). Plot. What was the temperature at $t = 5.2$? How fast was the object then cooling? When was the temperature 65°?

3. Radium decomposes continually. Table 3 shows the quantity (Q mg.) remaining after T yr., if the initial quantity was 1 gm. How

---

* More accurately, "acceleration along the path of motion." If an object moves along a curve, there is also an acceleration across the path.

much will remain after 400 yr.?   What is the instantaneous rate of change of Q at $T = 2000$?

4 S. In Ex. 3 about how much does Q decrease from $T = 2000$ to $T = 2010$?

TABLE 1		TABLE 2		TABLE 3		TABLE 4		TABLE 5	
t	N	t	T	T	Q	t	v	v	x
0	0.2	0	120	0	1000	0	0	0	0
1	0.6	2	80.7	1000	681	2	12	10	4.2
2	3.9	4	56.8	2000	463	4	40	20	17.0
3	28	6	42.3	3000	315	6	72	30	38.2
4	74	8	33.5	4000	214	8	96	40	68.0
5	127	10	28.2	5000	146	10	100	50	106.2
6	150	12	25	6000	99	12	72	60	153.0
7	149	14	23	7000	68	14	0	70	208.3

5. The speed of a moving object (v ft./min.) varied with the time (t min.) as in Table 4.   Plot; and read off the maximum speed.   Find the acceleration at $t = 6$.

6. Table 5 shows the distance (x ft.) normally required for stopping a certain auto, if running v miles per hr.   What speed would require 50 ft. for stopping?   How fast does x increase with v at $v = 30$?

7 S. In Ex. 6 how much greater is x if $v = 30.2$ than if $v = 30$?

8. Table 6 shows the distance (D knots) traveled by the S.S. *Bremen* in t hrs., on a certain voyage.   Plot.   What does the virtual straightness of the graph indicate?   Find the average speed for the first 20 hr.

TABLE 6		TABLE 7		TABLE 8					
t	D	W	N		A			A	
				t	(*Pre.*)	(*Obs.*)	t	(*Pre.*)	(*Obs.*)
0	0	74.1	40.6						
9.6	240	68.6	40.3						
32.6	849	55.3	41.6	0	—	56.6	36	10.5	11.0
55.6	1467	42.3	45.1	4	49.1	44.3	40	8.3	9.2
78.6	2089	28.0	48.4	8	42.0	42.0	44	6.0	6.5
101.6	2720	12.0	49.8	12	35.4	33.6	48	4.3	4.2
120	3220	1.6	49.7	16	29.7	30.2	52	2.9	3.1
				20	24.5	24.2	56	1.8	1.8
				24	20.1	22.1	60	0.7	1.1
				28	16.4	17.0	64	0.2	0.8
				32	13.2	13.6	68	Healed	

9. On the voyage in Ex. 8, the ship's latitude ($N°$, north) and the longitude ($W°$, west), at the corresponding times, are shown in Table 7. Plot.   (For easy comparison with Ex. 8, make an exception here, and let W increase toward the *left*, as it would in a map.)   At what average rate did N change with W between $W = 60$ and $W = 20$?   At what longitude was the ship farthest north?

10. With Dr. Carrel's method of treating deep wounds, the date of healing can be predicted accurately.* Table 8 shows the predicted and the observed size (A sq. cm.) of a typical wound t days after the first treatment. Plot together the theoretical and observed curves of healing. Theoretically, at what rate should the wound have been healing when $t = 20$?

§ 9. Interpolation: Proportional Parts.

The operation of finding a value of a variable quantity between those given in a table, and consistent with them, is called *interpolation*. One way to interpolate is to plot a smooth graph and read off the required intermediate value.

Another method, fairly accurate if the tabular intervals are not large, is that of "Proportional Parts." In this we regard the rate of increase as constant within the interval in question.

Ex. I. Find from Table I the weight of vapor in saturated air at 23° C.

TABLE I

TEMP. $T°$	WEIGHT W gm.
20	17.2
5 {	} 5.7
25	22.9

We simply have to find how much W will increase while T rises from 20° to 23°.

The 5° rise in T increases W by 5.7 gm.

∴ The 3° rise in T increases W by $\frac{3}{5}$ of 5.7 gm. (= 3.4 gm.)

Adding this increase to 17.2, the weight at 20°, gives 20.6 gm. as the weight at 23°. This is evidently a reasonable value.

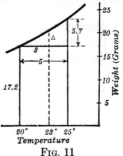

FIG. 11

Observe in Fig. 11 that if the graph were straight, this calculation would be strictly correct, as the increase in W between 20° and 23° (denoted by the Greek letter Δ, "delta")

---

would be exactly three fifths of the whole increase 5.7 gm.   The small or partial increases (3 and Δ) would be strictly "proportional parts" of the whole increases (5 and 5.7).

To avoid blunders in more complicated cases we may set the calculation down in detail, as in the following example.

Ex. II.   Table II gives the "reciprocals" of 4.42 and 4.43.* Find the number whose reciprocal is .22591.

TABLE II

NUMBER (N)	RECIPROCAL (R)
$.01\left\{\Delta\left\{\begin{array}{l}4.42\\ -\;?\\ 4.43\end{array}\right.\right.$	$\left.\begin{array}{r}.226244\\ .225910\\ .225734\end{array}\right\}334\left.\right\}510$

We first indicate the required value between the nearest given values, as shown here.   Then we form corresponding differences in the two columns, using Δ for the *difference between the required value of N and* 4.42.

For a constant rate of change, these corresponding differences should be proportional:

$$\frac{\Delta}{.01} = \frac{334}{510}.$$

That is, the partial difference in N is to the whole difference in N as the partial difference in R is to the whole difference in R.

Multiplying through by .01 gives $\Delta = 3.34 \div 510 = .0065$. Recalling what Δ stands for, we add it to 4.42, getting 4.4265. This result is reasonable, being between 4.42 and 4.43 and nearer the latter — as it evidently should be from a comparison of the given values.

Remarks.   (I) If we had used Δ to denote the difference between the larger value (4.43) and the required value, we should have *subtracted* the value of that Δ finally from 4.43.

(II) How inaccurate this method of "Proportional Parts" is, depends on how much the graph would deviate from a straight line in the interval considered.   In general, *it is a waste of time to calculate the value of Δ to many figures.*   A good graph is usually more accurate.

* If a definition of "reciprocal" is desired, see § 29.

Points for Self-Quiz

Meaning of interpolation; the two methods thus far given; advantages and disadvantages of each; what the method of Proportional Parts assumes about the table, and about the graph; meaning of "Δ" and how to decide whether to add or subtract it.

EXERCISES

In Exs. 1–5 use Proportional Parts

1. Table 1 gives the boiling point of water ($T°$) at various pressures (P mm.). Find T when $P = 825$. Also P when $T = 100.8$.

2. Table 2 gives the density of mercury (D gm. per cc.) at various temperatures ($T°$). Find D when $T = 28.8$; also T when $D = 13.531$.

3. Table 3 gives the squares of 3 numbers. From it find approximately the square of 87.4. Check.

4. Table 4 shows the reciprocals of 3 numbers. Find the reciprocal of 1.413.

5. Table 5 gives the square roots of 3 numbers. Find $\sqrt{6.71}$, and check by squaring the result.

TABLE 1		TABLE 2		TABLE 3		TABLE 4	
P	T	T	D	N	S	N	R
760	100	26	13.532	87	7569	1.40	.7143
787.7	101	28	13.528	88	7744	1.41	.7092
816	102	30	13.523	89	7921	1.42	.7042
845	103						

6. The amount ($\$A$) which a deposit of $1000 will yield after various intervals of time (T yr.), drawing interest at 5%, compounded annually, is shown approximately in Table 6. Find graphically and also by Proportional Parts when the original sum will have been quadrupled. How fast will A be increasing at $T = 10$? (Check by considering the interest rate.)

7. The probable error (E meters) of a range-finder at various ranges (R meters) is shown by Table 7. One of the values is given incorrectly. Plot, and find which one; also what the value should be.

8 S. In Ex. 7 find what change occurs in E from $R = 1000$ to $R = 1010$.

9 S. Make a table of squares for the numbers 0, 2, 4, 6, 8, 10. Plot. Read off $(6.8)^2$ and $\sqrt{72}$, and check. What change occurs in the square if the number increases from 5 to 5.01? Check.

TABLE 5	
N	$\sqrt{N}$
6.6	2.569
6.7	2.588
6.8	2.608

TABLE 6	
T	A
0	1000
5	1276
10	1629
15	2079
20	2653
25	3386
30	4322
35	5516

TABLE 7	
R	E
400	0.7
1000	4.4
1500	9.7
2000	17.0
2250	20.5
2500	27.0
2750	32.9
3000	39.0

10. Find by Proportional Parts the required p in Ex. 2, p. 9.

11. Likewise find the required t in Ex. 11, p. 10.

12. (*A*) Draw a rough sketch similar to Fig. 11, to illustrate Ex. 3. (*B*) The same for Ex. 4.

C. THE MEAN-VALUE PROBLEM

§ 10. Average Value of a Varying Quantity. We often speak of the average value of a quantity which is continually changing. This requires definition.

E.g., if the height of a graph is continually changing, what shall we take as the true average height throughout some interval? Not simply the average of the heights at the beginning and end of the interval. For the latter average takes no account of the way the height varies within the interval — whether the curve sags or arches upward. Nor would the height at the middle of the interval in general be the required average height.

FIG. 12.

By the average height throughout an interval let us understand: *That height which, multiplied by the base, would give the area under the curve in that interval.* In other words, let it be the height of a rectangle equivalent to the area under the curve and having the same base. (See *MN* in Fig. 12.)*

* In § 327 S we shall connect the average height, as thus defined, with the ordinary idea of an arithmetical average, when we try to apply the latter idea to an unlimited number of ordinates.

The average height as thus defined is called the *mean ordinate* of the curve in the strip considered. To approximate it closely, simply draw a horizontal line across the strip at about the right height, compare the triangular areas thus formed (to the right and left of N), and move the line up or down if either area appears to be the larger.

Likewise when a changing quantity Q is represented by the changing height of a graph, we regard as the "true average value" of the quantity in any interval that value $\bar{Q}$ (read "Q bar") which is represented by the mean ordinate of the graph. The uses which we shall make of this idea will be justified more fully later on.

§ 11. Distance Found from a Speed-Time Graph.

Suppose now that we have a graph such as Fig. 13. Here the changing speed of a moving object is represented by the changing height of the graph; and we assume that the average speed for any 5 minutes is represented by the corresponding mean ordinate.

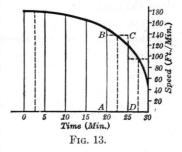

Thus the average speed during the interval AD was, according to the vertical scale, about 140 ft./min.; and the distance

FIG. 13.

traveled during these 5 minutes was about 140×5, or 700 feet. Similarly for each other interval. Adding results for all the intervals would give the total distance traveled.

Remarks. (1) We use intervals small enough for the eye to compare triangular areas with some assurance. A rapid rise or fall of the curve may necessitate using very narrow strips in some part of the curve.

(2) The area of rectangle $ABCD$ (Fig. 13) represents the distance traveled by the object during the 5 minute interval AD. (Why?) Hence the area under the graph also represents the distance traveled.

§ 12 S. Further Illustrations of Mean Ordinates.

Exercises 3, 5, 7–14, below, show various other uses of mean ordinates. But we may well contrast here two cases, somewhat alike, which are very important in scientific work.

(A) *Finding Momentum from a Force-Time Graph.* A force
acting upon an object imparts "momentum" to it. The
amount of momentum equals the average force, multiplied by
the length of time. *E.g.*, an average force of 35 lb. acting for
10 sec. imparts 350 lb.-sec. of momentum.

Suppose that the force varies, and that we have plotted it
as a function of the time. Then the average force in any
interval is represented by the corresponding mean ordinate.
By reading it off and multiplying by the length of time, we can
find the amount of momentum imparted during the interval.

(B) *Finding Work from a Force-Distance Graph.* The amount
of work done in moving an object is found by multiplying the
distance the object travels by the average force used in moving
it. *E.g.*, an average force of 35 lb., moving an object 10 ft.,
does 350 ft.-lb. of work.

If the force varies, and we have a graph exhibiting it as a
function of the distance, the average force for any distance is
represented by the mean ordinate. Hence the work can be
found.

The average force on the basis of distance may be different from
the average force on the basis of time.* Momentum is given by the
area under a force-time graph. (And *work* by what?) In many applications of mean ordinates we need to know the meaning of the
product of the two quantities plotted horizontally and vertically.
That product is the kind of quantity which the area under the graph
must represent — if it has a meaning.

Points for Self-Quiz

Definition of mean ordinate; how used in studying variables
in general; method of finding distance from a speed-time graph;
what represents the distance in such a graph; similar questions
as to momentum and work.

EXERCISES

1. The speed of an airplane (V ft./min.) after passing a certain
point varied with the time (T min.), as in Table 1. Plot, and find the
distance traveled during the hour covered by the table. How fast
was the speed changing at $T = 30$?

* Cf. the author's *Higher Course*, p. 286.

TABLE 1		TABLE 2		TABLE 3		TABLE 4	
T	V	t	v	t	$Hr.$	t	R
0	11900	0	0	0	8:32	0	192
10	12000	.01	76	30	7:59	1	194
20	11900	.02	139	60	6:52	2	198
30	11600	.03	183	90	5:34	3	205
40	11100	.04	198	120	4:18	4	216
50	10400	.05	183	150	3:24	5	231
60	9500	.06	139	180	3:16	6	248
		.07	76	210	3:58	7	262
		.08	0	240	4:56		

2. As an auto traveled at a certain fixed speed, a point P on a tire traveled with a varying speed (v ft./sec.), shown in Table 2 at various intervals of time (t sec.) during one revolution. Find graphically the speed of P at $t = .005$. Check by Proportional Parts. (Why is there a discrepancy?) Find also the length of the path traveled by P, through the air, during a turn.

3. In 1935 the time of sunrise in Edinburgh t days *after* Jan. 1 is shown in Table 3. Plot. How fast was the length of the forenoon increasing at the end of January? What was the average length of the forenoon during April?

4. The speed of a vertically falling body increases during each second by about 32 ft./sec. If thrown down with initial speed of 20 ft./sec., what speed has it after 2, 4, 6, 8, 10 sec.? Find graphically the total distance fallen from $t = 0$ to $t = 10$.

5. During exercise a man consumed oxygen at a rate (R cc./min.) which varied with the elapsed time (t min.) as in Table 4. Find how fast this rate R was increasing at $t = 3$. Also find the total consumption during the 7 min.

6. Table 5 shows the speed of Halley's Comet (V million mi./yr.) at various times (T yr), since it was nearest the sun. (A) Find the distance traveled until farthest away: 38.5 years. (B) Find how fast the speed was changing at $T = 5$.

TABLE 5

T	0	1	3	6	9	12	15	21	30	38.5
V	1000	375	225	155	120	90	72	50	28	16

7. The pull exerted by a locomotive in starting a train exceeded the resisting forces by F tons, varying with the time elapsed (t sec.).

as shown in Table 6.   Find the total momentum given to the train in 8 seconds.   Also find the rate of increase of F at $t = 2$.

8. A weighing spring was stretched from a length of 5 inches to a length of 5.8 inches, the pull used (f lb.) increasing with the length (L in.), as in Table 7.   Find the total work done in stretching the spring.

9. The resistance (R lb.) offered by a tug-of-war team after being pulled x ft. decreased as in Table 8.   Find the total work done in pulling the team 48 ft.

TABLE 6		TABLE 7		TABLE 8		TABLE 9		TABLE 10		TABLE 11	
t	F	L	f	x	R	d	f	t	i	t	P
0	0	5.0	0	0	2100	1.0	18400	0	0	0	0
1	26	5.1	5	9	1920	1.5	10720	.001	49.6	2	48
2	40	5.2	10	18	1545	2.0	7300	.002	71.8	4	160
3	40	5.3	15	24	1215	2.5	5420	.003	81.8	6	288
4	32	5.4	20	30	900	3.0	4250	.004	86.3	8	384
5	25	5.5	25	36	615	3.5	3450	.005	88.4	10	400
6	21	5.6	30	42	420	4.0	2900	.006	89.3		
7	19	5.7	35	48	300			.007	89.7		
8	18	5.8	40								

10. The force (f lb.) exerted by steam upon a piston varied with the distance from one end of the cylinder (d ft.), as in Table 9.   Find the work done in moving the piston from $d = 1.5$ to $d = 3$.

11. Table 10 shows the intensity (i amperes) of an electric current t sec., after the circuit was closed.   Find the rate of increase of i at $i = .003$; also the average intensity between $t = .002$ and $t = .003$.

12. The electric power (P kilowatts) used by a factory increased during the first 10 min. as in Table 11.   Find (*a*) the average P used 'etween $t = 6$ and $t = 8$;   (*b*) the average rate at which P increased .rom $t = 6$ to $t = 8$;   (*c*) how fast P was increasing at $t = 2$.

13. In Ex. 12 try to estimate in one step the average P used for the entire 10 min.; then check by finding the average for each 2 min. interval and averaging these results arithmetically.

14. In Ex. 1, p. 13, how would you proceed to find the average number of bacteria present during the time covered by the table? Likewise, to find the average temperature of the object, in Ex. 2, p.13?

§ 13. Geometrical Uses of Mean Ordinates.

(*A*) *To find the area within any closed plane curve* divide the figure into narrow strips by parallel lines, and approximate each strip by a rectangle.

In this way, if the curve in Fig. 14 were a "contour line" running around a hill at some given elevation, as determined by a survey, we

could find the area of the horizontal cross-section of the hill inclosed
by that contour line.

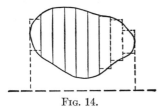

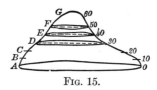

FIG. 14.   FIG. 15.

Engineers often use a "planimeter," which will measure any
small plane area approximately, however irregular the boundary.

(*B*) *To find the volume of an irregular solid,* say a hill, imagine
it cut into thin slices by parallel planes, and approximate each
slice by a cylinder. Any slice, such as *DE* in Fig. 15, equals a
cylinder of the same height whose base area is some *average
cross-section area* within the slice.

The areas of the various horizontal cross-sections *A, B, C,*
etc., can be found as in Fig. 14 above. Suppose this done, and
that we then *plot a graph show-
ing how the sectional area varies
with the elevation.* (Fig. 16.)
The average height of the graph
in any strip will represent the
average area in the corresponding slice of the mound. If this
is, say, 20,000 sq. ft. for the
slice *DE*, whose thickness is 10 ft., the volume of the slice
is 200,000 cu. ft. Similarly for the other slices.

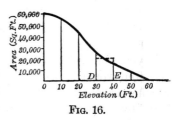

FIG. 16.

§ **14. Tables of Squares, etc.** To save time in many problems,
tables of squares and square roots, etc., are given in the Appendix, pp. 534–35. Some sample lines are shown here
in part. Larger tables are available.

N	N^2	$\sqrt{N}$	$\sqrt{10\,N}$
5.0	25.00	2.2361	7.0711
5.1	26.01	2.2583	7.1414

This means, for instance, that

$$5.1^2 = 26.01; \quad \sqrt{5.1} = 2.2583; \quad \sqrt{51} = 7.1414, \text{ etc.}$$

The numbers N given in the table all lie between 1 and 10. But the table can be used for larger or smaller values because of these facts:

(A) Moving the decimal point one place in a number will merely move it two places in the square.

(B) Moving the point two places in a number will merely move it one place in the square root.

	Ex. I		Ex. II
Since	$5.1^2 = 26.01$	Since	$\sqrt{5.1} = 2.2583$
hence	$51^2 = 2601$	hence	$\sqrt{510} = 22.583$
also	$.051^2 = .002601$	also	$\sqrt{.051} = .22583$
	etc.		etc.

The column $\sqrt{10\ N}$ gives the square root when the decimal point has been moved *one* place, or 3 places, etc. But in looking up a square root, the best way is not to think of "N" and "10 N," but to decide in advance what the first figure of the required root will be, and then look in the column where that figure occurs.

If you were going to extract the root without a table, the first step would be to point off "periods" of two places each, starting from the decimal point: the required first figure is found by extracting the square root of the leading period.

Illustrations

$\sqrt{5'10'00'00.}$ starts with 2; has 4 digits before the decimal point.

$\sqrt{51'00.}$ starts with 7; has 2 digits before the decimal point.

$\sqrt{.00'05'13'4(0)}$ starts with 2, in the second decimal place.

$\sqrt{.00'00'51}$ starts with 7, in the third decimal place.

In each case it is obvious which column of the table will give the required root: the correct leading figure occurs in only one!

Cube-root tables are used similarly; but the "periods" consist of three figures each. For illustrations see p. 535.

When N has several significant figures, we may either interpolate, or extract the root arithmetically. Logarithms will provide a much easier way. (Chapter VI.)

Remark. Squares and square roots are frequently needed in working with right triangles, where we use the Pythagorean theorem: *The square on the hypotenuse equals the sum of the squares on the two legs.*

Points for Self-Quiz

Suggest some good points yourself; likewise hereafter.

EXERCISES

1. A piece of land lies between a straight fence and a curved stream. Table 1 shows the distance from the fence to the stream (y yards) at various points (x yards) from one end of the fence. Map the land roughly and find its approximate area.

2. A ship's deck has an axis of symmetry running lengthwise. The semi-widths (w ft.) measured from this axis to one side of the deck vary with the distance from the bow (d ft.), as in Table 2. Find the approximate area of the deck.

3. The depth (D ft.) for a proposed railway "cut" for a level track through a hill will vary with the distance (x ft.) from one end, as in Table 3. Assuming the hill to slope smoothly, find the average depth for each 100 ft. How much earth must be removed for a cut 20 ft. wide with vertical sides?

TABLE 1		TABLE 2		TABLE 3		TABLE 4		TABLE 5		TABLE 6	
x	y	d	w	x	D	E	A	x	A	h	A
0	0	0	0	0	0	0	65	0	0	0	0
10	22	50	16	100	7	2	54	2	5	5	10900
20	39	100	26	200	20	4	47	4	16	10	15000
30	51	150 ⎫		300	23	6	42	6	27	15	15900
40	50	—		400	18	8	38.5	8	32	20 ⎫	
50	40	— ⎬	29	500	12	10	36	10	25	25 ⎬	16000
60	26	—		600	17	12	34	11	15	30 ⎭	
70	14	350 ⎭		700	22	14	32.5	12	0	35	15900
80	5	400	27	800	10						
90	0	445	13	900	0						
		450	0								

4. The area (A sq. ft.) of a horizontal section of a certain wall varies with the elevation (E ft.) above the base, as in Table 4. Find the volume of the wall, and also the rate at which A changes with E at $E = 10$.

5. A plumb-bob is to be made with its horizontal cross-section area (*A* sq. cm.) varying with the distance (*x* cm.) above the lowest point, as shown in Table 5. What will its volume be?

6. According to a naval architect's drawings, the horizontal sections of a certain ship at various heights (*h* ft.) above the keel will have the areas (*A* sq. ft.) shown in Table 6. What will the volume of the ship be, up to a height of 25 ft.?

7. Every horizontal section of a steeple is a square, whose side (*s* ft.) varies thus with the distance (*x* ft.) from the top: $s = .2 x$. Find the volume of the steeple from the top down to $x = 40$. (Hint: First find the area of the square section at $x = 0, 10, 20, 30, 40$.)

8. Like Ex. 7 for a conical steeple if the radius of any section *x* ft. below the top is $r = .2 x$.

9. Look up the squares of 2.8; 590; 3200; .81; .022. Test each result roughly by common sense.

10. Look up the square roots of 3.8; 4500; 18000; .087; .94. Check by common sense.

11. Look up the cube roots of 7.4; 400; 19000; .31.

12. (*A*) Look up the square and square root of 46.5, interpolating to take account of the given third figure. (*B*) The same for .208. (*C*) Also for .00523.

13. Indicate the first figure and the position of the decimal point in the square roots of 928600, and .0924. Also, in the cube root of .00831.

14. Find the hypotenuse of a right triangle, if the legs are 14 in. and 48 in. Likewise if the legs are 5 in. and 6 in.

15. The hypotenuse of a right triangle is 20 in.; one leg is 19 in. Find the other leg.

16. In Ex. 15, if one leg were double the other, find both legs.

[17.] An uncovered rectangular tank is to have a square base and contain 800 cu. ft. Materials for the base cost 40¢ per sq. ft., and for the sides 30¢ per sq. ft. Can you suggest some way to figure out approximately what dimensions would give the lowest cost?

D. The Extreme-Value Problem

§ 15. Maximum and Minimum Values: Trial Method. It is sometimes important to know the largest or smallest value of a variable quantity.

Such "extreme values" can be found approximately by *making experimental calculations and comparing results.* A graph is often helpful in locating the highest and lowest values.

Ex. I. Find the most economical dimensions for an open, rectangular, sheet-iron box, which is to have a square base and is to contain 24 cu. ft.

Let us try various dimensions, and calculate each time the number of square feet of material required. As in Fig. 17, let the height be h ft. and each side of the base be x ft.

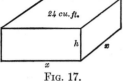
Fig. 17.

If $\qquad x = 2:$ $\qquad$ base area $= 4$ sq. ft.

To give a volume of 24 cu. ft., this requires a height of 6 ft. The total area of the four sides and base will then be

$$A = 4\,hx + x^2 = 4(6)\,(2) + 2^2 = 52.$$

In like manner for $x = 3, 4, 5$, etc., we find the other areas shown in Table I.*

TABLE I

x	A	x	A
2	52	5	44.2
3	41	6	52
4	40		

The smallest value here is $A = 40$ when $x = 4$; but *a smooth graph shows a still smaller value* between 3 and 4: viz. $A = 39.6$, at $x = 3.6$, approx. (Fig. 18.)

Thus the base should be about 3.6 ft. square, which requires a height of 1.8 ft., approx. (How could the best values of x and h be found still more closely?)

* An alternative procedure which may be preferable is to express A in terms of x alone. From $V = x^2h = 24$, we get $h = 24/x^2$. Hence the area formula, $A = 4hx + x^2$ can be written

$$A = 4\left(\frac{24}{x^2}\right) x + x^2,$$

or $\qquad A = \dfrac{96}{x} + x^2.$

Substituting values for x gives the table. (Verify.)

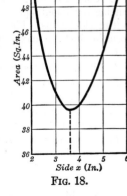
Fig. 18.

In any such problem it is well to start experimenting with values near those we think will be the best. But we should go on a little beyond any supposed maximum or minimum.

The table should have but two columns: The quantity for which we tried values and the quantity to be made a maximum or minimum.

§ 16. Caution. A few questions about maxima and minima can be answered by elementary geometry, but we should never jump at conclusions in such matters.

E.g., it would not do to argue that the box in § 15 should be a cube to have the least area. We were not dealing with a *complete* area: there was no top.

EXERCISES

(Work these by experimenting and plotting results.)

1. A rectangle is to have a perimeter of 26 in. For what dimensions will its area be greatest? Do these come out as you would expect?

2. A long sheet of tin 25 in. wide is to be made into a gutter, by  turning strips up vertically along the two sides. How many inches should be turned up at each side to secure the greatest carrying capacity, *i.e.*, the greatest sectional area?

3. A sheet of tin 21 in. square is to be made into an open box, by cutting out equal squares at the four corners and turning up the resulting side strips. Find the size of the square to cut out to give the resulting box the maximum volume. What maximum? (Hint: What if 1 in. squares are cut out? 2 in. squares, etc.?)

4. Like Ex. 3 for a sheet of tin 20 in. by 30 in.

5. A rectangular sheep pen including 130 sq. yd. is to be built against a long wall any part of which can be used as one side of the pen. What lengths should the three new sides have to require the smallest amount of new construction?

6. A rectangular stockade is to contain 1200 sq. yd. The fences running one way will cost $3 per yd., the other two $2 per yd. What dimensions will make the cost of fencing least, and how small?

7. One ship (*S*) was 60 mi. straight north of another (*S'*) at noon. But *S'* was sailing east 10 mi. per hour and *S* was sailing south 20 mi.

per hour. When were they nearest, and how near? (Calculate their distance apart at 1 P.M., at 2 P.M., etc. Use tables of square roots if desired.)

8. In Ex. 2 above suppose the tin 30 in. wide and a 10-in. strip turned up at each side, perhaps not vertically (Fig. 19). For what depth will the gutter have the greatest capacity? (For any chosen value of y, the value to be used for x must be: $x = \sqrt{100 - y^2}$. Why?)

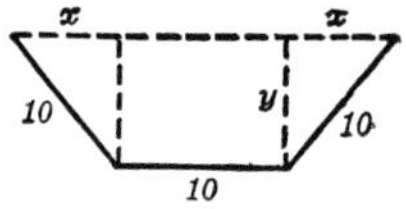

Fig. 19.

9. The load (L lb.) which a rectangular beam of a certain length can carry is $L = 20\ xy^2$, where x and y are the width and depth of beam in inches. Find what x and y give the strongest beam that can be cut from a circular log 30 in. in diameter.

10. In Ex. 9 what x and y will give the *largest* beam that can be cut from the given log? Do these come out as you would expect?

11. A printed page is to allow 80 sq. in. for printed matter and have a margin of $1\frac{1}{2}$ in. at each side and 2 in. at top and bottom. (Thus, if the print lines are 10 in. long, the height of the print column must be 8 in., making the page 13 in. wide and 12 in. high.) What shape of page will require the least paper?

12. For a package to go by parcel post the sum of its length and girth must not exceed 100 in. What are the dimensions and volume of the largest rectangular package, with square ends, that can go? (Note that the result does not give a cube: we are not asked to find the largest volume for a given area.)

13. Like Ex. I, p. 27, but containing 600 cu. ft.

14. A covered rectangular tank is to have a square base and contain 120 cu. yd. The base will cost $3 per sq. yd., the sides and top $2 per sq. yd. Find the most economical dimensions.

[15.] Suggest some way to solve the equation $4\ x^3 - 7\ x^2 + 15 = 0$. (Hint: The question really is this: What values for x will make the quantity $4\ x^3 - 7\ x^2 + 15$ equal to zero?)

E. The Zero-Value Problem

§ 17. Elementary Equations Reviewed. In practical work it is often necessary to solve an equation for some unknown quantity. This can be done in any numerical case, at least approximately, by a simple graphical process. Before discussing this, however, it may be well to recall that certain kinds of equations can be solved exactly by elementary algebra, as indicated below. If these methods are not already familiar, they should be *thoroughly mastered now.*

Linear Equations

An equation of the first degree (*i.e.*, involving only the first power of the unknown quantity) can be solved by a simple transposition and division.

Ex. I. Solve $\qquad 2x + 5 = 0.$

Evidently $2x = -5$, whence $x = -\frac{5}{2}$.

Check: Substituting $-\frac{5}{2}$ for x does make $2x+5$ equal to zero. Hence $-\frac{5}{2}$ is the required "root." *

Remark. In "transposing" the number 5 above, what we really do is to subtract 5 from both sides of the equation. Subtracting 5 from the left member leaves only $2x$; and subtracting 5 from 0 gives -5.

Quadratic Equations

An equation of the second degree can be solved by "completing the square." To understand this process observe that, in the square of any binomial such as

$$(x+7)^2 = x^2 + 14x + 49,$$

or, more generally,

$$(x+n)^2 = x^2 + 2nx + n^2,$$

the final term is *the square of one half the coefficient of x.*

Thus if the quantity $x^2 + 14x$ appeared in an equation, we could convert it into a perfect square by adding 7^2 or 49.

Ex. II. Solve $\qquad 3x^2 - 11x + 7 = 0.$

Transposing and dividing: $\qquad x^2 - \frac{11}{3}x \quad = -\frac{7}{3}.$

One half of $-\frac{11}{3}$ is $-\frac{11}{6}$. Adding $(-\frac{11}{6})^2$ or $\frac{121}{36}$ to both sides:

$$x^2 - \frac{11}{3}x + \frac{121}{36} = -\frac{7}{3} + \frac{121}{36} = \frac{37}{36}.$$

The left member is now the square of $(x - \frac{11}{6}.)$ Extracting square roots:

$$x - \frac{11}{6} = \pm \frac{\sqrt{37}}{6},$$

$$x = \frac{11 + \sqrt{37}}{6} \text{ or } \frac{11 - \sqrt{37}}{6}.$$

* A root of an equation is a number which, substituted for the unknown quantity, will make the two members of the equation equal.

Check: Direct substitution shows these to be roots of the equation:

e.g., $3\left(\dfrac{11 + \sqrt{37}}{6}\right)^2 - 11\left(\dfrac{11 + \sqrt{37}}{6}\right) + 7$, if simplified, will give zero.

Remark. If we approximate $\sqrt{37}$ by decimals, the results cease to be exact. But they will be more convenient for most purposes.

N.B. If a quadratic equation is given in factored form, like $(x - 4)\,(2\,x + 5) = 0$, or if we can see such factors by inspection, we need not complete the square. Rather, we reason that *the product of the two factors can be zero only if one factor is zero.* Setting $x - 4 = 0$ gives $x = 4$; and $2\,x + 5 = 0$ gives $x = -\frac{5}{2}$. Either of these values, 4 or $-\frac{5}{2}$, substituted for x in the original product, will reduce the product to zero and satisfy the equation.

Unfortunately, factors are not often evident in practical problems; but we can *always* complete the square in any actual quadratic equation. (See Chapter IX for further theory and methods.)

§ 18. Equations as Problems of Variation. Judged by the foregoing methods, the problem of solving an equation does not appear to be connected with our basic problem of determining how one quantity will vary with another. But the two problems can be linked together.

For instance, we may think of the equation in Ex. II above as follows: For every value of x, whether a root or not, the quantity $3\,x^2 - 11\,x + 7$ has a definite value, and it must therefore vary with x in a definite way. The problem of solving the equation

$$3\,x^2 - 11\,x + 7 = 0,$$

is simply the problem of *finding where this varying quantity $3\,x^2 - 11\,x + 7$ reaches the value zero.*

The same idea will evidently apply to any other equation. And this suggests the following general method of solution.

§ 19. Graphical Solution of Higher Equations. There is no very elementary algebraic method of solving equations of the third degree or above, unless factors can be seen by inspection. But the real roots of *any equation of any degree* can be approximated graphically, if the equation contains only one unknown quantity.

For instance, if we wish to solve the equation

$$2\,x^3 - 15\,x + 10 = 0,$$

we may *plot a graph showing how the polynomial* $2\,x^3 - 15\,x + 10$ *varies with* x, *and read off the values of* x *where the polynomial becomes zero.*

The first step is, of course, to calculate a table of values of the polynomial by substituting various values for x:

$x = 4$,   poly. $= 2(4)^3 - 15(4) + 10 = 78$;
$x = 3$,   poly. $= 2(3)^3 - 15(3) + 10 = 19$;
and similarly for the other values in the adjacent table.

Plotting these values gives the curve in Fig. 20, negative ordinates being drawn downward as usual. The height of this graph at any point represents the value of the polynomial at the corresponding value of x.

x	POLY.
4	78
3	19
2	− 4
1	− 3
0	10
− 1	23
− 2	24
− 3	1
− 4	− 58

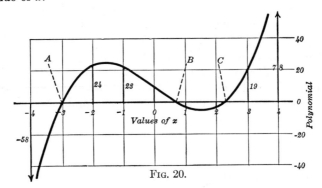

FIG. 20.

Evidently the polynomial becomes zero at the crossing points A, B, and C, where $x = -\,3.03$, $.71$, *and* 2.31, *approx.* These values are very close to the true roots of the given equation.*

These roots could be found *roughly* from the table without plotting. *E.g.*, since the polynomial is negative at $x = 2$, and positive at $x = 3$,

* The value of x at A, B, and C are also called the "zeros" of the polynomial.

we may set it equal to zero somewhere between, and use "Proportional Parts."

§ 20. Number of Roots: Imaginaries. An equation of the first degree has a single root; one of the second degree has two. (These two may, however, be equal, so that only one number satisfies the equation.) Similarly, in general, an equation of the nth degree has n roots. These may be either "real" or "imaginary."

By an imaginary number, you will recall, is meant a number involving the square root (or any even root) of a negative number — $e.g.$, $2 + \sqrt{-5}$. Such a number cannot be approximated by "real" numbers, either positive or negative. Hence imaginary values *cannot be represented graphically*, as long as we use scales consisting of real numbers. If any of the roots of an equation are imaginary, they will therefore not show in the graph.

So, if we find only a few roots for an equation of high degree, it may mean that the others are imaginary. Or it may mean that we have not carried the graph far enough.

The names "real" and "imaginary" are very misleading, as they suggest that one kind of number actually exists and that the other does not. The fact is, these are merely *different kinds* of numbers. Imaginary numbers can be given a perfectly concrete interpretation, which makes them exceedingly useful in Electrical Engineering and elsewhere. (Chapter XV.)

EXERCISES

1. Of what is $x^2 - 10\,x + 25$ the square? Verify by squaring your answer.

2. Add the appropriate number to $x^2 + 8\,x$ to form a perfect square. Of what binomial is your complete expression then the square? (Verify by squaring that binomial.)

3. Like Ex. 2 for $x^2 - 10\,x$; also for $x^2 - \frac{4}{5}\,x$.

4. Solve by completing the square:

(a)	$2\,x^2 - 11\,x + 3 = 0,$	(b)	$5\,x^2 - 4\,x - 12 = 0,$
(c)	$20\,x^2 - 11\,x + 3 = 0,$	(d)	$5\,x^2 + 4\,x + 8 = 0,$
(e)	$x^2 + 6\,x + 13 = 0,$	(f)	$11\,x^2 + 8\,x - 7 = 0,$
(g)	$x^4 - 10\,x^2 + 9 = 0,$	(h)	$2\,x^4 + 5\,x^2 - 1 = 0.$

5. By completing the square show that $x^2 - 8x$ can be written $(x - 4)^2 - n$, where n is a certain number. Hence show that the least possible value of $x^2 - 8x$ is -16.

6. If $M = 10x - x^2$, express M in the form $M = n - (x - a)^2$, where n and a are certain numbers; and thus show that the greatest value of M is 25.

7. In Ex. 2, p. 28, how many inches should be turned up to give the rectangle an area of 70 sq. in.?

8. How wide a margin (top, bottom, and sides alike) on a page 9 in. by 6 in. would leave 26 sq. in. for printed matter?

9. For a simple beam loaded and supported in a certain way, the "bending moment" at any distance (x ft.) from one end is $M = 30x - x^2$. For what value of x will $M = 180$ exactly?

10. Solve graphically:

(a) $x^3 - 4x + 1 = 0$,   (b) $x^2 - x - 5 = 0$,

(c) $x^3 - 3x + 7 = 0$,   (d) $x^4 + x^3 - 12x^2 + 2 = 0$.

11. In Ex. 10 (b) check by completing the square. Also find the roots directly from the table used in Ex. 10 (b). Why the discrepancies?

12. When a sphere of diameter 4 ft. and specific gravity $\frac{3}{4}$ floats in water, the depth of immersion (x ft.) is a root of the equation $x^3 - 6x^2 + 24 = 0$. Find that root. (Why must the other two roots be excluded?)

13. In finding the maximum deflection of a 25-ft. beam loaded in a certain way it is necessary to solve the equation

$$4x^3 - 150x^2 + 1500x - 3125 = 0$$

for x. Do this.

14. Determine the approximate location of the "real" roots of:

(a) $x^3 - 3x^2 - 3x + 18 = 0$,

(b) $x^3 - 41x^2 + 440x - 455 = 0$.

Apparently how many in each case?

15. In Ex. 14 (b) test the value of the given polynomial at $x = 20$. Does this indicate further roots?

16. Solve for x: $x + 2\sqrt{x - 1} = 9$.   Check your results.

17. Point out the error in the following "proof" that $12 = 0$:

Clearly, $\sqrt{x^2} + \sqrt{4y^2} = x + 2y$.

If $x = 6$ and $y = -3$, this equation becomes

$$\sqrt{36} + \sqrt{36} = 6 - 6.$$

I.e., $12 = 0.$

§ 21. Synthetic Substitution. When solving an equation graphically, the table of values is best calculated by the following method.

Illustration. To substitute 2 for x in the polynomial

$$5 x^3 + 13 x^2 - 16 x - 20,$$

multiply the first coefficient (5) by 2, and add to the next coefficient (13); multiply the sum by 2, and add to the next coefficient (-16), etc.

5	$+13$	-16	-20	$\lfloor 2$
	10	$+46$	$+60$	
5	$+23$	$+30$	$+40$	

The final result, 40, is the value of the polynomial when

$$x = 2.$$

This can be verified by substituting directly:

$$5(2)^3 + 13(2)^2 - 16(2) - 20 = 40.$$

The reason this process works is a simple one: Multiplying the 5 by any value of x and adding the 13 gives $5x + 13$; multiplying this sum by x and adding the -16 gives $5x^2 + 13x - 16$; multiplying this sum by x and adding the -20 gives $5x^3 + 13x^2 - 16x - 20$, which is the value of the polynomial. In other words, by multiplying by x at each stage, before introducing the next coefficient, we have multiplied each coefficient by x the proper number of times in all, and have thus built up the polynomial.

To illustrate further, let us substitute -4 for x:

5	$+13$	-16	-20	$\lfloor -4$
	-20	28	-48	
5	-7	$+12$	-68	

The result is -68. Check this. Also examine these steps carefully.

This process is quicker than direct substitution.* Also it shows with certainty when we have gone far enough to get all the real roots.

---

* This is especially true if we write the coefficients ($5, +13, -16, -20$) at the bottom of a loose slip of paper, and slide this down over the page of calculations instead of rewriting the coefficients for each successive substitution. The number substituted, like -4 above, can be written in the second line (instead of the first which is on the loose slip).

E.g., in the present case, there can be no root above 2 nor any below − 4. For substituting − 5 or − 6, etc., instead of − 4, would simply make each successive product and sum numerically larger, while keeping their signs alternately + and −, and could not produce a final zero. Nor could the substitution of + 3 or + 4, etc., instead of + 2. (Why not?)

In any case, we have gone far enough in the negative direction when the successive sums *alternate in sign, beginning with the leading coefficient*; and far enough in the positive direction when the sums *are all positive*.

If any power of x is lacking in a given polynomial, its coefficient is zero; and *this zero must be inserted*.

Thus, to substitute in $2x^5 - 15x^3 + x^2 + 7x$, use the coefficients

$$2 + 0 - 15 + 1 + 7 + 0,$$

since x^4 and the constant term are missing. (Observe the x^2 term here.)

EXERCISES

1. Find approximately the real roots of

(a) $x^3 + 4x^2 - 3x - 11 = 0,$ (b) $x^3 - 7x + 3 = 0,$
(c) $x^4 + 2x^3 - 8x^2 - 3 = 0,$ (d) $x^3 - 6x - 12 = 0,$
(e) $x^4 - x^3 - 20x^2 - 2 = 0,$ (f) $x^5 - 10x + 12 = 0,$
(g) $x^8 - 8x^4 - 15x^2 - 6 = 0,$ (h) $x^9 - 13x^3 + 14 = 0.$

2. The smallest safe diameter (d in.) for the bolts in a certain steel shaft is a root of the equation $d^4 + 320d^2 - 340d - 4290 = 0.$ Find it.

3. Determine the approximate location of all the real roots of the following equations:

(a) $x^4 - 39x^3 + 354x^2 + 640x - 2500 = 0,$
(b) $x^3 + 17x^2 + 40x - 290 = 0.$

(Suggestion: Try values widely separated at first to get an idea of how the polynomial runs.)

4. Solve for x and check carefully:

(a) $x + \sqrt{x^2 - 9} = 1,$ (b) $x + \sqrt{x - 9} = 11,$

(c) $x = \dfrac{9}{x},$ (d) $x + 3 = \dfrac{4}{x}.$

§ 22. Summary of Chapter I. It is often necessary to study the way in which some one quantity varies with another

What value will the one quantity have for any specified value of the other? What maximum and minimum values? What mean value? Is it ever zero? What is the average rate of increase in any interval? The rate at any instant?

If a table of values has been obtained — say experimentally — a graph can be plotted and used to answer such questions approximately. Precise answers should not be expected when our given information about the variable quantities is merely a table of values. More accurate methods will be sought in the following chapters.

Any quadratic equation can be solved exactly by completing the square. Tables of square roots can be used to approximate the results.

The real roots of an equation of any degree can be approximated graphically, the synthetic method of substitution affording a good test as to the sufficiency of the table. Interpolation by proportional parts may be too inaccurate here; but is valuable when the intervals in a table are very small.

Any large error in a table of values can usually be discovered from the resulting irregularity in the graph.

It would be well to read again at this point the suggestions on page 2 as to methods of study. Also, make sure that you know how to deal with each point mentioned in the above summary; and know the meaning of each technical term that has been defined. Do some "self-quizzing"!

EXERCISES

1. Make a list of the basic problems designated by letters (A)–(E) in this chapter. Show by rough drawings and brief statements the procedures for solving these problems.

2. Which quantity would you plot vertically and which horizontally if you wished to show the relation between: The death rate of bacteria and the amount of sunshine? The temperature in a mine and the depth below the surface of the ground? The pressure of superheated steam and the temperature?

3. The area of a wound, A sq. cm., decreased with the time, t days, as in Table 1. Plot the curve of healing. Find the rate at $t = 8$.

4. Table 2 shows the cash surrender value ($\$V$) of a certain life insurance policy after T years. Find graphically and by proportional parts what the value should be when $T = 22$. (Why is there a discrepancy?) What is the rate of increase per year at $T = 20$?

TABLE 1		TABLE 2		TABLE 3		TABLE 4		
t	A	T	V	p	L	$Yr.$	C	R
0	16.2	0	0	-2	79	1922	480	4.99
4	10.7	5	85	-1	94	1923	515	4.86
8	6.5	10	205	0	107	1924	580	4.63
12	3.8	15	351	1	119	1925	665	3.88
16	2.1	20	523	2	127	1926	860	3.29
20	1.0	25	735	3	127	1927	1025	3.12
24	0.4	30	1000	4	119	1928	1140	2.97
				5	86	1929	1215	2.94

5. For some partially deaf persons the loss of serviceable hearing (L units) varied with the pitch (p octaves above middle C) as in Table 3. Plot. At what p was L greatest? How fast did L increase per octave at middle C?

6. Table 4 shows the average annual consumption of electric energy (C kilowatt-hours) by Portland, Ore., homes in the years 1922 to 1929; also the average rate paid (R¢ per kwh.). Plot C and R over the same base line.

7. In testing electrically the structure of an oil deposit, the instrument readings (R units) varied with the horizontal distance (x mi.) as in Table 5. Plot. For what x would R be largest? (This locates the highest point in the oil pocket.)

8. In a gravitational test over an oil deposit, the variation in the time of swing of a pendulum (V millionths sec.) varied with the horizontal distance (x mi.) as in Table 6. Plot. (The graph indicates roughly the form of the upper surface of the oil pocket — inverted.) Where is V lowest?

TABLE 5		TABLE 6		TABLE 7		TABLE 8		TABLE 9	
x	R	x	V	t	S	$Hr.$	I	x	D
0	6.5	0	1.50	0	19	9	3300	0	0
1	11.0	1	1.05	4	36	10	4900	500	20
2	18.0	2	0.55	6	54	11	7100	1000	30
3	20.5	3	0.10	7	62	12	9000	1500	40
4	17.5	4	0.05	9	84	1	8300	2000	48
5	15.0	5	0.35	11	91	2	6100	2500	40
6	12.6	6	1.00	13	93	3	3600	3000	15
								3500	0

9. Cancer tissue placed in a nutrient solution increased in size (S units) after t days as in Table 7. Plot. One tabulated value of S is badly erroneous: correct it.

10. The intensity of the ultraviolet in direct sunlight (I units) at various hours of an April day is shown in Table 8. How fast was I changing at 11 A.M.? At 2 P.M.?

11. Table 9 gives the depth of a river (D ft.) at various distances x feet from one bank, going straight across. Find the approximate area of the cross-section of the river.

12. As a particle P in a pendulum swung from its lowest position L to its highest position H, and back, its speed (v in./sec.) varied with the time (t sec.), as in Table 10.* (a) Find v at $t = .3$; also how fast v was then changing. (b) How far did P travel in going from L to H?

13. The quantity (Q gal.) of a certain mineral water which can be sold at various prices ($P¢$ per gal.) is shown in Table 11. The total expense ($\$E$) of marketing those quantities is also shown. What price gives the greatest net profit? [Hint: Knowing how much is sold at a given price, how would you calculate the receipts? The profit?]

14. Find the radius and length of the largest cylindrical package which can go by parcel post. See Ex. 12, p. 29.

15. Solve graphically $x^2 + x - 10 = 0$. Check by completing the square. Also approximate one root by proportional parts. Why is this inaccurate?

16. Find approximately all the real roots of

$$(a) \qquad x^3 - 12\,x + 48 = 0,$$
$$(b) \quad x^4 - 2\,x^3 - 3\,x^2 + 2 = 0.$$

TABLE 10

t	v
0	6
0.2	4.85
0.4	1.85
0.6	-1.85
0.8	-4.85
1.0	-6

TABLE 11

P	Q	E
30	1400	145
40	1200	125
50	1000	105
60	800	85
70	600	65
80	400	45

* While an actual speed, or rate of motion, is always positive or zero, it is convenient here and in much later work to use a minus sign to indicate a *reversed direction* of motion. Thus, -1.85 in./sec. here means that P is moving at the rate of 1.85 in./sec., but that the motion is now *downward* along the path rather than *upward*.

CHAPTER II

AS TO EXACT RELATIONSHIPS

A. FUNCTIONS AND FORMULAS

§ 23. Formulas. A varying quantity can be represented graphically, subject to the uncertainties and inaccuracies of drawing the curve. Graphs are a suitable and valuable tool in applied mathematics; for comparatively few relationships between variables in the natural and social sciences are known with absolute exactness. Nevertheless exactness is an ideal, which can frequently be attained with the ideal variables of pure mathematics. For this purpose the relations between these ideal variables are generally expressed by means of equations or formulas. And the ideal variables often represent closely the actual varying quantities of science.

Illustration. If a ball be dropped vertically from an airplane, the distance (s ft.) through which it will have fallen when t sec. have elapsed is approximately

$$s = 16\,t^2. \qquad (1)$$

For instance, after 10 sec., $s = 16\,(10^2) = 1600$. That is, the ball will have fallen 1600 ft., approx.

More accurately, the coefficient of t^2 in formula (1) should be 16 plus a small fraction, depending on the latitude of the place. But even this would ignore the effect of air resistance, which is highly important in the case of a rapidly moving object like a pistol bullet, or a light object like a leaf. (In fact, the formula $s = \frac{1}{2}\,gt^2$, often used in Physics for a fall in a perfect vacuum, is not quite exact even there. It ignores the slight variations in the acceleration g during the fall, and certain other minute discrepancies.) So, in illustrative examples, we shall always use the value $16\,t^2$ for simplicity. Anyhow, it is permissible to make a purely mathematical study of an ideal point which would move *exactly* according to equation (1).

We shall, as in Physics, often use the notation s for the "space" or distance traveled, and v for the speed or quantitative measure of the "velocity." Do not mistake s for speed.

Evidently formula (1) is equivalent to a complete table of values of s for all positive values of t — until the ball strikes, after which the formula is no longer valid.

Formulas in general give very full information in a brief form; and they can be carried around much more easily than a graph, or can even be memorized. If themselves exact, formulas can be used to calculate certain related quantities exactly, even rates in very small intervals where a graph ceases to give reliable results.

To illustrate in the case of the falling ball, let us find from formula (1) the average speed, or rate of motion, during an interval of .01 sec. beginning at the instant $t = 3$.

At $\qquad t = 3, \qquad s = 16(3)^2 = 144.$
At $\qquad t = 3.01, \quad s = 16(3.01)^2 = 144.9616.$

During the .01 sec., therefore, the ball falls .9616 ft. Hence its average speed is

$$v = \frac{.9616}{.01} \text{ (ft./sec.)} = 96.16 \text{ (ft./sec.)}.$$

This average speed, by the way, cannot differ much from the *speed at the instant* $t = 3$.

Any algebraic expression involving x, whether it has any concrete meaning or not, may be regarded as a function of x, for it will vary with x in some definite way. *E.g.*, the quantity $2x^3 - 15x + 10$ varies with x, as shown in Fig. 20, p. 32. Any formula, then, such as $y = x^2$, *expresses y algebraically as a function of x.*

§ 24. **Increment Notation.** In calculating rates, etc., it is desirable to have a short notation for the change in one quantity produced by any change in another.

We have already used Δ (delta) to stand for a difference or change in a quantity. Hereafter we shall affix the name of the quantity to prevent any possible ambiguity. Thus

Δx will denote a difference or change in x;
Δy will denote the corresponding change in y.

Observe that Δx does not denote some quantity Δ times the quantity x, but simply the change in x, as stated.

In this notation the average rate of increase of y per unit change in x can be expressed simply as $\Delta y / \Delta x$.

Similarly, in § 23, since $s = 144$ when $t = 3$, and $s = 144.9616$ when $t = 3.01$, we may write

$$\Delta s = .9616, \qquad\qquad \Delta t = .01.$$

$$\therefore \frac{\Delta s}{\Delta t} = 96.16 \quad = \left\{ \begin{array}{l} \text{average rate of increase of } s \text{ per} \\ \text{unit change in } t \text{ during this .01 sec.} \end{array} \right.$$

§ 25. Plotting a Formula. From any given formula we can, if we like, calculate a table of values, and plot a graph — to be used thereafter as a ready computer in reading off further values. This is especially desirable when the formula is very complicated, even though the graph is less precise than the formula.

For instance, the graph of the cost of tanks, shown in Fig. 6, p. 5, saves the designer several hours on each calculation.

Any graph which happens to be straight makes a good computer, if drawn with a ruler on accurate paper.

EXERCISES

1. The assessed value ($\$V$) of a certain house t years after construction will be $V = 2000 - 40\,t$. Plot this from $t = 0$ to $t = 30$, calculating V every five years. What sort of graph do you get?

2. In the formula $y = ax + b$ what is the value of y when $x = 1, 2, 3, 4, k, k + 1$? How much does y increase every time that x increases by 1 unit? Hence what sort of graph must every formula of this type (first degree) have? How many points are needed to plot it?

3. The amount which would accumulate on an original sum of $\$100$ after t months with simple interest at 6% is $A = 100 + .5\,t$. (Why?) Plot this from $t = 0$ to $t = 80$. Read off A when $t = 55$.

4. The distance (s ft.) that an object will fall, from rest, in t sec. is $s = 16\,t^2$. (A) Calculate s at $t = 2$; also the average *speed* during .03 sec. beginning then. (B) Plot s as a function of t from $t = 0$ to $t = 5$; and check the calculated speed.

5. The height of a ball t sec. after being thrown straight upward was $h = 112\,t - 16\,t^2$ feet. Plot. When was the ball highest and how high? When was it 128 ft. high? Check the latter answer by putting $h = 128$ and solving the equation for t.

6. In Ex. 5 calculate the average rate at which the ball rose from $t = 2$ to $t = 2.01$. Check by the graph.

7. At any horizontal distance (x ft.) from the middle of a certain suspension cable the height (y ft.) above the lowest point is given by $y = .02\,x^2$. Plot the curve of the cable from $x = 0$ to $x = 80$. How fast does the cable rise on the average, per horizontal foot, between $x = 50$ and $x = 52$? Check graphically.

8. Every horizontal section of a reservoir is a square, whose side varies thus with the height (h ft.) above the bottom: $s = 30 + 3\,h$. (A) Plot s from $h = 0$ to $h = 10$. (B) Plot the area of the section as a function of h from 0 to 10.

9. In Ex. 8 find how much water must flow in to increase the depth from 4 ft. to 10 ft.

10. The speed of an object (v ft./sec.) after falling s ft. freely from rest is $v = 8\sqrt{s}$. (a) Plot from $s = 0$ to $s = 36$. (Hint: Use $s = 1, 4, \frac{25}{4}, 9$, and other perfect squares.) Read off v when $s = 10, 15, 20$. (b) A ball, dropped from the Washington Monument, had fallen 500 ft. when caught. What speed had it acquired?

11. The time (T sec.) of a complete swing for a pendulum of length l in. is $T = .32\sqrt{l}$. By changing the vertical scale make the graph in Ex. 10 serve for this formula. Read off T if $l = 6, 18, 30$.

[12.] Plot a graph showing how the quantity $y = 60/(x - 3)$ varies with x, from $x = -2$ to $x = 7$. Then find from the equation the value of y when $x = 3.01$, and when $x = 2.99$. Is there any indication of the upper and lower parts of the graph turning toward each other?

§ 26. Varieties of Graphs. The true nature of a function described by a formula can often be realized best by studying its graph: the character of the graph depends upon the type of formula.

E.g., if a formula is *linear* — *i.e.*, of the first degree, the graph is *straight*. (See Ex. 2, p. 42.) To plot it we need calculate but two points, well separated, and join these by a straight line. A third point is desirable as a check.*

Again, if a function is *irrational*, substituting certain values for x may give imaginary results — which cannot be plotted. Thus $\sqrt{25 - x^2}$ is real only between $x = -5$ and $x = +5$, and its graph does not go beyond these values.

Again, the graph of a *polynomial* — *i.e.*, the sum of integral powers of x with given coefficients — such as $2\,x^3 - 15\,x + 10$,

---

* A function like $20/(2\,x - 5)$ which involves x in the *denominator* is not called linear; but only expressions of the form $ax + b$.

is a *smooth curve*, as in Fig. 20, p. 32. But the graph of a
function which has x in the denominator may be startlingly
different. (See § 27.)

§ 27. A Necessary Precaution, illustrated. Let us plot
the graph of the function

$$y = \frac{60}{2 - x} \qquad (2)$$

from $x = -4$ to $x = 8$.

Substituting values for x gives the following table.

x	y	x	y
-4	10	3	-60
-3	12	4	-30
-2	15	5	-20
-1	20	6	-15
0	30	7	-12
1	60	8	-10
2	?		

(What happens when $x = 2$ will be discussed shortly.)

From -4 to 1 and from 3 to 8, the graph runs as indicated
by the curve in Fig. 21. Let us follow the left-hand branch
and see what happens *near* $x = 2$.

Substituting again in the given formula:

at $\qquad x = 1.9, \quad y = \dfrac{60}{2 - 1.9} = 600;$

at $\qquad x = 1.99, \quad y = \dfrac{60}{2 - 1.99} = 6000.$

Evidently the curve is climbing faster and faster, and is
not approaching the other branch. Follow the latter back:

at $\qquad x = 2.1, \quad y = \dfrac{60}{2 - 2.1} = -600;$

at $\qquad x = 2.01, \quad y = -6000.$

The farther we follow either branch toward $x = 2$, the farther it goes from the other — enormously! What is the explanation? How about y when $x = 2$ exactly?

The formula then reads: $y = \frac{60}{0}$. But **division by zero is impossible.** (§ 28, below.) Hence $\frac{60}{0}$ is a meaningless symbol: it does not stand for zero, nor for any other number. That is, no value exists for y when $x = 2$.

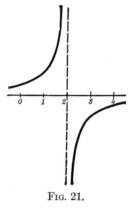

FIG. 21.

This explains the peculiarity of the graph. The curve *nowhere crosses the vertical line at* $x = 2$; for if it did, the ordinate at the crossing would give a definite value for y when $x = 2$. Hence the graph consists of two entirely separate branches. There is a tremendous break at $x = 2$: the function is "discontinuous" there.

Remark. In general, whenever a function involves a fraction, we must see whether any real value of x will reduce the denominator to zero, and the numerator to some other value. If so, the curve will break. To make sure about this, simply set the denominator equal to zero, solve for x, and then test near-by values.

§ 28. Operations with Zero. We can multiply by zero, add or subtract zero, subtract any number from zero, or divide zero by any other number — in short, perform every numerical operation with zero except one:

We cannot divide by zero.

For instance, to divide 60 by zero we should have **to find a** quotient which, multiplied by zero, would give 60:

$$\text{if } \frac{60}{0} = Q, \qquad \text{then } 60 = 0 \cdot Q.$$

But no such quotient exists: *any number whatever, multiplied by zero, gives zero* and not 60.

Erroneous statements are often made in this connection about "infinity" — whatever that may be. The correct statement is that we cannot divide by zero.*

* An explanation of the proper technical use of the term "infinity" may, of course, be given at this point, or postponed, at the discretion of the instructor. See Appendix, p. 528.

Observe further that such an expression as $7 + \frac{60}{0}$ would also be meaningless. We could no more add a number to $\frac{60}{0}$ than we could add a number to a color!

§ 29. Reciprocal Numbers.

One number is called the reciprocal of another if their product is $+1$.

Thus the reciprocal of 3 is $\frac{1}{3}$; the reciprocal of $-\frac{2}{3}$ is $-\frac{5}{2}$; etc. To find the reciprocal of any number, simply divide 1 by that number.

Every number except zero has a reciprocal. But $\frac{1}{0}$ does not exist.

EXERCISES

1. Find the reciprocals of 5, 2.5, .08, $-\frac{2}{7}$, $1\frac{2}{3}$, -100.

2. Show that $\frac{1}{2}(3 + \sqrt{5})$ and $\frac{1}{2}(3 - \sqrt{5})$ are mutually reciprocals; likewise, $\sqrt{2} + 1$ and $\sqrt{2} - 1$; also, $\sqrt{2}$ and $\frac{1}{2}\sqrt{2}$.

3. Carry out these operations with zero, wherever possible: $0 \div 8$, $0 - 7$, $1{,}000{,}000 \times 0$, $7 + \frac{1}{3}(0)$, $\frac{1}{4}(0 - 12)$, $.001 \div 0$, $\frac{1}{2}(-4 - 0)$, 0^3, $\sqrt{0}$, $5 + \frac{2}{0}$.

4. Draw the graphs of the following between $x = -20$ and $x = 50$; then read off the value of y at -8 and $+32$, and check.

    $(a)\ y = 2x - 15$, $(b)\ y = 30 - 6x$, $(c)\ y = x + 10$.

5. Plot these three formulas over the same base line: $y = \frac{3}{2}x + 5$, $y = \frac{3}{2}x$, $y = \frac{3}{2}x - 2$. Similarly for these: $y = x + 2$, $y = .4x + 2$, $y = -x + 2$. In the graph of $y = ax + b$, is the steepness determined by a or by b? What does the other constant determine?

6. The relation between Fahrenheit and Centigrade temperatures is given by $F = 1.8C + 32$. (Check the values for freezing and boiling water.) Plot the graph from $C = -100$ to $C = 200$. Read off F when $C = 135$, and C when $F = -13$. Check each.

7. Plot each of the following from $x = -4$ to $x = 5$, or for as much of this interval as possible:

    $(a)\ y = 2 - x$, $(b)\ y = (2 - x)^2$, $(c)\ y = 4 - x^2$,

    $(d)\ y = \sqrt{2 - x}$, $(e)\ y = \sqrt{4 - x^2}$, $(f)\ y = 10/(2 - x)$.

8. Plot $y = \dfrac{x - 3}{x + 1}$ from $x = -4$ to $x = 5$.

9. At what value of x, if any, would the graph of each following formula break?

    $(a)\ y = \dfrac{20}{x + 4}$, $(b)\ y = \dfrac{20x}{x^2 + 4}$, $(c)\ y = \dfrac{20x}{x^2 - 4}$.

10. When an object x in. away is photographed with a lens of "focal length" F in., the plate should be at a distance y in. from the lens, given by the formula $y = Fx/(x - F)$. Taking F as 25, plot y from $x = 0$ to $x = 90$. Read off y for $x = 12.5$, and for $x = 75$. (Values of x less than 25 correspond to imaginary or "virtual" images.)

11. The time of revolution (T yr.) for a planet at a distance of x units from the sun is $T = \sqrt{x^3}$. [For the earth, $x = 1$.] Plot from $x = 0$ to 35. Read off the value of T for $x = 30.1$ (*Neptune*); also x if $T = .24$ (*Mercury*).

[12.] If $y = k x^2$, where k is some constant, and if $y = 12$ when $x = 2$, find k. Likewise if $y = k/x^2$, and $y = 10$ when $x = 2$.

[13.] If $y = ax + b$, and if $y = 10$ when $x = 2$, and $y = 14$ when $x = 4$, find a and b.

§ 30. Discovering Linear Formulas.

In working with scientific formulas, the question naturally arises as to how they are obtained in the first place.

Some are derived by reasoning from known principles, but many others are *discovered empirically*. That is, experiments are performed, or observations made, and the results noted in the form of a table of values. The question then is purely mathematical: *To find a formula satisfied by all the values in a given table.*

There is no one process by which this can always be done. But we shall from time to time see how all the more common types of laws can be discovered. At present only the simplest case will be considered.

THEOREM. If a quantity y increases at a constant rate per unit change in an independent variable x, the formula for y in terms of x must be of the linear type: $y = ax + b$.

PROOF. Let a denote the constant rate of increase and b the value of y when $x = 0$. Then, when x has increased from 0 to any value X, y will have increased by aX (or a units per unit change in x). Thus y will equal its original value b plus its increase aX:

$$y = aX + b.$$

That is, for every value of x, y is given by a linear formula. (*Q.E.D.*)

To find what values a and b should have in any particular case, we may proceed as in Ex. I below.

Ex. I. Table I shows the amount of potassium iodide (W

grams) which will dissolve in 100 grams of water, at several temperatures ($T°$). Find a formula for the amount which will dissolve at any temperature.

TABLE I

T	W	T	W
10	136	40	160
20	144	50	168
30	152	60	176

By inspection of the table, W increases at a constant rate, .8 gm./deg. Hence the values satisfy a formula of the type:

$$W = aT + b. \qquad (3)$$

For instance,

$$136 = 10\ a + b,$$
$$144 = 20\ a + b, \text{ etc.}$$

To find a and b, we simply take any two such equations formed by substituting from the table, and solve simultaneously. Subtracting eliminates b and gives $a = .8$, the given rate, as should be expected. Substituting this in either equation gives $b = 128$.

That is, if formula (3) is to fit the given table, we must have $a = .8$ and $b = 128$. Thus the required formula is

$$W = .8\ T + 128.$$

Check: This fits all values in the table.

Remark. When a table runs at irregular intervals, we may not be able to tell by inspection whether the rate is constant. But we can tell by *plotting a graph and seeing whether this is straight.* If the rate is not constant, the formula is not linear, and we cannot find it as yet.

§ 31. **Writing Formulas for Laws of Variation.** Often a scientific law states that one quantity y *varies as* another quantity x. By this is meant that the ratio of y to x is some constant k. Or, what is the same thing:

$$y = k x.$$

Similarly, if y varies as x^2, then $y = k x^2$.

Observe that, in the first case, y is proportional to x; and doubling the value of x will double y. But, in the second case, doubling x makes y four times as great.

To say that y *varies inversely as* x^2 means that y varies as the *reciprocal* of x^2. That is, $y = k\,(1/x^2)$, or

$$y = \frac{k}{x^2}. \tag{4}$$

Again, to say that y varies as u *and as* v means that it varies as their product: $y = k\,(uv)$.

Observe that the phrase "varies as x" has a very definite technical meaning, but that y might vary *with* x in any way whatever, even fluctuating while x increases.

Tests given in Chapter VII are used by scientists to ascertain from an experimental table of values whether or not y varies (either directly or inversely) as some power of x. In Table I, § 30, notice that W is not proportional to T, and thus does not vary as T. But the changes in W and T, that is, ΔW and ΔT are proportional. This gives a constant *rate*, and hence a linear formula, $W = aT + b$. If, in another such case, b were zero, W would vary *as* T.

We can find the constant k in any of the cases above, if we know the value of y corresponding to any value of x — or to values of u and v.

Thus, in equation (4), if $y = 10$ when $x = 3$, then

$$10 = \frac{k}{3^2}, \qquad\qquad \therefore\ \ k = 90.$$

The definite formula for y is then: $y = 90/x^2$.

EXERCISES

In Exs. 1–6, show that the formula is linear. Find it, and check for some further value in the table.

1. Table 1 gives the weight of KBr salt (W grams) that will dissolve in 100 grams of water at various temperatures ($T°$). After finding and checking the formula, find W for $T = 17$.

2. The time (t sec.) required for a powder fuse to burn varied with the initial temperature ($T°$) as in Table 2. Find the formula for t.

3. In killing some bacteria by ultraviolet rays, the percentage P surviving after t hr. varied as in Table 3. Find the formula. What percentage had been killed at $t = 3.5$?

4. The *rate* of heat production (R units per sec.) of a muscle stimulated t sec. is shown in Table 4. (*A*) Find the formula. (*B*) Find the total *amount* of heat produced from $t = .5$ to $t = 2.5$.

TABLE 1		TABLE 2		TABLE 3		TABLE 4		TABLE 5	
T	W	T	t	t	P	t	R	V	N
0	54	− 40	38.0	0	100	0.5	6	3	4
20	64	0	35.6	2	81	1.0	10	8	11
40	74	20	34.4	4	62	1.5	14	18	25
60	84	40	33.2	6	43	2.0	18	28	39
80	94	100	29.6			2.5	22	33	46

5. The rate at which the indicator of a certain gas-meter revolves (N rev. per sec.) for various velocities of the gas in the pipe (V ft./sec.) is shown in Table 5. What is the formula? For what V is $N = 0$?

6. The cost ($\$C$) of publishing a certain pamphlet will vary with the number (N) printed, as shown in Table 6. Find C if $N = 3200$. What is the meaning of each constant in the formula?

In Exs. 7–9, there are slight irregularities in each table. Draw what seems to be the most probable straight line among the points; then read values from the line, and use these values to find the formula.

7. The latent heat of steam (L calories) is shown in Table 7 for various temperatures ($T°$). Find an approximate formula.

8. Table 8 gives the average weights (W lb.) of men of various heights (h in.). Express approximately the relation of W to h.

9. Table 9 gives the volume (V cc.) of a certain quantity of gas at several temperatures ($T°$). What formula? Find V at $T = 15$.

TABLE 6		TABLE 7		TABLE 8		TABLE 9	
N	C	T	L	h	W	T	V
1000	150	70	557	61	124	− 30	162
2000	165	85	546	63	132	− 9	176
4000	195	100	536	65	140	6	187
6000	225	115	526	67	148	27	199
7000	240	130	515	69	157	45	212
				71	166		

In the following exercises, obtain the formula expressing the law of variation, and calculate the further values asked for.

10. If y varies as x^4, and $y = 80$ when $x = 2$, what is the formula? Find y when $x = .1$. Find x when $y = 50,000$.

11. The pressure (P lb./sq. ft.) exerted by a wind against a wall varies as the square of the wind velocity (v mi./hr.). $P = 30$ when $v = 90$. Find the formula. What P for $v = 50$?

12. The amount (A gm.) of a substance digested in Q gm. of pepsin in one hour varies as the square root of Q. If $A = 7$ when $Q = 100$, what is the formula?

13. The volume of a gas at a constant temperature varies inversely as the pressure applied. If $V = 200$ when $P = 15$, what is the formula? Find V when $P = 30, 40, 50$.

14. When plants are in rows, the number to an acre varies inversely as the square of the distance (x ft.) apart each way. $N = 10890$ if $x = 2$. Find the formula; also find N if $x = \frac{1}{2}, 3, 6$.

15. The volume of oxygen (V cc.) taken up by some yeast in t min. was proportional to t. At $t = 60$, V was .156. Find the formula. What V at $t = 50$?

16. The sun's attraction (A dynes) upon a remote particle P of radius r cm. varies as r^3; and the repulsion (R dynes) of the sun's light upon P varies as r^2. If $A = .3$ and $R = .2$ when $r = .0001$, find formulas for A and R (valid for particles at that distance from the sun). For what r would $R = A$? What physical effect if R exceeds A?

17. The volume of a liquid flowing through a fine tube per sec., varies as the fourth power of the radius, inversely as the length, and directly as p, the difference in pressure at the ends. Express these facts by a single formula.

18. The fundamental frequency (n vibrations per sec.) of a taut string varies as the square root of the tension (T dynes), inversely as the radius (r cm.), inversely as the length (l cm.) and inversely as the square root of the density (d gm./cc.). Further, $n = 250$ when $r = .05$, $l = 20$, $d = 4$, and $T = 1\ 000\ 000\ \pi$. Find the formula.

§ 32. Negative and Fractional Exponents. It is highly useful to give a meaning to a power x^n even when the exponent n is negative, fractional, or zero.

A positive integral power denotes simply the product of several equal factors. Thus, x^5 stands for the product of five x's. But obviously x^{-5} can have no such meaning. Likewise $x^{\frac{2}{3}}$ and x^0 are quite absurd from this standpoint.

The meanings assigned to such powers may already be familiar to you from algebra. If not, master them thoroughly now.

Definitions	Illustrations

(1) x^{-p} shall stand for $\dfrac{1}{x^p}$; $10^{-3} = \dfrac{1}{10^3} = .001.$

(2) $x^{p/q}$ shall stand for $\sqrt[q]{x^p}$; $10^{\frac{2}{3}} = \sqrt[3]{10^2} = 4.642-.$

(3) x^0 shall equal 1;* $10^0 = 1;\ (-3)^0 = 1$, etc.

Remarks.   (I) These definitions are the only ones possible if the usual laws of exponents are to apply in all cases.

For instance, dividing x^3 by x^5 gives x^{-2} by subtracting exponents; but gives $1/x^2$ by canceling. Thus x^{-2} must equal $1/x^2$, if the law of subtracting exponents is to be valid here. Similarly x^0 would result from dividing x^3 by x^3, and hence must equal 1 if x is not zero.

Again, if the law of dividing exponents when extracting a root is always to apply: $\sqrt[3]{x^4} = x^{\frac{4}{3}}$, etc.

(II) These definitions suffice to determine the value of any numerical expression consisting of rational powers. For instance,

$$y = 7\,(32)^{-\frac{3}{5}} + 8^0 + \frac{1}{4^{-1} - 5^{-1}}$$

is the same thing as

$$y = \frac{7}{\sqrt[5]{32^3}} + 1 + \frac{1}{\frac{1}{4} - \frac{1}{5}} = 21\tfrac{7}{8}.$$

Observe here that the negative exponent -1 belonged to 4 and 5 separately, not to the denominator as a whole. Also, we may first extract the fifth root of 32 and then cube the result.

§ 33. **Power Laws or Formulas.**   We can now bring many varieties of scientific laws under one class. *E.g.*, if y varies as x^2, or inversely as x^2, or as $\sqrt{x}$, so that we have respectively:

$$y = k\,x^2, \qquad y = \frac{k}{x^2}, \qquad y = k\,\sqrt{x},$$

every one of these is included in

$$y = k\,x^n, \tag{5}$$

* However, further discussion is needed if x itself is zero. See the author's *Higher Course*, pp. 308, 313.

by taking, respectively, $n = 2$, $n = -2$, $n = \frac{1}{2}$. Similarly (5) can cover many other formulas by giving other values to n. Thus, if $n = -\frac{1}{2}$, we have $y = k\,x^{-\frac{1}{2}} = k/x^{\frac{1}{2}}$, or

$$y = \frac{k}{\sqrt{x}}.$$

That is, y varies inversely as $\sqrt{x}$.

It is a great advantage in dealing with scientific formulas to be able to study many at once, in the single equation (5). This is possible because we have *generalized the meaning* of a power, to allow n to be negative or fractional. Such generalizations are very typical of modern mathematics.

Whenever y varies as a power of x, in the generalized sense of (5), we say that "y varies according to the Power Law." We also call x^n a Power Function. The graph differs greatly according as n is positive or negative, integral or fractional. (Cf. Figs. 122–23, p. 313.)

§ 34. Exponential Formulas. It is well to contrast the two formulas

$$y = k\,x^2, \qquad\qquad y = k\,(2^x) \qquad (6)$$

The first y varies according to the Power Law: the other behaves very differently. *E.g.*, when $x = 10$, $x^2 = 100$ but $2^x = 1024$; when $x = 0$, $x^2 = 0$ but $2^x = 1$; when $x = -3$, $x^2 = 9$ but $2^x = \frac{1}{8}$. The second y doubles whenever x increases by 1 unit. Not so the first.

The second equation of (6) is called an *exponential* formula or law, because the variable x appears in the exponent. That is, we have a *constant raised to a variable power*. In a Power Formula, the reverse is true; *i.e.*, we have a variable raised to a constant power.

Many scientific laws are expressed by exponential formulas, with positive or negative exponents. (Chapter VII.)

EXERCISES

1. (*a*) Why do we take x^{-5} as standing for $1/x^5$, and x^0 as denoting 1? Illustrate by divisions, using definite powers. (*b*) If $x^{\frac{3}{4}} \cdot x^{\frac{3}{4}} \cdot x^{\frac{3}{4}} \cdot x^{\frac{3}{4}}$ be multiplied by adding exponents, what is the result? Hence, what is the suitable meaning of $x^{\frac{3}{4}}$?

2. When $x = 10$, what is the value of x^{-3}? Of $-x^3$? (Notice the big difference in the meaning of the $-$ signs. Also contrast $x^{\frac{1}{2}}$ with $1/x^2$).

3. What is the meaning of: $x^{\frac{2}{3}}$, $a^{\frac{7}{2}}$, $x^{\frac{1}{4}}$, $x^{-\frac{1}{2}}$, $x^{-\frac{2}{3}}$?

4. Find the values of these expressions:

(a) $2^{-1} - 5^{-1}$, (b) $8^0 + 3^{-2}$, (c) 75×10^{-4},

(d) 30×2^0, (e) $20^0 \div (2^{-1} - 3^{-1})$, (f) $(\frac{1}{5})^{-2} \times 10^{-3}$,

(g) $36^{\frac{3}{2}}$, (h) $27^{-\frac{2}{3}}$, (i) $\frac{3}{4}(16)^{-\frac{1}{4}}$.

5. Express in a form free from negative and zero exponents, and find the value of each quantity when $x = 2$:

(a) $6x^{-3} + x^{-2} + 1.5 x^0$, (b) $\dfrac{7x - 5x^0}{x^{-4}} + 3x^{-1}$.

6. If y varies inversely as x^3, and $y = 5$ when $x = 2$, write a formula for y in terms of x. May this be regarded as a special case of the *Power Law*, $y = kx^n$, for some values of k and n? Explain.

7. Express these equations in the form of the *Power Law*:

$$y = \frac{20}{x^4}, \qquad z = \frac{150}{7x^6}, \qquad r = \frac{\sqrt{v^3}}{5}.$$

In Exs. 8–12, find each formula; then write it as a Power Law, and list the values of k and n.

8. In projecting a lantern slide on a screen, the area (A sq. ft.) of the picture varies as the square of the distance (x ft.) from the lens; and $A = 100$ if $x = 30$.

9. The velocity of water (V ft./sec.) escaping from a dam, through an orifice h ft. below the surface, varies as the square root of h; and $V = 50$ when $h = 100$.

10. The frequency of a radio wave (f megacycles/sec.) is inversely proportional to the wave length (L meters); and $f = 100$ when $L = 3$.

11. The period (P sec.) of a 3-inch pendulum in different localities varies inversely as the square root of the gravitational acceleration (g ft./sec.^{2}); and $P = .5544$ when $g = 32\frac{1}{9}, = (5\frac{2}{3})^2$.

12. Taking as a unit the amount of solar energy received per sq. ft. at the earth, with the sun directly overhead 93 million miles away, write a formula for the energy E similarly received at any distance x million miles from the sun: E varies inversely as x^2.

13. Make a table of values for $y = x^3$ and $y = 3^x$ from $x = -2$ to $x = 6$. Note how differently the two functions change. Name each.

14. If the population P of a city doubles every decade for a half-century, beginning with 7000 people, make a table showing P after t decades, $t = 0$ to $t = 5$. Does this come under the Power Law? The Exponential Law?

15. In Ex. 14, obtain by inspection a formula for the table.

§ 35. Periodic Functions. Many variables studied in science rise to a maximum, fall to a minimum, and repeat this over and over in an unchanging pattern. Hence they are called periodic functions of the time. Their fluctuations can be studied effectively with the help of the following idea.

In a circle of any size (Fig. 22), let a radius OP turn steadily around the center O. The height y of the point P above the horizontal diameter varies with the angle A, rising to the

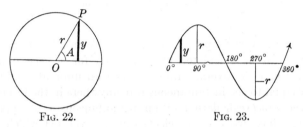

FIG. 22.   FIG. 23.

value r when $A = 90°$, and falling to zero when A reaches 180°. As A goes on to 270° and beyond, P goes below the base line and we consider y negative. When A passes 360°, y repeats its former values. Fig. 23 shows its variations.

In another circle with twice as large a radius, the value of y corresponding to a given value of A will be twice as great as here. But if we divide each y by its own r, the resulting *ratio* y/r will be exactly the same in both cases. Thus, the *ratio* depends only on the size of angle A, and not on the size of the circle. Hence we may say that y/r is a *function of A.*

Likewise if we consider the distance x of the point P to the right of the vertical diameter, x/r is a function of A, and runs through periodic oscillations. Similarly for y/x. All these ratios, and some others, are called *circular functions* of A. Another name is *trigonometric functions*.

These functions will be studied in detail later in the course. In Chapters V–VI we shall use them to solve important problems relating to triangles; and in X–XI to deal with periodically fluctuating quantities.

§ 36. Kinds of Functions. Many quantities vary, at least approximately, according to a Power formula, an Exponential formula, or in some periodic manner like a circular function. Far more do not. Indeed, y may vary with x in any manner whatever, and may have any form of graph. But most cases can be expressed very closely by a combination of a few or many terms of the kinds just mentioned.

Mathematics can study *ideal* variables which *exactly* obey certain laws. Science must deal with the actual variables encountered in nature or in the human world; and must seek, through mathematical means, approximations so close that the discrepancies are unimportant for the objectives in view.

§ 37. Our Next Step.* In formula work an average rate of increase can be calculated exactly, even for a very minute interval; and the average rate for such an interval would be nearly equal to the instantaneous rate anywhere in the interval. But the *exact* calculation of an instantaneous rate appears baffling, since we cannot select any interval for which the average rate will surely equal the required instantaneous rate.

Nevertheless the calculation can easily be made as soon as we see clearly *just what an instantaneous rate is.* This and similar questions will next be considered.

EXERCISES

1. If $y = 10\,x^2$, find the exact average rate at which y increases, per unit change in x, from $x = 3$ to $x = 3.0002$.

[2.] If $R = 25 + 200\,\Delta x$, how small must Δx be chosen in order to have R differ from 25 by less than .000 001?

[3.] In Ex. 1, express the exact average rate at which y increases, while x increases from $x = 3$ to $x = 3 + \Delta x$. How small must Δx be chosen to make this rate differ from 60 by less than .001?

4. The deflection of a beam varies as the cube of the length. If $D = .002$ when $L = 10$, find the formula giving D for any L. Find D when $L = 17$.

5. If the speed of an object (V ft./sec.) varies as the square of the elapsed time (t sec.); and if $V = 16$ when $t = 2$, find the formula for V. How much does V increase between $t = 5$ and $t = 8$? What average *acceleration* during this 3-sec. interval?

* If for any reason it is desired to take up Chapters V and VI early, an interruption of the course as here presented can be made conveniently at this point.

6. In testing the insulation of certain telephone lines it is necessary to find the resistance from the formula

$$R = \frac{15\ 000\ 000}{V} - 100\ 000,$$

for values of the voltage (V) running from 1 to 150. Plot the graph for this interval. Would the complete graph break?

7. Two burners A and B, 10 ft. apart, are of different power. At a distance of 1 ft., A gives 50 calories a second; B, 400 calories. The intensity varies inversely as the square of the distance. What point on the line AB receives the least heat from A and B combined; and how much heat? (§ 15.)

8. If the plates for printing a chart cost $40.00 and the cost of printing is 1.6 cents per copy, what will be the total cost of x copies? Plot from $x = 1000$ to $x = 10,000$. Read off the cost of 8750 copies. How many copies for $75?

9. A wire was stretched, its length $(L$ in.) varying with the pull $(P$ lb.), as in Table 1. Find the formula for L in terms of P. Check. Tell how you would find the work done in stretching the wire from $L = 42.5$ to $L = 43$.

10. Table 2 shows how long $(t$ hr.) after noon of Dec. 21 the winter solstice fell in various years. Plot. Are the breaks in this graph due to nature or to man?

TABLE 1			TABLE 2			
P	L		$Yr.$	t	$Yr.$	t
100	42.5		1924	10	1929	16
200	42.7		1925	16	1930	22
300	42.9		1926	22	1931	28
400	43.1		1927	28	1932	10
500	43.3		1928	10	1933	16

B. Some Basic Ideas Analyzed

§ 38. The Limit Concept. Suppose that y is a function of x; and that we let x approach some fixed value a very closely. Then, in many cases, y will approach some fixed value b, also very closely. By choosing x appropriately near to a, we may be able to bring y *as close to b as we please.* If so, we say that "y approaches the limit b, as x approaches a," written $y \to b$ as $x \to a$.

Ex. I.   Suppose $y = 100\,x + 17$; and let x come very close to 3.   Then y approaches very near to the value 317.   In fact, the difference between y and 317 is

$$D = y - 317 = (100\,x + 17) - 317 = 100\,x - 300;$$
i.e., $D = 100\,(x - 3)$.

Hence, if we wish to make y differ from 317 by less than .04, for instance — in other words, to make D less than .04, or $100\,(x - 3)$ less than .04 — it will suffice to take x so near to 3 that $(x - 3)$ is numerically less than .0004.   That is, x could be chosen anywhere between 3.0004 and 2.9996; and y would surely differ from 317 by less than .04.   Likewise, *no matter how small a positive number* (n) you might first name, we could proceed to make y differ from 317 by less than your n, by choosing x so close to 3 that $(x - 3)$ is numerically less than $\frac{1}{100}\,n$. Hence we may rightly assert that $y \rightarrow 317$ as $x \rightarrow 3$.

Ex. II.   If $Q = 4 - 16\,\Delta t$, and if we let $\Delta t \rightarrow 0$, then $Q \rightarrow 4$. For, if you name *any* small positive n you please, the difference between Q and 4, namely $-16\,\Delta t$, can be made numerically less than n, by choosing Δt numerically less than $\frac{1}{16}\,n$.

Remarks (I).   In saying, above, that *y approaches* 317 as *x approaches* 3, we are making no statement whatever as to what happens to y when x equals 3.   The latter question can, however, be settled by inspection.

(II).   The limit concept is one of the most important in higher mathematics, and lies at the basis of much of the work in this course. Hence the limit definition may well be stated concisely and formally, as follows:

To say that $y \rightarrow b$ as $x \rightarrow a$ means that, *for every pre-assigned positive number n,* however small, *there exists some corresponding positive number p,* such that, when $x - a$ is numerically less than p (though not zero), then $y - b$ is numerically less than n.

§ 39. Instantaneous Speed.

When we speak of the speed of a moving object at a certain *instant*, precisely what do we have in mind?

Not the average speed for the next hour, nor even for the next minute or second.   Nevertheless the average speed for a very short interval would closely approximate the "instantaneous speed" of which we are thinking.   And by making the interval shorter and shorter, we could bring the average speed closer and closer to the instantaneous speed — as close to the latter as we please.

In other words, the speed at any instant is simply **the limit which the average speed would approach,** if the interval were indefinitely shortened (*i.e.*, made to approach zero), while always including the instant.

This statement will be taken as our definition of instantaneous speed.

To calculate an instantaneous speed *exactly*, we must somehow find the limit in question. To do this we shall first find the average speed in an interval of arbitrary length — not a fixed interval such as .01 sec., but an elastic interval of *any* length. Then we shall squeeze this interval down as small as we please, and see what the average speed *approaches*.

Ex. I.   Find the speed at which a ball was rising 3 sec. after it was thrown straight upward, if the height (h ft.) after t sec. was

$$h = 100\,t - 16\,t^2. \tag{7}$$

Consider any interval beginning at $t = 3$; and let Δt denote the length of time in the interval — which therefore ends at $t = 3 + \Delta t$.

By (7) the heights at the beginning and end of the interval were:

at $t = 3$, $h = 100\,(3) - 16\,(3)^2 = 156$;
at $t = 3 + \Delta t$, $h = 100\,(3 + \Delta t) - 16\,(3 + \Delta t)^2$.

Multiplied out and simplified, this latter h reduces to

$$h = 156 + 4\,\Delta t - 16\,\Delta t^2,$$

where Δt^2 denotes the square of Δt, — since Δt is a single quantity. The difference of the two heights, $\Delta h = 4\,\Delta t - 16\,\Delta t^2$, is the distance the ball rose during the interval of Δt sec. (Fig. 24.) Dividing by Δt:

$$\frac{\Delta h}{\Delta t} = 4 - 16\,\Delta t = \text{av. speed during } \Delta t.$$

For instance, if $\Delta t = .01$, we have $4 - 16\,(.01)$, or 3.84, ft./sec. as the average speed from $t = 3$ to $t = 3.01$.

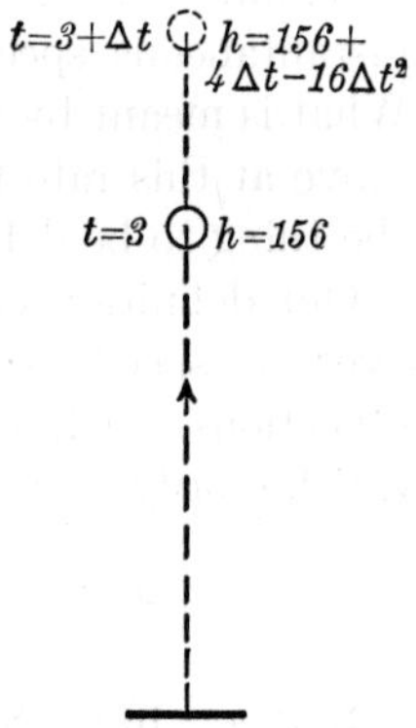

Now let Δt approach zero. The *limit* approached by the average speed $4 - 16\,\Delta t$ is precisely 4. That is, the *instantaneous speed* at $t = 3$ is precisely 4 (ft. per sec.).

$t=3+\Delta t$ $h=156+$
     $4\,\Delta t-16\Delta t^2$

$t=3$ $h=156$

Fig. 24.

Remarks. (I) We do not say that the average speed 4 − 16 Δt will ever be exactly equal to 4. Neither will it ever be equal to the instantaneous speed. But the *limit* which the average speed is *approaching* is exactly 4; and this limit is called the instantaneous speed. Observe that we did not get the latter by letting $\Delta t = 0$.

(II) If our resulting speed had come out *negative*, it would indicate that the ball was *falling* — i.e., that the height was decreasing. (For it would show that the value of h at $t = 3 + \Delta t$ was smaller than the value at $t = 3$, which we subtracted — at least, that this would be so when Δt became small.)*

§ 40. The Limit Idea is Essential to a satisfactory definition of an instantaneous speed.

The distinction between an interval of time and an instant is like that between a line-segment and a point: an interval has some length or extent, but an instant has none. No distance whatever can be traveled "during an instant," for an instant has no duration. Hence it would be meaningless to define an instantaneous speed as "the distance traveled during the instant divided by the length of time in the instant" (!).

Neither can we employ any such idea as "the speed during the shortest possible interval of time." There is no such thing: any interval, however short, has some definite extent, and can be subdivided into billions of still shorter intervals.

Again, it is useless to give any such vague definition of instantaneous speed as "the rate of motion at the instant." What is meant by the "rate at an instant" if the object doesn't move at this rate for even a short interval? This is precisely the thing to be defined.

Our definition of an instantaneous speed as the limit of an average speed is, however, definite, and free from logical objections. Many other familiar concepts can be defined satisfactorily only by using a similar idea.

EXERCISES

1. If $y = 10x + 8$, what limit does y approach as $x \to 3$? Show that you can choose x so near to 3 that y will differ from 38 by less than .0002. Likewise, by less than any assigned positive number n.

* Cf. footnote, p. 39.

2. If $Q = 5 + 1000 \, \Delta t$, what limit does Q approach as $\Delta t \to 0$? Show that you can choose Δt so small that Q will differ from 5 by less than .03. By less than any assigned positive n.

3. Like Ex. 2, if $Q = 5 - 20 \, \Delta t$.

4. The distance (s ft.) that a ball had rolled down an incline after t sec. was $s = 4 \, t^2$. How far had it rolled when $t = 10$? When $t = 10 + \Delta t$? What average speed from $t = 10$ to $t = 10 + \Delta t$? What if $\Delta t = .0001$? Exactly what speed at the instant when $t = 10$?

5. A ball rolled up an incline, its distance from the starting point after t sec. being $s = 60 \, t - 6 \, t^2$. What was its average speed from $t = 2$ to $t = 2 + \Delta t$? Its exact speed at $t = 2$?

6. A stone was dropped from an airplane. Its height above ground t sec. later was $h = 8000 - 16 \, t^2$. Find the rate of fall at $t = 20$.

7. The speed (v ft./sec.) of a car t sec. after starting, and until full speed was reached, varied thus: $v = 4 \, t - .1 \, t^2$. What was the speed at $t = 10$? At $t = 10 + \Delta t$? What was the average *acceleration* during this interval Δt? What acceleration at the instant $t = 10$?

8. The volume of a balloon (V cu. ft.) t hr. after starting was $V = 4000 + 50 \, t^2$. At what average rate did V increase between $t = 3$ and $t = 3 + \Delta t$? How fast was V increasing at the instant $t = 3$?

[9.] If water is flowing from a reservoir more and more slowly, how may we accurately define the *instantaneous* rate of flow at 2 P.M.?

[10.] Precisely what is meant by the "area" or "number of square feet" within a given curve? Such a space cannot be cut up exactly into square feet.

§ 41. Instantaneous Rates in General.

If we say that a balloon "is now expanding at the rate of 50 cu. ft. per min.," precisely what do we mean? Simply this:

The average rate of expansion for any short interval beginning now will be very approximately 50 cu. ft. per min.; and *the limit which this average rate would approach,* if the interval were indefinitely shortened, *is exactly 50 cu. ft. per min.**

---

* Persons unfamiliar with this limit idea are generally unable to explain the precise meaning of such a statement as the one above concerning the balloon. For instance, they will often say: "This means that, if the balloon kept on just as it is now growing, it would expand by 50 cu. ft. in the next minute." (And so it would.) But precisely what is meant by "just as it is now growing"? What is meant by the way, or rate at which, the balloon is expanding at the instant? This is precisely the thing to be explained! Such an explanation merely leads around a circle, and explains nothing at all.

Similarly in general, when we speak of the rate at which any quantity is increasing "at a certain instant," we mean: the limit approached by the average rate in an adjoining interval, as the interval is indefinitely shortened.

To calculate an instantaneous rate, then, we simply get the average rate for an arbitrary adjoining interval, and see what happens to this as the interval approaches zero.

Ex. I.   The volume (V cu. in.) of a certain weight of a gas varies thus with the pressure (p lb. per sq. in.):

$$V = \frac{200}{p}. \tag{8}$$

Find the rate at which V changes per unit change in p, at the instant when p reaches the value 17.

Solution:

At $p = 17$, $\qquad\qquad V = \dfrac{200}{17}.$

At $p = 17 + \Delta p$, $\qquad V = \dfrac{200}{17 + \Delta p}.$

The change in V due to the increase Δp is

$$\Delta V = \frac{200}{17 + \Delta p} - \frac{200}{17}.$$

Reducing to a common denominator and then subtracting gives *

$$\Delta V = \frac{-200\,\Delta p}{17\,(17 + \Delta p)}. \tag{9}$$

Dividing by Δp, the average rate of increase per unit is

$$\frac{\Delta V}{\Delta p} = \frac{-200}{17\,(17 + \Delta p)}. \tag{10}$$

The instantaneous rate is the limit approached by this as Δp approaches zero:

$$\text{Inst. rate} = -\frac{200}{17^2} = -\frac{200}{289}.$$

That is, the volume is at the instant in question *decreasing* at the rate of $\frac{200}{289}$ cu. in. per unit increase in p.   (What shows that the volume is decreasing?   Should that be expected?)

* For the two fractions become, respectively:

$$\frac{3400}{17\,(17 + \Delta p)}, \quad \text{and} \quad \frac{3400 + 200\,\Delta p}{17\,(17 + \Delta p)}.$$

§ 42. Length. As a basis for certain later deductions, let us ask just what is meant by the "length" of a *curved line*, or the "distance" along a curve?

Consider how you would proceed to measure it approximately. Obviously you would measure only a small arc at a time — which would be nearly straight and hence practically coincide with a part of your ruler. In reality, however, you would be measuring not the small arc itself but its *chord*.

The combined lengths of all the chords (Fig. 25) would approximate closely the thing which we call "the length of the curve." The latter we define, then, simply as the *limit* approached by the total length of the chords as their number is indefinitely increased and the length of each approaches zero.

FIG. 25.

E.g., we define the circumference of a circle as the limit approached by the perimeter of a regular inscribed polygon, when the number of sides is indefinitely increased.

The limit idea is essential to a satisfactory definition. Thus it would not do to say merely: "the length of a line is the number of inches it contains." A curved line cannot be cut up into parts each of which would coincide with an inch rule or some fraction thereof. The phrase, "the number of inches which it contains," is meaningless by itself. To speak of "the number of inches *to which it is equivalent*," would be no better. For what is meant by their being "equivalent" other than that they "contain" the same number of inches?

Nor is it any definition to say that the "length of a curve is the length which it would have if straightened out." A geometrical curve must be taken as it is. So must the curved edge of a table, for instance.

Again, if we defined the length of a curve as the length of a rule which would roll along the curve from one end to the other without slipping, we should be presupposing an accurate definition of "rolling without slipping" — which would itself be found to involve the limit idea.

In fact, the idea of a limit is needed to define fully *even the length of a straight line segment.* *E.g.*, the side and diagonal of a unit square are incommensurable.   The diagonal "contains" the unit an irrational number of times (viz. $\sqrt{2}$ times); but this needs explanation, and sooner or later involves the idea of a limit.

§ 43. Area and Volume.   The "area" of any plane figure can be approximated by dividing it into narrow strips and replacing each strip by a rectangle.   (See Fig. 14, p. 23.)   This idea could be used in *defining* the area — say as the limit approached by the sum of the rectangular areas, as each strip becomes indefinitely narrow.

The definitions of the area of a curved surface and the volume of a solid are somewhat similar, but more complicated.

EXERCISES

1. Explain briefly the precise meaning of the following statements. (Each necessarily involves the idea of a limit, approached as an interval is indefinitely shortened.)

(*a*) The water in a basin was flowing out at the rate of 30 cu. in. per min. at the instant when it was 6 in. deep.

(*b*) A wound was healing at the rate of .05 sq. cm. per hr. just five days after the first treatment.

(*c*) Some salt was thrown into a pan of water; 50 sec. later it was dissolving at the rate of .02 oz. per sec.

2. The hourly consumption of coal (*y* tons) in a locomotive varies thus with the speed (*V* mi./hr.): $y = .005 V^2$.   At what average rate does *y* change, per unit increase in *V*, from $V = 30$ to $V = 30 + \Delta V$? What is the instantaneous rate at $V = 30$?

3. The temperature ($T°$) in a wire varied thus with the distance (*x* in.) from one end: $T = 12 x - x^2$.   Find the average rate at which *T* changed, per unit increase in *x*, from $x = 4$ to $x = 4 + \Delta x$; also the instantaneous rate at $x = 4$.

4. The height (*h* ft.) of a suspension cable above a river at a horizontal distance of *x* ft. from the middle, is $h = 100 + .02 x^2$.   Find the instantaneous rate at which the cable rises, per horizontal foot, at $x = 30$.

5. In Ex. 4, plot the curve of the cable from $x = 0$ to $x = 50$; and check graphically the instantaneous rate in question.

6. A square metal plate is heated and expands.   Find the rate at which the area is increasing, per unit change in the edge *x* in., at the instant when $x = 8$.

7. Like Ex. 6 for a circular plate. Find the rate at which A is increasing, per unit change in the radius, when $r = 5$.

8. If $y = 70/x$, at what average rate does y change, per unit increase in x, from $x = 9$ to $x = 11$? From $x = 9$ to $x = 9 + \Delta x$? At what instantaneous rate when $x = 9$?

9. The strength (i amp.) of an electric current varied thus with the resistance (R ohms): $i = 40/R$. Find the instantaneous rate of change of i per ohm, at $R = 9$.

10. The time (T hr.) required for a certain air trip varies thus with the mean speed maintained (V mi./hr.): $T = 1000/V$. How fast does T change with V, at $V = 150$?

11. Two runners, one with a long and the other with a short stride, run a quarter mile on a curved track. If their footsteps follow the same curved line, which steps the greater distance?

12. Criticize the following "Explanation." To say that the volume of a sphere is 200 cu. ft. means that the sphere "contains" 200 cu. ft., or that the "amount of space" is the same as in 200 foot cubes.

[13.] What is meant by a tangent to a circle? Can you draw any sort of curve to which that definition of a tangent line would not apply? Can you suggest any definition which would always apply?

§ 44. Instantaneous Direction.   A moving object usually travels along a curved path, and thus does not move in any one direction during even a small fraction of a second. What then is meant when we say that it "is *now* moving in a certain direction"?

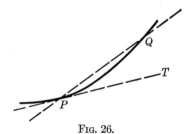

FIG. 26.

The short arc PQ (Fig. 26) passed over in a short time is nearly straight, and hence nearly coincides with its chord. The secant line containing this chord approximates closely what we regard as the instantaneous line of motion — the shorter the time, the better.

The instantaneous direction of motion is simply the *limiting direction* of the secant, as the time-interval (or the length of the chord) approaches zero.

It is often said that the direction of motion at any instant, or the direction of a curve at any point, is the direction of the tangent line.   But why?   Simply because *the tangent line PT is the limiting position approached by the secant line PQ, as Q approaches P along the curve.*

§ 45. Definition of a Tangent Line.   The last statement above will be taken as our definition of a tangent to any curve. Memorize it.

The limit idea is essential.   Various definitions sometimes given for a tangent to a circle are worthless for more complicated curves.

(1) For example, the idea that a tangent is "a line perpendicular to a radius" cannot be applied to either curve in Fig. 27 — unless we can say what constitutes a "radius" of such a curve.   (Not even a short arc of one of these could be a part of a circle, because of the continual change of curvature.)

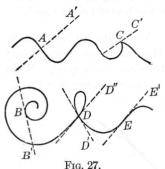

FIG. 27.

(2) The idea that a tangent is "a line meeting the curve at only one point" is unsound. For evidently AA' in Fig. 27 is not what we mean by a tangent, while BB' is clearly tangent at B although meeting the curve at several points.

(3) The idea that a tangent is "a line touching the curve at a point without crossing it there," is also unsatisfactory.   For instance CC' in Fig. 27 meets the curve at C without crossing it but is not what we mean by a tangent — its direction differing from that of the curve at C — while, on the other hand, EE' has the direction of the curve at E, and should be regarded as tangent though it crosses.   (Would you hesitate to call EE' tangent if considering only the part of the curve to the right or left of E alone?)

The important question is not whether a line crosses a curve, but whether it has the *same direction* at the common point.   Our definition of a tangent as the limiting position of a secant insures that the direction will be the same.

If different limiting positions are approached from the right and left, as at D, there are two tangents. If because of any peculiarity of the curve the secant fails to approach a limiting position, no tangent is defined.

§ 46. **Slope or Grade.** To describe the rate at which a line or curve rises, per horizontal unit, we speak of its *slope* or *grade*.

In the case of a straight line, the slope is simply the number of units the line rises in each and every horizontal unit. If it rises 47 ft. in 100 ft. horizontally its slope is .47. Or its grade is 47%.

The slope of a horizontal line is zero. There is no such thing as the slope of a vertical line.

Of course a line may be very nearly vertical and yet have a slope. The slope increases without limit if the line approaches a vertical position indefinitely.

In the case of a curve we speak of the *average slope* in any interval, and also of the *slope at any point.*

By the average slope is meant the average rise per horizontal unit during the interval. (This would equal $\Delta y/\Delta x$ in Fig. 28.) By the slope at any point P is meant the limit approached by the average slope $\Delta y/\Delta x$ as $\Delta x \to 0$.

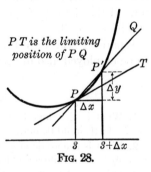

P T is the limiting position of P Q

Fig. 28.

Observe in Fig. 28 that $\Delta y/\Delta x$ is also the slope of the secant line PQ. Its limit is, therefore, the slope of the tangent line PT. Thus the average slope of a curve in any interval is the same as the slope of the secant; and the slope at any point is the same as the slope of the tangent PT.*

Ex. I. The height (y ft.) of a certain suspension cable above its lowest point, at any horizontal distance (x ft.) from the center, is
$$y = .002\ x^2.$$
Find the slope at the point where $x = 100$.

* See footnote, p. 12.

Solution: We first calculate the average slope in any interval, from $x = 100$ to $x = 100 + \Delta x$:

At $x = 100$, $y = .002 \, (100)^2 = 20$;

At $x = 100 + \Delta x$, $y = .002 \, (100 + \Delta x)^2 = 20 + .4 \, \Delta x + .002 \, \Delta x^2$.

The difference of the two heights, $\Delta y = .4 \, \Delta x + .002 \, \Delta x^2$, is the distance the cable rises in the horizontal distance Δx.

$$\therefore \frac{\Delta y}{\Delta x} = .4 + .002 \, \Delta x = \text{av. slope.}$$

Next we let the interval Δx become smaller and smaller, and see what *limit* is approached by this average slope.   Evidently it is .4.

That is, the slope of the curve or of the tangent line at $x = 100$ is .4. Or the "grade" is 40%.

Remark.   When a calculated slope comes out negative, it means simply that the curve is falling toward the right, inasmuch as the new value of y after x has increased is smaller than the original value which was subtracted from it.   (*Cf.* Remark II, § 39.)

§ 47. Drawing a Tangent.   Calculating the slope of a tangent line furnishes a means of drawing the line *exactly*.*

E.g., if the slope is .4, simply draw a line through the given point of tangency, rising .4 units in each horizontal unit, toward the right.   If the slope is $-\frac{4}{3}$, draw a line which falls toward the right $\frac{4}{3}$ of a unit in each horizontal unit — or, say, 4 units in any 3.

Whatever scales are used in plotting a curve are, of course, to be employed also in drawing any tangent line.

EXERCISES

1. What is the slope of a line which rises 8 in. in each horizontal foot?   18 ft. in 30 ft. horizontally?

2. What is the grade of a sidewalk which rises 6 ft. in 50 ft. horizontally?   Of a railroad which rises 66 ft. in 1 mi.?

3. Draw straight lines with these slopes: $2/5$, $-5/2$, $-3/8$; also lines with these grades: 20%, 100%, 60% down grade.

4. What is the grade of a line if the slope is .05?   .85?   7.85?

5. Plot the graph of $y = x^2$ from $x = -3$ to $x = 3$, using the same scales horizontally and vertically.   Draw an apparent tangent at $x = 1$ and measure its slope.   Also *calculate* exactly the rise of this

---

* In the same sense that the constructions of elementary geometry are exact.

curve from $x = 1$ to $x = 1 + \Delta x$. What average slope? What slope at $x = 1$? How could an exact tangent be drawn to this curve?

6. In Ex. 5 calculate also the slope at $x = 2$. Draw a line having that slope.

7. The height (y ft.) of a suspension cable x ft. from the middle is $y = 150 + .01\, x^2$. Calculate the slope at the point where $x = 50$. Show by drawing a line just how steep the cable is at that point.

8. The height (y in.) of a curve, x in. from a certain point horizontally, is $y = .6\, x - .05\, x^2$. Find the slope at $x = 5$.

9. Plot the graph of the function $y = 1/x$ from $x = -3$ to $x = 6$, using the same scale horizontally as vertically. Calculate the exact slope of the tangent line at $x = 2$; and draw the line having that slope — thus checking your curve. (*N.B.* In getting the average slope from 2 to $2 + \Delta x$ it is necessary to subtract one fraction from another. How is this always done?)

§ 48. General Conclusions.

From foregoing examples it seems clear that any term containing Δx, Δx^2, or Δx^3, etc., as a factor, will approach zero as $\Delta x \to 0$, no matter how large a coefficient it may have; also that the sum of any fixed number of such terms must approach zero. That is:

(I) $\ k\, \Delta x^n \to 0$,

(II) $\ a\, \Delta x + b\, \Delta x^2 \ldots + k\, \Delta x^n \to 0$

as $\Delta x \to 0$. (Each coefficient $a, b, \ldots, k$ may be either positive or negative.)

Detailed proofs of these two conclusions are given in more advanced courses.

§ 49. Further Limit Notation.

To denote the limit which a quantity approaches as $\Delta x \to 0$, we shall write the symbol $\underset{\Delta x \to 0}{L}$ before the quantity. Thus $\underset{\Delta x \to 0}{L} (17\, \Delta x^2)$ stands for the limit of $17\, \Delta x^2$ as $\Delta x \to 0$.

In this notation, statements **(I)** and **(II)** above may be re-written thus:

(I) $\ \underset{\Delta x \to 0}{L} (k\, \Delta x^n) = 0$,

(II) $\ \underset{\Delta x \to 0}{L} (a\, \Delta x + b\, \Delta x^2 \ldots + k\, \Delta x^n) = 0$.

These notations should be studied until thoroughly familiar.*

§ 50. Functional Notation.
The letter f is often used to denote a function, the independent variable being written in parentheses after f. Thus $f(x)$ does not mean some quantity f times x, but some function of x — read briefly "f of x." For instance, $f(x)$ might stand for $4 x^3 + 7$, or for 10^x, etc.

The value of $f(x)$ when $x = 3$ is denoted by $f(3)$. Thus if

$$f(x) = 2 x^3 - 15 x,$$
then $$f(3) = 2 (3)^3 - 15 (3) = 9.$$

The statement that "when $x = 3$ the function $= 9$" is summed up in the brief equation $f(3) = 9$.

To distinguish between different functions in the same problem, we denote them by $f(x)$ and $F(x)$, or by $f_1(x)$ and $f_2(x)$, etc.

EXERCISES

1. Exactly what is meant by saying that: As x approaches 2, $(x^2 + x - 1)$ approaches 5 as a limit?

2. Tell in detail exactly what these statements mean:

(a) $$x^4 \rightarrow 16 \text{ as } x \rightarrow 2,$$

(b) $$\underset{x \to 3}{\mathbf{L}} (x^2 - x - 5) = 1,$$

(c) $$\underset{\Delta x \to 0}{\lim} (9 + 20 \Delta x + 5 \Delta x^2) = 9.$$

3. What is the numerical value of $\underset{x \to 10}{\mathbf{L}} (x^3 - 7 x^2 + 80 x - 800)$? Of $\underset{x \to 2}{\lim} \left(\dfrac{x^3 + 1}{x + 4} \right)$? Of $\underset{\Delta x \to 0}{\lim} \left(\dfrac{30 + \Delta x}{5 - \Delta x} \right)$?

4. Point out precisely what is wrong with these notations:

(a) $\underset{x \to 0}{\mathbf{L}} (6 + 5 x) \rightarrow 6,$ (b)   As $x \rightarrow 0$, $(x^2 + 5) = 5.$

5. (a) If $f(x) = x^2 + 10 x$, find $f(1)$, $f(20)$, $f(a)$, $f(2.5)$.

(b) If $F(x) = x^3 - 8$, find $F(0)$, $F(k)$, $F(2 + \Delta x)$, $F(3 + \Delta x)$.

6. If $Q = 30 + 1000 \Delta x$, prove that $Q \rightarrow 30$ as $\Delta x \rightarrow 0$.

---

* Still another notation is to write lim in place of the **L** above. *E.g.*,

(I) $\underset{\Delta x \to 0}{\lim.} (k \Delta x) = 0.$

7. Multiply out, or otherwise expand, and keep the results for reference:

$$(a)\ (x+h)^3, \qquad (b)\ (x+h)^4, \qquad (c)\ (x+h)^5$$

8. (*a*) Calculate the slope of the tangent to the graph of $y = x^3$ at $x = 2$.

(*b*) The angle ($A°$) turned by a wheel after t sec. was $A = t^3$. Calculate the average speed of rotation from $t = 2$ to $t = 2 + \Delta t$. Also the instantaneous speed when $t = 2$.

(*c*) The edge of a cube is increasing. Calculate the instantaneous rate of increase of its volume when the edge $x = 2$. Also the instantaneous rate when $x = a$, any value.

9. Find the slope of the curve $y = 12\,x - x^2$ at $x = 5$; and draw a line having that slope.

10. The repulsion (F dynes) between a certain pair of electrical charges varies thus with the distance (x cm.) apart, $F = 40/x^2$. Find how fast F changes with x, at $x = 3$. (See Ex. 9, p. 69, note.)

11. In Ex. 10 does F vary according to the Power Law, p. 52? If so, what are k and n in this case?

12. In what sense can we say that a ball thrown straight upward is "instantaneously at rest" when it reaches the highest point, and not similarly "at rest" at other instants?

13. "The speed of a pendulum is neither increasing nor decreasing at the lowest point of the swing." Explain what this statement means, in view of the fact that the speed is *not constant* during any interval.

[**14.**] If a smooth curve, such as that in Ex. 9 above, rises to a maximum height and then descends, what slope has it at the highest point?

§ 51. Summary of Chapter II.

A relation between two mathematical variables x and y can often be expressed exactly by a formula. If a table of values shows that y changes with x at a constant rate, the formula must be linear: $y = ax + b$. If y varies as a power of x, we have the Power Law: $y = k\,x^n$. By defining negative and fractional exponents, many apparently different cases can be brought under this one law — including cases of inverse variation. (Adequate tests for this law, and for others involving exponential terms like 2^x, etc., will be given in later chapters.)

With a formula, exact calculations can be made, including instantaneous rates, etc. But it is sometimes advantageous to replace a formula by its graph. The shape of the latter depends upon the type of formula: the curve will break if any value of x makes a denominator equal to zero; or will end abruptly if a radical becomes imaginary.

The idea of a *limit* is essential to a satisfactory definition of an instantaneous speed, slope, or rate, tangent line, direction or length of a curve, area, or volume, etc. Indeed, the idea has much wider application.

But it might conceivably happen in some cases that no limit would be approached. For example, a curve might be so full of sudden turns that a secant line through a given point would approach no definite limiting position while the interval was indefinitely shortened. There would then be no tangent line, nor any slope for the curve, at that point. Likewise, if the sum of the chords inscribed in an arc approached no limit as each was indefinitely shortened, we would not consider the curve as having a "length." Each of our quantities should be defined *conditionally*; for example, "**if** the average rate . . . . . approaches a limit . . . . . , this limit is called the instantaneous rate."

Critical analysis such as we have attempted here — the effort to get at the inner meaning of terms — is the very essence of all accurate thinking. Much fruitless controversy would be avoided in daily life by insisting upon clear ideas and accurate definitions.

Several apparently distinct problems — such as finding the speed of a moving object, the slope of a curve, and the rate of expansion of a metal cube — may in reality be one and the same problem. (Cf. Ex. 8, p. 71.) In fact, a single process will suffice for calculating all instantaneous slopes, speeds, and rates. And so, in the next chapter, we shall reduce this process to a system, whereby we can *write formulas for these quantities at sight,* and can use the formulas readily for many purposes.

CHAPTER III

DIFFERENTIATION

SOME IMPORTANT PHASES OF THE RATE PROBLEM

§ 52. Rate-Formulas. If we wish to know the speed of a moving object at several different instants, we can save time by deriving once for all a general *formula* for the speed at any instant whatever. Similarly for slopes and rates in general.

Ex. I. The height (y ft.) of a vertically thrown ball after t sec. was $y = 100\,t - 16\,t^2$. Find the speed at any instant.

We proceed as when calculating the speed at $t = 3$ (§ 39), but do not specify a particular value for t.

At any instant, $y = 100\,t - 16\,t^2$.
Δt sec. later, $y = 100\,(t + \Delta t) - 16\,(t + \Delta t)^2$.

Simplifying the latter value of y and subtracting the former gives * $\Delta y = 100\,\Delta t - 32\,t\,\Delta t - 16\,\Delta t^2$.

This difference in height is the distance traveled during the Δt sec.

$$\therefore \frac{\Delta y}{\Delta t} = 100 - 32\,t - 16\,\Delta t.$$

This is the average speed during Δt sec. beginning at any time t. The limit approached by this as $\Delta t \to 0$ is

$$\underset{\Delta t \to 0}{\mathbf{L}} \left(\frac{\Delta y}{\Delta t} \right) = 100 - 32\,t. \tag{1}$$

This is the instantaneous speed at the beginning of our interval Δt; *i.e., the speed at any time, t sec. after the ball was thrown.*

For instance:

at $t = 0$,   speed $= 100 - 32\,(0) = 100$ (ft./sec.),
at $t = 3$,   speed $= 100 - 32\,(3) = 4$ (ft./sec.).

This last result was found in § 39. But now we can get the speed at any number of instants, by merely substituting values for t in (1).

---

* Δt will not combine with t as Δt^2, for it is not a product $\Delta \cdot t$ but simply the *difference in t* or "increment" of t. (§ 24.)

From this speed-formula we can also find *exactly when the ball was highest*. For the speed was then exactly zero:

$$100 - 32\,t = 0. \qquad\qquad \therefore\ t = \tfrac{100}{32} = \tfrac{25}{8}.$$

At that instant, $y = 100\,(\tfrac{25}{8}) - 16\,(\tfrac{25}{8})^2 = 156\tfrac{1}{4}$. That is, the maximum height reached was $156\tfrac{1}{4}$ ft.

EXERCISES

1. A bomb was fired straight up, its height (y ft.) after t sec. being $y = 400\,t - 16\,t^2$. Find the speed at any time. In particular what speed at $t = 10$? At $t = 20$? When was the bomb highest? How high?

2. Plot the graph of $y = x^2 - 5\,x + 7$ from $x = 0$ to $x = 4$. Calculate the exact slope at any point. What slope at $x = 2$ and $x = 3$? Find the value of x at which y has its minimum value. What value?

3. A volume of gas (V cu. in.) varied thus with the pressure (P lb./sq. in.): $V = 800/P$. Find the rate of increase of V per unit change in P at any instant. What rate at $P = 20$?

4. As a ball rolled down an incline its distance (x ft.) from the top varied thus with the time (t sec.): $x = 3\,t^2$. Find the speed (v ft./sec.) at any instant. Show that $v = \sqrt{12\,x}$, continually.

5. Calculate the slope of a suspension-cable curve, whose height is $y = .005x^2$ at any point. Where does the slope equal 2?

6. A spherical balloon expands. Find the rate of increase of the volume, per unit change in the radius, at any time.*

7. In Ex. 4, express the last equation as a Power Law. What values have k, n?

§ 53. Derivative of a Function.

Rate, slope, and speed calculations present one and the same problem. Let us, therefore, save time by formulating the problem abstractly in such a way as to cover all these calculations at once — and perhaps others also.

Let y be any function of x. Then if x starts from any value and increases by any amount Δx, y will increase by some Δy (positive, negative, or zero). If Δx is made very small, Δy will usually become very small also; but the fraction $\Delta y/\Delta x$ will ordinarily approach some definite limiting value.

* Formulas for volumes, etc., are given in the Appendix, p. 526.

DEFINITION: *The limit of* $\Delta y/\Delta x$ *as* Δx *approaches zero* is called the *derivative of* y *with respect to* x, and is denoted by dy/dx. That is,

$$\frac{dy}{dx} = \operatorname*{L}_{\Delta x \to 0}\left(\frac{\Delta y}{\Delta x}\right). \tag{2}$$

The notation dy/dx is read "$d\,y$ over $d\,x$"; but we are not using it to denote some quantity dy divided by some dx. We are using it simply as a notation for the limit approached by $\Delta y/\Delta x$.

Though a derivative is thus defined abstractly, yet it has many possible concrete interpretations — and hence everything that we learn about derivatives will apply at once to many different problems. The definition and the following facts should therefore be learned with the greatest care.

§ 54. Interpretations of dy/dx.

Some of the more fundamental interpretations of derivatives will now be mentioned.

(*a*) If y denotes the distance traveled by a moving object, and x denotes the time, then $\Delta y =$ the additional distance traveled in an additional time Δx; and

(*a*)

$$\frac{\Delta y}{\Delta x} = \frac{\text{distance}}{\text{time}} = \text{average speed during } \Delta x;$$

$$\therefore \frac{dy}{dx} = \textit{limit of average speed} = \textit{instantaneous speed.}$$

(*b*) If y denotes the height of a graph and x the horizontal distance from a fixed point, then $\Delta y =$ the rise in a small horizontal distance Δx, starting from some point P; and

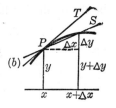

(*b*)

$$\frac{\Delta y}{\Delta x} = \text{average slope of curve during interval } \Delta x;$$

$$\therefore \frac{dy}{dx} = \textit{limit of average slope} = \textit{slope at point } P.$$

(*c*)

FIG. 29.

(*c*) If y denotes any quantity which varies with another, x (*e.g.*, the volume of a fluid, with the temperature x), Δy is the increase (in volume) produced by a rise of Δx (in temperature); and

$\quad \dfrac{\Delta y}{\Delta x}$ = average rate of increase (cubic inches per degree).

$\therefore \dfrac{dy}{dx}$ = *limit of average rate* = *instantaneous rate.*

Thus the derivative dy/dx means instantaneous speed, slope, rate etc., according to the meaning of x and y.

Always, in fact, dy/dx gives the instantaneous rate at which y is changing per unit change in x. Speed is simply the rate at which the traveled distance is increasing per hour (or second, etc.). Slope is the rate at which a curve is rising per horizontal unit.

To find the rate at which any quantity is changing, simply get the derivative of the quantity.

§ 55. Differentiation.

The process of calculating a derivative is called *differentiation*. It is the same as that of finding a formula for an instantaneous rate, speed, or slope; but is usually condensed as follows.

Ex. I.   Differentiate $y = x^3$.

After x has increased, the new value of the function will be the original value y plus some increment Δy.

$$\therefore y + \Delta y = (x + \Delta x)^3,$$

i.e., $\quad\quad y + \Delta y = x^3 + 3\,x^2\Delta x + 3\,x\Delta x^2 + \Delta x^3.$

$$\therefore \Delta y = 3\,x^2\Delta x + 3\,x\Delta x^2 + \Delta x^3.$$

$$\therefore \frac{\Delta y}{\Delta x} = 3\,x^2 + 3\,x\Delta x + \Delta x^2.$$

$$\therefore \frac{dy}{dx} = 3\,x^2.$$

Observe that we get the final value, dy/dx, not by putting $\Delta x = 0$ (which would make $\Delta y/\Delta x$ meaningless), but rather by seeing *what limit* $\Delta y/\Delta x$ *approaches as* $\Delta x \rightarrow 0$.

The resulting derivative, just obtained, may be given various concrete interpretations:

1. If y is the distance traveled by an object in any time x, and $y = x^3$, then the *speed* at any instant is $3\,x^2$.

2. If y is the height of a graph at any horizontal distance x from some fixed point, and $y = x^3$, then the *slope* at any point is $3 x^2$.

3. If y and x are the volume and edge of a metal cube which is being heated, then $y = x^3$, and the rate of increase of the volume per unit change in the edge is at every instant equal to $3 x^2$.

§ 56. Increasing or Decreasing?

We shall often need to test whether a given function $y = f(x)$ is increasing or decreasing, as x increases and passes through some particular value.

Now the graph of a function is rising toward the right at any point where its slope is positive; and falling where its slope is negative. (Cf. Remark, § 46.) That is,

$$y \text{ is increasing where } dy/dx = +,$$
$$y \text{ is decreasing where } dy/dx = -. \tag{3}$$

Remarks. (I) In some cases y increases or decreases steadily through points where $dy/dx = 0$ — that is, where the slope is zero. (Discussed later: § 65.)

(II) It is not a real test of increasing to compare the value of y at the given point with some near-by value. For y might be increasing at the point, and yet have decreased before reaching the comparison value.

But the test given in (3) above is never misleading. For if $\Delta y/\Delta x$ is *ultimately* positive, the neighboring point must ultimately be the higher, and hence y must be increasing.

EXERCISES

1. Differentiate the following functions, and test whether each is increasing or decreasing at $x = 1$ (or $t = 1$):

(a) $y = x^2$,	(b) $y = x^3$,	(c) $y = x^4$,
(d) $y = 5 x^2 - 17$,	(e) $y = x^2 - 5 x + 8$,	(f) $y = 3/x$,
(g) $y = 42 t - 6 t^2$,	(h) $y = t^2 + 20/t$,	(i) $y = 100 t^3$.

2. A ball rolled up an incline so that its distance from the starting point after t sec. was $y = 42 t - 6 t^2$. By Ex. 1 (g) what was the speed at $t = 0, 2, 5$? When was it farthest up, and how far?

3. In Ex. 1 (e), plot y from $x = 0$ to $x = 5$. What is the exact slope at $x = 2$? At $x = 3$? (Check.) Exactly what x gives the minimum y? How small a value?

4. If y denotes the *speed* of a moving object and x the *time*, what is the meaning of $\Delta y/\Delta x$, and of dy/dx?

5. If the speed of a car t sec. after starting was $V = 6\,t - .2\,t^2$, what was the *acceleration* at any time? What at $t = 0, 10, 20$?

6. Along an arch of a bridge the height (y ft.) above the water at any horizontal distance (x ft.) from the center is $y = 90 - .006\,x^2$. Find the slope at any point, and in particular at $x = 50$.

7. Find the derivatives of the following quantities. Substitute some numerical value and interpret each result as a statement about rates.

(a) The distance a ball had fallen after t sec. was $s = 16\,t^2$.

(b) The height of a cable x ft. from the middle is $y = .004\,x^2$.

(c) When a certain locomotive rounds a certain curve at a speed of V mi./hr., the centrifugal force (F tons) is $F = .09\,V^2$.

(d) The repulsion (R dynes) between a certain pair of electrical charges varies thus with their distance apart (x cm.): $R = 20/x^2$.

[**8.**] Compare the results in Ex. 1 (a), (b), (c), above. What would you expect for dy/dx, if $y = x^5$? If $y = x^{10}$? If $y = x^n$?

§ 57. Differentiating x^n by Rule.

As we have noted, it is very common for one quantity (y) to vary as some fixed power of another (x), say

$$y = kx^n. \tag{4}$$

To study rates of increase easily in such cases, we shall now obtain a formula for differentiating any power at sight.

The adjacent table shows the derivatives of three powers of x, as found in Ex. 1, p. 77. These results suggest that the derivative of any positive integral power x^n would be nx^{n-1}. Let us see.

y	$\dfrac{dy}{dx}$
x^2	$2\,x$
x^3	$3\,x^2$
x^4	$4\,x^3$

If $y = x^n$, then $y + \Delta y = (x + \Delta x)^n$.

Multiplied out, $(x + \Delta x)^n$ always gives *

$$(x + \Delta x)^n = x^n + nx^{n-1}\,\Delta x + ax^{n-2}\,\Delta x^2 + bx^{n-3}\,\Delta x^3 + \ldots$$
$$+ nx\,\Delta x^{n-1} + \Delta x^n,$$

where we do not need to know the values of the coefficients a, b, etc.

* If not familiar with the Binomial Theorem, you can check this expansion as follows. $(x + \Delta x)^n$ means $(x + \Delta x) \cdot (x + \Delta x) \cdot (x + \Delta x) \cdot (x + \Delta x) \cdots$ to n factors. Multiplying together the x's of all the n factors gives x^n. Multiplying the Δx in any one factor by the x's in all the others gives $x^{n-1}\,\Delta x$ — and this term will occur n times in all when we use the Δx of one factor after another. Multiplying the Δx's in two or more factors gives terms containing Δx^2 or Δx^3, etc. — whose coefficients we do not need to know.

Subtracting $y = x^n$ gives

$$\Delta y = nx^{n-1} \, \Delta x + ax^{n-2} \, \Delta x^2 + \ldots + \Delta x^n.$$

$$\therefore \frac{\Delta y}{\Delta x} = nx^{n-1} \quad + ax^{n-2} \, \Delta x + \ldots + \Delta x^{n-1}.$$

The limit of this as $\Delta x \to 0$ is simply nx^{n-1}. (§ 48, II.) Thus

$$\frac{dy}{dx} = n\,x^{n-1}. \tag{5}$$

In words: *the derivative of any positive integral power of x equals the exponent of the given power, times the next lower integral power of x.*

By this remarkable rule, we may write certain derivatives at sight. Thus

$$\text{if } y = x^6, \quad \text{then } \frac{dy}{dx} = 6\,x^5;$$

$$\text{if } y = x^{100}, \quad \text{then } \frac{dy}{dx} = 100\,x^{99}.$$

Memorize carefully the verbal statement of rule (5), and that of each similar rule that follows.

N.B. An important special case is the derivative of x itself:

$$\text{if} \quad y = x \, (= x^1), \qquad \frac{dy}{dx} = 1 \cdot x^0 = 1. \qquad (\text{Cf. § 32})$$

This result may also be obtained directly. Thus

$$\text{if} \quad y = x, \qquad \text{then} \qquad y + \Delta y = x + \Delta x.$$

$$\therefore \frac{\Delta y}{\Delta x} = 1, \qquad \text{and} \qquad \frac{dy}{dx} = 1.$$

This means that the rate at which y increases, per unit change in x, is 1 — which is obvious, since $y = x$.

§ 58. Effect of a Constant Multiplier.

What will be the derivative of the product of a function of x by any constant k?

If $y = kf$, then $y + \Delta y = k\,(f + \Delta f)$,

whence

$$\frac{\Delta y}{\Delta x} = k\,\frac{\Delta f}{\Delta x},$$

$$\therefore \frac{dy}{dx} = k\,\frac{df}{dx}.$$

A constant multiplier k simply multiplies the derivative by k.*

     Ex. I.   If $y = 10\,x^3$, $\dfrac{dy}{dx} = 10\,(3\,x^2) = 30\,x^2$.

This means simply that $10\,x^3$ increases just ten times as fast as x^3.

     Ex. II.   If $y = -\tfrac{1}{3}\,x^8$, $\dfrac{dy}{dx} = -\tfrac{1}{3}\,(8\,x^7) = -\tfrac{8}{3}\,x^7$.

     Ex. III.   If $y = 17\,x$, $\dfrac{dy}{dx} = 17\,(1) = 17$.

§ 59. Effect of an Added Constant.

How does a constant which is added to a function affect the derivative?

If $y = f + k$, then $y + \Delta y = (f + \Delta f) + k$.

Obviously k drops out in subtracting to get Δy. Thus $\Delta y / \Delta x$, and hence dy/dx, has the same value as if we were differentiating $y = f$ alone. That is, *a constant added to a function contributes nothing to the derivative.*

     Ex. I.   If $y = x^4 + 1000$, $\dfrac{dy}{dx} = 4\,x^3$.

This means that $(x^4 + 1000)$ increases at the same rate as x^4.

Graphically speaking, adding a constant to a function simply raises or lowers the entire graph by a fixed amount, and does not change the *slope* at any point.

The derivative of an isolated constant is zero. For, if $y = k$, the increment Δy corresponding to any change in x is zero.

     Ex. II.   If $y = 2^{10}$ continually, $\dfrac{dy}{dx} = 0$.

Indeed, the rate of change of 2^{10} is zero.

Though the formula for differentiating x^n has been proved only when n is a positive integer, it holds also when $n = 0$ (if $x \neq 0$). For, if $y = x^0$ the formula would give $dy/dx = 0\,(x^{-1}) = 0$ — the same result as we get by differentiating the equivalent form $y = 1$.

---

* As to variable multipliers, see § 61.

§ 60. Differentiating a Sum. If y is the sum of two functions of x, say $y = f + F$, and if x increases by Δx, then

$$y + \Delta y = f + \Delta f + F + \Delta F.$$

$$\therefore \ \frac{\Delta y}{\Delta x} = \frac{\Delta f}{\Delta x} + \frac{\Delta F}{\Delta x}.$$

$$\therefore \ \frac{dy}{dx} = \frac{df}{dx} + \frac{dF}{dx}.$$

That is, *the derivative of the sum of two functions is simply
the sum of their separate derivatives.*

The same is evidently true for the sum of any specified
number of terms.

Ex. I.   If $y = x^{17} + 4\,x^{10}$, $\dfrac{dy}{dx} = 17\,x^{16} + 40\,x^9$

Ex. II.   If $y = \frac{5}{3}\,x^8 - 15\,x + 4$, $\dfrac{dy}{dx} = \frac{40}{3}\,f^{z}$

We can now write at sight the derivative of any "polynomial," and
use it to solve problems on rates, slopes, etc.

§ 61. Differentiating a Product or Fraction.

Ex. I.   Differentiate $y = (x^2 + 6)(x^3 - 4)$.
Multiplied out: $y = x^5 + 6\,x^3 - 4\,x^2 - 24.$

Differentiated: $\dfrac{dy}{dx} = 5\,x^4 + 18\,x^2 - 8\,x.$

Could this result be obtained by differentiating the factors $(x^2 + 6)$
and $(x^3 - 4)$ separately, and then multiplying the two derivatives
$2\,x$ and $3\,x^2$ together?

Ex. II.   Differentiate $y = \dfrac{x^3 + 72}{x}.$

Divided out: $y = x^2 + \dfrac{72}{x}.$

Since we have as yet no rule for terms with x in the de-
nominator, we resort to the "Δ-process" (§ 55); and get finally

$$\frac{dy}{dx} = 2\,x - \frac{72}{x^2}.$$

This result cannot be obtained by differentiating the numerator and denominator separately.

These examples show that *the derivative of the product or quotient of two functions is NOT equal to the product or quotient of the two derivatives.* At present we differentiate a product by first multiplying out; and use the "Δ-process" for a fraction having x in the denominator.

EXERCISES

1. Differentiate the following functions at sight, writing the functions and their derivatives in parallel columns, like a table:

$$x^{200}, \quad 5\,x^{40}, \quad \tfrac{7}{3}\,x^6, \quad -18\,x, \quad .002\,x^5, \quad -.045\,x^8, \quad \tfrac{25}{2}\,x, \quad \frac{6\,x^{11}}{17}, \quad \frac{-x^3}{12},$$

$$x^4 - 3\,x, \qquad .03\,x^2 - \frac{x}{7}, \qquad \frac{x^3}{5} + x - 10^5, \qquad \frac{7}{2}\,x^4 + \frac{x^3}{9} - \sqrt{7}.$$

2. The same as **Ex. 1** for the following, in which a, b, and c denote constants:

$$x^3 + ax^2 - bx + c; \qquad \frac{5\,ax^6}{3} + \frac{2\,x^4}{b}; \qquad \frac{5\,x^2}{4} - \frac{11\,c}{3}; \qquad \pi x^2.$$

3. Differentiate:

(a) $20\,x^2\,(9 - x)$; (b) $(x^3 - 1)\,(x^2 + 2\,x + 5)$; (c) $(3\,x^2 - 5)^2$.

4. The same as **Ex. 1** for the following, differentiating with respect to the variable named in each case:

$$1.5\,t^3, \quad -9\,t^2/64, \quad 20\,t, \quad r^4, \quad -.07\,v^2, \quad \pi r^2, \quad \tfrac{4}{3}\,\pi r^3.$$

5. The range of a certain gun for various muzzle velocities is $R = .02\,V^2$. How fast does R increase with V at $V = 1200$?

6. Find how fast the volume of a cube increases with the edge x in., when $x = 20$.

7. The speed of a car t sec. after starting was $V = .09\,t^2 - .001\,t^3$. Find the acceleration at $t = 40$.

8. As water leaked out of a pail, the volume (V cu. in.) remaining after t sec. was $V = 2000 - 40\,t + .2\,t^2$. Find how fast the volume was decreasing at $t = 30$.

9. At a temperature of $T°$ the voltage of a certain new battery is $E = 1.454 - .0015\,T + .00001\,T^2$. Find the rate of change of E per degree at $T = 30$. Increasing or decreasing?

10. The volume (V cu. ft.) of a certain ship's hull up to a height of x ft. above the keel is $V = 1600\,x^2 - 80\,x^3 + 2\,x^4 - .02\,x^5$. Find how fast the volume of water displaced increases with the draught (*i.e.,* how fast V increases with x) at $x = 20$.

11. The momentum of a locomotive t min. after starting was $M = 5\,t^2\,(t-20)^2$. Find how fast M was changing at $t = 5$ and at $t = 15$. Increasing or decreasing?

12. The height (y ft.) of a ship's deck, going forward from a certain point A, varies as the square of the horizontal distance (x ft.) from A. If $y = 5.6$ when $x = 200$, find the formula for y at any x. Find the slope of the curve at $x = 200$. Express this as a "grade."

13. The distance (D ft.) required for stopping an auto under normal conditions varies as the square of the speed (V mi./hr.). If $D = 18$ when $V = 20$, write the formula, giving D for any V. Also find how fast D increases with V at $V = 20$; at $V = 60$.

14. Plot $y = x^3 + 5$ from $x = -3$ to $x = 3$, calculating y at $x = \frac{1}{2},$ $-\frac{1}{2}$. Calculate the exact slope at $x = 0$ and 1. Compare the graph.

15. (a) Plot $y = 1.2\,x + 3$ from $x = 0$ to $x = 10$. Measure its slope; and calculate the same by differentiation.

(b) Prove that the graph of any linear function $y = ax + b$ has a constant slope. Hence what sort of graph?

16. Differentiate $y = (x^3 + 6\,x^2 + 8)/x$.

(Hint: Divide out; then differentiate by the Δ-process, § 55.)

17. The same as Ex. 16 for $y = (x^4 - 9\,x^2 + 13)/x^2$.

[18.] The force (F lb.) applied to an object varied thus with the time (t min.): $F = 40\,t - t^2$. Find how fast F was increasing at $t = 10$. Hence, about how much did F increase in the next .03 min.?

19. In Ex. 18 was F increasing or decreasing at $t = 21$?

20. Does each following y increase with x, or decrease, at $x = 10$? (a) $y = 61\,x - 3\,x^2$; (b) $y = x^3 - 31\,x$; (c) $y = x^8 - 11\,x^7$.

§ 62. Note on Mensuration Formulas.

Some elementary formulas for volumes, areas, etc., often used in what follows, are given in the Appendix, p. 526. Recalling certain facts which are proved in geometry may help to fix those formulas in mind.

FIG. 30.

(I) An area is always the product of *two* linear dimensions, while a volume is the product of *three*. Thus a volume formula could never be $2\,\pi rh$, say.

(II) *The same formulas apply to cylinders as to prisms.* The reason is that a cylinder is the limiting form approached by an inscribed prism, when the number of sides of the base is indefinitely increased. For either solid:

$$Volume = (area\ of\ base) \times (height).$$

N.B. "Height" means the perpendicular distance between bases.

(III) *The same formulas apply to cones as to pyramids,* a cone being the limiting form approached by an inscribed pyramid. For either solid:

$$Volume = \tfrac{1}{3}\ (area\ of\ base) \times (height).$$
$$Lateral\ area = \tfrac{1}{2}\ (perimeter\ of\ base) \times (slant\ height).$$

The term "slant height" is meaningless, however, unless the cone is a right circular cone and the pyramid is regular.*

(IV) *The area and circumference of a circle are*

$$\mathbf{A} = \pi r^2, \quad \text{and} \quad \mathbf{C} = 2\,\pi r.$$

(V) *The area and volume of a sphere are*

$$\mathbf{A} = 4\,\pi r^2, \qquad V = \tfrac{4}{3}\,\pi r^3.$$

That is, the area exactly equals four "great circles" cut through the center — a very surprising fact.

The volume equals one third the area times the radius — just as if the sphere were composed of tiny pyramids with their vertices at the center and their bases in the surface.

§ 63. Approximate Increments. For a small interval Δx, the fraction $\Delta y/\Delta x$ and its limit dy/dx are nearly equal. Thus, approximately,

$$\frac{\Delta y}{\Delta x} = \frac{dy}{dx}, \quad \text{or} \quad \Delta y = \left(\frac{dy}{dx}\right)\Delta x. \tag{6}$$

That is, *the change in y, due to a small change in x, is approximately equal to the derivative times* Δx.†

Ex. I. If $y = x^{10}$, how much will y increase when x changes from 2 to 2.003?

Here $\dfrac{dy}{dx} = 10\,x^9, \quad = 5120$ at $x = 2$.

$\therefore\ \Delta y = \left(\dfrac{dy}{dx}\right)\Delta x = (5120)\ .003 = 15.36$, approx.

* Hereafter when we speak of a "cylinder" or a "cone," we shall mean a right circular cylinder or cone, unless something is said to the contrary.

† As to the error in this approximation, see *Higher Course*, pp. 252, 254.

To find Δy *exactly* we should have to calculate $y + \Delta y = (2.003)^{10}$ and subtract $y = 2^{10}$. This tedious operation gives $\Delta y = 15.464\cdots$, nearly the same as the approximation obtained so easily above.

Ex. II.   The edge of a cube was measured as 20 in. but was really 19.98 in.   About how much was the calculated volume in error?

The question amounts to this: By how much would the volume change, if the edge changed from 19.98 to 20 in.?

$$V = x^3,$$

$$\therefore \frac{dV}{dx} = 3\,x^2, \ = 1200 \text{ at } x = 20.$$

$$\therefore \Delta V = \left(\frac{dV}{dx}\right)\Delta x = (1200)\,(.02) = 24, \text{ approx.}$$

The error in the calculated volume was about 24 cu. in.

Remarks.   (I) This result would be affected very little by taking the value of dV/dx at $x = 19.98$ instead of $x = 20$.   *We chose the simpler value.*

Compare the approximate formula $\Delta V = 3\,x^2\Delta x$ with Fig. 31.

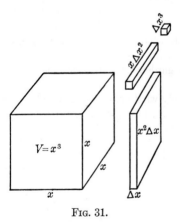

Fig. 31.

(II) In Ex. I if x had changed from 2.001 to 1.998, we should have had $\Delta x = -\,.003$, and would still have calculated dy/dx at $x = 2$, getting $\Delta y = 15.36$, approx.

EXERCISES

1. If $y = 2.5\,x^2$, approximately how much does y increase while x increases from 9.97 to 10.02? Exactly how much?

2. If $y = x^5 - 6\,x^3 + 12\,x - 68$, approximately how much does y increase while x goes from 2 to 2.0002? By about how much should x increase, from $x = 2$, to change y by .007?

3. The factory cost ($\$y$) of producing x tons of a substance daily is $y = 20 + 60\,x - .075\,x^2$. Approximately how much will y increase while x increases from 20 to 20.5? Exactly how much?

4. A 30 gm. mass moving with a speed of v cm./sec. has the kinetic energy, $E = 15\,v^2$. About what change in E if v rises from 9.99 to 10.02?

5. If the population of a city t yr. after Jan. 1, 1900 was $P = 51000 + 800\,t - 10\,t^2$, about what increase in P occurred from $t = 10$ to $t = 10.05$? About how soon after $t = 10$ had P increased by 18?

6. If a metal cube expands so that its edge x increases from 20 in. to 20.002 in., approximately what change in its volume? In its total area? About what change in x would increase the area by .6 sq. in.?

7. Find the approximate change in the volume and area of a ball bearing if it wears down from a radius of 5 mm. to one of 4.96 mm.

8. About what change would be necessary in:

(a) The radius of a spherical balloon, to increase the volume by 16 cu. ft., if the radius is approximately 20 ft.?

(b) The radius of a cylinder, to increase the volume by 4 cu. ft., if the height is constantly 20 ft. and r is about 5 ft.?

9. Approximately what errors will there be in the calculated area

(a) Of a sphere if the radius is taken as 6 in. when really 6.01 in.?

(b) Of a circular garden if the *diameter*, measured as 40 ft. is erroneous by .02 ft.?

10. Approximately what errors would be allowable in the measured

(a) Side of a square (about 20 cm.), if the error in the calculated area is not to exceed 1.25 sq. cm.?

(b) Diameter of a sphere (about 40 cm.), if the calculated volume is not to be in error by more than 10 cc.?

11. In Exs. 9–10 what is the approximate percentage error in each case?

12. The maximum deflection of a beam varies as the cube of the length. If $D = .4$ when $l = 10$, write a formula for D. Approximately how much larger is D for $l = 20.08$ than for $l = 20$?

13. For certain trees of a given height, the volume (V cu. ft.) varies as the square of the diameter (x in.); and $V = 62$ when $x = 20$. Approximately how much larger is V for $x = 30.25$ than for $x = 30$?

14. The heat radiation from an object (H units) varies as the fourth power of the absolute temperature ($T°$), and $H = 81$ when $T = 300$. Approximately what change in H while T increases from 299 to 301?

[**15.**] Criticize this "proof" that $1 = 2$: If $x = 1$, $x^2 - x = x^2 - 1$. Hence, factoring out $x - 1$, we get: $x = x + 1$. That is, $1 = 2$.

§ 64. Note on Zero Factors and Fractions.

As we have previously noted: *A product is zero if any one of its factors is zero;* and, conversely, a product can be zero *only if* some factor is zero.

If we were solving the equation

$$5\,x^4 - 10\,x^3 - 40\,x^2 = 0,$$

and canceled out $5\,x^2$, we should lose the root $x = 0$ — one out of three possible values.

The indiscriminate canceling of factors may easily lead to an erroneous conclusion.

For instance, we might infer from the equation $kx = 17\,x$ that $k = 17$ necessarily — which is not so; k might be 1000, or any other number. For if x happens to be *zero*, $kx = 17\,x$, no matter what value k has.

We can, however, assert that, since $kx - 17\,x = 0$,

$$\therefore\ (k - 17)\,x = 0.$$

And hence, *either* $x = 0$, *or else* $k - 17 = 0$ (making $k = 17$).

Never cancel a factor out of an equation without considering the possibility of its being zero.

Another important principle is this: A fraction can be zero only if its *numerator* is zero.

E.g., if
$$\frac{2\,x^2 - 50}{\sqrt{x^2 + 25}} = 0,$$

then $\qquad 2\,x^2 - 50 = 0, \qquad\qquad \therefore\ x = \pm\,5.$

§ 65. Horizontal Tangents.

Any graph has a horizontal tangent wherever its slope $dy/dx = 0$. Usually it is then turning from rising to falling or vice versa — as at A or B in Fig. 32, p. 88.

But not always. *E.g.*, in the graph of $y = x^3$ (Fig. 33), the slope $dy/dx\ (= 3\,x^2)$ is zero at $x = 0$: but the curve rises through C, being lower everywhere to the left and higher everywhere to the right.

A sure test as to whether there is a turning point can be made by noting the *sign of* dy/dx just before and after. If the sign

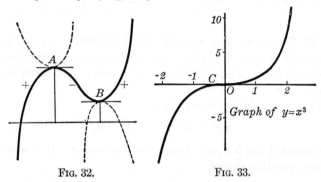

FIG. 32. FIG. 33.

runs $+ - +$ as in Fig. 32, the curve must rise to A, fall to B, and then rise again.

N.B. This curve to the left of A is regarded as a rising rather than a falling curve, because we always think of *going toward the right, with x increasing.*

§ 66. Extreme Values.

As any ordinary (rational algebraic) function y approaches a maximum or minimum value, its graph rises or falls very slowly. At the turning point, the slope is zero.

By using this latter fact, we can locate the extreme values (maxima and minima) of y without plotting. We have simply to set $dy/dx = 0$, solve for x, and substitute in the y equation. To determine whether each result is a maximum or minimum, we simply test the sign of dy/dx for values of x just before and after each.

Ex. I. Find the maximum value of $y = 11\,x - 2\,x^2$.

Here $$\frac{dy}{dx} = 11 - 4\,x.$$

Setting $dy/dx = 0$, and solving for x:

$$11 - 4\,x = 0, \qquad \therefore\ x = \tfrac{11}{4}.$$

DIFFERENTIATION 89

Substituting this value of x in the original equation:

$$y = 11 \left(\tfrac{11}{4}\right) - 2 \left(\tfrac{11}{4}\right)^2 = \tfrac{121}{8} = 15\tfrac{1}{8}.$$

Testing dy/dx at values near $x = \tfrac{11}{4}$, before and after, say at $x = 2$ and $x = 3$, we find:

at $x = 2$, $\dfrac{dy}{dx}$ is $+$, $\therefore$ y is increasing;

at $x = 3$, $\dfrac{dy}{dx}$ is $-$, $\therefore$ y is decreasing.

Clearly, dy/dx can change sign *only* at $x = \tfrac{11}{4}$. Hence y increases until it reaches the value, $y = 15\tfrac{1}{8}$; and then decreases. Thus $15\tfrac{1}{8}$ is the maximum y.

There is no minimum in this case: the graph (Fig. 34) would have no lowest point if continued indefinitely.

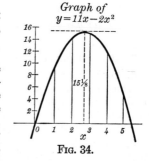

Graph of $y = 11x - 2x^2$

Fig. 34.

Remarks. (I) At A in Fig. 32 the ordinate y reaches a "relative maximum," greater than any near-by value on either side, but not the greatest value anywhere along the graph. There is, frequently, no absolute maximum. Our process will give turning points where a relative maximum or minimum is reached by a function whose graph is a smooth, unbroken curve.

(II) There are some kinds of maximum and minimum problems in which the derivative could not be used. *E.g.*, suppose we ask for the largest integer whose square does not exceed 105. Evidently the answer is 10; but differentiation is not applicable as we are considering only isolated numbers, 1, 2, 3, etc. Or, again, suppose that the height of a ball (h ft.) above ground, t sec. after being dropped from a window, was $h = 400 - 16\,t^2$ — the formula applying only during the free fall. The smallest height was $h = 0$, at $t = 5$; but this could not be found by putting the speed $dh/dt = 0$. (Indeed, the ball struck the ground with considerable speed.) The quantity $400 - 16\,t^2$ would go on decreasing if t went beyond 5; but the free fall to which the formula applies ends at $t = 5$. Thus the minimum is an end-value — a sort of accidental minimum — and is not a turning minimum, down to which h decreases and then increases. (Even if the ball bounced, the same formula did not apply after the impact.)

Still another kind of maximum problem is this: What form should a curve have in order to enclose the greatest possible area for a given perimeter? Questions like this are discussed in a more advanced branch of Mathematical Analysis.

EXERCISES

1. What sure conclusion as to the value of x can you draw from each following equation:

$$(a)\ x^2 = 30\ x? \qquad (b)\ 4\ \pi^2\ x^2 = 25\ \pi x? \qquad (c)\ \frac{2\ x + 3}{x - 5} = 0?$$

2. Test each following function for maximum and minimum values. Check by finding a near-by value of y on each side. Show the general form of the graph near by, indicating the maximum or minimum y.

$$(a)\ y = 9\ x - x^2, \qquad\qquad (b)\ y = x^2 - 8\ x + 10,$$
$$(c)\ y = 12\ x - x^3, \qquad\qquad (d)\ y = x^3 - 5\ x^2 + 3\ x,$$
$$(e)\ y = 100 - x^4, \qquad\qquad (f)\ y = x^4 - 8\ x^2 + 9.$$

3. Plot $y = 4\ x^3 - x^4$ from $x = -2$ to $x = 5$. Test the slope carefully at $x = 0$ and near-by. Any maximum or minimum?

4. For a beam loaded in a certain way the deflection (y ft.) at any horizontal distance (x ft.) from one end is $y = .00001\ (30\ x^2 - x^3)$. Plot a graph showing how y varies with x from $x = 0$ to $x = 30$. [This graph will be the curve of the beam, exaggerated and inverted.] Calculate the maximum y; and check.

5. The work done by exploding a mixture of 1 cu. ft. of coal gas with x cu. ft. of air is $W = 83\ x - 3.2\ x^2$. Find the maximum value of W. (Find dW/dx by the Δ-process, for review.)

6. The speed of a point on a fly-wheel t sec. after starting was $V = 20\ t^2 - t^3$. Was this increasing or decreasing at $t = 13$, and how fast? When was V greatest?

7. In Ex. 2, p. 28, express the area in terms of x, and find its maximum value.

8. A number x minus its square is to be made a maximum. Find x. Check by calculating the difference, for some near-by values.

9. Given a formula for any quantity, how would you find the rate of increase at any instant? The amount of increase in any very small interval? The maximum and minimum values? Whether increasing at any point?

§ 67. Applied Maxima and Minima.
Practical problems concerning maximum and minimum values are usually stated verbally rather than in terms of formulas or functions. In

such cases we must first set up a formula for the quantity in question, expressing it *in terms of some one variable,* say x. Then we can differentiate and proceed as formerly.   (§ 66.)*

Ex. I.   If a rectangle is to have a perimeter of 40 in., what is its greatest possible area?

(Perhaps you could prove geometrically that the rectangle should be a square?   But let us try out our new method.)

The area of *any* rectangle is

$$A = bh. \qquad (7)$$

And if the perimeter is to be 40 in.,

$$2\,b + 2\,h = 40,$$

then $b = 20 - h$.   Substituting this in (7) gives

$$A = (20 - h)\,h = 20\,h - h^2. \qquad (8)$$

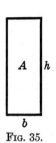

Fig. 35.

A is now expressed in terms of a single variable, h; and we are to find what value of h will make A greatest.   Differentiating:

$$\frac{dA}{dh} = 20 - 2\,h.$$

Equating this derivative to zero gives $h = 10$.   Testing the signs of dA/dh at $h = 9$ and $h = 11$, shows a maximum at 10; viz.

$$A = 20\,(10) - (10)^2 = 100.$$

Remarks.   (I) $h = 10$ requires also $b = 10$: a square.

(II) To keep the perimeter constant, b must change with h in a definite way.   Thus A, though expressed in (7) in terms of two variables b and h, is really a function of either alone; and is not ready for differentiation until so expressed, as in (8).

Ex. II.   Find the volume of the largest right circular cone which can be inscribed in a sphere of diameter 10 in.

For any cone, inscribed or not:

$$V = \tfrac{1}{3}\,\pi r^2 h. \qquad (9)$$

---

* We thus obtain in this way only maxima and minima of the "relative" or turning type. See Remark (II), p. 89.

But in the present case we have, from the right triangle in Fig. 36:

$$r^2 + (h - 5)^2 = 5^2,$$

whence
$$r^2 = 10\,h - h^2.$$

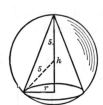

Substituting this value for r^2 in (9) above gives

$$V = \tfrac{1}{3}\,\pi\,(10\,h - h^2)\,h = \frac{\pi}{3}\,(10\,h^2 - h^3). \quad (10)$$

$$\therefore \frac{dV}{dh} = \frac{\pi}{3}\,(20\,h - 3\,h^2),$$

$$\frac{dV}{dh} = 0 \text{ when } h = 0 \text{ or } \tfrac{20}{3}.$$

FIG. 36.

A test shows that $h = 20/3$ makes V a maximum; viz.

$$V = \frac{\pi}{3}\left[10\left(\frac{20}{3}\right)^2 - \left(\frac{20}{3}\right)^3\right] = \frac{4000\,\pi}{81} = 155.1+.$$

N.B. Similarly in any other problem, we first draw a figure (if needed) and write some formula for the quantity which is to be maximized or minimized. Then by using the hypothesis or requirements of the problem, we express everything *in terms of one variable alone* — the choice of this one variable being simply a matter of convenience. (Cf. footnote, p. 104.)

When in doubt, it is well to ask: What is to prevent our making *all* the quantities as large or small as we please? This will direct attention to the limitation or specified relation among the several quantities.

EXERCISES

1. Find as in Ex. I above the largest possible area for a rectangle of perimeter 50 in. Similarly show that, for any specified perimeter P, the area is largest when the rectangle is a square.

2. Find two numbers whose sum shall be 11 and whose product P shall be as large as possible. Check by calculating P for some near-by values.

3. The sum of three sides of a rectangle is to be 50 in. and the area is to be a maximum. Find the sides.

4. What are the dimensions and volume of the largest rectangular box with square ends which can go by parcel post? (See Ex. 12, p. 29.)

5. Of all rectangular boxes having a given length and *given girth*, show by Ex. 1 that the largest end-area (and volume) will occur in the box which has square ends.   If Ex. 4 had not specified square ends, should we have chosen them square anyhow for best results?

6. In Ex. 7, p. 29, express the distance between the ships t hr. after noon.   [*Ans.*, $y = \sqrt{500\,t^2 - 2400\,t + 3600}$.]   Find the minimum value of y^2; and how large y was then.

7. In Ex. 9, p. 29, express L as a function of x alone.   [*Ans.*, $L = 18000\,x - 20\,x^3$.]   What x and y will give the strongest beam?

8. In Ex. 5, p. 28, express the combined length of the three new sides in terms of x — parallel to the wall.   [*Ans.*, $L = x + 260/x$.] Find the minimum L, getting dL/dx by the Δ-process.

9. Find the volume of the largest cone contained in a sphere of diameter 6 in.

10. Like Ex. 9 for the largest cylinder in that sphere.

11. A Norman window has vertical sides and a horizontal base, but the top is a semicircle.   If the perimeter is 10 ft., what dimensions will give the largest possible area?

12. At a price of \$$x$ each, the maker of an article can sell monthly a number $y = 180 - 5\,x$, the cost of which to him was $C = 600 + 4\,y$ (dollars).   What x would maximize his profit?

13. In Ex. 13, p. 39, show that the tabulated values of Q and E satisfy the formulas: $Q = 2000 - 20\,P$, $E = 205 - 2\,P$.   Express the net profit at any price.   [*Ans.*, in cents, $N = 2200\,P - 20\,P^2 - 20500$.]   What P gives the maximum N?   How much?

[14.] Differentiate $y = 1/x^2$ by the Δ-process.   Also differentiate by rewriting y as x^{-2} and using the formula for $y = x^n$.   Reconcile.

§ 68. Differentiating Negative Powers.

Let us now see about a rule for differentiating any *negative* power at sight. Can the standard formula for any positive power $y = x^n$ be used here?

This formula, applied for instance to $y = x^{-10}$, would give

$$\frac{dy}{dx} = -10\,x^{-11};$$

since going down one unit from the exponent -10 would bring us to -11.*

The correctness of this result can be tested by the original increment method of differentiating.   (§ 55.)

---

* Think of the analogy to temperatures below zero.

Since $y = x^{-10} = 1/x^{10}$, we have here $y + \Delta y = 1/(x + \Delta x)^{10}$,

$$\therefore\ \Delta y = \frac{1}{(x + \Delta x)^{10}} - \frac{1}{x^{10}} = \frac{x^{10} - (x + \Delta x)^{10}}{(x + \Delta x)^{10}\, x^{10}}. \qquad (11)$$

By § 57, $(x + \Delta x)^{10} = x^{10} + 10\, x^9\, \Delta x + (ax^8\, \Delta x^2 + \cdots + \Delta x^{10})$.

Subtracting this expansion from x^{10} in (11) gives

$$\Delta y = \frac{-10\, x^9\, \Delta x - (ax^8\, \Delta x^2 + \cdots + \Delta x^{10})}{x^{10}\, (x + \Delta x)^{10}}.$$

$$\therefore\ \frac{\Delta y}{\Delta x} = \frac{-10\, x^9 - (ax^8\, \Delta x + \cdots + \Delta x^9)}{x^{10}\, (x + \Delta x)^{10}}.$$

Now take the limit of this fraction as $\Delta x \to 0$:

$$\frac{dy}{dx} = -\frac{10\, x^9}{x^{20}} = -10\, x^{-11}.$$

This is the same result as was obtained above from the formula for $y = x^n$. Hence that formula works correctly in the case of $y = x^{-10}$.

By precisely the same steps it can be shown to work in the case of any negative power $y = x^{-n}$. (Ex. 20 below.) Hence we can differentiate many fractions without further recourse to the increment method — by simply regarding the fractions as negative powers.

E.g., suppose that $y = 4/x^{100}$.
This is 4 times $1/x^{100}$, or $4\, x^{-100}$.

$$\therefore\ \frac{dy}{dx} = -400\, x^{-101}, \quad = -\frac{400}{x^{101}}\left[\text{not} -\frac{1}{400\, x^{101}}\right].$$

Notice how complicated this differentiation would be by the Δ-process.

Negative powers often arise in problems on maxima and minima.

Ex. I. An open rectangular tank is to contain 500 cu. ft. What is the least possible cost, if the base costs $3 per sq. ft. and the sides $2 per sq. ft.?

The base must be a square.   (Cf. Ex. 5, p. 92.)

The four sides contain 4 hx sq. ft. and cost 8 hx dollars.   The base costs 3 x^2 dollars.   Hence the total cost is

$$T = 3\,x^2 + 8\,hx.$$

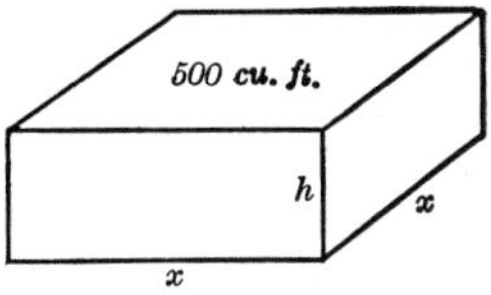

But as the volume is to be 500 cu. ft.,

$$x^2h = 500, \quad \text{or} \quad h = \frac{500}{x^2}. \quad (12)$$

FIG. 37.

$$\therefore\ T = 3\,x^2 + 8\left(\frac{500}{x^2}\right)x = 3\,x^2 + 4000\,x^{-1}.$$

T is now expressed in terms of x alone.   To minimize it:

$$\frac{dT}{dx} = 6\,x - \frac{4000}{x^2} = 0.$$

$$\therefore\ x = \sqrt[3]{2000/3} = 8.74, \text{ approx.,}$$

giving $\quad h = 6.55$, and $T = 687.5$, approx.

Remark.   To find the *relative values* of h and x in this tank, we had best re-write equation (12) as follows:

$$h = \frac{500\,x}{x^3}; \quad \therefore\ h = \frac{500\,x}{2000/3}.$$

Simplified, this gives $h = \frac{3}{4}\,x$; and $T = 9\,x^2$.

EXERCISES

1. Differentiate, and write the results in tabular form:

(a) x^{-7}, $\quad 7\,x^{-5}$, $\quad -\frac{5}{3}\,x^{-6}$, $\quad \dfrac{35}{x^3}$, $\quad \dfrac{-9}{8\,x^{40}}$, $\quad \dfrac{k}{x^2}$, $\quad \dfrac{c}{2\,x^{10}}$;

(b) $x^6 + \dfrac{100}{x^4}$, $\quad \pi x^2 - \dfrac{50}{x}$, $\quad \dfrac{14}{3\,x^6} - 96\,x$, $\quad \dfrac{k}{x^3} + \dfrac{c}{x^2}$.

2. For a certain weight of a gas the volume varied thus with the pressure: $V = 800/P$.   Find the rate of increase of V at $P = 20$. About how much did V change while P increased from 20 to 20.037?

3. Gravitational acceleration (g ft./sec.^{2}) varies thus with the distance (r miles) from the center of the earth: $g = 512000000/r^2$. Find the approximate change in g from $r = 4000$ to $r = 4000.01$.

4. The electrical resistance of a wire varies inversely as the square of the diameter x. If $R = 20$ when $x = 5$, find the formula for R. Also find the rate of change of R at $x = 5$.

5. The current in an electric circuit varies inversely as the resistance. If $c = 60$ when $R = 5$, find the rate of change of c per unit change in R at $R = 20$.

6. Find the minimum value of y in each case:

$$(a) \ y = 2\,x^2 + \frac{500}{x}, \qquad (b) \ y = 4\,x + \frac{200}{x}.$$

7. Find the lowest possible cost of enclosing a rectangular area of 200 sq. yd. with end walls costing \$2 per yd. and side fences costing \$1 per yd.

8. Find the most economical dimensions of an open rectangular box which is to contain 80 cu. ft., if the base costs 50¢ per sq. ft. and the sides 20¢ per sq. ft.

9. The same as Ex. 8, if the base and sides both cost \$2 per sq. ft.

10. An open cylindrical cup is to contain $1000\,\pi$ cu. in. What dimensions will require the least material?

11. The same as Ex. 10, for a closed cylindrical can, to contain
(a) $250\,\pi$ cu. in., (b) 231 cu. in.

12. (a), (b). The same as Ex. 11 (a), (b), if the can is to have its top and bottom of double thickness.

13. Find by using the derivative the smallest possible perimeter for a rectangle whose area is to be 200 sq. in.

14. Find the least possible area for a printed page which shall contain 80 sq. in. of printed matter, with margins 1 in. wide at the sides and 2 in. wide at the top and bottom.

15. A rectangular box with a square base is to contain 45 cu. in. and have a cover cap which will slide on tight for 2 inches. Express the total surface of the box and cap — virtually two open boxes — and find its minimum value. [The resulting equation will need to be solved by trial. § 21.]

16. Similar to Ex. 15 but with a volume of 144 cu. in., and a cap which slides on, half way down.

17. If the total cost (\$$T$) of producing x units of a commodity is $T = 25 + 10\,x + .02\,x^2$, what x will give the lowest cost per unit?

18. Find the least possible cost for a voyage of 1000 mi., if the hourly cost (\$$y$) at a speed of v mi./hr. is $y = 160 + .01\,v^3$.

[19.] The distance (y ft.) traveled by an object in the first t min. was $y = 30\,t^2 - t^3$. Find the speed and acceleration at $t = 10$.

20. Prove the differentiation formula (5) correct for any negative integral power, $y = x^{-n}$. [The steps are the same as for x^{-10} above.]

§ **69. Further Notation.**   The derivative of any function $f(x)$, being itself some function of x, is often denoted by $f'(x)$, read "f prime of x."   Thus:

$$\text{if} \quad f(x) = x^4, \qquad \text{then} \quad f'(x) = 4\,x^3.$$

A derivative is often denoted also by writing $\dfrac{d}{dx}$ or $\dfrac{d}{dr}$, etc., before the function differentiated.   *E.g.*,

$$\frac{d}{dx}\,(x^4) = 4\,x^3, \qquad\qquad \frac{d}{dr}\,(\pi r^2) = 2\,\pi r.$$

Thus, if $y = f(x)$, the following notations are equivalent:

$$\frac{dy}{dx} = \frac{d}{dx}\,(y) = \frac{d}{dx}\,f(x) = f'(x) = \underset{\Delta x \to 0}{\text{L}}\left(\frac{\Delta y}{\Delta x}\right).$$

§ **70. Repeated Differentiations.**   Suppose we have given a formula for the distance (y ft.) traveled by an object in t min., say

$$\text{dist.,} \quad y = 20\,t^3 - t^4. \tag{13}$$

And suppose we wish to find the *acceleration* at any time — *i.e.*, the rate at which the speed is changing.

Differentiating (13) gives the speed at any time:

$$\text{speed,} \quad v = 60\,t^2 - 4\,t^3.$$

But we wish to know how fast the speed is changing.   Hence we must differentiate the speed.   (The fact that we have already performed a differentiation in getting the speed makes no difference.)

$$\therefore\ \text{accel.} = \frac{dv}{dt} = 120\,t - 12\,t^2.$$

For instance, at $t = 5$, the acceleration is $120\,(5) - 12\,(5)^2$ or 300 units.   That is, the speed is increasing at the rate of 300 ft./min. gained per min.   This is abbreviated 300 ft./min.[2]

To make this calculation, we had to differentiate twice in succession.   If we had wished to know the rate at which the acceleration is increasing, we should have had to differentiate a third time.

In general, *to find the rate at which any quantity is changing, we must find the derivative of that quantity* — no matter how many differentiations may already have been performed in getting that quantity.

There are many problems requiring repeated differentiations. Another illustration follows.

Ex. I.   The height of a curve at any horizontal distance x from a fixed point O is

$$y = x^3 - 15\,x^2.$$

Find how fast the slope is changing per horizontal unit at $x = 10$.

Solution.   Differentiating once gives the slope:

$$\text{slope,} \quad l = 3\,x^2 - 30\,x. \tag{14}$$

Differentiating again gives the rate at which the slope is changing:

$$\text{rate,} \quad \frac{dl}{dx} = 6\,x - 30, \quad = 30 \text{ at } x = 10.$$

That is, the slope is increasing at the rate of 30 per horizontal unit. To check this, let us calculate the slopes at $x = 9$ and $x = 11$. By (14) these are $l = -27$ and $l = +33$. The increase is $\Delta l = 60$ in two horizontal units, making the average rate 30 per unit.

Definition.   The rate at which the slope of a curve is changing at any point is called the *flexion*.

§ 71. Derivatives of Any Order.

§ **71. Derivatives of Any Order.**   The derivative of the derivative dy/dx is called the "second derivative" of the original function $y = f(x)$, and is denoted* by $\dfrac{d^2y}{dx^2}$ or $f''(x)$. These symbols are read: "$d\,2\,y$ over $d\,x$ square" and "f second of x."

Similarly the derivative of $f''(x)$ is called the "third derivative," and is denoted by $f'''(x)$ or $\dfrac{d^3y}{dx^3}$. And so on.

---

* Observe where the indices 2 are written. We may think of these as indicating that the operation denoted by $\dfrac{d}{dx}$ is to be performed twice upon y.

Ex. I.   If $y = x^{10} + 1/x^2$, find d^3y/dx^3.

$$\frac{dy}{dx} = 10\,x^9 - 2\,x^{-3},$$

$$\frac{d^2y}{dx^2} = 90\,x^8 + 6\,x^{-4},$$

$$\frac{d^3y}{dx^3} = 720\,x^7 - 24\,x^{-5}.$$

EXERCISES

1. Find the second derivatives of the following·

$y = x^6 + 2\,x^3 + 35\,x,$ $\qquad$ $y = 1.5/x^{10},$ $\qquad$ $y = 30\,t^2 - t^5,$

$P = x + 8 + \dfrac{400}{x^2},$ $\qquad$ $V = \tfrac{4}{3}\,\pi r^3,$ $\qquad$ $S = t\,(30 - t^2).$

2. Find the fourth derivative of $y = x^5 + 6\,x^2 - 27\,x + 25.$

3. Find d^5y/dx^5 if $y = .02\,x^{10} + x^3/2 + 1/x.$

4. For a ball thrown straight upward the height after t sec. was $y = 88\,t - 16\,t^2$. Find the speed and acceleration at any instant.

5. The distance (y ft.) that a ball rolled in t sec. was $y = 20\,t + 10\,t^2$. Find the speed and acceleration at $t = 3$.

6. In the curve $y = x^3$ find the slope and flexion at $x = 5$.

7. The same as Ex. 6 for a suspension cable if $y = .4\,x^2$.

8. The same for the curve of a beam if $y = .001\,(x^3 - 60\,x^2)$.

9. How fast is the slope of the curve $y = x^3 - 2\,x + 1$ changing (per horizontal unit) at $x = 2$?   Check by computing the exact slopes at $x = 1.99$ and 2.01.

10. In t seconds after brakes were applied a train moved a distance (s ft.) given by $s = 44\,t - 4\,t^2$.   Find how fast it was moving when $t = 2$.   Also how fast its speed was then decreasing.

11. The distance an object traveled in t minutes was $y = 8\,t^3 - .1\,t^4$. Plot a graph showing y as a function of t from $t = 0$ to 60, substituting 0, 10, 20, etc.

[**12.**] Plot a graph showing how the speed v increased with t in Ex. 11. What were the maximum and minimum values of v — by the graph, and by calculation?

13. How would you proceed to find the rate at which the acceleration of a moving object is increasing at any instant: (a) If given a formula for the speed at any time?   (b) If given a formula for the distance traveled?

§ 72 S. Derived Curves. The slope of any given curve f varies with x in some definite way. This variation is most clearly shown by plotting another

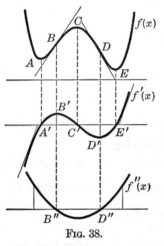

curve f', whose height is everywhere equal to the slope of curve f, or derivative of $f(x)$. (Fig. 38.)

Observe how the zero slope of f at A, C, and E appears in the "derived curve" f', as a zero height, at A', C', E'. Again, the maximum and minimum slopes of f at B and D give maximum and minimum ordinates for f' at B' and D'.* When curve f descends, it has a negative slope, and f' a negative height.

FIG. 38.

A further derived curve can be drawn to show how the slope of f' changes; *i.e.*, the variation of $f''(x)$. (This is often done, as far as $f^{\text{iv}}(x)$, in studying the bending of loaded beams.) We may, then, interpret $f''(x)$ either as the flexion of curve f, or as the slope of f'. or as the height of the second derived curve f''.

§ 73 S. Points of Inflection. In drawing an accurate graph it is helpful to locate the "points of inflection" (such as B and D, in Fig. 38), where the curve has a maximum or minimum slope. For near such points the curve is very nearly straight, almost coinciding with its tangent line for some distance.

Ex. I. Find the maximum and minimum slopes of curve f in Fig. 38, if the height at any point is

$$y = x^4 - 8\,x^2 - x + 16. \tag{15}$$

The slope at any point is

$$l = \frac{dy}{dx} = 4\,x^3 - 16\,x - 1. \tag{16}$$

---

* Slope is not simply a measure of steepness. It has a *sign*, and at D the slope of f has fallen to a negative value lower than that on either side for some distance.

To make this slope a maximum or minimum, we make *its* derivative zero:

$$\frac{dl}{dx} = 12\,x^2 - 16 = 0. \tag{17}$$

This gives $\qquad x = \pm \sqrt{4/3} = \pm 1.155$, approx.

Testing $x = -2, -1, 1, 2$, in (17) shows l to be a maximum at $x = -1.155$, and a minimum at $x = 1.155$. By (16) these maximum and minimum slopes are 11.32 and -13.32; and by (15) they occur at points B and D, having $y = 8.19$ and 5.96.

Observe that the derivative to be tested "before and after" is the one which we have set equal to zero.

§ 74 S. Maximum Rates. It is often important to know when a quantity will be increasing most rapidly. This is very different from the question as to when the quantity will be greatest.

For instance, in Fig. 38, the slope of curve f is greatest at B, but is changing very slowly in that vicinity. Again, in the same curve, the height is increasing most rapidly at B, but is greatest at C. Another illustration follows.

Ex. I. The distance (y ft.) traveled by an object in t min. was

$$y = 6\,t^5 - t^6.$$

Find when the acceleration was increasing most rapidly.

The question is not when the acceleration was greatest but when *its rate of increase* was greatest.

$$v = \frac{dy}{dt} = 30\,t^4 - 6\,t^5, \ = \text{speed},$$

$$a = \frac{d^2y}{dt^2} = 120\,t^3 - 30\,t^4, \ = \text{accel}.$$

The rate of increase of the acceleration is

$$R = \frac{d^3y}{dt^3} = 360\,t^2 - 120\,t^3, \ \textit{to be max.} \tag{18}$$

$$\therefore \frac{dR}{dt} = 720\,t - 360\,t^2 = 0.$$

This gives $t = 0$ or 2.   The latter value makes R a maximum,

for at $$t = 1 \text{ and } 3 : \frac{dR}{dt} = +, - \cdot$$

To find the maximum R, substitute $t = 2$ in (18).

Remark.   It is helpful to label successive derivatives and introduce a single letter (as R above) for the quantity which is to be a maximum or minimum.   Decide at the outset which quantity that is, and when you reach it in differentiating set *its* derivative equal to zero.

EXERCISES

1. The distance traveled by an object in t min. was $y = 30\,t^4 - t^5$. Find when the speed was a maximum; likewise the acceleration.

2. In Ex. 1 find when the acceleration was increasing most rapidly.

3. If the distance traveled in t min. was $y = 60\,t^3 - t^4$, find the acceleration a at $t = 20$.   Was a then increasing or decreasing, and how rapidly?   Find the maximum acceleration.

4. The height of a curve is $y = 36\,x^2 - x^4$.   Where is the slope a maximum?   Where is the slope increasing most rapidly?

5. The height of a curve is $y = 6\,x^4 - x^5$.   Find where the slope is a maximum, and where the flexion increases most rapidly.

6. The kinetic energy of a motorcycle t minutes after starting was $E = 100\,t^4 - 20\,t^5 + t^6$.   Find when E was increasing most rapidly.

7. A beam loaded in a certain way bends so as to form the curve $y = .00002\,x^4 - .003\,x^2$.   Plot y on a large scale, from $x = 0$ to $x = 10$. Show the exact tangent at any point of inflection.

8. Plot $y = x^3 - 12\,x + 10$ from $x = -4$ to $x = 4$.   Where does y reach a maximum or minimum?   What slope at any point of inflection?

9. (A) In Ex. 8, measure the slope at several points; and plot the derived curve f'.   Check some points of f' by calculation.

(B) Check further by measuring some slopes for f', and see whether these will make the second derived curve f'' straight.

[10.] Find dy/dx from $y = (x^5 + 1)^3$ after multiplying out.   Reduce to $dy/dx = 15\,x^4\,(x^5 + 1)^2$.   Can you see any simple rule which would give this same result without multiplying out?

§ 75. Indirect Dependence.

Heretofore each function that we have differentiated has been expressed directly in terms of its independent variable — say y in terms of x.   But there are cases in which y is given in terms of some other quantity u, and u in terms of x. y is then in reality a function of x, although expressed as such only indirectly.

For instance, if $y = u^5$ and $u = x^2$, then $y = x^{10}$.

In this instance, it is easy to change from the indirect relation between y and x in terms of u, to the direct relation $y = x^{10}$. And if we wish to know the rate of increase of y per unit change in x, we simply differentiate this last equation, getting $dy/dx = 10\,x^9$.

But it is sometimes very inconvenient to change to the direct relation between y and x; and we therefore need some method of finding dy/dx even while y is expressed indirectly in terms of u.

Notice the difference between dy/dx and dy/du. The latter would be the rate of increase of y *per unit change in u*. We want dy/dx.

(To distinguish verbally between dy/dx and dy/du, we call one the derivative with respect to x, and the other the derivative with respect to u.)

§ **76. Differentiating a Function of a Function.** If y is given as a function of u, and u as a function of x, say

$$y = F(u), \qquad u = f(x), \tag{19}$$

how can we find dy/dx immediately?

Increasing x by Δx would evidently increase u by some Δu, and hence y by some Δy. We seek dy/dx, the limit of $\Delta y/\Delta x$. But evidently

$$\frac{\Delta y}{\Delta x} = \frac{\Delta y}{\Delta u} \cdot \frac{\Delta u}{\Delta x}. \tag{20}$$

Taking the limits of these fractions (if the limits exist) gives

$$\frac{dy}{dx} = \frac{dy}{du} \cdot \frac{du}{dx}. \tag{21}$$

That is, to find dy/dx in (19) above, we have merely to *find dy/du from the first equation, and du/dx from the second, and then multiply the results.*

Thus if y is increasing at the rate of 10 units per unit change in u, and u at the rate of 6 units per unit of x, then y is increasing at the rate of 60 units per unit of x.

Ex. I. If $y = u^7 + 2\,u^4$, and $u = x^5 + 1$, find dy/dx.

Here $\dfrac{dy}{du} = 7\,u^6 + 8\,u^3$, $\dfrac{du}{dx} = 5\,x^4$.

Hence by (21), $\dfrac{dy}{dx} = (7\,u^6 + 8\,u^3)\,(5\,x^4)$.

It would be possible here to express y directly in terms of x, multiply out, and then differentiate. But this would be inconvenient.

Formula (21) will be used in deriving further differentiation formulas; and should be carefully memorized.*

§ 77. Differentiating a Power of a Quantity. Let u denote any function of x, or quantity involving x. Then if

$$y = u^n,$$

$dy/du = nu^{n-1}$, and hence by (21) above:

$$\frac{dy}{dx} = n\,u^{n-1}\,\frac{du}{dx}. \tag{22}$$

That is, *the derivative of any integral power of a quantity equals the given exponent times the next lower power of that same quantity, times the derivative of that quantity.*

By this theorem we can now differentiate at sight any integral power of a quantity, without first multiplying out or using the Δ-process.

Ex. I. $y = (x^2 + 3\,x - 7)^{100}$.

Here $\dfrac{dy}{dx} = 100\,(x^2 + 3\,x - 7)^{99} \cdot (2\,x + 3)$.

For any numerical value of x, this result can be calculated very quickly by logarithms. (Chap. VI.)

---

* Formula (21) also shows why, in maximizing or minimizing a quantity V which depends on two related variables x and y (as in § 67), we get the same result whether we express V as a function of x alone or of y alone. Since

$$\frac{dV}{dx} = \frac{dV}{dy} \cdot \frac{dy}{dx},$$

$dV/dx = 0$ and $dV/dy = 0$ simultaneously — provided dy/dx is finite and not zero.

N.B. Here y is given directly in terms of x, but not as a *power* of x. To differentiate by the short power-rule, we must regard y as a power of a *quantity* u ($= x^2 + 3x - 7$); and thus from the practical standpoint the case is one of indirect dependence, coming under (22) or (21) above

Ex. II. $\quad y = \dfrac{4}{(10-x)^3} \qquad$ *i.e.*, $y = 4(10-x)^{-3}$.

Here $\quad \dfrac{dy}{dx} = -12(10-x)^{-4}(-1), = \dfrac{12}{(10-x)^4}.$

(The factor -1 comes in as the derivative of the quantity in parentheses.)

EXERCISES

1. In the following cases of indirect dependence find dy/dx:

(a) $y = u^3 - 6u + 4, \quad u = x^3 - 1;$ (b) $y = u^5 + 5/u, \quad u = x^2 + 10;$
(c) $y = u^{50} - .02u^{10}, \quad u = 7x + 3;$ (d) $y = u^{20} - 75, \quad u = x^6.$

2. In Ex. 1 (d) express y in terms of x, differentiate, and compare.

3. In the following find the derivative with respect to t:

(a) $V = x^3, \quad x = 8t^{40} - 17;$ (b) $A = \pi r^2, \quad r = 2.5t^2 + t.$

[**4.**] The edge of a cube (x in.) increased at the rate of .002 in./hr. Can you find how fast the volume was increasing at the instant when $x = 20$? (Hint: We know dx/dt and wish to find dV/dt.)

5. Write at sight the derivatives of the following:

(a) $y = (x^4 + 2)^{1000}$, (b) $y = (36 - t^2)^9$,

(c) $z = .08(2x + 7)^6$, (d) $V = \tfrac{4}{3}\pi(2-x)^3$,

(e) $y = \dfrac{120}{(t^3-1)^7}$, (f) $y = \dfrac{15}{4(9+x)^2}$,

(g) $u = \dfrac{3}{7(8-t)}$, (h) $Q = \dfrac{15}{4(9+x^2)}.$

6. The kinetic energy of a moving object, t sec. after starting, was $E = 5(40t - t^2)^2$. How fast was this increasing at $t = 10$?

7. In Ex. 7, p. 57, express the total amount of heat as a function of the distance x from A. Find the minimum value of H.

8. The resistance (R ohms) of an electric wire 100 M. long varies thus with the radius (x cm.): $R = .0048/x^2$; and x varies thus with the absolute temperature ($T°$): $x = .1991 + .000\ 003T$. How fast does R change with T, per degree, at $T = 300$?

9. In a factory the monthly expenditure ($\$E$) varies thus with the output (u units): $E = 2000 + 18\ u - .01\ u^2$. To sell the output and operate steadily, u is regulated by the selling price ($\$x$ per unit): $u = 2000 - 20\ x$. How fast does E change with x, at $x = 20$?

10. In Ex. 9 what x would give the greatest profit? How much?

§ 78. Rate Problems Requiring Indirect Differentiation.

EXAMPLE: The edge (x in.) of an expanding metal cube is increasing at the rate of .04 in./hr. How fast is the volume increasing (per hour) at the instant when $x = 10$?

This is in effect a problem of indirect dependence: We know how V depends on x, and how x varies with the time t:

$$V = x^3, \quad \text{and} \quad \frac{dx}{dt} = .04;$$

and we are to find how V varies with t at a certain instant. V depends on t — but through the medium of x, so to speak.

By § 76,

$$\frac{dV}{dt} = \frac{dV}{dx} \cdot \frac{dx}{dt}, \tag{23}$$

i.e.,

$$\frac{dV}{dt} = 3\ x^2 \frac{dx}{dt}. \tag{24}$$

At the specified instant this becomes

$$\frac{dV}{dt} = 3\ (10)^2\ (.04) = 12.$$

I.e., the volume is increasing at the rate of 12 cu. in./hr.

Notice particularly the factor dx/dt in (24). This should not surprise us; for the rate at which V changes per hr. must depend upon the rate at which x changes per hr., or vice versa. It would be absurd to write simply $dV/dt = 3\ x^2$; and thus assert in effect that the rate at which V changes has nothing to do with the rate at which x changes.

On the other hand, the equation $dV/dx = 3\ x^2$ is reasonable. It merely gives the rate at which V changes *per unit change in x*.

In general, whenever we have one quantity (y) expressed in terms of another (x), and we differentiate with respect to the time, or any other third variable (t), the result will be *the ordinary derivative (dy/dx) multiplied by an extra factor (dx/dt):*

$$\text{if} \quad y = f(x), \qquad \text{then} \quad \frac{dy}{dt} = f'(x) \cdot \frac{dx}{dt}. \qquad (25)$$

This is, in fact, precisely what the general theorem on in-direct dependence shows, merely changing u and x in (21) to x and t.

Hereafter, then, we may differentiate with respect to a third variable t as just stated without explicitly thinking of (21).

Ex. I. $y = x^6$.   Here $\dfrac{dy}{dt} = 6\,x^5\,\dfrac{dx}{dt}$.

Ex. II. $S = 4\,\pi r^2$.   Here $\dfrac{dS}{dt} = 8\,\pi r\,\dfrac{dr}{dt}$.

N.B.   Compare Ex. I carefully with this differentiation:

$$y = (t^{10} + 1)^6, \qquad\qquad \frac{dy}{dt} = 6\,(t^{10} + 1)^5 \cdot 10\,t^9.$$

In each case we are differentiating with respect to t a power of a *quantity*, not simply t. In one case the quantity is $(t^{10} + 1)$, in the other x.

§ 79. Related Rates.   It is profitable to look at the fore-going problem of the expanding cube from another angle.

There we had given *two related quantities* V and x,

$$V = x^3,$$

and the rate at which one of them was changing,

$$dx/dt = .04,$$

and we had to find *how fast the other was changing.*

This is typical of many problems which arise in scientific work. In any such case we simply differentiate the given equation of relationship (like $V = x^3$) *with respect to t,* and substitute any given values.

Ex. I. From a conical filter whose height is three times the radius, a fluid filtered out at the rate of .3 cu. in./min. How fast was the level falling, when the fluid was 6 in. deep in the middle? (Fig. 39.)

For the shrinking fluid cone we have

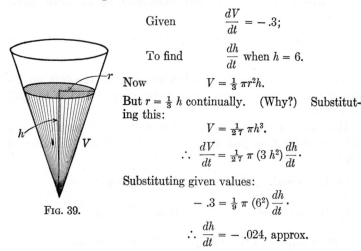

$$\text{Given} \qquad \frac{dV}{dt} = -.3;$$

$$\text{To find} \qquad \frac{dh}{dt} \text{ when } h = 6.$$

Now $\qquad V = \frac{1}{3}\pi r^2 h.$

But $r = \frac{1}{3}h$ continually. (Why?) Substituting this:

$$V = \tfrac{1}{27}\pi h^3.$$

$$\therefore \frac{dV}{dt} = \tfrac{1}{27}\pi\,(3\,h^2)\frac{dh}{dt}.$$

Substituting given values:

$$-.3 = \tfrac{1}{9}\pi\,(6^2)\frac{dh}{dt}.$$

$$\therefore \frac{dh}{dt} = -.024, \text{ approx.}$$

Fig. 39.

The level was falling at the rate of .024 in./min.

EXERCISES

1. Find the derivative with respect to t of each following quantity (assuming all the letters, except π, to vary with t):

$y = x^9,$ $\qquad y = 4\,x^{30},$ $\qquad y = .015/x^4,$ $\qquad y = .2\,x^3 - 7\,x,$

$Q = x^{-5},$ $\qquad V = \frac{4}{3}\pi r^3,$ $\qquad W = \frac{5}{2}\,s - s^2,$ $\qquad T = h^2 + 6/h.$

2. Like Ex. 1 for the following quantities:

$$y = 2.5\,(9 - x^2)^4, \qquad Q = x^2 + y^2 + z^2, \qquad M = \frac{200}{(12 + p)^2}.$$

3. The radius of a spherical balloon increased at the rate of .02 ft./min. How fast was the volume increasing at the instant when $r = 15$? Likewise the surface area?

4. The volume of a cube was increasing at the rate of 300 cu. in./min. at the instant when the edge was 20 inches. How fast was the edge changing?

5. The height of a cone constantly equals the diameter of the base. If the volume increases at the rate of 50 cu. in./hr., find the rate of change of the radius when $r = 5$.

6. Sand, falling at the rate of 3 cu. ft./min., forms a conical pile whose radius always equals twice the height. How fast is the height increasing when $h = 10$? [How do you account for the very small answer?]

7. Solve Ex. I, § 79, taking the given rate as .06 cu. in./min., and the specified depth as 3 in.

8. A cylinder contracts so that its height always equals four times its radius. If the volume is decreasing at the rate of 2 cu. in./hr., how fast is r decreasing when $r = 10$?

9. A sphere is expanding at the rate of 12 cu. in./min. Find how fast the radius and surface area are increasing when $r = 20$. About how much will they increase in the next 6 sec.?

10. The volume of a quantity of gas varied thus: $V = 800/p$. If p increased at the rate of .5 lb./min., how fast was V changing when $p = 20$?

11. The volume (V cc.) of a kilogram of water varies with the temperature ($T°$ C.) thus: $V = 1000 - .0576\,T + .00756\,T^2 - .0000351\,T^3$. If T rises at the rate of .02 deg./min., how fast will V be increasing when $T = 20$?

12. The volume of a balloon was increasing with the temperature at the rate of 10 cu. ft./deg., when the radius r was 10 ft. How fast was r then increasing, per degree?

13. (a) Obtain equation (24) by the Δ-process. [Observe that $\Delta V/\Delta t$ will contain a factor $\Delta x/\Delta t$, which gives rise to dx/dt.] (b) Similarly show that if $S = 4\,\pi r^2$, $dS/dt = 8\,\pi r\,dr/dt$.

§ 80 S. Differentiating Implicitly.

EXAMPLE: A ship A sailing eastward at the rate of 12 mi. per hr. left a certain point five hours before another ship B arrived from the north coming at 16 mi. per hr. How fast was the distance AB changing two hours after A left?

Let Fig. 40 represent the positions at any time. Then

$$\frac{dx}{dt} = 12, \quad \frac{dy}{dt} = -16,$$

and we are to find dz/dt when $x = 24$ and $y = 48$.

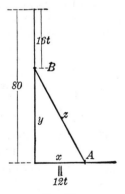

FIG. 40.

At any time, t hr. after A left, we should have

$$x = 12\, t, \qquad y = 80 - 16\, t. \tag{26}$$

$$\therefore\ z = \sqrt{x^2 + y^2} = \sqrt{6400 - 2560\, t + 400\, t^2}.$$

We have as yet no formula for differentiating such a function, as this radical is a *fractional* power. But we can proceed as follows.

Since z^2 and $x^2 + y^2$ are constantly equal, they must be changing at the same rate. Hence their derivatives with respect to t are equal. In other words, since

$$z^2 = x^2 + y^2,$$

$$\therefore\ 2\, z \frac{dz}{dt} = 2\, x \frac{dx}{dt} + 2\, y \frac{dy}{dt}^{*}. \tag{27}$$

Substituting the given values, with the corresponding value of z, $= \sqrt{24^2 + 48^2}$ or $\sqrt{2880}$:

$$2 \sqrt{2880}\ \frac{dz}{dt} = 2\,(24)\,(12) + 2\,(48)\,(-16).$$

$$\therefore\ \frac{dz}{dt} = \frac{-480}{\sqrt{2880}} = -8.95.$$

That is, the distance AB was decreasing at the rate of 8.95 mi./hr.

Remarks. (I) This method of finding dz/dt without first solving explicitly for z is called *implicit differentiation*. Notice carefully the reasoning involved; also that the result would have been badly erroneous if we had overlooked the negative sign for dy/dt.

(II) When one side of a varying triangle remains fixed, its numerical value should be used from the outset, rather than an unknown letter. One term in the equation corresponding to (27) is then zero.

(III) The minimum value of z above can be found thus:

Put $dz/dt = 0$, and by equation (27) we must have

$$x \frac{dx}{dt} + y \frac{dy}{dt} = 0.$$

That is, $12\, x - 16\, y = 0$. Or introducing t by (26) above:

$$12\,(12\, t) - 16\,(80 - 16\, t) = 0.$$

Solving this for t gives $t = 3.2$, whence $z = 48$ — the minimum.

---

* If in doubt as to this, denote z^2 by Q; and note that, if $Q = z^2$, then $dQ/dt = 2\, z\, dz/dt$. [Cf. (25).] Similarly for the derivatives of x^2 and y^2.

EXERCISES

1. What form would equation (27) take if the equation preceding it were changed to $z^2 = x^2 + 2500$?   What if we had $x^2 + y^2 = 100$ constantly?

2. A ladder 25 ft. long leans against a vertical wall.   If its foot is pulled away horizontally at the rate of .06 ft./sec., how fast is the top descending when 20 ft. high?

3. An airplane flying horizontally at the rate of 200 ft./sec. passes straight over a pool, at an elevation of 6000 ft.   How fast is its distance from the pool increasing 40 sec. later?

4. A launch is pulled upstream by a cable fastened to a bridge 16 ft. higher.   If the cable is pulled into the boat at the rate of 2 ft./min., how fast will the boat be advancing when 34 ft. of cable are out?

5. The baseball "diamond" is a square 90 ft. on each side.   A ball was batted along the third-base line with a speed of 120 ft./sec.   How fast was its distance from first base changing 1 sec. after starting?

6. A train running straight east at the constant rate of 30 mi./hr. left a town 2 hours before another arrived from the north, coming at the rate of 40 mi./hr.   Find how fast the distance between the trains was changing one hour after the first started.

7. In Ex. 6 when were the trains nearest?   How near?

8. A balloon B was descending straight over a railroad track at the rate of 20 ft./sec.   An engine E was approaching at the rate of 40 ft./sec.; but was 1300 ft. away from the point directly below B, when B was 1400 ft. high.   How fast was the distance BE changing 10 sec. later?   When was BE least, and how small?

9. An auto running constantly 80 ft./sec. passed directly under a balloon just as a ball was dropped.   If the height of the ball after t sec. was $h = 700 - 16\,t^2$, how fast was the distance between the ball and the auto changing when $t = 5$?

10. In Ex. 9 when were the ball and the auto nearest?

11. A rectangle is inscribed in a circle of diameter 25 in.   If we increase the base at the rate of .4 in./min., how fast will the altitude be decreasing when equal to 24 in.?

12. In a hemispherical cistern of radius 10 ft. the water level is rising .02 ft./hr.   How fast is the radius of the upper surface of the water increasing, when 6 ft. below the top?

§ 81 S. Differentiating Fractional Powers.   The formula for differentiating u^n applies to fractional as well as integral powers.

For instance, if

$$y = u^{\frac{5}{3}},$$

then,

$$\frac{dy}{dx} = \tfrac{5}{3} u^{\frac{2}{3}} \frac{du}{dx}.$$

Many irrational quantities can now be differentiated by first writing them as fractional powers.

Ex. I. $\qquad y = \sqrt{58 - x^2}, \quad = (58 - x^2)^{\frac{1}{2}}.$

$$\frac{dy}{dx} = \tfrac{1}{2} (58 - x^2)^{-\frac{1}{2}} (- 2 x) = \frac{- x}{\sqrt{58 - x^2}}.$$

Ex. II. $\qquad y = \sqrt{6 x^3}, \quad = \sqrt{6} \, x^{\frac{3}{2}}.$

$$\frac{dy}{dx} = \sqrt{6} \cdot \tfrac{3}{2} x^{\frac{1}{2}} (1) = \frac{3 \sqrt{6 x}}{2}.$$

Ex. III.   A later problem involves finding the minimum value of a function like the following:

$$y = \frac{\sqrt{x^2 + 24}}{5} + \frac{180 - x}{7};$$

i.e., $\qquad y = \tfrac{1}{5} (x^2 + 24)^{\frac{1}{2}} + \tfrac{1}{7} (180 - x).$

Here $\qquad \dfrac{dy}{dx} = \tfrac{1}{10} (x^2 + 24)^{-\frac{1}{2}} (2 x) - \dfrac{1}{7},$

$$= \frac{x}{5 \sqrt{x^2 + 24}} - \frac{1}{7}.$$

Equating this to zero (§ 66), transposing, squaring, etc., we find

$$x = 5, \qquad y = \tfrac{7}{5} + 25 = 26\tfrac{2}{5}.$$

Testing dy/dx at 4 and 6 shows this value of y to be a minimum.

§ 82 S. Abrupt Extremes.   The graph of

$$y = x^{\frac{2}{3}} + 1$$

falls sharply to a minimum height of 1 at $x = 0$, and then rises sharply. (Fig. 41.)   It does not have a horizontal tangent at the lowest point.

As always, the slope dy/dx is negative just before the minimum and positive just after it. But here dy/dx changes from $-$ to $+$ by "jumping" — not by going through zero. The slope becomes indefinitely great, positively on one side and negatively on the other, as we approach the point. The "derived curve" (§ 72) would have a break at $x = 0$, though there is no break in the original graph.

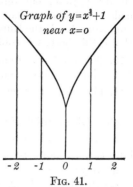

Graph of $y=x^{\frac{2}{3}}+1$ near $x=0$

Fig. 41.

The only powers of x which allow this combination at a maximum or minimum are fractional powers.

EXERCISES

1. What is the meaning of $x^{\frac{5}{3}}$, $x^{\frac{1}{4}}$, $x^{-\frac{1}{7}}$, $x^{-\frac{3}{2}}$?

2. Differentiate $y = 5\,x^{\frac{7}{3}}$ and express the result in a form free from fractional powers. Likewise for $y = 2\,x^{-\frac{1}{3}}$.

3. Express as powers, differentiate, and simplify the results:

$$y = \sqrt[4]{x^5}, \qquad y = 9\sqrt{x^7}, \qquad y = 10/\sqrt[3]{x}, \qquad y = 20/\sqrt{x^3}.$$

4. The speed (v ft./sec.) acquired in falling freely s ft. from rest is $v = 8\sqrt{s}$. How fast does v increase with s, at $s = 25$?

5. The period (T sec.) of a pendulum l in. long in latitude 30° is $T = .32\sqrt{l}$. How fast does T increase with l at $l = 4$? About how much longer is the period if the pendulum is 4.1 in. long than if 4 in. long?

6. The period of a 3 in. pendulum varies with the gravitational acceleration (g ft./sec.^{2}): $T = \pi/\sqrt{g}$. About what change in T if g changes from $32\frac{1}{9}$ to $32\frac{2}{9}$? [Cf. Ex. 11, p. 54.]

7. A planet, distant x units from the sun, revolves in T yr. given by $T = \sqrt{x^3}$. About what change in T if x decreases from 30.1 to 29.9?

8. Differentiate the following fractional powers of quantities:

(a) $y = (x^6 + 1)^{\frac{5}{3}}$, (b) $y = (x^8 - 5)^{\frac{7}{2}}$, (c) $y = \sqrt{400 - x^4}$,

(d) $z = \sqrt{9 - x^2}$, (e) $s = 2\sqrt[3]{7.5 - x}$, (f) $u = \sqrt[4]{x^2 + 2\,x - 10}$,

(g) $y = \dfrac{30}{\sqrt{x^4 + 9}}$, (h) $z = \dfrac{-5}{2\,(t^2 - 1)^{\frac{3}{4}}}$, (i) $w = \dfrac{500}{11\sqrt[3]{100 - t^3}}$.

9. Two towns A and B are 60 mi. apart on a straight coast; an island C is 15 mi. out, directly off A. The trip from C to B is to be made by a launch and auto, meeting somewhere along the shore, say x mi. from A. If the launch goes 15 mi./hr. and the auto 25 mi./hr., what is the shortest possible time for the trip?

10. Plot $y = 5 - x^{\frac{2}{3}}$ from $x = -8$ to $x = 8$. (Take $x = 8$, $\frac{27}{8}$, 1, $\frac{1}{8}$, etc.) Note the maximum.

11. Plot another graph showing how dy/dx varies with x in Ex. 10.

§ 83. Differential Notation. In some work it is convenient to be able to deal with a derivative dy/dx as a fraction $dy \div dx$. This can be done by giving suitable meanings to dy and dx separately:

Let dy and dx denote any two quantities, large or small, whose ratio $dy \div dx$ equals the derivative $f'(x)$ or dy/dx. That is,

$$\frac{dy}{dx}, \text{ derivative} \quad = \frac{(dy)}{(dx)}, \text{ fraction.} \tag{28}$$

The quantities dy and dx are called *differentials*.

An equation like

$$\frac{dy}{dx} = 3\,x^2 \tag{29}$$

may now be written also in the form

$$dy = 3\,x^2\,dx, \tag{30}$$

by simply multiplying through by dx.

Treating a derivative as a fraction allows great freedom of operation. For instance, a product like

$$\frac{dy}{du} \cdot \frac{du}{dx}$$

may be simplified by merely canceling du. The value (dy/dx) thus obtained is correct by the theorem on indirect dependence, (21), p. 103.

If we regard y as a function of either of two related variables u and x, the derivatives dy/du and dy/dx are usually different in form and value, but the differential dy has the same value in each case. Thus, if $y = u^3 + 20$, and $u = x^2$, then $y = x^6 + 20$. The first and last of these equations give

$$dy = 3\,u^2\,du, \qquad\qquad dy = 6\,x^5\,dx.$$

But since $3\,u^2 = 3\,x^4$, and $du = 2\,x\,dx$, the two values of dy are equal.

Differentials are used very extensively in more advanced courses. Here, however, we merely need to know their meaning and the fact that a differential equation like (30) above is only another way of expressing the value of a derivative, as in (29).

The following concrete interpretations of differentials may, nevertheless, be of interest.

§ 84 S. Interpretations of Differentials. In Fig. 42 let PT be tangent to the graph of $y = f(x)$. Then the ratio of HT to PH equals the rate at P — i.e., equals $f'(x)$. Hence HT and PH may be taken as dy and dx, respectively.

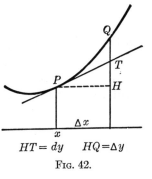

$HT = dy \qquad HQ = \Delta y$

Fig. 42.

Now HT is the amount that y would increase while x increased by PH if the rate remained constant. Hence we may say:

The differential of a function y is the amount that y would increase while x increased by any amount (dx) if the rate remained the same as at the instant considered.

Moreover, if dx is small, dy is nearly equal to Δy (or HQ). But by (28), $dy = f'(x)\,dx$. Hence Δy, the small change in y produced by a small increase in x, is approximately equal to the derivative times the latter increase. (Cf. § 63.)

We usually take dx positive, letting x actually increase. But dy may then turn out to be negative, indicating that y would make a negative "increase" or actually a decrease, if the rate remained constant.

Observe also that dy is a function of x and dx, two independent variables, while the derivative is a function of x alone.

EXERCISES

1. Differentiate the following, finding dy:

$$y = x^4, \qquad y = x^{-2}, \qquad y = 6\,x^{\frac{5}{2}}, \qquad y = x^7 - 7\,x^3 + 3 - 16/x.$$

2. Write the differential of V, if $V = x^6$. Verify that either dV/dx or dV/dt is obtainable correctly from this by simply dividing.

3. Simplify by inspection:

$$\frac{dV}{dx} \cdot \frac{dx}{dt}, \qquad\qquad \frac{dS}{dr} \cdot \frac{dr}{dt}, \qquad\qquad \frac{dy}{du} \cdot \frac{du}{dx}, \qquad\qquad \frac{dp}{dv} \cdot \frac{dv}{dt}.$$

4. By what would you multiply $\dfrac{dy}{dp}$ to get $\dfrac{dy}{dt}$?

$$\frac{dr}{ds} \text{ to get } \frac{dr}{dx}? \qquad\qquad \frac{dV}{dx} \text{ to get } \frac{dV}{dt}? \qquad\qquad \frac{dy}{dx} \text{ to get } \frac{dy}{ds}?$$

5. Express in an equivalent form each of these statements:

$$dy = x\,dx, \qquad\qquad dx = 2\,t^5\,dt, \qquad\qquad dV = 4\,\pi r^2\,dr.$$

6. If $y = x^2 + 30$ is the curve in Fig. 42, and if x increases from 2 to 2.01, find dy and also Δy.

§ 85. Summary of Chapter III. To find the rate at which any given quantity is increasing at any instant, we have merely to find its *derivative* — *i.e.*, to differentiate.

The derivative is defined abstractly as a certain *limit*, but it may have various concrete interpretations, such as instantaneous rate, slope, speed, acceleration, etc.

Derivatives can often be written at sight. In such cases it is easier to find instantaneous rates than average rates. (Cf. § 37.) Indirect differentiation with respect to a third variable, say t, is possible. This introduces an extra factor, dx/dt.

The *amount* of change in y while x changes by a small dx is approximately dy or $f'(x)\,dx$. The effect of an error of measurement can be estimated in this way.

To locate the maximum and minimum (turning) values of any quantity, we set its derivative equal to zero, and test the same derivative before and after. (We also see whether the derivative can change from + to −, or *vice versa*, by "jumping.") In practical problems it is first necessary to obtain a formula for the quantity to be maximized or minimized — and express this in terms of a *single variable*.

To find when a quantity is increasing most rapidly — *i.e.*, at the greatest rate — requires repeated differentiations. So do some problems on acceleration, flexion, etc.

Observe that although we can find the *slope* of a tangent line, we cannot as yet find its *inclination* — *i.e.*, the *angle* at which it rises from the horizontal. This problem will be treated later. (§ 114.)

EXERCISES *

1. What is meant by the derivative of y with respect to x? When does it give the slope of a curve? The speed of an object? An acceleration? A flexion? Given a formula for any quantity, how would you find the rate of increase at any instant? The amount of increase in any very small interval? The maximum and minimum values? Whether increasing or decreasing at any point?

2. Differentiate $y = x^3 - 30\,x + 7$ by the Δ-process.

3. Differentiate at sight:

(a) $y = x^5 + \frac{1}{4}\,x^3 - x/9 + 200$;

(b) $z = 6\,\sqrt[3]{x^7} + 8/x$;

(c) $y = \dfrac{3}{\sqrt{x}} - \dfrac{12}{(5 - x^2)^2}$;

(d) $w = \dfrac{\sqrt{3 + 4\,t - t^2}}{10}$.

4. In the Power Law, $y = kx^n$, how does dy/dx compare with y/x in value? Can you interpret this result, as to rates?

5. The quantity of sugar present in a certain chemical reaction, t min. after starting, was $Q = c/(1 + kt)$, where c and k are constants. Show that the rate of decrease was always k/c times Q^2.

6. A rectangular box is to contain 160 cu. ft. The materials for the base cost 30¢ per sq. ft., for the sides 10¢ per sq. ft., and for the top 20¢ per sq. ft. What is the smallest possible total cost, and what dimensions will give it? (See Ex. 5, p. 92.)

7. The space within a mile race-track consists of a rectangle with a semicircle at each end. To make the rectangle as large as possible, how much of the mile should be given to the straight sides and how much to the curved ends?

8. If the quantity (Q units) of a commodity that can be sold at any price ($\$x$ per unit) is $Q = 400000 - 5000\,x$, and if the expense ($\$E$)

---

* Attention is also called to exercises indicated by a **C** with the numeral (*e.g.*, **8 C**) in Chapters V, VI, which may be worked at this point by any classes that have already covered those chapters.

of making and selling Q units is $E = 25000 + 10\,Q$, what x will give the maximum possible profit?   How much?

9. A circular ripple spreads over a pond, the radius increasing steadily at the rate of 3 ft./sec.   How fast is the disturbed area growing when 1 sec. has passed?   10 sec.?

10. The height (h in.) of a conical stalactite is continually ten times the diameter.   If the volume is increasing at the rate of 2 cu. in./yr., how fast is the height increasing when $h = 20$?

11. The lowest flying speed (V ft./sec.) for a certain airplane varies as the square root of the wing loading (w lb./sq. ft.).   If $V = 57$ when $w = 9$, give the formula.   Approximately what change in V if w is increased from 9 to 9.06?

12. The radius of a sphere is measured as 10 in.   About how accurate must this measurement be, if the calculated volume is not to be erroneous by more than 5 cu. in.?

13. Plot $y = 4 + 6\,x^3 - x^4$, showing any points of maximum or minimum height or slope.   What is the flexion at $x = 1$?

14. The distance traveled by an object in t min. was $y = 60\,t^3 - t^4$. Find the maximum speed.   Was the acceleration increasing or decreasing when $t = 20$, and how rapidly?

15. A baseball is batted along the third-base line, going 60 ft./sec. How fast is its distance from first base changing one second after it started?   How fast when passing third base?

16. Solve Ex. 8, p. 111, taking the initial height of B as 1500 ft. and the rate of descent as 30 ft./sec.

17. In each of the following, first write a formula for the variable quantity, or function, in question; then find the required rate.

(a) The "moment of inertia," I, of a flat circular disk varies as the fourth power of the radius.   If $I = 40$ when $r = 2$, find how fast I increases with r, at $r = 5$.

(b) In a railway curve the elevation of the outer rail should vary inversely as the radius.   If $E = 2.5$ (in.) when $R = 3000$ (ft.), find how fast E changes, at $R = 2000$.

[**18.**] The height of a ball t sec. after being thrown straight up was $y = 50 + 80\,t - 16\,t^2$.   Show that the acceleration $= -32$ ft./sec.^{2} constantly.   What terms in this formula might have been different without modifying this result?   Write some other formulas to illustrate this.

[**19.**] A ball rolls up an incline, its distance from the bottom after t sec. being $x = a + bt - 3\,t^2$.   Show that the acceleration $= -6$ ft./sec.^{2} For what values of a, b, would x equal 10 and the speed 100 at $t = 0$?

[**20.**] The speed of an object after t sec. varied thus: $v = 30\,t^2 - 4\,t^3$. Can you find the distance traveled at any time?

CHAPTER IV

INTEGRATION

THE RATE PROBLEM REVERSED

§ 86. Differentiation Reversed. We have seen how to find the rate at which a given quantity is changing at any instant. Consider now the reverse problem:

Given the rate at which a quantity is changing, to find how large the quantity will be at any time. (Of course, we must also know how large it was at some particular time.)

If the given rate is constant, the problem is merely one of arithmetic. But if the rate varies, we must in general proceed as follows:

The given rate is the derivative of the quantity whose value is required. Hence we are *given the derivative* of a function, and are to *find the function itself*. That is, we must reverse the differentiation process.*

Ex. I. A stone was dropped from an airplane 8000 ft. high: t seconds later its height (h ft.) was decreasing at the rate of $32\,t$ (ft./sec.). Find the height at any instant.

The given rate or derivative is

$$\frac{dh}{dt} = -32\,t. \qquad\qquad (\text{Why} - ?)$$

To find h, then, we must think of some function which, if differentiated, would give $-32\,t$. One such function is

$$h = -16\,t^2.$$

But there are others. For instance, $h = -16\,t^2 + 500$, and $h = -16\,t^2 - 40$, both have this same derivative $-32\,t$. So does

$$h = -16\,t^2 + C, \qquad\qquad (1)$$

C being any constant whatever, positive or negative.

In other words, the given rate of change of h does not by itself determine the value of h at any time. But we were

---

* Of course we might solve the problem approximately by some graphical method. See Ex. 5, p. 21

told also the height of the stone at the start, viz. $h = 8000$ at $t = 0$, when we began to count time. This fact requires the constant C in (1) to have the value 8000; and (1) becomes

$$h = -16\,t^2 + 8000. \tag{2}$$

Check: This formula is a correct solution of our problem. For at $t = 0$ it reduces to $h = 8000$, and by differentiation $dh/dt = -32\,t$, the specified rate.

It is instructive to compare the foregoing problem with one in which the given rate is constant:

Ex. II. A captive balloon is being pulled down at the rate of 50 ft./min. How high will it be t min. hence?

Evidently, $h = C - 50\,t$, where C denotes the present height, what-ever that may be. In other words, C is the value of h at $t = 0$, when we begin to count time.

In each problem *the value of h at any instant is completely determined by the original value and the rate of change at all times.*

§ 87. Integration.

The process of reversing a differentia-tion, to find an original function when given its derivative, is called **integration**. The required original function is called the **integral** of the given derivative.

When integrating, we must always add an arbitrary con-stant C. For the given *rate* determines only the amount of *increase*. And the total value of the function at any time equals this increase *plus the original value*.

The value of this added "constant of integration" becomes

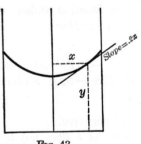

FIG. 43.

definite if the value of the function is known at some instant or point. For instance, in Ex. I of § 86, the value of C was determined by the fact that $h = 8000$ at $t = 0$. Another illustration follows.

Ex. I. The water in a rotating pail, of radius 5 in., has its upper surface hollowed out, forming a curve whose slope at any distance x in. from the axis of rotation is $.2\,x$.* (Fig. 43.) If the

* It is shown in Physics, by considering the forces involved, that for any constant speed of rotation, the slope must equal *some* constant times x.

water is 8 in. deep at the highest point, find its depth at any other point.

We are to find y as a function of x, having given

$$\frac{dy}{dx} = .2\,x, \quad \text{and } y = 8 \text{ when } x = 5.$$

We therefore seek a function which, if differentiated, would give $.2\,x$. One such function is $.1\,x^2$.   But any constant might be added, making

$$y = .1\,x^2 + C. \tag{3}$$

By the problem, however, $y = 8$ when $x = 5$.   In (3) this gives

$$8 = .1\,(5)^2 + C,$$

or $C = 5.5$.   And hence the required depth at any distance x in. from the center is

$$y = .1\,x^2 + 5.5.$$

(Here again C is the value of y at $x = 0$, as substitution would show.)

EXERCISE

[1.] Find by inspection a function which if differentiated will give $dy/dx = x^3$.   (Check your answer.)   Likewise for $dy/dx = x^{10}$, and x^n. Hence, integrating x^n with respect to x will give what result?

§ 88. Integration Formula.   To save labor let us systematize the integration process.

Differentiating any power of x leads to the next lower power. Hence integrating leads to the next higher.   Thus

$$\frac{dy}{dx} = x^n \quad \text{gives} \quad y = \frac{x^{n+1}}{n+1} + C. \tag{4}$$

The coefficient $1/(n+1)$ is required to cancel the multiplier $(n+1)$ which would come from the exponent in differentiating.

By this formula, we can integrate various powers at sight. Thus

$$\frac{dy}{dx} = x^{10} \quad \text{gives} \quad y = \frac{x^{11}}{11} + C;$$

$$\frac{dy}{dx} = x^{-4} \quad \text{gives} \quad y = \frac{x^{-3}}{-3} + C;$$

$$\frac{dy}{dx} = x^{\frac{7}{5}} \quad \text{gives} \quad y = \frac{x^{\frac{12}{5}}}{\frac{12}{5}} + C.$$

These last two results can be simplified, giving

$$-\frac{1}{3\,x^3} + C, \quad \text{and} \quad \tfrac{5}{12}\, x^{\frac{12}{5}} + C.$$

These integrations should be checked by differentiating the results.

Formula (4) fails, however, if $n = -1$. For then $n + 1 = 0$ and cannot be used as a divisor. (It is clear anyhow that x^{-1} could not be obtained by differentiating the next higher power x^0.) The integral of x^{-1} must be some other kind of function, not a power of x. (Treated in § 185.)

Remark. The effect of a constant multiplier is simply to multiply the resulting integral by the same factor. For instance:

$$\frac{dy}{dx} = 20\, x^6 \quad \text{gives} \quad y = 20\left(\frac{x^7}{7}\right) + C.$$

But to integrate the product of two *variable* factors we must first multiply out. (Cf. § 61.)

To integrate the *sum* of several terms, we integrate term by term. It is unnecessary to introduce a constant for each term integrated. For a single C can have any value whatever — say the sum of the values which several C's might have.

§ 89. Uniqueness.

If to an integral of a given derivative any constant be added, the result will still be an integral. For the constant would disappear on differentiating.

But may there not be some entirely different function which would also be an integral — perhaps a very complicated function, whose derivative would simplify down to the given quantity? No, this is impossible. In other words:

Two functions which have the same derivative can differ only by a constant.

For if the derivatives are equal, the functions must be changing at the same rate; and hence their difference is not changing but remains constant. One function equals the other plus a constant.

Thus an integration can give only one result, aside from the possibility of an added constant.

EXERCISES

1. Given each following value for dy/dx, find y itself, including the arbitrary constant. Check each answer by differentiation.

(a) $dy/dx = x^7,\quad x^4,\quad x,\quad 9\,x^2,\quad -\frac{5}{2}\,x^3,\quad \frac{3}{2}\,x,\quad 30,\quad -4;$

(b) $dy/dx = x^{\frac{3}{2}},\quad x^{\frac{2}{3}},\quad x^{\frac{1}{4}},\quad 2\,x^{\frac{1}{2}},\quad \frac{9}{5}\sqrt{x},\quad -\frac{7}{4}\sqrt[3]{x},\quad 8\sqrt{x^5}+7;$

(c) $dy/dx = x^{-8},\quad x^{-3},\quad x^{-\frac{7}{8}}.\quad 1/x^4,\quad 5/x^{\frac{3}{5}},\quad k/x^{10},\quad k+2/\sqrt[5]{x^6}.$

2. Similarly find y if dy/dx has each following value:

(a) $4\,x^5 - 3\,x + 6\sqrt{x} - 7 + \dfrac{5}{x^2};$ (b) $6\,x^2\,(x^3 - 7\,x^2 + ax + b).$

3. In the following, find y as a definite function of x, determining the constant of integration:

(a) $dy/dx = x^4 - 9\,x + 200,$ and $y = 100$ at $x = 0,$

(b) $dy/dx = 6\sqrt{x} + 25 - 8\,x^3,$ and $y = 30$ at $x = 1.$

4. If $dV = x^3\,dx$ and $V = 0$ when $x = 2$, express V as a function of x.

5. Express A as a function of x, if $dA = x^2\,dx$, and $A = 0$ when $x = 3$.

6. The weight of a column of air, whose cross-section is 1 sq. ft. and height is h ft., increases with h about as follows, while h is not too large: $dW/dh = .0805 - .00000268\,h$. Express W as a function of h, knowing that $W = 0$ when $h = 0$. Find the weight of a column 2000 ft. high.

7. The slope of a certain suspension cable at any horizontal distance x ft. from the center is $.006\,x$. Find the height (y ft.) at any point if $y = 20$ at $x = 0$.

8. In Ex. I, § 87, change the slope to $.4\,x$ and the depth at the center to 5 in., and find y at any point. Plot from $x = -3$ to $+3$.

9. The speed of a car t sec. after starting was $60\,t^2 - 4\,t^3$. Find a formula for the distance (y ft.) traveled at any time.

10. When a car had run for t sec., its momentum M was increasing at a rate equal to $(3\,t^2 + 2\,t)$. Find M at any time; at $t = 10, 20, 30$.

11. In studying the growth of yeast the equation $dS = kT\,dT + nl\,(l + bT^2)\,dT$ was encountered. Here k, n, l, and b are constants. Integrate to express S as a function of T.

12. The following table shows the rate (R lb. per hr.) at which a piece of ice was melting t hours after being cut. Find the total amount which melted during the ten hours. (Hint: Plot a graph whose height shall represent the rate of melting at any instant. What, then, will represent the average rate during any interval?)

t	0	2	4	6	8	10
R	40	32.4	25.6	19.6	14.4	10

13. In Ex. 12 the formula for R at any time is $R = 40 - 4\,t + .1\,t^2$. Calculate the quantity melted from $t = 0$ to $t = 10$, and check your graphical result. (Hint: How is the given rate R related to the *quantity*?)

§ 90. Repeated Integrations.
In some practical problems it is necessary to integrate several times in succession.

To determine the value of the constant of integration which enters at each step, we must know the numerical value, at some instant or point, of the quantity represented by the integral obtained at that step — say, flexion, slope, or height of a curve; or acceleration, speed, or distance traveled by a moving object; etc.

§ 91. Projectiles, Thrown Vertically.
When an object is thrown straight upward, its speed v decreases by 32 ft./sec. in each second.* Thus if the speed is 140 ft./sec. at the start, after 1 sec. it will be 108 ft./sec.; etc. (See table.) After 5 sec. the object will be *falling* with a speed of 20 ft./sec., then 52 ft./sec., etc. Calling these downward speeds negative, we can say that v is still decreasing algebraically, though increasing numerically. In fact, every value of v down the entire table is

t	v
0	140
1	108
2	76
3	44
4	12
5	-20
6	-52
7	-84

obtained by *subtracting* 32 from the preceding value. (Verify.)

That is, *the acceleration or rate of change of v, is -32 ft./sec.^{2} whether the object is rising or falling.*

To express this fact mathematically, recall that the speed is the rate at which the height (y ft.) is changing: $v = dy/dt$, whence the acceleration is

$$\frac{d^2y}{dt^2} = -32. \tag{5}$$

By remembering this one simple equation, we can solve all ordinary problems concerning vertically thrown projectiles, if we understand the process of integrating. Separate for-

* The remarks as to accuracy made in § 23 apply here also.

mulas for upward and downward motion, as commonly used in elementary physics, are unnecessary.

Remark. A negative acceleration is sometimes called a positive *deceleration.*

Ex. I. A ball was thrown from a height of 2000 ft. with an initial speed of 80 ft./sec. straight downward. Find its height t sec. later.

Integrating (5) gives the speed at any time:

$$\frac{dy}{dt} = -32\,t + C.$$

But the speed was -80 at the start: *i.e.*, $dy/dt = -80$ at $t = 0$. Hence $C = -80$.

$$\therefore \ \frac{dy}{dt} = -32\,t - 80. \tag{6}$$

Integrating again:

$$y = -16\,t^2 - 80\,t + k.$$

But the height at the start was $y = 2000$. Hence $k = 2000$. Thus, finally,

$$y = 2000 - 80\,t - 16\,t^2. \tag{7}$$

Observe the physical meaning of this result: The height at any instant equals the original height (2000) minus the distance (80 t) the ball would have fallen in t seconds if it had kept on at the original speed (80 ft./sec.), and minus also the distance (16 t^2) that gravity would pull it down in t seconds starting from rest.

EXERCISES

1. Point out the physical meaning of formula (6) above, as has just been done for formula (7).

2. A ball was thrown straight up from a roof 96 ft. high with an initial speed of 80 ft./sec. Find its height after t seconds, and point out the physical meaning of each term.

3. In Ex. 2 when did the ball strike the ground, and with what speed?

4. Some shot were fired straight up from an airplane 3200 ft. high with an initial speed of 160 ft./sec. Find when they were highest and how high. When did they pass the 3500 ft. level rising? Falling?

5. How long would it take a stone to reach the ground if dropped from a window 1024 ft. high? What speed would it have acquired?

6. The same as Ex. 5, if the stone were hurled downward with an initial speed of 192 ft./sec.

7. Derive the general formula for the varying height of an object thrown vertically from any initial height h, with any initial speed v (which can be positive or negative). How would you proceed to find the speed with which the object reaches the ground? When highest (if started upward)?

8. By Ex. 7, or independently, find the height of an airplane if a ball dropped from it requires 20 sec. to reach the ground.

9. A sliding object, starting with a speed of 60 ft./sec., was retarded by friction, the deceleration being 12 ft./sec.^{2}. Express the distance traveled in t sec. Find the total distance traveled.

10. A point on the rim of a flywheel was moving at the speed of 40 in./sec. when the power was cut off. The speed thereafter decreased at the rate of 4 in./sec.^{2}. Find when the wheel stopped and how far the point moved in stopping.

11. The same as Ex. 10, if the rate of decrease was 6 ft./sec.^{2}, and the original speed 120 ft./sec.

12. An elevator starts up with a constant acceleration of 4 ft./sec.^{2} for 5 sec.; then maintains the same speed for 38 sec., and finally stops with a deceleration of 10 ft./sec.^{2}. How high does it go?

§ 92. Integral Notation.

The integral of any function $F(x)$, with respect to x, is denoted by the symbol

$$\int F(x)\, dx.$$

For instance, $\int x^2\, dx$ denotes the integral of x^2 with respect to x.

$$\therefore \quad \int x^2\, dx = \tfrac{1}{3} x^3 + C.$$

This is usually read simply "The integral of x square $d\,x$."

In this notation the integration formula (4), p. 121, reads:

$$\int x^n\, dx = \frac{x^{n+1}}{n+1} + C. \tag{8}$$

This fails, however, if $n = -1$ (p. 122). That case is treated later (§ 185).

A constant multiplier simply multiplies the result. *E.g.,*

$$\int 4\,\pi r^2\, dr = 4\,\pi \int r^2\, dr = \tfrac{4}{3}\,\pi r^3 + C.$$

Thus a constant factor can be moved from one side of the integral sign to the other. Variable factors, however, cannot be so moved, for a product of two variable factors cannot be differentiated by merely differentiating one factor.

Observe that the expression following the integral sign ∫ is in the *differential form* (§ 83). That is, the sign ∫ stands for a *quantity whose differential is* whatever follows.

Thus $\int x^2\, dx$ stands for the quantity whose differential is $x^2\, dx$. But of course this is the same thing as the quantity whose derivative with respect to x is x^2.

How the use of the *differential* form in the integral notation originated, will appear later. One of its advantages is that, while a quantity y has different derivatives with respect to different variables, it has only one differential dy.

§ 93. A Growing Area. Many geometrical and physical quantities can be calculated quickly and exactly by integration. The underlying idea is much the same in all cases. Let us consider first the typical case of the area under any given graph — supposing of course that the graph is free from breaks, so that an area is actually bounded.

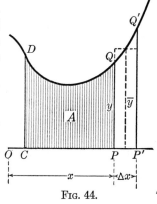

Fig. 44.

In Fig. 44 if CD is fixed and PQ moves to the right, the area A will vary with x in some definite way. If we can determine its *rate of increase*, dA/dx, we can find A by integrating.

To get a vivid idea of the growing area A imagine a rubber sheet with one end fastened at CD and the other end PQ being pulled along, while the sides, attached to wires, constantly fit along the base line and the curve. The area of the stretching sheet is the "growing area" A, of which we are speaking.

While x increases by Δx, A increases by

$$\Delta A, \ = \text{area of strip } PP'Q'Q, \ = \overline{y}\, \Delta x,$$

where $\bar{y}$ is the mean ordinate (read "y bar").

$$\therefore \frac{\Delta A}{\Delta x} = \bar{y}.$$

This is the average rate of increase of A per x-unit.   Its limit is

$$\frac{dA}{dx} = \underset{\Delta x \to 0}{\mathrm{L}} (\bar{y}) = \overline{PQ} = y. \tag{9}$$

That is, *the rate at which the area A is increasing at any instant is equal to the height of the curve at that point.**

§ 94. Areas Found Exactly.   Since the rate of growth of the area A in Fig. 44 is $dA/dx = y$, we have simply

$$A = \int y\, dx. \tag{10}$$

Thus we can find the area under any graph, if we know a formula expressing the height y at any point in terms of the horizontal distance x from some fixed point, and if we can integrate the expression $y\, dx$.

To illustrate, let us find the area under the curve $y = x^3$ between a fixed ordinate erected at $x = 1$ and a moving ordinate.

Equation (10) becomes in this case

$$A = \int x^3\, dx = \tfrac{1}{4} x^4 + C. \tag{11}$$

This is our growing area, and it is to start at $x = 1$.   That is, $A = 0$ when $x = 1$.

Substituting these values in (11) gives

$$0 = \tfrac{1}{4}(1)^4 + C, \quad \text{or} \quad C = -\tfrac{1}{4}.$$

Hence the required area from $x = 1$ to any other value of x is simply

$$A = \tfrac{1}{4} x^4 - \tfrac{1}{4}.$$

E.g., from $x = 1$ to $x = 3$, we have $A = \tfrac{1}{4}(3)^4 - \tfrac{1}{4} = 20$.   Likewise, from $x = 1$ to $x = 10$, $A = \tfrac{1}{4}(10)^4 - \tfrac{1}{4} = 2499\tfrac{3}{4}$.   And so on.

* This result is reasonable.   For suppose the ordinate PQ to move say .001 inch to the right.   Evidently the tiny strip added to the growing area A would be almost exactly .001 y (sq. in.).   The average rate of growth during this tiny interval would be practically y (sq. in. per horizontal inch).   The instantaneous rate is exactly y.

If we sought an area under this curve starting at some other value than $x = 1$, however, we should have to redetermine the constant C accordingly.

Observe, then, that we find an area between two fixed ordinates by regarding it as the value to which a varying area will grow, starting from one of the ordinates.

EXERCISES

1. Find the following integrals:

(a) $\int x^5 \, dx$, $\qquad \int 350 \, x^{-3} \, dx$, $\qquad \int 4 \, t \, dt$, $\qquad \int 6 \, t^{\frac{1}{2}} \, dt$;

(b) $\int \left(x^6 + \dfrac{2 \, x^3}{5} - \dfrac{x^2}{11} + 5 \right) dx$, $\qquad \int \sqrt[3]{x} \, dx$, $\qquad \int \dfrac{dt}{t^2}$.

2. Plot from $x = 0$ to 10 a line whose height at any point is $y = 2\,x + 3$. Find by elementary geometry the area under it. Calculate the same area by integration.

3. Find by integration the area under the line $y = 6\,x + 4$, from $x = 2$ to 8. Can you check this result by geometry without plotting?

4. Find the area under the curve $y = x^2$ from $x = 3$ to any other x; from $x = 3$ to $x = 10$.

5. Find the area under each of the following curves:

(a) $y = x^3 - 4\,x + 10$, from $x = 2$ to 4; $\qquad$ (b) $y = \sqrt{x}$, 9 to 16;

(c) $y = x^{10} - 6\,x^2 + 8$, from $x = 0$ to 1; $\qquad$ (d) $y = \sqrt[3]{x}$, 1 to 8;

(e) $y = \dfrac{1}{x^4}$, from $x = 2$ to 4; $\qquad$ (f) $y = \dfrac{1}{\sqrt{x}}$, 1 to 9.

6. In a certain curve the height varies as the square of the horizontal distance x from a certain point, and is 5 at $x = 2$. Find the area under the curve from $x = 1$ to 4.

7. Plot that part of the curve $y = 15\,x - 3\,x^2$ in which y is positive. Calculate the area under it.

8. Find the area between the base line and the curve $y = 9 - x^2$ from $x = 3$ to $x = 6$. [To interpret the negative result, see whether the curve is above or below the base line in this interval. Cf. equation (9).]

9. Find the area between the curves $y = 9 - x^2$ and $y = x^2$ from $x = 0$ to 1.

10. Like Ex. 9 for the curves $y = x^2$ and $y = x^3$.

[**11.**] An object is moved against a force (F lb.) which varies thus with the distance x ft.: $F = 5\,x - x^2$. Plot F as a function of x from

$x = 0$ to $x = 5$.   Find graphically the work done from 0 to 5.   Can you calculate this work exactly?

§ 95 S. **Momentum.**   Consider the momentum M imparted to a moving object by a varying force in t seconds after starting.   (§ 12.)

In an additional interval Δt, further momentum ΔM is imparted.   This equals the average or mean force $\overline{F}$ acting during Δt, multiplied by the time Δt: $\Delta M = \overline{F}\,\Delta t$.   Hence the average rate of increase of M per sec. is

$$\frac{\Delta M}{\Delta t} = \overline{F}.$$

As $\Delta t \to 0$, $\overline{F}$ approaches the value of F at the instant considered:

$$\therefore \ \frac{dM}{dt} = F.$$

$$\therefore \ \boldsymbol{M = \int F \, dt}. \tag{12}$$

This agrees with our earlier statement (§ 12) that M is represented by the area under a force-time graph.   For y in that graph is F and x is t, so that the area $A = \int y\,dx$ becomes $A = \int F\,dt$.

Ex. I.   Find the momentum generated from $t = 3$ to any other instant if the force varies thus: $F = 16 - .6\,t^2$

By (12): $M = \int (16 - .6\,t^2)\,dt;$

i.e., $M = 16\,t - .2\,t^3 + C.$

And, since $M = 0$ when $t = 3$, we find on substituting: $C = -42.6$.

§ 96 S. **Work.**   Consider the work done by a variable force in moving an object any distance x.

In an additional distance Δx, additional work ΔW is done.   This equals the mean force $\overline{F}$ acting during Δx, multiplied by the distance: $\Delta W = \overline{F}\,\Delta x.$

$$\therefore \ \frac{\Delta W}{\Delta x} = \overline{F}.$$

The instantaneous rate at which W is increasing is therefore:

$$\frac{dW}{dx} = F.$$

$$\therefore \ W = \int F \, dx. \tag{13}$$

This indicates that W is represented by the area under a force-distance graph. For there $y = F$ and $\int y \, dx$ becomes $\int F \, dx$.

§ **97. Volumes.** Let Fig. 45 represent any solid, and let V be the volume between a fixed plane CD and a moving plane PQ at a varying distance x from some fixed point O.

While x increases by Δx, V increases by some ΔV:

$$\Delta V = \text{volume of slice}$$

$$PP'Q'Q = \overline{A}\Delta x,$$

where $\overline{A}$ ("A bar") is the mean cross-section area in the slice. Hence the average rate of increase of V per x-unit is

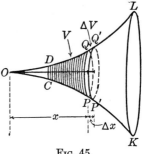

Fig. 45.

$$\frac{\Delta V}{\Delta x} = \overline{A}.$$

$$\therefore \ \frac{dV}{dx} = \mathop{\mathrm{L}}_{\Delta x \to 0} (\overline{A}), \ = \text{area } \overline{PQ} = A_s. \tag{14}$$

That is, *the rate of increase of V at any instant equals the area of the cross-section A_s*, at the point just reached.

$$\therefore \ V = \int A_s \, dx. \tag{15}$$

Hence we can find the volume of any solid, if we can do two things: (1) Express the area of a *moving* cross-section *in terms of its distance x* from some fixed point and (2) integrate the expression thus obtained.

Ex. I.   Suppose the moving section in Fig. 45 to be a circle and its radius to vary thus: $r = .05 \, x^2$.   Find the volume between two planes CD and LK located at $x = 3$ and $x = 10$, respectively.

$$A_s = \pi r^2 = \pi \, (.05 \, x^2)^2 = .0025 \, \pi x^4.$$

$$V = \int .0025 \, \pi x^4 \, dx = .0005 \, \pi x^5 + C.$$

This is the growing volume between some fixed plane (to be taken at CD) and the moving plane PQ.   When PQ was just starting from CD, the volume was zero: $V = 0$ at $x = 3$.

$$\therefore \; 0 = .0005 \, \pi \, (3)^5 + C.$$

This requires $C = -.1215 \, \pi$; and the growing volume is

$$V = .0005 \, \pi x^5 - .1215 \, \pi.$$

When PQ reaches LK, $x = 10$ and $V = 50 \, \pi - .1215 \, \pi = 156.7$, approx.

Remark.   In finding a volume by integration we need not know the *shape* of the solid.   It suffices to know the *area* of each plane section perpendicular to a given line.   Solids of different shapes may lead to the same problem in integration. In some of the following exercises where the shape of a cross-section is given, from which the area can be ascertained, the form of the solid cannot be fully identified.

EXERCISES

1. The force (F lb.) moving an object varied thus: $F = 180 \, t - 6 \, t^2$. Find the momentum generated from $t = 1$ to $t = 4$.

2. Like Ex. 1 for a force varying in each of these ways:

(a) $F = 40 \, t$, $t = 3$ to 20;   (b) $F = 8.6 \, t + 20$, $t = 0$ to 10;

(c) $F = 125 - t^3$, $t = 0$ to 10;   (d) $F = 12\sqrt{t} + 25$, $t = 1$ to 9.

3. The force (F lb.) required to stretch a certain spring x inches is $F = 30 \, x$.   Find the work done in stretching it from its normal length to an elongation of 4 in.

4. The force (F dynes) with which two spheres carrying certain electrical charges will attract each other when their centers are x cm. apart is $F = 20/x^2$.   Find the work done in moving them apart, from $x = 2$ to $x = 10$; from $x = 2$ to $x = 1000$.

5. When an electron E is x cm. from a surface S, it is attracted toward S with a force (F dynes) given by the formula: $F = 5.25 \, (10^{-20})/x^2$. Find the work necessary to draw E away from S, from $x = 5$ to $x = 15$.

6. The force (F lb.) exerted on a piston varied thus with the distance x in. from one end of the cylinder: $F = 360000/x^{\frac{4}{3}}$. Find the work done from $x = 8$ to $x = 27$.

In the following problems draw a rough figure for yourself even where one is shown.

7. A certain horn has an axis of symmetry. Each section perpendicular to this axis is a circle, whose radius varies thus with the distance x from one end: $r = .02\ x^2$. Find the volume of the space within the horn from $x = 10$ to $x = 20$. (Cf. Fig. 45.)

8. In a certain steeple any horizontal section x ft. from the top is a square, whose side s ft. varies thus: $s = .01\ x^2$. Find the volume, if the total height is 40 ft.

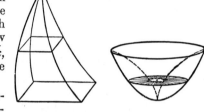

9. Every horizontal section of a solid is a rectangle, whose sides y and z vary thus with the distance (x in.) below the highest point: $y = 14\ \sqrt{x}$, $z = x^2/3$. Find the volume from $x = 0$ to $x = 16$.

10. Every horizontal section of a solid is a ring between two concentric circles, whose radii (R, r ft.) vary thus with the distance x ft. above the lowest point: $R = \sqrt{x}$, $r = x^2$. Find the volume, $x = 0$ to 1.

11. The base of a solid is a quarter circle of radius 10 in. (Fig. 46.) Every section parallel to one face is a right triangle, whose altitude equals 1.4 times its base. Find its volume.

(Hint: The area of the moving triangular section, $.7\ y^2$, must be expressed in terms of x. This is easy, since x and y are legs of a right triangle in the base, whose hypotenuse is the radius, 10 in.)

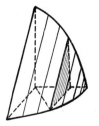
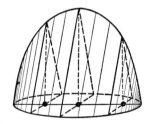

Fig. 46.

12. The base of a solid is a circle of radius 10 in., but every section perpendicular to one diameter is an isosceles triangle, whose height equals half its base. Find the volume. (Has this solid any relation to the type of solid in Ex. 11? Cf. Fig. 46.)

13. Find by integration the volume of a hemisphere of radius 10 in. Check by geometry. (Hint: What sort of section is made by any plane x in. from the flat side or base? What area, A_s?)

14. Find the volume of a segment cut from a sphere of radius 20 in. by a plane 5 in. from the center.

15. (*a*) Find the volume of air in a hall 200 ft. long if the ends, and all sections parallel to them, have the form of the area under the curve $y = 30 - .03\,x^2$, from $x = -20$ to $x = 20$. (*b*) Draw and measure this area as a check.

§ 98. Setting up the Area-Formula.

In finding a volume the area A_s can often be expressed immediately in terms of the dimensions of the moving section. But before integrat-

ing, this must be put in terms of x, the distance of the section from some fixed point. The transformation is often effected by the Pythagorean theorem or a proportion.

For instance, suppose we wish to find the volume of a wedge 7 in. high cut off from a cylinder of radius 5 in. by a plane passed through a diameter of the base. (Fig. 47.)

Fig. 47.

Any section perpendicular to that diameter is a right triangle. (Why?) Its area is

$$A_s = \tfrac{1}{2}\,y\,z. \tag{16}$$

But we must get this expressed in terms of x.

The radius, if drawn to the end of y, would form in the base plane a right triangle with legs x and y, and hypotenuse 5.

$$\therefore\ y = \sqrt{25 - x^2}. \tag{17}$$

Moreover, the vertical sectional triangle is similar to the central right triangle whose sides are 5 in. and 7 in. (Why?)

$$\therefore\ \frac{z}{y} = \frac{7}{5},$$

whence $\qquad z = \tfrac{7}{5}\,y = \tfrac{7}{5}\,\sqrt{25 - x^2}.$

Substituting the values of y and z in terms of x in (16) above gives

$$A_s = \tfrac{1}{2}\,\sqrt{25 - x^2}\cdot\tfrac{7}{5}\,\sqrt{25 - x^2} = \tfrac{7}{10}\,(25 - x^2).$$

This is now ready to integrate:

$$V = \int \tfrac{7}{10} (25 - x^2) \, dx = \tfrac{7}{10} (25 \, x - \tfrac{1}{3} \, x^3) + C.$$

If we consider half the wedge, starting the "growing volume" at $x = 0$, then $C = 0$. The moving plane finally comes to $x = 5$, making

$$V = .7 (125 - \tfrac{125}{3}) = \tfrac{175}{3} = 58\tfrac{1}{3}.$$

Doubling this gives the volume of the entire wedge.

N.B. Observe once more that the area which we integrate is not the area of some special fixed section (like the central triangle), but rather the area of a *general moving section*, expressed in terms of its distance x from some fixed point.

§ 99. Original Meaning of $\int$.

When we write $A = \int y \, dx$, we mean that A is a quantity whose derivative with respect to x is equal to y.

But historically the sign $\int$ was originally an S, denoting *"sum of."* The area under a curve was regarded as composed of innumerable strips — each having a tiny base dx, a practically constant height y, and hence an area $y \, dx$. (Fig. 48.) The whole area was the sum of these tiny "elements" of area, or, as then written:

$$A = \int y \, dx. \qquad (18)$$

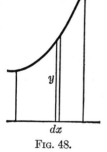

"The integral" originally meant simply "the whole," and integration was the process of making whole. From this point of view formula (18) has a very tangible meaning.

dx

Fig. 48.

Unfortunately, however, this reasoning is a bit crude. No matter how narrow a strip may be, its area is not exactly $y \, dx$. To get the exact value of A from (18) it is necessary to use the sign $\int$ not in the old sense of the sum of elements $y \, dx$, but as denoting the integral in the modern sense — *i.e.,* a quantity whose derivative with respect to x is y.

The old conception, nevertheless, can be modified slightly so as to be free from logical objection. (This will be done in Chap. XII.) And, when properly understood, this idea of tiny elements will afford the simplest means of setting up integral formulas. In fact, it is the method regularly used by scientific men. Some further illustrations will make the idea clearer.

(A) *Volume of a Solid.* According to the old conception, we may consider the solid as composed of exceedingly thin slices, say like a soap film — so thin that the area of each face of the slice is the same. The volume of the slice is this area A_s (which depends on the distance x from some fixed point) multiplied by the thickness of the slice dx. The whole volume is the sum of these slices:

$$V = \int A_s \, dx.$$

This will give a strictly correct result, if we integrate instead of summing — as we know from (15) above.

(B) *Distance Traveled at a Varying Speed.* According to the old conception, we may consider so short an interval of time dt that the speed v remains constant. The distance traveled during this interval is $v \, dt$; and the whole distance is the sum of all these tiny distances:

$$s = \int v \, dt.$$

If we integrate instead of summing, we get an exact value. For since the speed is the derivative of the distance, the distance is the integral of the speed.*

(C) *Work Done by a Variable Force.* According to the old conception, we may consider so short a distance dx that the force is constant. The work done in this tiny distance is $F \, dx$; and the sum of all these little bits of work is

$$W = \int F \, dx.$$

This formula, too, as we know by (13), gives an exact value if we integrate instead of summing.†

---

* Observe that this integral is also precisely the one which would have to be calculated, if we wished to find the area under the speed-time graph, for there v takes the place of "y" and t the place of "x." That is, the distance is represented exactly by the area under the speed-time graph. Cf. § 11.

† Why this crude reasoning, despite its fallacy of considering certain variable quantities as temporarily constant leads to these formulas which are strictly exact when we interpret the sign $\int$ in the modern sense, will become clear in Chap. XII. We shall also see how to tell when this reasoning can be relied upon.

EXERCISES

1. If the height of a cone is 6 in. and the radius of the base is 3 in., what is the area of a horizontal section x in. from the vertex? Calculate the volume by integration, and check by geometry.

2. The same as Ex. 1, for a cone of height 24 and radius 9.

3. The same as Ex. 1, for a cone of any height h and radius r.

4. Draw the curve $y = x^2$, roughly. Calculate the volume which would be generated by revolving the area under this curve about its base-line from $x = 0$ to $x = 2$. (Hint: What sort of figure will any section perpendicular to the base-line be? With what radius?)

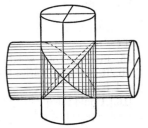

5. The same as Ex. 4, for the line $y = 2x + 3$ from $x = 1$ to $x = 4$.

6. Find by integration the volume of a sphere of radius 3 inches; also the volume cut off from that sphere by a plane 2 inches from the center.

7. Find the volume of a wedge 6 in. high cut from a cylinder of radius 5 in. by a plane passing through a diameter of the base.

8. The same as Ex. 7, if the wedge has any height h, and the cylinder any radius r.

9. The base of a solid is a quarter-circle of radius 9 in. Every section parallel to one vertical face is a right triangle whose altitude is twice its base. Find the volume of the solid.

10. Find the volume common to two equal cylinders of radius 5 in. whose axes meet at right angles. (Hint: In the figure above, show that every section one way is a square, whose area is $100 - 4x^2$.)

11. Water is poured from a cylindrical cup 6 in. tall and 6 in. in diameter. Find the volume remaining when the surface of the water just bisects the bottom of the cup.

12. Two cylinders have a common upper base, and tangent lower bases — all circles of radius 10 in. Find the volume of the common solid, if the height between bases is 30 in. (See the figure on p. 138.)

13. By using the idea of the summation of tiny "elements," set up the integrals which express:

(*a*) The momentum generated by a variable force;

(*b*) The volume of a sphere of radius 20 in., regarded as composed of thin concentric shells at a varying distance r in. from the center. [Hint: What are the area and thickness of any shell?]

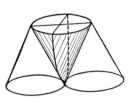

(c) The area of a circle of radius 10 in., regarded as composed of narrow concentric rings, at a varying distance, r in. from the center.

(d) The increase in the national wealth during any period if the rate of increase is some variable quantity R — supposed known as a function of t.

14. During a decade the rate of emigration from a country (R persons per yr.) varied approximately thus with the elapsed time (t yr.): $R = 10000 + 800\,t - 30\,t^2$.   Find the total emigration between $t = 2$ and $t = 8$.

15. Find the total weight of a rod 10 ft. long if its weight per foot (y lb./ft.) steadily varies thus with the distance (x ft.) from one end: $y = 4 + .3\,x - .03\,x^2$.

[16.] Could the quantity $(x^3 + 1)^{10} \cdot 3\,x^2$ be obtained by differentiating some power of $(x^3 + 1)$, possibly multiplied by a numerical factor? If so, find $\int (x^3 + 1)^{10}\,3\,x^2\,dx$.

§ 100 S. Water Pressure: Total Force.   An important engineering problem is this: To calculate the total force with which water will press horizontally against a vertical wall or dam.

The pressure, that is to say, the number of pounds per sq. ft., is different at different depths: 1 ft. below the surface it is 62.5 lb. per sq. ft.; 2 ft. below, it is twice this; and so on, proportionally.*

To find the total force against a dam, with the pressure varying all the way down, we may proceed in either of two ways.

(I) *By using the old conception of "tiny elements."*

According to this we may consider a very narrow strip across the dam as being all at one depth, x ft. below the surface of the water.   The pressure against this strip is, then,

$$p = 62.5\,x \text{ (lb. per sq. ft.)}.$$

The number of square feet in the strip is $w\,dx$, where w denotes the width of the dam at this depth.   Multiplying the

---

* Actually, 62.4 is closer for pure water; but 62.5 is a convenient working figure, and is a satisfactory average when impurities are considered.

number of pounds per sq. ft. by the number of square feet, we get the total force, or number of pounds, against the strip:

Force against strip = 62.5 $x\,w\,dx$ (lb.).

The total force against the dam is the sum of all these little forces:

$$F = \int 62.5 \; x \; w \; dx. \tag{19}$$

If we can get a formula for the width of the dam at any depth x, the total force can be found by integrating (19).

If no such formula is obtainable for w, then F can merely be approximated by figuring out the force against many narrow strips, and adding.

(II) *By reasoning exactly about a "growing force."*

Let F denote the total force against the dam down to any depth x. Then while x increases by Δx, F increases by some ΔF (the force against the narrow strip in Fig. 49).

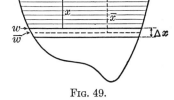

$$\Delta F = 62.5 \; \overline{x} \; \overline{w} \; \Delta x,$$

Fig. 49.

where $\overline{x}$ and $\overline{w}$ are some average depth and width in the strip.

The average rate of increase of F, per foot increase in x, is, then,

$$\frac{\Delta F}{\Delta x} = 62.5 \; \overline{x} \; \overline{w},$$

and the limit of this as $\Delta x \to 0$ is

$$\frac{dF}{dx} = 62.5 \; x \; w,$$

whence we have (19) again, the $\int$ denoting "integral of." *

Ex. I. The width of a dam x ft. below the surface of the water is $w = 400 - x^2$. Find the total force against it down to a depth of 20 ft.

* For oil instead of water, the only change in (19) would be a different numerical factor in place of 62.5. This is the weight of a cubic foot of water, and would be replaced by the weight of a cubic foot of the oil.

Substituting in (19) the given value of w we have

$$F = \int 62.5\, x\, (400 - x^2)\, dx = 62.5 \int (400\, x - x^3)\, dx.$$

$$\therefore F = 62.5\, (200\, x^2 - \tfrac{1}{4}\, x^4) + C.$$

But $F = 0$ at the surface, where $x = 0$. Hence $C = 0$. And when $x = 20$, we have the whole force, $F = 62.5\, (80000 - 40000)$, $= 2500000$ (lb.).

§ 101 S. Integrating a Power of a Quantity.   Can we ever integrate an expression which involves a product, or a power of a quantity, without first multiplying out?   Yes, if the given expression happens to be the derivative of a higher power — aside from a constant multiplier perhaps.

By (22), p. 104, we know that *differentiating* any power u^n gives $nu^{n-1}\, du/dx$. Hence if we are to integrate a given expression and come out with u^n, the expression must consist of *a power of u, multiplied by the derivative of u*, and possibly also by a constant.

Ex. I.   Integrate $(x^4 - 25)^9\, 4\, x^3\, dx$.
This is the 9th power of the quantity $(x^4 - 25)$ times the derivative of that quantity.   Hence it would result from differentiating the 10th power of that same quantity — aside from a numerical factor $\tfrac{1}{10}$.

$$\therefore \int (x^4 - 25)^9\, 4\, x^3\, dx = \tfrac{1}{10}\, (x^4 - 25)^{10} + C. \qquad (20)$$

Observe that the factor $4\, x^3$ is used up in integrating the power $(x^4-25)^9$. This will probably be clearer if you differentiate the result, and compare.

In the foregoing example, if we had been given $7\, x^3$ instead of $4\, x^3$, the desired form $4\, x^3$ could be found by taking the 7 outside, and multiplying and dividing by 4:

$$\int (\cdots)^9\, 7\, x^3\, dx = 7 \int (\cdots)^9\, x^3\, dx = \tfrac{7}{4} \int (\cdots)^9\, 4\, x^3\, dx.$$

The result would have been $7/4$ times the result in (20) above.

If, however, we had been given *a different power of x*, say x^5 instead of x^3, this could not be remedied by multiplying and dividing, for a variable cannot be moved from one side of the integral sign to the other.   [In fact, an x^5 obviously would not arise in differentiating $(x^4 - 25)^{10}$.] We should have to multiply out before integrating.

Ex. II.   Find $y = \int \sqrt{9 - x^2} \; x \; dx$.

We need $-2x$ outside the radical.   So we change the form thus:

$$y = -\tfrac{1}{2} \int (9 - x^2)^{\tfrac{1}{2}} \cdot - 2\,x\,dx = -\tfrac{1}{2} [\tfrac{2}{3}(9 - x^2)^{\tfrac{3}{2}}] + C.$$

Ex. III.   Find $\int \sqrt{x^3 + 16} \; dx$.

This is not yet possible, the factor x^2 being absent outside the radical.

EXERCISES

1. A gate of a canal "lock" has a constant width of 40 ft. and a height of 40 ft.   When the water level is 10 ft. from its top, what is the total force against it?   Calculate this by integration, and also without.

2. The width of a certain dam at a depth of x ft. is $w = 300 - x^2$. Calculate w at $x = 0, 2, 4, 6, 8, 10$; and make a rough drawing of the dam down to that depth.   Estimate its area and the total force of water pressure against the part drawn.   Calculate this force.

3. Find the total force of water pressure down to a depth of 10 ft. if the width of a dam varies thus: $w = 400 - 4\,x^2$.

4. Find the total force against one face of a triangular board immersed in water, if one vertex is at the surface, one side (6 ft. long) is vertical, and the base (2 ft. long) is horizontal.

5. A triangular gate in a vertical dam is 4 ft. high, and is 4 ft. wide at its level top 10 ft. below the surface of the water.   Find the force against the gate.   (Hint: Show that $w = 14 - x$.)

6. Find the following integrals and check each by differentiation:

(a) $\int (8 + x^3)^{\tfrac{5}{2}} \, 3\,x^2 \, dx$,

(b) $\int \sqrt{4 - x^4} \; 4\,x^3 \, dx$,

(c) $\int \sqrt{16 - x^2} \; x \, dx$,

(d) $\int 7\,(x^6 + 9)^{-\tfrac{1}{2}} \, x^5 \, dx$,

(e) $\int 6\,x^4\,(1 - x^5)^{20} \, dx$,

(f) $\int \left(x / \sqrt{x^2 + 25}\right) dx$.

7. Find $\int (x^2 + 10)^2 \, x \, dx$ in two ways, and reconcile the answers.

8. Find the total force on the end of a cylindrical boiler of radius **3** ft., placed horizontally, and half full of water.   (Hint: The depth

x and half-width $w/2$ are sides of a right triangle whose hypotenuse is 3 ft. Integrate the final expression as in Ex. 6 c.)

9. The same as Ex. 8, if the radius is 6 ft.

10. Explain precisely what is meant by the "number of lb. per sq. ft. *at the depth of x ft.*" We cannot have a square foot of vertical wall all at the same depth, x ft., no matter how narrow the strip.

11. A rectangular floor 60 ft. long and 20 ft. wide carries a load, whose amount per sq. ft. (y lb.) varies thus with the distance (x ft.) from one end: $y = 2\,x$. Express the total load as an integral: (*a*) By using the old idea of elements; (*b*) By a consideration of rates.

§ 102 S. Further Applications. Many physical quantities calculated by integration are too complicated to discuss at present. One more case will be cited, however:

The total attraction of a uniform rod upon an exterior particle M, in its axis produced. By the law of gravitation: Every particle m of the rod attracts M with a force proportional to the product of the masses divided by the square of the distance apart: $F = GMm/x^2$, where G is a cer-

FIG. 50.

tain gravitational constant. But there are particles at all distances, within certain limits. (Fig. 50.)

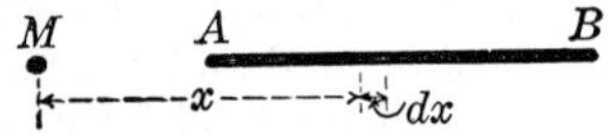

Using the old conception, consider a tiny piece of the rod at any distance x from M. Its mass equals D, the mass per unit length, multiplied by dx, its length. The attraction of this tiny mass $D\,dx$ upon M is $GMD\,dx/x^2$. And the whole force is

$$F = \int \frac{GMD\,dx}{x^2}, \quad = \frac{-GMD}{x} + C. \qquad (21)$$

To check this, consider the growing attraction exerted by a varying portion of the rod, over to a distance x from M. Increasing x by Δx takes in an additional force ΔF which equals $GMD\Delta x/\bar{x}^2$, where $\bar{x}$ is some average or mean distance from M to points of the added portion Δx. Then $\Delta F/\Delta x = GMD/\bar{x}^2$, and $dF/dx = GMD/x^2$. Hence we have (21) again, but with the sign $\int$ used in its modern sense, to denote a quantity whose derivative is GMD/x^2.

§ 103. Summary of Chapter IV.   Integration is the reverse of differentiation:

$$\int f(x)\ dx = F(x) \quad \text{means} \quad dF(x) = f(x)\ dx.$$

Its uses are of two sorts: (I) to derive a formula for some varying quantity whose rate of change is known — *e.g.*, the height of a projectile at any time; and (II) to calculate some fixed geometrical or physical magnitude, such as area, work, etc.

But as each fixed area, etc., is the value to which some varying area, etc., will grow, problems of type (II) in reality come under type (I).

The constant of integration can be determined if we know the value of x, or t, etc., at which the growth is regarded as starting.

In elementary geometry each new area and volume is calculated by some new plan.   But by integration we find all volumes by one and the same process: Expressing the sectional area A_s in terms of the distance x from some fixed point, and then integrating $A_s\ dx$.*   Similarly all plane areas can be found by one process, all momenta by one process, etc.   Moreover many problems which we have not yet analyzed yield to the same general method.

The science of calculating derivatives (or differentials) and integrals is known as *Differential and Integral Calculus*.   It was invented by Sir Isaac Newton about 1670, and by Gottfried Wilhelm Leibnitz independently, a little later.   Each made many notable calculations with his new invention — Newton's work in astronomy and physics being especially remarkable, although his notation was much less convenient than that of Leibnitz, which we are using.

In Differential Calculus the fundamental problem is to find the rate at which a given quantity is changing; in Integral Calculus it is the reverse: Given the rate, to find the value of the varying quantity.

Our work up to this point is, of course, barely a start in this field.

EXERCISES †

1. Which of these forms can be integrated by some method already studied?   (Do not work out.)

(a) $x^3\ (x^4 + 8)^{\frac{1}{2}}\ dx,$ (b) $x^2\sqrt{16 - x^4}\ dx,$

(c) $(x^2 + 1)^{10}\ dx,$ (d) $x\ (10 - x^2)^{10}\ dx.$

* If no formula for A_s is known, we can often find one by a preliminary integration.   This will be discussed in Chapter XII.

† See footnote, p. 117.

2. A point moved in such a way that $d^3y/dt^3 = 72$, y being the distance traveled. At $t = 0$ the speed was 200 and the acceleration $- 6$. Find y at any time.

3. A stone was thrown straight down from an airplane 18000 ft. high with an initial speed of 30 ft./sec. Derive a formula for its height after t sec. How would you proceed to find the speed with which the stone struck the ground?

4. A stone was dropped from a helicopter 2400 ft. high when an automobile running 60 ft./sec. passed directly beneath. (*a*) How far apart were the stone and automobile 10 sec. later, and how fast was their distance changing? (*b*) When were they nearest?

5. A bullet was fired straight up from an airplane 9600 ft. high, with an initial speed of 800 ft./sec. Find its height after t sec. When did it strike the ground? When was it highest? How high?

6. A beam loaded in a certain way has its curve defined by the equation $d^4y/dx^4 = - .000036\,x$. Find y as function of x, if at $x = 0$ we have $y = 0$, slope $= -.008$, flexion $= 0$, and rate of increase of flexion $= .0012$.

7. Find the area under the curve $y = 1/x^2$ from $x = 2$ to $x = 20$.

8. In stretching a spring, the force (F lb.) varied as the elongation (x in.) and was 30 lb. when $x = 1$. Find the work done in producing an elongation of 5 in., starting from normal length.

9. The force (F lb.) with which steam drove a piston varied thus: $F = 3000/x^{\frac{4}{3}}$. Find the work done from $x = 1$ (in.) to $x = 27$ (in.).

10. The base of a solid is a circle of radius 20 inches, and every section perpendicular to one diameter is an isosceles triangle whose height equals twice its base. Find the volume of the solid.

11. A wedge 6 in. tall is cut off from a cylinder of radius 6 in. by a plane passing through a diameter of the base. Find its volume.

12. Find the volume within the surface generated by revolving the curve $y = x^2 - 1$ about its base line, from $x = 1$ to $x = 3$.

13. A triangular board is immersed vertically in water, its vertex being at the surface and its horizontal base being 8 ft. below. If the base is 6 ft. long, find the total force of water pressure against one face of the board.

14. Express and calculate the attraction in Fig. 50 if $M = .60$, $D = 3$, $G = .000\,000\,067$, the rod is 30 cm. long, and the particle 10 cm. away.

15. A rod 20 cm. long has a mass of .08 gram per cm. Find its total attraction on a particle of mass 3 grams, placed 6 cm. from the rod, and in line. Take G as in Ex. 14.

16. Find the total weight (W lb.) of a rod 8 ft. long if its weight per foot (w lb./ft.) varies thus with the distance (x ft.) from one end: $w = .06\, x$. (Set up the integral in two ways.)

17. Find the total load on a beam 25 ft. long if the rate of loading (y lb. per ft.) varies thus with the distance (x ft.) from one end: $y = 10\, x$. (Set up the integral in either way.)

18. Like Ex. 11, p. 142, for a floor 40 ft. by 25 ft., if y varies thus: $y = 10 + 1.2\, x$.

19. The loading (y lb. per sq. ft.) on a circular floor of radius 20 ft. varies thus with the distance (x ft.) from the center: $y = 10 + 1.2\, x$. Find the total load on the floor.

[20.] Find by geometry the area of the smaller segment cut from a circle of radius 20 in. by a chord which subtends an angle of 120° at the center. Why would it be more difficult to find the area if the central angle were 100° instead of 120°?

Exs. 21–25 use this idea: Any given curve may be regarded as the derived curve (§ 72) of some original or "primitive" curve.

21. (a) If the given curve has the equation $y = x^2$, what is the equation of the primitive curve? Explain any indefiniteness. (b) Determine that particular primitive in which $y = 10$ when $x = 3$.

22. Find the equation of the primitive having $y = 8$ at $x = 0$, if the given curve is $y = 18x - 3x^2$.

23. (a) Explain how, if a curve were given without its equation, the primitive could be constructed by measuring certain areas and adding these to the initial value of y in the required primitive. (b) Illustrate by plotting the curve given in Ex. 22, and constructing the primitive. Check some ordinates of the primitive by calculations from the formula.

24. (a) Find by measurement or geometry the area under the line $y = 2\, x$ from $x = 0$ to each of the values $x = 0, 1, 2, \ldots, 7$. Use these results to plot a primitive curve, with $y = 0$ at $x = 0$. (b) Check by integration. (c) Check also by measuring slopes of the primitive curve, and comparing the ordinates of the given graph.

25. (a)–(c). Like Ex. 24 (a)–(c) for the given curve $y = x^2$.

§ 104. Unknown Integrals. We are not yet able to integrate some expressions which arise in simple problems.

Ex. I. The area under the curve $y = \dfrac{1}{x}$ is

$$A = \int \frac{1}{x}\, dx.$$

No integration formula has yet been given for $\int x^{-1}\, dx$. (See § 88, p. 122.)

Ex. II.   The area of the circular segment BCD in Fig. 51 is

$$A = 2 \int y \, dx = 2 \int \sqrt{100 - x^2} \, dx.$$

We cannot effect the integration as yet.   (Cf. Ex. III, § 101.)

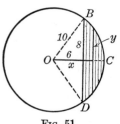

Later on we shall see how to perform both of these integrations.   In the meantime we can at least solve such problems approximately by the graphical method of § 13.

In fact, *any unknown integral* can be approximated graphically.   For

Fig. 51.

$$\int F(x) \, dx = \text{area under graph of } F(x),$$

and to find the value of such an integral we need merely plot the function $F(x)$, and measure the area under the graph.

Remark.   The question naturally arises as to whether the area of the segment in Ex. II above can be calculated by elementary geometry.

$$A = \text{sector } OBCD - \text{triangle } OBD.$$

The area of OBD is clearly 48 sq. in.   The sectorial area is to the entire area of the circle as $\angle BOD$ is to 360°.

The size of $\angle BOD$ is definitely fixed by the length of its chord BD (= 16 in.).   But we have as yet no means of finding just how many degrees there are in the angle.

If we knew the precise relation of an angle of a triangle to the sides, we could find the required area.

§ 105.   Survey of Chapters I–IV.   At the beginning of the course we defined a *function* as a quantity which varies with another in some definite way.   And the central problem all along has been to learn just how a function varies.

When given merely a *table of values*, we could only plot the function and study it graphically.   Average and instantaneous rates could be approximated; also extreme values, mean values, and any quantity which is represented by the area under a graph.

When the function was given by a *formula* we could make some of these calculations exactly.   But we did not at first see how to find an instantaneous rate exactly, nor the area under a graph.

On defining an instantaneous rate accurately as a *limit*, we saw that to calculate it we must find the limiting value approached by an average rate, whose interval is being indefinitely shortened. This brought us to differentiation, the chief operation of the Differential Calculus. We wrote derivatives of power functions at sight, and used them for various purposes.

Finally, we saw how to calculate various quantities by the Integral Calculus. But the usefulness of the integration process is limited at present by our inability to integrate many simple expressions; *e.g.*

$$\sqrt{100 - x^2}\, dx, \qquad \frac{1}{x}\, dx.$$

Functions exist which have these differentials; but they are of different sorts from any which we have studied. So our next project will be to study some *further kinds of functions*. These will be highly useful of themselves.

As suggested by the problem of the circular segment (§ 104) and that of the inclination of a curve (§ 85), we need to know the *relations between the sides and angles of a triangle*. To this matter we now turn our attention.

CHAPTER V

TRIGONOMETRIC FUNCTIONS

THE SOLUTION OF TRIANGLES

§ 106. Some Preliminary Ideas. The branch of mathematics which deals with the relations between the angles and sides of a triangle is called *Trigonometry* — from two Greek words meaning "to measure a triangle." It also deals with matters of a very different kind, relating to periodically oscillating quantities. Thus it is the basis of surveying, and of many calculations in engineering, physics, astronomy, navigation, and other sciences.

Before proceeding with the subject proper, let us note some elementary ideas as to the drawing and measuring of figures.

An angle of any size can be measured or drawn by using a protractor. (See Appendix, p. 528). Hence, any ordinary triangle problem, arising in surveying or elsewhere, can be solved approximately by simply *drawing the figure to some chosen scale, and reading off the required distances or angles.*

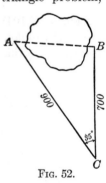

FIG. 52.

With good instruments and practice the percentage of error can be kept very low. Thus we can check roughly the more refined methods developed presently, which use trigonometry proper.

Ex. I. Find the distance AB across a pond (Fig. 52), if the distances CA and CB and $\angle C$ have been measured as 900 ft., 700 ft., and 35°.

We draw an angle of 35° with a protractor, and lay off sides of 9 cm. and 7 cm., to represent CA (= 900 ft.) and CB (= 700 ft.), respectively. Joining the ends of these lines we get a triangle which must be similar to the actual large triangle ABC. (Why?) The third side of the constructed triangle measures 5.4 cm.; hence the distance AB is 540 ft.

§ 107. Locating Points by Coordinates. In mapping it is necessary to describe accurately the location of any important point P.   Usually this is done by giving the distances x and y of P from two mutually perpendicular lines, YY' and XX'. (Fig. 53.)

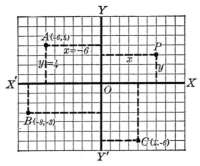

Fig. 53.

To show on which side of each reference line or axis the point P lies, we use a $+$ or $-$ sign, calling x negative for points to the left of YY', and y negative for points below XX'. Thus for the point A, $x = -6$, $y = 4$; for B, $x = -8$, $y = -3$; and for C, $x = 4$, $y = -6$.

The x and y of a point are called its "rectangular coordinates": x the *abscissa* and y the *ordinate*. O is called the *origin*.

To designate a point we simply write its coordinates within parentheses, x first.   Thus $(-6, 4)$ denotes the point at which $x = -6$ and $y = 4$.

This idea of rectangular coordinates, closely related to our earlier plotting, is also used in daily life.   *E.g.*, we direct a man to some point by saying that it is two miles east and three miles north.

In mapping, the positive X-axis is taken eastward and the positive Y-axis northward.

Another way of describing location is illustrated in daily life when we say that a town is "20 miles from here in a direction 12° north of east," or that a golf flag is "500 yd. away in a direction 30° west of south."   That is, the location of a point P is described by stating its *distance* from some chosen origin O, and the direction angle which the line OP makes with some chosen axis of reference.   (Fig. 54.)

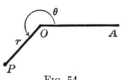

In Mathematics the direction angle is generally measured **counter-clockwise** *from* the axis *OA to* the line *OP*; and is denoted by θ (Greek letter *theta*).   The line *OP* is called the "radius vector," and is denoted by *r*.   The origin *O* is also called the *pole*; and the values (*r*, θ) are called the *polar coordinates* of *P*.   In this chapter we regard *r* as positive and let θ take any value from 0° to 360°, according to the location of *P*.   This subject will be discussed further in Chapter X.

Fig. 54.

EXERCISES

1. Draw any triangle, measure its three angles, and check their sum by geometry.

2. Draw two triangles with their sides respectively 2, 3, 4, and 4, 6, 8.   Measure and compare corresponding angles.

3. Draw a straight line which rises from the horizontal at an angle of 35°.   By making suitable measurements calculate its slope.

4. To find the distance *AB* through a hill, lines *AC* = 400 ft., and *BC* = 640 ft. were measured; also ∠ *C* = 60°.   Find *AB*.

In Exs. 5–12 it is desirable to use rectangular graph paper.

5. Plot the point *P* whose rectangular coordinates are (12, 5). Exactly how far is it from the origin *O*?   By measurement, what angle does *OP* make with the positive *X*-axis?   The same for the point *P* (− 8, 6).

6. Map a pentagonal piece of ground whose corners are: *A* (5, 3); *B* (− 5, 3); *C* (− 8, − 1); *D* (0, − 7); *E* (8, − 1).   Apparently which sides are equal?   Any right angles?   Check by measurement or calculation.

7. With Seattle as (0, 0) and a mile as the unit, Mt. Rainier has the position (27, −52).   By measurement, how far is the mountain from Seattle and how many degrees south of east?   What is its direction angle θ, measured counterclockwise from the east?

8. Three cities have the following coordinates, referred to New York as (0, 0):   Providence (130, 70);   Ithaca (−130, 115);   Philadelphia (−65, −60).   Find the distance and direction of each from N.Y., describing the direction by an acute angle from E, N, W, or S.   Also give the direction angle θ for each, measured counterclockwise from the east.

9. Niagara Falls is 19 mi. from Buffalo, 30° west of north.   Restate this location by giving polar coordinates for the Falls, with Buffalo as pole, and the direction axis eastward.   Also read off rectangular coordinates for the Falls.

10. With Los Angeles as pole and the axis eastward, Mt. "Baldy" has the position (37, 26°). How far east, and how far north, is it from L.A.? State this by giving rectangular coordinates for the mountain.

11. With Chicago as pole and the axis eastward, map these cities: Detroit (240, 8°); Minneapolis (350, 140°); Kansas City (410, 208°); Cincinnati (260, 310°). Read off the rectangular coordinates of each.

[**12.**] At several points on one side of an acute angle, erect perpendiculars, and measure the sides of each right triangle so formed. Divide the leg opposite the given angle by the hypotenuse in each case, and compare. Likewise the opposite leg by the adjacent leg.

§ 108. Trigonometric Functions of an Acute Angle.

If we erect perpendiculars at various points of either side of any acute angle (Fig. 55), the right triangles thus formed are all similar. (Why?) Hence their corresponding sides are proportional. *E.g.,*

$$\frac{a}{b} = \frac{a'}{b'} = \frac{a''}{b''}, \text{ etc.}$$

Thus the ratio a/b does not depend at all upon the size of the triangle. But if we change the size

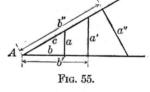

FIG. 55.

of angle A, the triangle changes shape, and a/b no longer has the same value. In fact, a/b varies with A in some definite way, and is therefore some function of A.

Likewise a/c, b/c, etc., are functions of A. All of these ratios are called "trigonometric functions" of A; and each has a name.

DEFINITIONS. In any right triangle, large or small, containing a particular acute angle A (Fig. 56), let a denote the leg opposite angle A, b the adjacent leg, and c the hypotenuse. Then the "sine" and "tangent" of angle A (abbreviated sin A, tan A) are defined as follows:

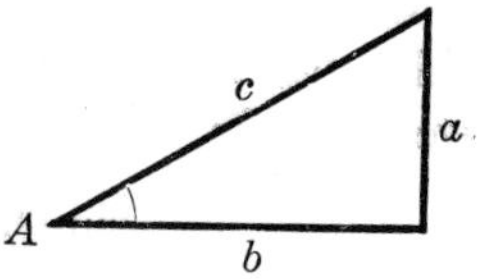

FIG. 56.

$$\sin A = \frac{a}{c} = \frac{\text{opposite leg}}{\text{hypotenuse}};$$

$$\tan A = \frac{a}{b} = \frac{\text{opposite leg}}{\text{adjacent leg}}.$$

(1)

152 TRIGONOMETRIC FUNCTIONS

Likewise the "cosine" and "cotangent" are defined as:

$$\cos A = \frac{b}{c} = \frac{\text{adjacent leg}}{\text{hypotenuse}};$$

$$\text{ctn } A = \frac{b}{a} = \frac{\text{adjacent leg}}{\text{opposite leg}}.$$

(2)

Note that in the first pair it is the *opposite* leg that is divided by another side; in the second pair, or "co-functions," it is the *adjacent leg*. Also observe that the sine and cosine have the hypotenuse as the divisor. These definitions should be memorized thoroughly.

Two other functions, needed in a later chapter, are the *secant* and *cosecant*: $\sec A = c/b$, $\csc A = c/a$. We shall here deal with the functions defined above, and shall refer to them as "the four functions."

§ 109. Numerical Illustrations. Suppose a right triangle to be formed as in Fig. 57 by bisecting an equilateral triangle whose sides are 2 units long. The altitude, or leg opposite the 60° angle, equals $\sqrt{3}$. (Why?) Hence we read off:

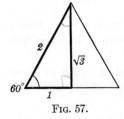

FIG. 57.

$$\sin 60° = \frac{\sqrt{3}}{2}, \qquad \tan 60° = \frac{\sqrt{3}}{1},$$

$$\cos 60° = \frac{1}{2}, \qquad \text{ctn } 60° = \frac{1}{\sqrt{3}}.$$

This indicates that there are some special angles, whose functions are easily found by geometry. For most angles we refer to tables (§ 110), calculated by methods described later. (§ 345.)

In Fig. 57 the other acute angle is 30°. The leg opposite this angle is adjacent to the 60° angle, and vice versa. Hence, we read off:

$$\sin 30° = \frac{1}{2}, \qquad \tan 30° = \frac{1}{\sqrt{3}},$$

$$\cos 30° = \frac{\sqrt{3}}{2}, \qquad \text{ctn } 30° = \frac{\sqrt{3}}{1}.$$

Thus, $\sin 30° = \cos 60°$, and $\cos 30° = \sin 60°$; etc.

More generally, if any two angles A and B are *complementary* (*i.e.*, have their sum equal to 90°), the sine of either equals the cosine of the other, and the tangent of either equals the cotangent of the other. For both A and B will appear in any right triangle which contains either; and the side opposite one will be adjacent to the other.

In fact, the name "cosine" is merely a contraction of "the complement's sine." Likewise for "cotangent" and "cosecant."

Finding all the functions from one. Given any function of an acute angle A, we can construct the angle and read off the other functions. Always, ctn $A = 1 \div$ tan A.

Ex. I. tan $A = \frac{4}{3}$; find the other functions.

Recalling the definition of tan A, we draw a right triangle, making the leg opposite A equal to 4 and the adjacent leg 3. (Fig. 58.) The hypotenuse must be 5. Hence we read:

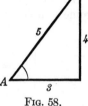

$$\sin A = \tfrac{4}{5}, \qquad \tan A = \tfrac{4}{3},$$
$$\cos A = \tfrac{3}{5}, \qquad \text{ctn } A = \tfrac{3}{4}.$$

Also, if desired: sec $A = 5/3$, csc $A = 5/4$.

Fig. 58.

EXERCISES

1. Draw a right triangle with the legs 5 and 12. Calling the smaller acute angle A and the larger B, read off the four functions of A. Likewise those of B.

2. Like Ex. 1 for a right triangle with hypotenuse 10 and one leg 6.

3. The same, with the hypotenuse 17 and one leg 15.

4. Re-draw Fig. 57 with the hypotenuse 10 and other sides accordingly. Read off the functions of 60° and 30°; and simplify to the values in § 109.

5. Draw an isosceles right triangle, choose convenient legs, and read off the four functions of 45°.

6. Given tan $A = 7/24$, construct A; and read off the other three functions.

7. Like Ex. 6, given each following function:

(*a*) sin $A = \frac{3}{5}$;   (*b*) cos $A = \frac{9}{41}$;   (*c*) ctn $A = \frac{2}{3}$.

8. Show that sin A can never exceed 1; but that tan A can range from very small to very large values. How about cos A? ctn A?

9. Draw a right triangle containing an angle of 35°. Measure the legs and hypotenuse, and compute approximate values for the four functions of 35°. Also label your results so they could be used for 55°.

10. Like Ex. 9 for 20° (and 70°).

11. Express each following function as another function of some other acute angle: sin 10°, sin 85°, tan 80°, tan 15°.

12. Like Ex. 11 for the following: cos 4°, cos 79°, ctn 6°, ctn 88°.

§ 110. Arrangement of Tables. When the functions of 20° are printed in a table, these can also be regarded as certain other functions of 70°. Likewise for any two complementary angles. Thus, a table need run only from 0° to 45°, provided it gives suitable labels to show at a glance to what functions and angles each tabulated value belongs.

The common arrangement is that used on p. 539, from which some sample items are reproduced here.

ANGLE	SINE	TANGENT	COTANGENT	COSINE	
0°	.0000	.0000	. . . . .	1.0000	**90°**
1°	.0175	.0175	57.290	.9998	**89°**
2°	.0349	.0349	28.636	.9994	**88°**
3°	.0523	.0524	19.081	.9986	**87°**
—	—	—	—	—	—
—	—	—	—	—	—
45°	.7071	1.0000	1.00000	.7071	**45°**
	Cosine	Cotangent	Tangent	Sine	Angle

The heavy labels at the bottom and right side go together. These call attention, for example, to the fact that 57.290 which is printed as ctn 1° is also tan 89°; and that .0523 which is printed as sin 3° is also cos 87°.

As ∠A runs from 0° to 90°, its sine runs through the values shown down the first column, .0000 to .7071; and then through the values up the last column, .7071 to 1.0000. The cosine values start by running down the last column, and then run up the first. Similarly for tan A and ctn A, respectively.

The table exhibits each quantity (sin A, etc.) as a function of A. The variations are shown more clearly by graphs. (§ 276.)

§ 111. Solution of Right Triangles. Finding the unknown "parts" (*i.e.*, angles or sides) of a definitely specified triangle is called *solving the triangle*. This can be done roughly by measuring a drawing, or accurately by using trigonometric tables.

Ex. I. To find the distance a between two points on opposite sides of a stream, a surveyor laid out a line 200 ft. long perpendicular to a, and measured the 33° angle shown in Fig. 59. Solve for a.

[Here we know an angle and the adjacent leg; and are to find the opposite leg. So we choose the *tangent*: opposite leg ÷ adjacent leg.]

$$\tan 33° = \frac{a}{200}.$$

But tan 33° = .6494   (by table).

Fig. 59.

$$\therefore \frac{a}{200} = .6494.$$

$$\therefore a = 129.9 \qquad \text{(nearly)}.$$

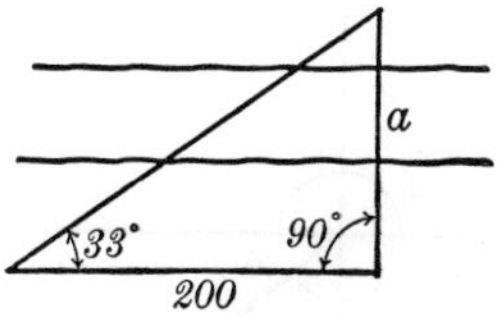

This result has been rounded off to four figures, because the table is not accurate to more. See the *Remark* below.

Ex. II. A ship sails 25° south of west. How far must it go to advance 20 miles southward? (Fig. 60.)

[We are to find the hypotenuse c, knowing an angle and the opposite leg. We choose the *sine*: opposite leg ÷ hypotenuse.]

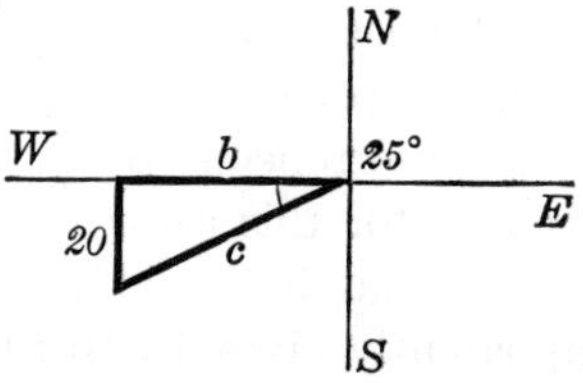

Fig. 60.

$$\sin 25° = \frac{20}{c} = .4226 \quad \text{(by table).}$$

Multiplying through by c gives 20 = .4226 c.

$$\therefore c = \frac{20}{.4226} = 47.33.$$

If we wished to know also the westward distance, b mi., we could now use any of these functions:

$$\frac{b}{20} = \text{ctn } 25°, \qquad \frac{20}{b} = \tan 25°, \qquad \frac{b}{c} = \cos 25°.$$

With the last of these, any error in the previously calculated value
of c would affect b as well. With the second, a long division would be
necessary to obtain b, as in finding c above. The first is best; it ob-
tains b directly from *given* values, and by a simple *multiplication*
because it has b in its *numerator*.

The hypotenuse c appears in the numerator of the secant and
cosecant; but, unfortunately, tables of these functions are not commonly available. Hence solving for c involves division. (It would
here take even longer to find c as $\sqrt{20^2 + b^2}$).

Ex. III.   Find the polar coordinates of the point $(6, -5)$.

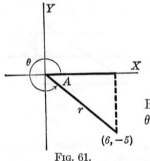

Fig. 61.

Using a table of square roots,

$$r = \sqrt{6^2 + 5^2} \;\; = \sqrt{61} \;\; = 7.8102.$$

Also for the acute angle A (Fig. 61):

$$\text{ctn } A = \tfrac{6}{5} = 1.2000$$

By tables, $A = 39°.8$; whence we find
$\theta = 360 - A° = 320°.2$.

REMARK.   Numerical results usually have as large a percentage error
as the least accurate number that enters the calculation.
E.g., suppose we multiply 42.183 by .112, where each factor
may be erroneous by $\tfrac{1}{2}$ in the third decimal place. For the
first factor this error would be only 1 part in 84000; but for
the second it would be 1 part in 224. The multiplication
apparently gives 4.7245; but this may be erroneous by 1 part
in 224, or slightly over .02. The true product for exact numbers that may be represented by 42.183 and .112 can lie anywhere between 4.70 and 4.75, approx.*

Hence, when working with 4-place tables we mislead ourselves if we keep more than four significant figures in our
results. Engineers and others who apply mathematics must
ascertain the possible error in each number employed. Here,
however, we shall assume all our given numbers to be accurate
to as many figures as the best of them, and to be as accurate as
our tables.

* Test this for 42.1825 × .1115 and 42.1835 × .1125.

EXERCISES

1. Read off from the table, p. 539, the four functions of 35°; likewise those of 75°.

2. Read off the functions of 55°. Check by drawing and measurement.

3. Interpolate, p. 539, to find the four functions of 20° 40′.

4. Like Ex. 3 for 60°.4.

5. Find A to the nearest degree if

(a) $\sin A = .04$,   (b) $\cos A = .2$,   (b) $\tan A = 1.8$,   (d) $\operatorname{ctn} A = 7$.

6. If $\tan A = .41$, find A to the nearest tenth of a degree.

In Exs. 7–25, first solve by drawing to scale and measuring the required part. Then solve by the table, directly from the given parts without using your measurements, getting angles to the nearest degree. Compare results.

7. The hypotenuse of a right triangle is 20 ft.; one angle is 37°. Find the legs and the other angle.

8. If one leg of a right triangle is 450 ft. and the hypotenuse is 500 ft., find the angles and other leg.

9. One angle of a right triangle is 72° and the opposite leg is 100 in. Find the other leg and the hypotenuse.

10. The hand rail of a stairway rises 20 ft. in a horizontal distance of 30 ft. At what angle does it ascend?

11. Find the vertical height of Niagara Falls, if this subtends an angle of 11° at a point 840 ft. away on the level of the top.

12. A ladder 20 ft. long leans against a vertical wall, and makes an angle of 75° with the level ground. How high does it reach? How far from the wall is its foot?

13. A cog railway near Interlaken rises 1420 meters in 7 km. of track. At what angle would the track have to ascend if the rise were uniform?

14. The Leaning Tower of Pisa is 180 ft. high and its top is 14 ft. out of plumb. Find what angle its axis makes with the vertical.

15. Mt. Jefferson is 74 mi. from Portland, Ore., in a direction 53° south of east. How far south is it, and how far east, from the city?

16. What direction is Mt. Hood from Portland, if 12.34 mi. south, and 49.54 mi. east?

17. A diagonal street runs 30° south of west. How far west must it go to have advanced 3 mi. to the south?

18. An airplane flew 65° north of east. When it had gone 200 mi. north, how far east had it traveled?

19. Find the polar coordinates of each following point:

(a) A $(7, -3)$;   *(b)* B $(-7, 3)$;   *(c)* C $(-5, 8)$.

20. Find the rectangular coordinates of the points whose polar coordinates are:

(a) D $(9, 100°)$,   *(b)* E $(25, 250°)$,   *(c)* F $(15, 305°)$.

§ 112. Further Geometric Figures.   Many problems relating to structure and design, regular polygons, chords of circles, etc., require a consideration of *isosceles triangles*.   Any such triangle can be cut into two equal right triangles, and hence can be solved by the foregoing methods.

Ex. I.   A regular octagon has a perimeter of 240 ft.   Find its area.

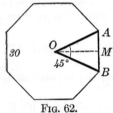

Each of the eight equal sides, as AB (Fig. 62) is 30 ft. long, and must subtend at the center O an angle of $\frac{1}{8}$ (360°) or 45°.   Bisecting this gives a right triangle, with $\angle MOA$ = 22°.5, and the opposite leg MA = 15 ft.

Fig. 62.

$$\frac{OM}{15} = \text{ctn } 22°.5 = 2.4142 *$$

$\therefore$ OM = 15 (2.4142) = 36.213.

The area of $\triangle AOB$ is $OM \times MA$; and the area of the octagon in sq. ft., is eight times this:

$$8 \ (36.213) \ (15) = 4345.6.$$

Or, take OM as the common altitude of the eight triangles AOB, etc.   Thus the area of the octagon = $\frac{1}{2} (OM) \times$ (perimeter), = 120 OM.

§ 113. Inclination Angles.   The inclination of a line is the angle I which the line makes with a horizontal plane.

The inclination of the line of sight as we look at an object is called the object's *angle of elevation or depression.*

Thus in Fig. 63, E is the angle of elevation of H as observed from the lower point L. And D is the angle of depression of L as observed from the higher point H. Each angle, being the *inclination* of the line of sight, is measured from the horizontal.   Evidently $D = E$.

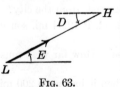

Fig. 63.

Since the slope l of any line is the num-

* This value is from a larger table.   Interpolation on p. 539 would give 2.4155.

ber of units the line rises in one horizontal unit (Fig. 64 *a*), we evidently have tan $I = l/1$, or

$$l = \tan I. \qquad (3)$$

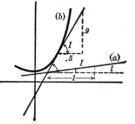

For instance, if a hillside has an inclination of 15°, its slope is $l = \tan 15° = .2679$. In other words, its grade is 26.79%.

Again, if a ship's deck has a slope of $\frac{1}{12}$, its inclination is given by

$$\tan I = .0833, \qquad I = 5°, \text{ nearly.}$$

§ 114 S. Inclination of a Curve.

FIG. 64.

The slope of a curve, or of its tangent line, at any point is easily found by differentiation: $l = dy/dx$. The inclination can then be found by using formula (3). Thus, in Fig. 64 *b*

$$\tan I = \frac{.9}{.5} = 1.800. \qquad \therefore I = 61°.$$

If l is negative the curve falls as x increases. We then consider the inclination I as negative; but find its numerical value by looking up the numerical value of l, as if positive.

N.B. The angle between two lines or curves in the same vertical plane can be found by subtracting the inclination of the one from that of the other.

EXERCISES

Solve by tables, taking angles to the nearest degree unless otherwise directed. Check by drawing and measurement where feasible.

1. As seen from Gorner Grat (10290 ft. high), the top of the Matterhorn (14703 ft. high) has an elevation angle of 7°. Find the air-line distance between the two points.

2. Eiffel Tower is 984 ft. high; the Empire State Building, 1250 ft. What would be the angle of elevation of the top of each, if viewed from a point 1 mile from the base on level ground?

3. Seen from an airplane 4000 ft. high a town has a depression angle of 6°. How far away is it, horizontally? In an air line?

4. At a point where the Grand Canyon is 1 mile deep, how wide is it if the line of sight from either rim to the center below has an inclination of 14°?

5. Seen from a ship's deck 40 ft. above the water the angle of elevation of a lighthouse 300 ft. above the water is 2°. How far out is the ship?

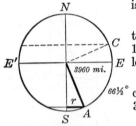

FIG. 65.

6. Find, to the nearest tenth of a degree, the angle of elevation of the sun if a pole 100 ft. high casts a shadow 84 ft. long on level ground.

7. Find the radius of the "Antarctic circle," taking the radius of the earth as 3960 mi. (Latitude 66° 30', S. Fig. 65.)

8. Find similarly the radius of the "Tropic of Cancer," 22° 30' N.

9. (a) Draw lines with inclinations of 4°, 45°, 80°. Find the slope of each, and express it also as a "grade."

(b) Find the inclination of a line if the slope is $\frac{1}{5}$, $\frac{4}{3}$, 3; also if the grade is 23%, 90%, 196%.

10. The steepest inclination of a cog railway is 34°.2. Find the maximum grade.

11. A ship's deck rises 1 inch in 15 inches horizontally. What is its inclination to the nearest tenth of a degree?

12. The rafters of a roof are inclined 38°. Find the height of the ridge above the eaves if the distance between eaves is 30 ft.

13. In a circle of radius 8 in., how long a chord would subtend an angle of 70° at the center?

14. In Ex. 13, what angle would be subtended by a chord 6 in. long?

15. Find the perimeter and area of a regular polygon of 15 sides, inscribed in a circle of radius 19.98 inches.

16. A regular 9-sided room is to have a perimeter of 180 ft. Find the floor area.

17. Find the area of the segment cut off from a circle of radius 10 in. by a chord 12 in. long.

18. Like Ex. 17 for a chord which subtends a central angle of 40°.

19. Find the volume of water in a horizontal cylindrical boiler of radius 25 in. and length 8 ft. when the water is 10 in. deep in the middle.

[20.] If the hypotenuse of a right triangle is c, and one acute angle is A, express the lengths of the two legs a and b. Using this result, draw several triangles with various angles and hypotenuses and write at sight expressions for the legs of each.

21. In laying out the circular arc of a railway curve several chords are constructed end-to-end, each 200 ft. long and making an angle of 170° with the preceding. Find the radius of the curve.

Exercises involving Calculus

22 *C*. Find the inclination of the curve $y = x^3$ at $x = .52$.

23 *C*. At what point on the curve $y = x^2$ is the inclination 42°?

24 *C*. The curve of a suspension cable is $y = .005\,x^2$. Find its inclination at $x = -225$.

25 *C*. Find the greatest inclination of the curve $y = 30\,x^2 - x^3$ between $x = 0$ and $x = 20$.

26 *C*. Like Ex. 25 *C* for $y = 20\,x^3 - x^4$.

§ 115. Projections. We shall frequently need to consider the projection of a given line-segment s upon some other line l — *i.e.*, the distance p between perpendiculars dropped from the ends of s upon l. (Fig. 66.) Time will be saved by getting a formula for the value of such a projection in any case.

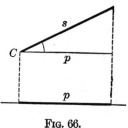

FIG. 66.

Now $p/s = \cos C$, and therefore,

$$p = s \cos C. \tag{4}$$

That is, *the projection equals the segment itself, multiplied by the cosine of the included angle.*

The same equation holds good for the projection of any plane area upon another plane.

E.g., suppose $BQFB$ (Fig. 67) is the projection of any area $BPFB$, determined by dropping perpendiculars from all points of the bounding curve BPF. We may regard each of the two areas as the area under a curve, whose height above the base-line FB at any point is y or Y. But $y = Y \cos C$ by (4) above; that is, y is a constant fraction of Y. Hence the lower curve BQF could be obtained from the upper by a mere change of scale. And the area, if found by mean ordinates (§ 13), would

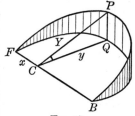

FIG. 67.

be reduced in the same scale. That is, the original or sloping area s and the projection p satisfy equation (4).

The proof is more concise by the methods of Chapter IV; for p and s are given by the integrals

$$p = \int y \, dx, \qquad s = \int Y \, dx.$$

Substituting $y = Y \cos C$ in the first integral gives

$$p = \int (Y \cos C) \, dx = \cos C \int Y \, dx = s \cos C$$

Observe that the projection of a line or area is always located at the feet of the perpendiculars; and is smaller than the original line or area, unless $C = 0$. What then?

§ 116. Component Speeds.

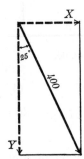

FIG. 68.

If a man is walking 400 ft. per min. in a direction 25° east of south, we may represent his rate of motion as in Fig. 68. In 1 min. he would go 400 ft. in the direction shown, and thereby would advance certain distances east and south. We therefore regard him as having an eastward speed, X ft./min., and a southward speed, Y ft./min., represented by the two arrows drawn with dashed lines. These theoretical speeds are called the "component speeds" eastward and southward.

The arrows or directed lines (often called "vectors") which represent X and Y in Fig. 68 are simply projections of the 400 vector on the horizontal and vertical directions.

$$\therefore X = 400 \cos 65°, \qquad Y = 400 \cos 25°.$$

In general, any plane motion can be regarded as combining or resulting from two component motions — mutually perpendicular in our discussions. We may be interested in only one of the component speeds. As above, we see that *the component of the actual speed V*, in a direction making an angle C with the actual direction of motion, is $V \cos C$.

§ 117. Sides by Inspection.

To save time and writing, we

should be able to read off a desired leg or hypotenuse in terms of a known side and angle, without first writing a ratio. Thus, in Fig. 69, instead of writing

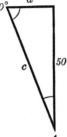

$$\frac{a}{50} = \text{ctn } 70°, \qquad \frac{50}{c} = \sin 70°,$$

we should simply think of these equations, and immediately write

$$a = 50 \text{ ctn } 70°, \qquad c = \frac{50}{\sin 70°}.$$

It is important to practice such writing.

Fig. 69.

EXERCISES

1. Find the horizontal and vertical projections of a line 20 ft. long if inclined 17°. If inclined 80°.

2. If a line 80 ft. long has a vertical projection of 28 ft., what is its inclination?

3. If a line inclined 14° has a horizontal projection of 45 ft., how long is it? Likewise, if inclined 77°?

4. Find the floor area covered by a shed roof, of area 1000 sq. ft., if the roof is inclined 16°.

5. With the sun directly overhead, a circular sheet of tin of radius 5 in. was held at an inclination of 50°. Find the area of its shadow on the level ground.

6. How large a roof inclined 32° is needed to cover 300 sq. ft. of floor?

7. Like Ex. 6 for 285 sq. ft. of floor, and a roof inclined 60°.

8. The same for a circular floor of radius 20 ft.

9. What will be the apparent shortest diameter of a wheel of radius 9.8 inches if its axle makes an angle of 65° with the line of sight?

10. The same as Ex. 9, for a diameter of 25 in. and an angle of 26°.

11. What area in a pipe of radius 8 inches would be obstructed by a damper turned 75° from the position of complete obstruction?

12. What fractional part of the area would be obstructed in any pipe with the damper turned 45°?

13. An erect cylinder of radius 10 in. is cut by a plane inclined 30°. Find the area and the longest diameter of the sloping section.

14. In Fig. 70 read off all lettered sides in terms of each acute angle.

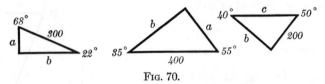

FIG. 70.

15. In Fig. 69 read off a and c in terms of angle A.

16. In Fig. 68 read off X in terms of 25°, and Y in terms of 65°.

17. If a ship is sailing 20° north of east at the rate of 13 mi. per hour, what are its component speeds, northward and eastward?

18. Similar to Ex. 17, but sailing 27.3 mi./hr., 36° south of west.

19. In target practice a wind is blowing 14.5 ft./sec. and crosses the direction of fire at an angle of 48°. What are its component velocities along and perpendicular to the direction of fire?

20. Same as Ex. 19, if the wind velocity is 9.8 m./s., crossing at an angle of 22°.

21. While a ship sails east 20 ft./sec., a marble rolls directly across a deck 30 ft./sec., starboard to port (right to left). How fast is the marble moving relative to the earth, and in what direction?

22. Like Ex. 21 for a man walking similarly across deck 4 mi./hr. on a ship moving west 12 mi./hr.

23. How large a board held perpendicular to the sun's rays would shade 1 sq. ft. of level ground when the sun is 60° above the horizon? 20° above? (What connection has this with the cause of the seasons?)

24. If $\sin A = \frac{15}{17}$, find $\cos A$, $\tan A$, $\operatorname{ctn} A$ without tables.

25. The summit of Mt. Hood has an elevation angle of 14° 10′ when viewed from Government Camp, 7345 ft. lower. Find the air-line distance between the two points.

Exercises involving Calculus

26 *C.* Find the (negative) inclination of the curve $y = 1/x$ at $x = 2$.

27 *C.* A ball rolled down a walk inclined 12°. The distance (y ft.) traveled in t sec. was $y = 2.39\,t^2$. Find the horizontal and vertical components of speed at $t = 5$.

28 *C.* Find the volume cut from a circular cylinder of radius 10 in. by a plane through a diameter of the base inclined 35°.

29 *C.* A solid has a quarter-circular base of radius 10 in. Every vertical section parallel to one side is a triangle whose base angles are 90° and 61°. Find the volume.

§ 118. Larger Tables. The four-place tables used thus far are accurate enough for some practical work. Five places will nearly always suffice — though some scientific work requires even seven or eight places. There is no point in using tables which are much more accurate than the data of the problem (measurements, etc.).

A few lines are reproduced here from a typical five-place table. The labels at the bottom are to be used with the minutes at the right — as in the small tables. For example:

$$\sin 72° 58' = .95613, \quad \tan 72° 59' = 3.2675.$$

17°

′	Sin	Tan	Ctn	Cos	
0	.29237	.30573	3.2709	.95630	60
1	265	605	.2675	622	59
2	293	637	.2641	613	58
—	—	—	—	—	—
—	—	—	—	—	—
60	.30902	.32492	3.0777	.95106	0
	Cos	Ctn	Tan	Sin	′

72°

For intermediate values interpolate by proportional parts. Check by common sense, noting whether your interpolated value lies between the tabulated values and nearer the right one. If it does not, you may have overlooked the fact that *the cosine and cotangent grow smaller as the angle increases.*

EXERCISES

1. Look up the five-place values of the sine, cosine, tangent, and cotangent of 35° 24′; also of 35° 24′.3, interpolating.

2. Like Ex. 1 for 88° 42′ and 88° 42′.8.

3. Find A to the nearest tenth of a minute if
$\tan A = 4.5215, \quad \cos A = .86610, \quad \text{ctn } A = .36375.$

4. In railroad construction a 6° curve is one in which a chord of 100 ft. subtends a central angle of 6°; similarly for a 5° curve, etc.

(*a*) Find the radius of a 5° curve.

(*b*) If the radius is 3000 ft., what is the degree of curvature?

5. As in Ex. 4, find the radius of a $4\frac{1}{2}$° curve. Also the curvature in a circle of radius 1 mi.

6. Find the area of either plane section common to two cylinders of radius 3 in. whose axes cross at right angles.

7. The same as Ex. 6 for two cylinders of radius 10 in., crossing at an angle of 80°.

8. A steel plate $\frac{3}{8}$ in. thick is to be bent 32° along a certain line. How much longer will the outer surface be than the inner, if both remain flat right up to the turn?

9. The same as Ex. 8 for a plate .45 in. thick if bent 21° 42′.

Exercises involving Calculus

10 *C*. Find the inclination of the curve $y = x^2$ at $x = .22$.

11 *C*. A triangular hole through a vertical dam is 6 ft. wide at the top, and both sides are inclined 51° 20′. Find the total force of water pressure against a gate closing the hole, if the surface of the water is level with the top of the hole.

12 *C*. The top of a 20 ft. ladder rests against a vertical wall. The foot is pulled away at the rate of .4 ft./min. How fast is the top descending when the inclination is 70°?

13 *C*. Solve Ex. I, p. 108, for a filter whose vertex angle is 106°.

§ 119. Oblique Triangles. The trigonometric functions have been defined as ratios of the sides of right triangles. They can, however, be used in solving oblique triangles as well. We have merely to drop a perpendicular from some vertex to the opposite side, and work with the right triangles thus formed.

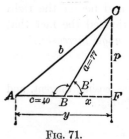

FIG. 71.

Any triangle whatever can be solved in this way if enough parts are given to fix its size and shape — in other words, enough parts to let us draw the triangle. By elementary geometry, this is possible if we know *the three sides*, or *two sides and any angle*, or *one side and any two angles*.*

NOTATION. In discussing these matters more fully we shall use a convenient notation: Capital letters will denote angles, and the corresponding small letters the opposite sides.

* For one ambiguity, see § 124. To have the three angles given would not suffice, as these alone do not fix the size of the triangle. In fact, three angles are no better than two. For if two are known, the third can be found from the fact that the sum of all three is 180°.

Thus, for instance, A will always stand for the angle opposite side a, and hence included between sides b and c.

Ex. I. Given $a = 77$, $c = 40$, $B = 121°$. Solve completely.

Plan: Let $B' = 180° - B = 59°$. Solve $\triangle BCF$ for p and x. Then $y = 40 + x$. Knowing p and y, find b and A from $\triangle ACF$. Find C from A and B.

Results: $x = 39.658$, $p = 66.002$; $A = 39°38'.6$, $b = 103.45$, etc.

Ex. II. Given $a = 75$, $b = 65$, $c = 80$.   Find the angles.

Plan: Too few parts of either right triangle are known to solve it alone. But by equating the values of p^2 in the two triangles, we easily find x. Thus

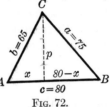

$$p^2 = 65^2 - x^2 = 75^2 - (80 - x)^2,$$

which, simplified, gives $160\,x = 5000$, or $x = 31.25$. Then $80 - x = 48.75$; and angles A and B are easily found, also C. [*Results:* $A = 61° 15'.8$, $B = 49° 27'.5$, $C = 69° 16'.7$.]

Fig. 72.

EXERCISES

(Large tables should be used in Exs. 1–2, at least.)

1. $(a) - (b)$ Carry out the method of solution outlined above for the triangles in Figs. 71, 72.

2. Solve the following oblique triangles similarly:

(I) Given $A = 19° 43'$,	$B = 82° 55'$,	$c = 6892$;
(II) Given $a = 725.7$,	$b = 842.4$,	$C = 33° 21'$;
(III) Given $a = 255$,	$b = 388$,	$A = 38° 16'.5$.
(IV) Given $a = 85$,	$b = 95$,	$c = 110$.

3. Find the distance AB across a pond if measurements from a third point C give: $CA = 400$, $CB = 500$, $\sin C = \frac{3}{5}$.

4. A triangular lot has the sides, $a = 80$, $b = 50$, $c = 70$ (ft.). Find C.

5. In Ex. 4 find the area of the lot.

6. A triangular lot contains 4000 sq. ft. Find the angle between two of the sides, which measure 100 ft. and 90 ft.

§ 120. Cosine Law. To avoid the labor of dissecting oblique triangles, let us now derive some formulas which will show how the calculation must turn out in each case.

Proceeding as in Ex. II, § 119, for an acute-angled triangle of any sides a, b, c, we should have:

$$p^2 = b^2 - x^2 = a^2 - (c - x)^2, \tag{5}$$

or, solving this for a^2,

$$a^2 = b^2 + c^2 - 2\,cx. \tag{6}$$

But x is the projection of b on c, and by § 115 equals $b \cos A$. Substituting this value for x in (6), we find:

$$\boldsymbol{a^2 = b^2 + c^2 - 2\,bc\,\cos A.} \tag{7}$$

That is, *the square of one side of a triangle is equal to the sum of the squares of the other two sides, minus twice the product of those sides by the cosine of their included angle.*

This theorem is called the "Cosine Law." It should be carefully memorized. Applied to b and c it gives,

$$b^2 = c^2 + a^2 - 2\,ca\,\cos B. \tag{8}$$
$$c^2 = a^2 + b^2 - 2\,ab\,\cos C. \tag{9}$$

(Observe that in each case the formula begins and ends with the same letter.)

What modifications, if any, must be made in these formulas to apply them to obtuse angles will be discussed in § 123.

By using the Cosine Law we can solve an acute-angled oblique triangle very easily if given *the three sides* or *two sides and their included angle.* We have merely to substitute the values of the given parts in equation (7), (8), or (9) as required, and solve for a required part. If some other combination of parts is given, it is best to use a different formula (§ 121).

Ex. I. Solve the triangle: $a = 75$, $b = 65$, $c = 80$.

By (7): $75^2 = 65^2 + 80^2 - 2\,(65)\,(80)\cos A.$

∴ $\cos A = .48077$, $A = 61°\ 15'.8$.

Angles B and C are found likewise by starting with 65^2 or 80^2.

Ex. II. Solve the triangle: $b = 750$, $c = 860$, $A = 40°$.

By (7) $a^2 = 750^2 + 860^2 - 2\,(750)\,(860)\cos 40°,$

whence a is known. Angles B and C can be found as in Ex. I, or as in § 124. Tables of squares and square roots may be used.

Remark. *If a given angle is* 90°, the triangle should not be solved by the Cosine Law but as a right triangle. *If an unknown angle happens to be* 90°, this fact will soon be discovered, for the square of one side will equal the sum of the squares of the other two.

§ 121. Sine Law.   From the two right triangles in Fig. 73 we find

$$p = a \sin B, \qquad\qquad p = b \sin A.$$

Hence $a \sin B = b \sin A$, or $\dfrac{a}{\sin A} = \dfrac{b}{\sin B}.$

Similar equations can be derived likewise for sides a and c, and for b and c.

$$\therefore \; \frac{a}{\sin A} = \frac{b}{\sin B} = \frac{c}{\sin C}. \qquad (10)$$

That is, *the three sides of a triangle are proportional to the sines of the opposite angles.*   [Memorize.]

What, if any, modifications are necessary when the triangle contains an obtuse angle will be discussed in § 123.

By using this "Sine Law," we can solve an oblique triangle easily if given a side and two angles, or two sides and the angle opposite one of them.   In the latter case there are often two possible triangles, one of which involves an obtuse angle.   This case is postponed to § 124.

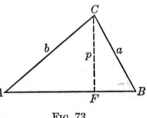

Fig. 73.

Ex. I.   Solve the triangle: $b = 750$, $A = 40°$, $C = 80°$.   The third angle is known at once: $B = 60°$.

$$\frac{a}{\sin 40°} = \frac{750}{\sin 60°} = \frac{c}{\sin 80°}. \quad \text{(Sine Law.)}$$

One of these equations gives a and the other gives c.

Remarks.   (I) When the two given angles are complementary, or one of them is 90°, the triangle should be solved as a *right triangle.*

(II) The Sine Law will not solve a triangle in the cases covered by the Cosine Law, though it may be helpful after some unknown part has been found.   The simplest rule as to which law to use in solving any given triangle is this: Use the Cosine Law if given the *three sides* or *two sides and their included angle*; and the Sine Law in *all other cases.*

EXERCISES

(Check all results by drawing to scale and measuring.   Use small tables if preferred, in the even-numbered exercises.)

1. Given $b = 1450$, $A = 64° 23'$, $C = 41° 54'$.   Find a, c, B.

2. Find a, b, C, given $c = 200$, $A = 80°$, $B = 30°$.

3. Find a, B, C, given $b = 125$, $c = 204$, $A = 25° 50'$.

4. Given $a = 600$, $b = 750$, $C = 40°$.   Find c, A, B.

5. Given $a = 55$, $b = 75$, $c = 80$.   Find A, B, C — independently of one another.   Check by adding.

6. Like Ex. 5, with $a = 5$, $b = 6$, $c = 7$.

7. To find the distance from a gun (G) to a target (T) a line $GO = 2375$ yd. long was measured to an observation post (O), and angles TGO and TOG were measured as $72° 15'$ and $80° 30'$.   Find GT.

8. To find the distance from a gun G to a target T beyond a hill an observer at O found by a range finder $GO = 2000$ yd., $OT = 3200$ yd., $\angle TOG = 69°$.   Find GT.

9. On a certain day the distances of the earth and Venus from the sun were 90,200,000 mi. and 66,200,000 mi. respectively.   The angle ESV between their directions was $69° 45'$.   Find EV, their distance apart, at that time.

10. Like Ex. 9 for the earth and Mars, with the distances 92,000,000 mi. and 140,000,000 mi., and $\angle ESM = 60°$.

11. To find the distance AB through a hill, lines $AC = 740$ ft., and $BC = 680$ ft., were measured, also $\angle C = 50°$.   Find AB.

§ 122. Functions of Any Angle.

The definitions of the sine, cosine, etc., in terms of sides of a right triangle are meaningless in the case of an obtuse angle.   We could not even get such an angle into a right triangle — much less speak of the opposite leg, hypotenuse, etc.

But, without changing the meaning for acute angles, we can re-word the definitions so that they will apply to angles of any size.   We employ the idea of coordinates, which was used in mapping points (§ 107).

Any angle θ, regarded as starting from some initial line OI and ending at some terminal line OT, can be placed on a pair of rectangular axes in what is called "trigonometric position," *i.e.*, with its initial side on the X-axis and its vertex at the origin. (Fig. 74.) Then any point P on the terminal side of θ has some rectangular coordinates (x, y) and a radius vector r.

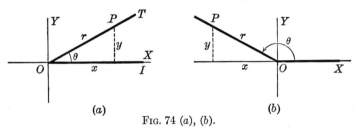

(a)   (b)

FIG. 74 (a), (b).

In the right triangle containing the acute angle θ in Fig. 74 *a*, our old definitions give:

$$\sin \theta = \frac{y}{r}, \qquad \cos \theta = \frac{x}{r}. \tag{11}$$

Similarly $\tan \theta = y/x$, $\operatorname{ctn} \theta = x/y$, $\sec \theta = r/x$, $\csc \theta = r/y$.

Hence equations (11), and the similar equations for $\tan \theta$, etc., could be taken as *defining* the functions of θ. Instead of "opposite leg ÷ hypotenuse," etc., we shall say henceforth:

$$\sin \theta = \frac{y}{r} = \frac{\text{ordinate of } P}{\text{radius vector of } P},$$
$$\cos \theta = \frac{x}{r} = \frac{\text{abscissa of } P}{\text{radius vector of } P}, \tag{12}$$

etc., where θ is in trigonometric position and P is any point on its terminal line. This statement has a meaning for angles of any size.*

For the obtuse angle θ in Fig. 74 *b*, observe that y is positive and x negative. Hence the sine of an obtuse angle is positive, and the cosine negative. Again, suppose the obtuse angle θ in Fig. 74 *b* and the acute θ in Fig. 74 *a* are supplementary (*i.e.*, have a sum of 180°). Then choosing equal r's in the

---

* The older form of statement was necessary for solving right triangles. By waiting until now for the new form we avoided having to learn both at once.

two cases would give numerically equal x's and also y's.   Hence the rule:

sine of an obtuse $\angle$ = sine of the supplementary acute $\angle$,   (13)
cosine of an obtuse $\angle$ = − cosine of supplementary acute $\angle$.

> *E.g.,* $\sin 170° = \sin 10°,$ $\cos 170° = -\cos 10°,$
> $\sin 100° = \sin 80°,$ $\cos 100° = -\cos 80°,$ etc.

§ 123. Obtuse-Angled Triangles.   With our generalized definitions, the Sine Law and Cosine Law apply to all triangles, even those involving an obtuse angle.

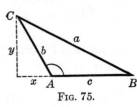

FIG. 75.

Proof. In the large right triangle of Fig. 75,
$$y = a \sin B.$$
But by (12):
$$y = b \sin A.$$
Equating these we get finally the Sine Law:
$$\frac{a}{\sin A} = \frac{b}{\sin B}, \text{ etc.}$$

Also in Fig. 75, since x is negative, the base of the large right triangle is $c - x$ (which is greater than c, as the entire base should be).

$$\therefore \ a^2 = y^2 + (c - x)^2 = y^2 + x^2 - 2cx + c^2.$$

But $y^2 + x^2 = b^2$; and by (12), $x = b \cos A$.

$$\therefore \ a^2 = b^2 + c^2 - 2bc \cos A.$$

Thus the Sine Law and Cosine Law are both valid.

In solving any triangle, then, whether acute-angled or obtuse-angled, we use the same formulas.   But in looking up the sine or cosine of an obtuse angle, we must remember the relations to acute angles [(13), above].

Ex. I.   Solve the triangle: $A = 110°,$ $B = 40°,$ $b = 75.$

$$\frac{a}{\sin 110°} = \frac{75}{\sin 40°} = \frac{c}{\sin 30°} \quad \text{(Sine Law.)}$$

To look up the sine of 110°, simply look up the sine of the supplement 70° — which it equals by § 122.   Then proceed as formerly.

Ex. II.   Solve the triangle: $A = 110°,$ $b = 75,$ $c = 95.$
$$a^2 = 75^2 + 95^2 - 2(75)(95) \cos 110°. \quad \text{(Cosine Law.)}$$

To look up cos 110°, merely find cos 70° and prefix a negative sign. (This will make the final term in the equation positive, and a^2 greater than $b^2 + c^2$ — as it should be, by Fig. 75.)

When a is known, find angles B and C by the Sine Law.

§ 124. Solving for an Angle. If we find from a triangle that the cosine of an angle is negative, this means that the angle is obtuse.

For instance, if $\cos A = -.76604$, then A is obtuse, and its supplement A' has its cosine equal to .76604. By the table $A' = 40°$; hence $A = 140°$.

When we find from a triangle the value of the sine of an angle, the angle may be acute, or may be obtuse. For instance, if $\sin B = .34202$, this may mean either that $B = 20°$ — by tables — or that $B = 160°$. Both values should be tested out. (This is the "ambiguous case" of elementary geometry.)

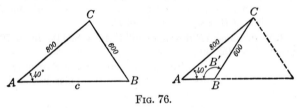

FIG. 76.

Ex. I. Solve the triangle: $a = 600$, $b = 800$, $A = 40°$.

$$\frac{600}{\sin 40°} = \frac{800}{\sin B} = \frac{c}{\sin C}.$$

This gives $\sin B = .85705$, whence B is either 58° 59′, or the supplement of this angle, viz. $B' = 121°$ 1′. There are two possible triangles, both having the given parts a, b, and A.[*]
In one of these triangles, $A = 40°$, $B = 58°$ 59′, and hence $C = 81°$ 1′; etc. In the other, $A = 40°$, $B = 121°$ 1′, and hence $C = 18°$ 59′; etc.

N.B. If the larger of the two given sides were opposite the given angle, only one triangle would be possible. (Test this by construction.) The fact would be discovered automatically in the process of solving: the second value of B would be too large to go into a triangle with $\angle A$.

---

[*] When this case arises in a practical problem, we have to decide by means of additional information which triangle is the one we want.

174   TRIGONOMETRIC FUNCTIONS

EXERCISES

1. Look up the sine and cosine of 106°;   168° 2′;   152° 12′.7;
128° 51′.2.

2. Find the angles whose cosines are: −.91706, −.44630, and
−.10265.   Also find the obtuse angles whose sines are: .36731, .84049,
and .25654.

3. Find the distance *AB* across a pond if *AC* = 395 ft., ∠*BAC* = 20°,
and ∠*ACB* = 106° 52′.

4. Two angles of a triangle are 30° and 40°; their included side is
200 ft.   Find the shortest side.

5. A mountain peak *P* had an elevation angle of 15° 7′ when observed from a point *A*, and one of 26° 45′ when observed from *B*,
on the same level as *A* and two miles from *A* directly toward the
mountain.   Find the air-line distance *AP*; also the height of *P* above
A or *B*.

6. Seen from an airplane *P*, two villages, *A*, *B* straight north and
3 mi. apart on a level plain, had depression angles of 9° and 7° respectively.   Find *PB*; also the height of *P*.

7. Find the distance *AB* through a hill if *AC* = 800 ft., *BC* = 700 ft.,
and angle *ACB* = 102° 39′.

8. On a certain date the distances of Jupiter and Saturn from the
sun, in astronomical units, were 5.2 and 9.1.   Their included angle
at the sun was 120°.   Find their distance apart.

9. Mt. St. Helens and Mt. Jefferson are respectively 53 mi. and
74 mi. from Portland, Ore., the angle between their directions being
115° 31′.   Find their distance apart.

10. Certain parts of some triangles are given below.   Find the
missing parts.   (Use any convenient table.)

	a	b	c	A	B	C
i.	71.5	48.2	46.9			
ii.	930	810	650			
iii.	6.35	8.51				34° 17′
iv.		.92	1.03	138°		
v.		6848	5928		43° 12′.8	
vi.	40		60	29°		
vii.	9800				95° 13′	26° 29′.2
viii.	.064			15°		86°

11 (*i* − *viii*).   Find the area of each triangle in Ex. 10 (i–viii).

§ 125. Successive and Simultaneous Triangles.   To find
an unknown distance or angle, we often have to solve two

triangles in succession, or else obtain simultaneous equations from two triangles.

Ex. I.   Find x in Fig. 77; given $A = 20°$, $B = 30°$, $AB = 2000$ (ft.).

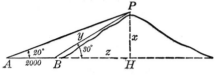

FIG. 77.

(1) *Solution by successive triangles.*   We first solve $\triangle ABF$ for y; then we use y to find x in the right triangle BHP.

In $\triangle ABP$, $\angle P = 10°$ (since $\angle B = \angle A + \angle P$).

$$\therefore \frac{y}{2000} = \frac{\sin 20°}{\sin 10°} = \frac{.34202}{.17365},$$

whence $y = 3939.2$.   Then in $\triangle BPH$, $x = y \sin 30° = 1969.6$.

(2) *Solution by simultaneous right triangles.*

In $\triangle AHP$: $2000 + z = x$ ctn $20° = x$ (2.7475).

In $\triangle BHP$: $z = x$ ctn $30° = x$ (1.7321).

$\therefore$ 2000 $= x$ (1.0154),   [subtracting]

$$\therefore x = \frac{2000}{1.0154} = 1969.6.$$

Observe here that ctn 30° − ctn 20° does not equal ctn 10°; and that sin 20° does not equal twice sin 10°.

EXERCISES

1. In Fig. 77 change the angles to 15° 8′ and 25° 46′ and the given distance to 3500 ft., and find x.

2. Two houses in line with the base of a hill are 4000 ft. apart on level ground.   Observed from the hilltop they have depression angles of 11° and 18°.   Find the height of the hill.

3. Two boat landings 2000 ft. apart on the farther side of a river are 61° 40′ and 70° 40′ downstream as seen from a landing on this side. How wide is the river?

4. Two men 1 mi. apart observe a balloon directly above the line joining them, at elevation angles of 50° and 73°, respectively. How high is the balloon?

5. Seen from the foot F of a tree on a cliff, a rock R in the sea has a depression angle of 40° 10′; seen from a point 25 ft. up the tree, it has a depression angle of 44° 20′. How much higher is F than R?

6. Looking straight across a stream from a hill some distance away and 125 ft. higher, the lines of sight to the nearer and farther banks have inclinations of 59° and 17°, respectively. How wide is the stream?

7. Viewed from a certain point the top and bottom of a nearly vertical waterfall 650 ft. high have respectively an elevation angle of 68° 47′ and a depression angle of 47° 10′. How far is the waterfall from the observer horizontally?

8. The top and bottom of a lighthouse which is 170 ft. tall are seen from a boat to have elevation angles of 5°.8 and 3°.1. How far out is the boat, horizontally?

9. Observed from a point 78.5 ft. higher than the foot of a nearly vertical waterfall, the top of the fall has an elevation angle of 46° 28′, and the bottom has a depression angle of 32° 19′. Find the height of the fall.

10. A flag-pole 120 ft. high standing at the top of a hill is viewed from a lower point A, the elevation angles of its top T and bottom B being 55° and 40°. Find the horizontal and vertical distances of A from B.

11. From a cliff 250 ft. high two ships are observed, one straight west with a depression angle of 8° 15′, the other 22° 47′ north of west with a depression angle of 5° 29′. Find the distance between the ships. (Hint: Three triangles are to be solved.)

12. A meteor was seen directly over a long straight road, between two points A and B on the road, 5 mi. apart. At A the elevation angle was 88° 15′; at B, 86° 40′. Find the height of the meteor when seen.

§ 126 S. **Force Problems.** If two forces, acting in the directions OA and OB (Fig. 78), are simultaneously applied

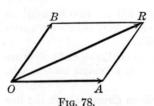

FIG. 78.

to an object at O, the object will move neither along OA nor along OB, but in some intermediate direction. More definitely, the principle is this:

If two forces are represented, in magnitude and direction, by two sides of a parallelogram OA and OB, drawn from a common vertex, they are together equivalent to a single force represented on the same scale by the diagonal of the parallelogram OR drawn from that vertex.

The resulting motion would be along that diagonal. The single force represented by the diagonal is called the **resultant** of the two given forces.

To find the resultant of two given forces graphically: Simply draw the forces on some chosen scale, as in Fig. 78, complete the parallelogram, and draw the appropriate diagonal. The *magnitude* of the resultant is given by the length of the diagonal, while its *direction* can be ascertained by measuring the angle which it makes with one of the given forces.

For more accurate results we solve a triangle of the figure by trigonometry. The applications of trigonometry to various kinds of force problems are extremely important.

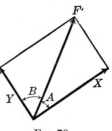

FIG. 79.

§ 127 S. Component Forces. Any two forces X and Y, which would together be equivalent to a single force F, are called *components* of F. If mutually perpendicular — which is the way components are taken unless otherwise stated — they are easily found.

$$X = F \cos A, \qquad Y = F \cos B. \tag{14}$$

Thus, *the component of a force in any direction is equal to the force itself, multiplied by the cosine of the included angle.*

The value of Y in (14) is the same as $Y = F \sin A$. (Why?)

Ex. I. Find the two components N and T of the weight of the block in Fig. 80, if the plane is inclined 20°.

The angles at the block are 20° and 70°. Hence

$$N = 1000 \cos 20° = 940,$$
$$T = 1000 \cos 70° = 342.$$

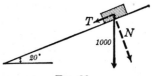

FIG. 80.

That is, the force with which the block presses against the plane is 940 lb., and the force tending to move the block down along the plane is 342 lb. If there were no friction, a pull of 342 lb. up the plane would just keep the block from sliding.

EXERCISES

(Solve graphically and by trigonometry.)

1. Two forces act on an object O: 240 lb. pulling north, and 320 lb. pulling east. Find the resultant and its direction.

2. Like Ex. 1 if the forces are 50 lb. south, and 130 lb. east.

3. Find the resultant R for two forces, $X = 150$ lb. and $Y = 90$ lb., whose included angle is 60°. Also find the angle which R makes with X.

4. The same as Ex. 3, but with $X = 800$ lb., $Y = 500$ lb., and their included angle 120°.

5. A weight of 50 lb., hanging from an airplane by a short rope, encounters a steady horizontal wind force of 22.8 lb. Find the inclination of the rope, and the actual tension in it.

6. A 90-lb. boy stands on a "merry-go-round" at a point where he is subject to a centrifugal force of 36 lb. At what angle should he lean inward to be perfectly balanced?

7. A horizontal force OH of 160 lb. and a vertical force OV of 120 lb. are balanced by a single force F. Find the intensity and inclination of F. (Hint: F must be directly opposite and equal to the resultant of OH and OV.)

8. The same as Ex. 7, but with $OH = 330$ lb. and $OV = 440$ lb.

9. Find the horizontal and vertical components of a force of 6500 lb. inclined 72° 45′.

10. In Fig. 80 change the weight to 300 lb. and the inclination of the plane to 29°. Find N and T.

11. Likewise find N and T in Fig. 80 if the weight is 5 tons and the inclination of the plane is 7° 15′.

12. A force F, inclined 36°, has a horizontal component of 950 lb. (a) Find F. (b) Find its vertical component.

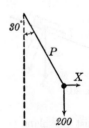

Fig. 81.

13. (a) If a force F is inclined 40° and has a vertical component of 2000 lb., find F. (b) Find the horizontal component.

14. A guy wire runs from a point 12 ft. high on a vertical pole to a point on the ground 16 ft. from the foot of the pole. What horizontal pull will the wire exert when the tension in it is 600 lb.?

15. A 200-lb. weight at the end of a rope swings around in a horizontal circle, the rope making an angle of 30° with the vertical, as in Fig. 81. Find the centrifugal force, X lb., and the pull in the rope, P lb.

§ 128 *S*. **Equilibrium of Forces: Component Method.** The
unknown forces needed to balance a
given force, or forces, can be found without drawing a force triangle or polygon.

To illustrate, let us find the forces
F and X acting along the two members
of a bridge-structure (shown in Fig. 82)
if the supporting force exerted by the
pier is 200 tons.

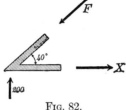

Fɪɢ. 82.

We first tabulate the horizontal and vertical components
of all the forces:

Fᴏʀᴄᴇ	Hᴏʀɪᴢ.	Vᴇʀᴛ.
F	$F \cos 40°$	$F \cos 50°$
X	X	0
200	0	200

(Clearly the 200-ton force can have no effect horizontally,
nor can X have any vertically.)

The component of a force along any direction measures its
tendency to produce motion in that direction. Hence, *the
vertical components must balance one another*.

$$F \cos 50° = 200, \qquad \therefore \ F = \frac{200}{\cos 50°} = 311.14.$$

Similarly, the horizontal components must balance:

$$F \cos 40° = X. \qquad \therefore \ X = 238.36.$$

In like manner — as is shown in treatises on Statics — it is possible
to go on to the other joints of a structure and find the forces acting
at each. Thus the forces along all the members can be found if the
supporting forces exerted by the piers are known. The principle by
which those forces are found is a very familiar one.

§ 129 *S*. **Moment of a Force.** As everyone knows, a 50-lb.
boy can balance a 100-lb. boy on a "teeter" board by sitting
just twice as far from the supporting rail or fulcrum. This
is because the "moment" of each weight (*i.e.*, its tendency
to produce rotation about the point of support) is proportional to its distance from that point.

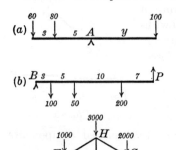

General Principle: The moment of any force about any point equals the product of the force by its arm — that is, by the perpendicular distance from the point to the line of action of the force.

Thus, in Fig. 83 (*a*), we have about the point *A*:

Force	Arm	Moment
80 lb.	5 ft.	400 lb.-ft.
60 "	8 "	480 "
100 "	y "	$100\,y$ "

The first two forces tend to turn the beam about *A* in one direction; and the third in the opposite direction. If the latter is just to balance the other two, *its moment must equal the sum of their moments*:

$$\therefore\ 100\,y = 880. \qquad \therefore\ y = 8.8.$$

Likewise in Fig. 83 (*b*), if the force *P* is just large enough to prevent the other forces from rotating the beam about *B*, its moment must balance theirs:

$$P\,(25) = 100\,(3) + 50\,(8) + 200\,(18). \quad \therefore\ P = 172.$$

And again, in Fig. 83 (*c*), if the force F_D is to prevent rotation *about C*,

$$F_D\,(40) = 1000\,(10) + 3000\,(20) + 2000\,(30). \quad \therefore\ F_D = 3250.$$

Similarly, to prevent rotation *about D*

$$F_C\,(40) = 1000\,(30) + 3000\,(20) + 2000\,(10). \quad \therefore\ F_C = 2750.$$

Check: $F_C + F_D$ equals the sum of the three loads, $1000 + 3000 + 2000$.

EXERCISES

1. A beam 20 ft. long weighing 10 lb. per ft. rests on a post at one end *A* and is supported by a vertical cable at the other end *B*. It carries a load of 1500 lb., 8 ft. from *A*. Find the pull in the cable.

(Hint: Regard the weight of the beam as a single force acting at its center.)

2. Like Ex. 1 but with an additional load of 100 lb., 4 ft. from *B*.

3. In Fig. 83 (*c*), what forces are exerted by the piers if the loads are 18000 lb., 25000 lb., and 12000 lb. at distances of 10 ft., 20 ft., and 30 ft. from pier C?

4. Like Ex. 3, if the three loads are 2000 lb., 1000 lb., and 4000 lb.

5. The two piers C and D at the ends of a bridge beam carry loads of 25000 lb. and 20000 lb. respectively, due to the weight of the bridge. If a car weighing 3000 lb. is placed on the bridge one fourth way from C to D, what load will D then carry?

6. In Fig. 82, change the supporting force to 5000 lb., the angle to 38°, and find F and X.

7. Find the pull (P lb.) in the cable, and the horizontal thrust (T lb.) exerted at O by the arm of the crane in Fig. 84 to support the weight of 500 lb.

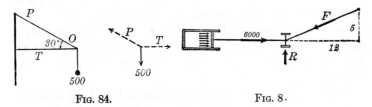

Fig. 84.   Fig. 8.

8. The same as Ex. 7, but with the given angle 42° 18′ and the weight 7500 lb.

9. Solve Ex. 15, p. 178, by the component method.

10. A weight of 100 lb. is supported by two wires, each inclined 27° 36′. Find the pull or tension in each wire.

11. The reaction R of the guide is vertical in Fig. 85. Find the force F.

12. Like Ex. 11, doubling the given force, and replacing 5 and 12 by 7 and 24, respectively.

Exercises involving Calculus

13 C. On a horizontal beam 60 in. long the loading (w lb. per in.) varies thus with the distance (x in.) from one end A: $w = 20 + .6\,x$. Find the moment about A of the load. [Hint: Consider the moment of the tiny load resting on a length dx, at any distance x from A.]

14 C. A sled is pulled on level ice by a force (F lb.) inclined constantly 12°, and varying thus with the elapsed time (t min.): $F = 20\,t - t^2$. Ignoring friction, what momentum would be generated from $t = 0$ to $t = 6$? [Only the horizontal component of F generates momentum.]

15 C. A beam 6 ft. long and weighing 200 lb. rests on a pier at one end A and is supported by a cable at the other end B. A load

(W lb.) travels from A to B, but W varies thus with its distance (x ft.) from A: $W = 100 - 6\,x$. Find the pull (P lb.) in the cable when $x = 2$. How fast was P then changing, per unit increase in x?

16 C. A 200-lb. block of ice slides down a plane inclined 17° 12′. Ignoring friction its acceleration (a ft./sec.²) would be constantly .16T, where T lb. is the component of the weight along the plane. Find the distance traveled in t sec. starting from rest.

§ 130. Summary of Chapter V.

In a right triangle the ratios of the sides will vary in a definite way with either acute angle; and are consequently *functions* of either angle.

By using the tabulated values of these functions, we can solve right triangles — and also oblique triangles, by dropping perpendiculars or using the Sine Law or Cosine Law.*

Coordinates are useful in mapping. They also provide a convenient means of *generalizing the definitions* of the functions. The sine and cosine of an obtuse angle are then easily found from the supplementary acute angle.

By the principle of the parallelogram of forces, all problems on equilibrium of concurrent forces reduce to triangle problems. They can be solved more easily by considering *components* — a procedure which is useful also in studying speeds. A closely related idea is that of *projections*.

In solving triangles we use the theorem that the sum of the angles of any triangle is 180°. You will recall from geometry that the proof of this theorem rests upon the *assumption* that through a given point one and only one line can be drawn parallel to a given line. *We are not obliged to accept this assumption.* There are "Non-Euclidean" geometries, perfectly logical, in which the assumption is denied. According to these geometries, the angle-sum differs from 180° — but imperceptibly in triangles of ordinary size. *No one knows which system of geometry is true* of the space in which we live — nor, indeed, whether *any* system exists which perfectly describes this physical space. But the "Euclidean" geometry and trigonometry which we have studied are *simpler* than other systems, and are always used in practical work.

§ 131. Our Next Step.

So much numerical calculation is necessary in solving triangles, in finding the values of deriva-

---

* The tables were calculated approximately in ancient times by means of certain formulas, but were greatly enlarged and improved in the sixteenth century, chiefly by G. J. Rheticus, a German.

tives and integrals, and in other scientific work, that it is imperative to know the best methods of computing. This matter will be considered in the next chapter; and some alternative methods of solving oblique triangles will be found.

A further development of trigonometry, dealing with questions of a very different kind, is given in Chapters X–XI. If it is desired to proceed earlier with that development, Chapters VII–IX (together with §§ 146–48, 151–54, 160–63 of Chapter VI) can be postponed without inconvenience.

EXERCISES

1. The hypotenuse and one leg of a right triangle are respectively 109 in. and 91 in. Find without tables all four functions of the smaller acute angle.

2. What is the grade of a mountain trail if the inclination is 16°?

3. What angle does a straight line of slope 1.28 make with one of slope −.7?

4. Find the slope and inclination of a roof which rises 7.8 ft. in a horizontal distance of 20 ft.

5. Find the air-line distance from the summit S of a snow peak to a hut 8147 ft. lower, whose depression angle observed from S is 12° 6′.

6 (a) In what direction should a level tunnel run through a hill to emerge at a point T 985 ft. north and 1170 ft. west from the starting point S? (b) Find its length ST.

7. An observer saw a color incorrectly when the object R was 24° from his central line of vision. If R was 18.5 ft. to his right, how far forward was it?

8. If two cylindrical tunnels of diameter 20 ft. cross at an angle of 55°, what is the area of either common plane section? Also the longest diameter of that section?

9. An oblique cylinder has a vertical height of 5 in. and circular bases of radius 3 in. The center of the upper base is directly over a point on the circumference of the lower. Find the longest and shortest diameters of a plane section of the cylinder passed at right angles to the axis.

10. An opening 5 feet square passes vertically through a ship's deck at a place where the deck's slope is .08 going forward and −.05 going outboard across-ship. How much higher is the highest corner of the opening than the lowest?

11. Find the perimeter and area of a regular hexagon circumscribed about a circle of radius 25 ft.

12. Draw to scale a triangle whose sides are 25, 30, and 40 units. Measure the smallest angle. A student tried to calculate this angle as follows:

$$\cos A = \frac{30}{40} = .750, \qquad \therefore\ A = 41° \ 25'.$$

What is wrong with this method?

13. A horizontal cylindrical oil tank has an inner diameter of 48 in. and length of 96 in. Find the volume of oil in it when the oil is 18 in. deep in the middle.

14. (a) Look up the sine and cosine of 108°, 166° 47′, 122° 15′.3.

(b) Find ∠A if cos A = −.08947, and two possible values of ∠B if sin B = .20677.

15. If the sides of a triangle are 45, 60, and 80, find the smallest angle.

16. A triangle ABC on level ground has $B = 60°$, $C = 105°$, $a = 300$ ft. Find the height of a tree standing at A, if the elevation angle of its top observed from B, is 7° 15′.

17. A field is a parallelogram with sides 30 and 40 chains long, and an area of 72 acres. Find its shorter diagonal. (1 acre = 10 sq. ch.)

18. Find by measurement and by trigonometry side c of a triangle if $a = 315$, $b = 521$, and $C = 40°$.

19. At a certain time the distances of the earth and Venus from the sun were respectively 91,400,000 mi. and 66,300,000 mi., the angle ESV between their directions being 108° 12′. Find EV, their distance apart at that time.

20. Given $b = 10620$, $A = 48° 54′$, $C = 76° 18′$; find the other parts.

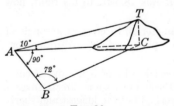

Fig. 86.

21. Find TC (the height of the mountain summit in Fig. 86), if $AB = 4852$ ft. and A, B, C are in a horizontal plane.

22. Like Ex. 21, but making $AB = 3625$ ft., $∠BAC = 81° 17′$, $∠ABC = 90° 45′$, and the elevation angle at $A = 4° 15′$.

23. A tree standing erect on a hillside whose inclination is 18° 42′ subtends at two points A and B directly in line down the incline angles of 10° 24′ and 16° 18′. If $AB = 392$ ft., find the height of the tree.

24. A 45-foot flag-pole on top of a building is observed from a point A on a level street to have elevation angles of 56° and 48°, top and bottom. How far is A from a point on the ground directly below the pole?

25. A tall cone of vertex angle 40° is cut by a plane inclined 25°. The highest point of the sloping section is 5 in. from the vertex. Show that the longest diameter of the section is 5 sin 40°/sin 45°.

26. Two stars A and B are at distances 3.5×10^{15} and 4×10^{15} miles from the earth; and the angle between their directions (from here) is 120°. Find their distance apart.

27. The sides of the triangular base of a prism are 9×10^{-4}, 6×10^{-4}, and 5×10^{-4} cm. Find the largest angle.

28. Two forces $OA = 24$ lb. and $OB = 15$ lb. have an included angle of 120°. Find their resultant R, and the angle which it makes with OA. Check by a protractor.

29. Like Ex. 28 but with $OA = 225$ lb., $OB = 105$ lb., and the included angle equal to 34°.

30. Two forces of 50 lb. and 70 lb. have a resultant of 90 lb. Find their included angle.

31. A lawnmower weighing 22 lb. is pushed on level ground with a force of 30 lb. directed along the handle which is inclined 35°. How large a force produces the forward motion? With what total force do the wheels press against the ground?

32. How great a weight could be suspended by two ropes each inclined 27°, if the greatest pull which either can sustain is 375 lb.?

33. Solve Ex. 7, p. 181, changing the given angle to 33° and the given weight to 1250 lb.

34. A vertical flywheel of radius 5 ft. is making 2 revolutions per sec. How fast is a point on the rim moving? How fast horizontally and vertically, when 3 ft. above the horizontal diameter?

35. A 20-ft. ladder weighing 50 lb. leans against a slippery vertical wall 16 ft. above ground. A 100-lb. boy is three fourths of the way up. What horizontal resistance does the wall exert on the top of the ladder? [Hint: Consider moments around the foot of the ladder.]

36. A wheelbarrow and its load make up a weight of 300 lb. acting vertically 16.8 in. from the axle. How large a vertical pull on the handles 40 in. from the axle will just raise the barrow?

37. Find the rectangular coordinates of the points whose polar coordinates are: A (10, 50°); B (10, 130°); C (10, 230°); D (10, 310°).

38. Find the polar coordinates of E (48, 14), F (−15, 20), G (15, −20).

Exercises involving Calculus

39 C. A point moves in a direction 31° north of east, the distance (y ft.) traveled in the first t sec. being $y = 1200\,t^2 - 4\,t^3$. Find its speed and acceleration at $t = 20$; also the component speeds and accelerations northward and eastward.

40 *C.* A right triangular plate with one angle 35° and the hypotenuse *h* in. expands. Approximately what is the change in area if *h* increases from 9.98 to 10.01?

41 *C.* A 25-foot ladder leans against a vertical wall. If its foot is pulled away horizontally at the rate of .4 ft./sec., how fast is the top descending when the inclination is 53° 7′.8?

42 *C.* Find the slope and inclination of the curve $y = .3\,x^2$ at $x = 2$.

43 *C.* A long horizontal rod weighing 4 lb. per ft. is to carry a load of 100 lb. four feet from one end which rests on a pier. The other end is to be supported by a vertical cable. For what length of rod (*x* ft.) will the pull in the cable (*F* lb.) be least?

44 *C.* Find the vertex angle of the largest cone which can be sent by parcel post. (See Ex. 12, p. 29.)

45 *C.* Find ∠*A* from the equation $(\tan A)^3 + (\tan A) = 47$, first letting $\tan A = x$. (Equations like this often arise in finding the position of a comet.) Use § 19; also § 63 if helpful.

46 *C.* Solve Ex. 6, p. 109, if the shape of the pile is changed so as to make the vertex angle 130°.

47 *C.* Find the total force of water pressure against a trapezoidal dam, whose longer base (= 20 ft.) is at the surface, whose acute angles are both 70°, and whose lower base is 8 ft. below the surface.

48 *C.* The base of a solid is a quarter-circle of radius 10 in. Every vertical section parallel to one side is a triangle whose base angles are 90° and 35°. Find the volume.

CHAPTER VI

LOGARITHMS

NUMERICAL CALCULATION

§ 132. Estimating Results. In making a numerical calculation it is important to estimate the result roughly in advance. This will check any gross error — such as misplacing the decimal point, etc.* Moreover, for some purposes, rough estimates suffice in themselves, making accurate calculations unnecessary. The following devices are frequently useful.

(I) *To estimate a product or quotient,* use "round numbers," and cancel when convenient.

$$E.g., \quad \frac{681.6 \times 7\ 946\ 000\ 000}{20\ 600\ 000 \times (30.27)^2} = \frac{700 \times 8\ 000\ 000\ 000}{20\ 000\ 000 \times 900} = 300, \text{ approx.}$$

The actual value is about 273.6; but we are much better off to know that it is *somewhere near 300* than to have no idea at all whether it is nearer, say, 5 or 5 000 000.

To make a closer estimate, notice whether each factor has been increased or decreased, and by about what fractional part. Make rough allowances accordingly.

(II) *To estimate a root,* use round numbers and group the figures according to the index of the root, as in § 14. Treat a fourth root as the square root of a square root, etc.

$$E.g., \quad \sqrt{265\ 800} = \sqrt{27\ 00\ 00} = 500^+, = 520, \text{ say;}$$
$$\text{also} \quad \sqrt[3]{.0000\ 7969} = \sqrt[3]{.000\ 080} = .04^+, = .043, \text{ say.}$$

§ 133. Scientific Notation. In scientific work, numbers which are very large or small are expressed briefly in such a form as 3.67×10^{12}, or 5.94×10^{-8}, instead of being written out in full. This avoids operations with long rows of zeros or decimal places.

To write out in the ordinary way any number given in this "Scientific Notation," we simply perform the indicated mul-

* In using a Slide Rule, an estimate is the only simple means of pointing off the result.

tiplication — *i.e.*, move the *decimal point* a number of places equal to the exponent, supplying as many zeros as may be needed.* *E.g.*,

$$7.69 \times 10^6 \ = 7\ 690\ 000. \qquad \text{(Point moved 6 places.)}$$
$$4.27 \times 10^{-5} = .000\ 0427. \qquad \text{(Point moved 5 places.)}$$

Conversely, *to express in "Scientific Notation"* any number given in the ordinary way, we simply factor out the proper power of 10. Placing the decimal point wherever we want it, we note how many places it was moved to get it there. Thus,

$$27\ 180\ 000 = 2.718 \times 10^7$$
$$.000\ 00483 = 4.83 \ \times 10^{-6}.$$

For reasons which will soon appear, we usually place the decimal point *after the first significant figure.* Thus, 2.718×10^7 is preferable to 27.18×10^6 or $.2718 \times 10^8$ — unless we have to compare this number with other numbers carrying the factor 10^6 or 10^8, or unless we need, say, 10^6 in order to extract a cube root evenly, etc.

In calculating with numbers expressed in scientific notation, we combine the various powers of 10 according to the laws of exponents, viz.

(A) *Multiplying:* $\qquad 10^x \cdot 10^y = 10^{x+y}$

(B) *Dividing:* $\qquad 10^x \div 10^y = 10^{x-y}$

(C) *Finding powers:* $\quad (10^x)^n \ = 10^{nx}$

(D) *Finding roots:* $\qquad \sqrt[n]{10^x} \ = 10^{\frac{x}{n}}.$

Ex. I. Calculate

$$f = \frac{(18\ 900\ 000)^3\ (.000\ 000\ 00615)}{\sqrt[3]{34\ 180\ 000\ 000\ 000}}.$$

Rewritten $\quad f = \dfrac{(1.89 \times 10^7)^3 \times (6.15 \times 10^{-9})}{\sqrt[3]{34.18 \times 10^{12}}} = \dfrac{1.89^3 \times 6.15 \times 10^{12}}{\sqrt[3]{34.18} \times 10^4}.$

Estimate $\qquad f = (7 \times 6 \div 3^+) \times 10^8 = 14 \times 10^8.$

By calculation $f = 12.794 \times 10^8.$

Notice that the powers of 10 are combined much more easily than

* Since 10^{-n} means $1/10^n$, multiplying by a negative power of 10 is the same as dividing by the corresponding positive power — *i.e.*, moving the decimal point to the left.

their coefficients 1.89, 6.15, etc. If the latter could also be expressed as powers of 10, the whole calculation would be very simple.

EXERCISES

1. Translate into ordinary notation: 4.79×10^6; 9.08×10^{-3}; diameter of a molecule of water $= 3.8 \times 10^{-8}$ cm.

2. Translate into "Scientific Notation," with the decimal point after the first digit:

1 day = 86 400 sec.,	1 watt = 10 000 000 ergs,
1 mi. = 161 000 cm.,	1 cm. = .000 006 21 mi.
1 gm. = .0022 lb.,	1 cc. = .0610 cu. in.

Air weighs .00129 gm./cc.; helium, .000 177 gm./cc.

In Exs. 3–13 estimate the answer very roughly. Then calculate it, accurate to three figures.

3. One wave of certain X-rays has a length of 1.28×10^{-8} cm. How many waves to 1 mi.?

4. How many miles does light travel in 1 hr. if its velocity is 3.00×10^8 meters/sec.?

5. The energy needed to raise the temperature of 1 gm. of water by 1° C. is 4.16×10^7 ergs. How many tons of water can be raised 10° in temperature by 5.66×10^{16} ergs?

6. If water molecules could be placed in line touching one another, how many would there be in 1 ft.? (Cf. Ex. 1.)

7. The average speed of an oxygen molecule in air is .31 mi./sec., and it averages 5×10^9 collisions per sec. Find the "mean free path" (*i.e.*, the average distance traveled between collisions).

8. A charge of 1 electron $= 1.59 \times 10^{-19}$ absolute coulombs. If a lamp takes .5 coulomb per sec., how many electrons does it take per sec.?

9. The energy quantum (e ergs) for light of any frequency (f vibrations per sec.) is $e = 6.54 \times 10^{-27} f$. Find e for violet light having $f = 7.5 \times 10^{14}$.

10. The Mississippi River carries about 3×10^7 cu. ft. of sediment to the Gulf daily. How thick a layer would this make on a city block 250 ft. by 400 ft.?

11. In Ex. 10 how large a cube would the volume of sediment make?

12. The distance from the sun to the earth is 9.29×10^7 mi.; to Pluto, 3.84×10^9 mi., and to nearest fixed star 2.5×10^{13} mi. Representing the distance to the earth by 1 inch, how far would it be on this scale to Pluto? To the nearest star?

13. The earth receives energy from a beam of sunlight 1 sq. mi. in cross-section at the rate of 4.7×10^6 horsepower, approx. Find the total rate of radiation from the sun. (Hint: How many square miles would there be in a spherical surface around the sun as center, at the distance of the earth, 9.29×10^7 mi.?)

[**14.**] Writing each exponent as a common fraction, recall the meaning of $10^{.25}$ and $10^{.125}$; and indicate how the value of each could be found by extracting square roots only.

[**15.**] If $a = 10^{.42917}$ and $b = 10^{.23812}$, what power of 10 would $a^2 \div b$ equal? Also $\sqrt[3]{a^2/b}$?

§ 134. Calculating by Combining Powers of 10.

We come now to the best system of numerical computation ever invented — by which we can make calculations in a few minutes that would otherwise require days or even years.

Here is the idea in essence: *Every positive number is some power of 10*, and can be expressed as such by means of certain tables. Hence to make a calculation we have merely to *combine exponents.*

For instance, suppose we wish to find $\sqrt[11]{a^3/b}$ where a and b denote some given numbers. And suppose the tables show that

$$a = 10^{.91021}, \quad b = 10^{1.10054}.$$

We build up the required quantity as follows:

$$a^3 = 10^{2.73063} \qquad \text{(Multiplying the exponent .91021 by 3.)}$$
$$b = 10^{1.10054}$$

$$\therefore \frac{a^3}{b} = 10^{1.63009} \qquad \text{(Subtracting the exponent 1.10054.)}$$

$$\therefore \sqrt[11]{\frac{a^3}{b}} = \sqrt[11]{10^{1.63009}}$$

$$= 10^{.14819} \qquad \text{(Dividing the exponent 1.63009 by 11.)}$$

And when we have seen from the tables what number this final power of 10 equals, we shall have found the required root.

Notice that in using these exponents the operation of cubing a is replaced by the mere multiplication of an exponent by 3; a long division ($a^3 \div b$), by the subtraction of an exponent; and the very difficult extraction of an eleventh root, by the mere division of an exponent by 11.

Very little more work would be required to find even a 67th root or a 211th root.

The tables are easily used, but to understand them thoroughly we must first note some further facts concerning powers of 10.

§ 135. Numbers as Powers of 10. The statement that every positive number is some power of 10 should perhaps be explained briefly.

Consider, for instance, the number 75, which is clearly not an integral power, being greater than 10^1 and less than 10^2. Neither is it a fractional power. For a fractional power is a *root*; and it can be shown that extracting a root of any integral power of 10 could never give 75 exactly.

When we say that 75 is some power of 10, we mean an *irrational* power.

That is, fractional powers can be found which will approximate 75 as closely as we wish:

$$10^{1.875} = 74.99, \qquad 10^{1.87506} = 74.9998, \text{ etc.}$$

And the *limit* approached by a certain sequence of such fractional powers, as the exponent approaches a certain irrational limiting value, is exactly 75.

Similarly for other positive numbers. Negative numbers will be considered later. (§§ 148, 352.)

§ 136. Common Logarithm Defined. In the equation

$$75 = 10^{1.87506\cdots}, \tag{1}$$

the exponent $1.87506 \cdots$ is called the *logarithm* of 75, written *log 75*. Thus,

$$\log 75 = 1.87506 \cdots.$$

In general, the logarithm of any number is *the exponent of the power to which 10 must be raised to produce the number.**

A logarithm usually consists of two parts: an integer and a decimal. The decimal is found from a table, the integer by inspection — as will be explained shortly.

---

* Observe that we do not define a logarithm as a *power*. In equation (1), 75 is a power of 10: the logarithm is the *exponent* of the power.

The logarithms now under consideration are often called "common logarithms" to distinguish them from some others, mentioned later.

§ 137. Logarithms of Numbers between 1 and 10. A principle which is very basic and will be used continually is this:

If a number N lies between 1 and 10, its logarithm consists of a decimal only.

For N lies between 10^0 and 10^1, and hence

$$N = 10^{0+\text{decimal}}, \qquad \text{or} \qquad \log N = 0 + \text{decimal}.$$

Conversely, *if log N is a positive decimal only, then N lies between 1 and 10.* (Proof?)

§ 138. Use of Tables. The logarithms of numbers between 1 and 10 can be read directly from a table. The logarithms of other numbers are obtainable from them. (§ 139.)

Five-place tables are accurate enough for most purposes, and their arrangement is like that of larger tables. A part of a typical page is reproduced here.

N	0	1	2	3	4	5	6	7	8	9
150	17609	638	667	696	725	754	782	811	840	869
51	898	926	955	984	*013	*041	*070	*099	*127	*156
52	18184	213	241	270	298	327	355	384	412	441
53	469	498	526	554	583	611	639	667	696	724

Explanation. The first three figures of the *number* are shown in the *N*-column at the left, and the fourth figure in the *N*-line at the top. A decimal point is to be understood after the first figure in the *N*-column, so that these numbers are really 1.50, 1.51, etc.

The logarithms appear in the body of the table, and are understood to be decimals only, and of five places throughout. Their first two figures are printed (only occasionally) in the 0 column at the left.

Ex. I. To find the logarithm of 1.502, we look opposite 150 under 2. We read 667, with 17 at the left. Hence

$$\log 1.502 = .17667, \qquad \text{or} \quad 1.502 = 10^{.17667}.$$

Ex. II. To find log 1.514, we look opposite 151 under 4:

$$\log 1.514 = .18013, \qquad \text{or} \quad 1.514 = 10^{.18013}.$$

(The asterisk indicates that the first two figures of the logarithm have changed from 17 to 18, as the last three figures have changed from 984 to 013.)

Conversely, if we have given a logarithm and wish to find the number, we simply locate the given logarithm in the body of the table and see what number corresponds to it.

Ex. III.   If given $\log N = .18355$, we locate this value opposite 152 and under 6.

$$\therefore\ N = 1.526; \qquad i.e., \qquad 10^{.18355} = 1.526.$$

If a given logarithm does not appear exactly in the table, we take the one nearest to it, or else interpolate by proportional parts.   (This is made easy in § 143.)   Similarly if a given number has more than four places.   If it has fewer than four, we mentally affix zeros; e.g., $1.5 = 1.500$.

§ 139. Logarithms of Larger or Smaller Numbers.   The logarithm of a number greater than 10 or less than 1 can be found by using the idea of Scientific Notation.

Ex. I.   1514000 would be 1.514×10^6.

And 1.514, which lies between 1 and 10, can be found in the table: $1.514 = 10^{.18013}$.   Multiplying this by 10^6 and adding exponents,

$$1514000 = 10^{6.18013}, \qquad\text{or}\ \ \log 1514000 = 6.18013.$$

Ex. II.   .01514 would be 1.514×10^{-2}.
$$\therefore\ .01514 = 10^{.18013} \times 10^{-2} = 10^{.18013-2}.$$

For reasons to be explained presently (§ 141), it is customary in cases like this not to combine the negative integer with the positive decimal, but rather to keep the exponent expressed as a difference.

Observe that the decimal part of the logarithm is the same for all these numbers: 1.514; 1514 000; and .01514.   So would it be for any other number having these same digits, 1, 5, 1, 4, in this same order.   (Why?)

To find a number when given its logarithm, we simply reverse the steps above — as in the following examples.

Ex. III.   Given $\log N = 4.18013$, or $N = 10^{4.18013}$.
This is evidently the same as $N = 10^4 \times 10^{.18013}$.   And the latter exponent, being a decimal only, can be found among the logarithms of the table: $10^{.18013} = 1.514$.

$$\therefore\ N = 10^4 \times (1.514) = 15140.$$

Ex. IV.   Given $\log N = .18184 - 3$,   or $N = 10^{.18184-3}$.

By tables this decimal power of 10, without the -3, would equal 1.52.   The effect of the -3 is to multiply by 10^{-3}, making

$$N = 1.52 \times 10^{-3} = .00152.$$

With practice all these operations may be abbreviated and performed rapidly — merely by inspection.

§ **140. Summary.**   (I) Every positive number is some real power of 10: the exponent of the power is the **logarithm of** the number.

(II) The integral part of a logarithm (or **characteristic,** as it is called) is found by inspection:

For any number between 1 and 10, the characteristic is zero.
Thus, $1.52 = 10^{.18184}$,   or $\log 1.52 = 0.18184$.

For any other number, think of its Scientific Notation.
Thus, $37200 = 3.72 \times 10^4 = 10^{\text{dec.}+4}$, or $\log 37200 = \text{dec.} + 4$;
and $.00458 = 4.58 \times 10^{-3} = 10^{\text{dec.}-3}$, or $\log .00458 = \text{dec.} - 3$.
Of course, we need not *write out* all these steps.*

(III) The decimal part of a logarithm (or **mantissa,** as it is called) is read from a table.   It is the same for all numbers which differ only in the position of the decimal point.

(IV) *In going from a logarithm back to the number*, we locate the mantissa in the body of the table, and read off the figures in the number.   If the characteristic is zero, the decimal point falls in the standard position, after the first figure.   If there is a characteristic $(\pm c)$, the point moves to the right or left c places from the standard position.

(V) Calculations can be made by *combining powers of 10.* The work should be so arranged that the exponents to be combined will be near one another, and in a column.

---

* Simply point with the pencil at the standard position of the decimal point after the first significant figure, and count up the power of 10 which would factor out.   Try this on the following:

$6981 = 10^{3+\text{dec.}}$	$25\,000\,000 = 10^{7+\text{dec.}}$
$28.9 = 10^{1+\text{dec.}}$	$314.16 = 10^{2+\text{dec.}}$
$.657 = 10^{\text{dec.}-1.}$	$.000\,000\,99 = 10^{\text{dec.}-7}$

Ex. I. Compute $f = \dfrac{(151.4)^2 \times 6927}{\sqrt[3]{735\,000\,000}}$.

$151.4 = 10^{2.18013}$ $\qquad\qquad \therefore\ (151.4)^2 = 10^{4.36026}$

$\qquad\qquad\qquad\qquad\qquad\qquad\qquad\qquad 6927 = 10^{3.84055}$

$\qquad\qquad\qquad\qquad\qquad\qquad\qquad \overline{\text{Product} = 10^{8.20081}}$

$735\,000\,000 = 10^{8.86629}$ $\qquad \therefore\ \sqrt[3]{735\,000\,000} = 10^{2.95543}$

$\qquad\qquad\qquad\qquad\qquad\qquad\qquad \overline{\therefore\ f = 10^{5.24538}}$

Looking up the mantissa .24538 we find 1.759. The characteristic 5 moves the point five places. Hence $f = 175\,900.$

Remark. Many rates, maxima, areas, etc., as found by differentiation or integration, must be calculated numerically by means of logarithms. And that is possible only because a logarithm varies with its number in a definite way. The tables show this variation: in other words, they give the values of a certain **function** called the "logarithm."

EXERCISES

1. Express these numbers as powers of 10:

(*a*) 37150; $\qquad$ 20 890 000. (First write the Scientific Notation.)

(*b*) 63.17; $\qquad$ 140 000. (Think of the Scientific Notation.)

What is the logarithm of each of these numbers?

2. Write as powers of 10 the numbers whose logarithms are

$\qquad$ 2.69566, $\qquad$ 6.92210, $\qquad$ 3.09734, $\qquad$ 1.39794.

Look up each number, reading the fourth figure which is nearest.

3. Find the product of the numbers in 1 (*a*). Likewise in 1 (*b*). Check each by actual multiplication.

4. Make each of the following calculations (to four figures) by expressing the given numbers as powers of 10, in a vertical column, and combining. Estimate each result roughly in advance as a check.

(*a*) $40.93 \times 7736 \times 2.198$, $\qquad$ (*b*) $(6.035)^4 \times 31230$,

(*c*) $8\,425\,000 \div 319.6$, $\qquad\qquad$ (*d*) $\sqrt[3]{136.8}$,

(*e*) $(98.35)^2 \times 50.47 \div 3980$, $\quad$ (*f*) $\sqrt{2890} \div 14.8$,

(*g*) $(41.08)^5 \div \sqrt{24830000}$, $\quad$ (*h*) $10\,000 \div (78.23 \times 6.983)$,

(*i*) $\dfrac{(6.7)^5 \times 28.23}{\sqrt{500300}}$, $\qquad\qquad$ (*j*) $\sqrt[3]{\dfrac{943.6}{29.2 \times 5.119}}$.

5. Proceed as in Ex. 1 (*a*) for the numbers .00035 and .6372; also as in 1 (*b*) for .0858, .000 099, and .005208.

6. Find what numbers the following powers of 10 equal:

$$10^{.81505-4}, \qquad 10^{.49136-6}, \qquad 10^{.73022-1}.$$

7. Calculate: (a) $.004937 \times 81390$; (b) $.0005166 \div 4.268$.

8. Interpolate by proportional parts to show that $\log \pi = .49715.*$

9. When a ball has fallen freely s cm. from rest, its speed v cm./sec. is $v = \sqrt{2\,gs}$, g cm./sec.[2] being the gravitational acceleration. Find v if $g = 980.4$ and $s = 2150$.

10. Plot a graph showing how $\log x$ varies with x from $x = 1$ to $x = 10$. If the logarithms of two numbers were known exactly, would interpolation by proportional parts give too large or too small a value in finding an intermediate logarithm?

11. When a particle of mass m gm. travels uniformly around a circle of radius r cm. in T sec., the "centrifugal force" (F dynes) is $F = 4\,\pi^2 mr/T^2$. Calculate F if $m = 38.75$, $r = 6.44$, and $T = 3.085$.

§ 141. Avoiding Negative Mantissas.

It would be inconvenient at the end of a calculation to come out with such a result as

$$N = 10^{-.39685},$$

for the tables give only positive mantissas. And if we used the definition of a negative power, writing $N = 1 \div 10^{.39685}$, we should have to look up the latter power and then perform a long division to get N.

To avoid such difficulties we usually arrange to keep our mantissa positive at every step of a calculation. This can be done, even when we have to subtract a larger logarithm from a smaller, by using a simple device:

Increase the smaller logarithm by some integer, making it now the larger, *and at the same time indicate the subtraction of a like integer,* so as to keep the net value unchanged.

Ex. I. Calculate $x = \dfrac{1.58}{4326}$ [Estimate, $x = .000\,35$.]

By tables: $1.58 = 10^{.19866}$ and $4326 = 10^{3.63609}$.
Increase the first exponent by 4, with -4 affixed. $1.58 = 10^{4.19866-4}$
Subtract the exponent 3.63609. $\underline{4326 = 10^{3.63609}}$
$$x = 10^{.56257-4}$$

Look up the resulting positive mantissa, and point off according to the characteristic -4. $x = .000\,3652.$

---

* Since π is used often, this logarithm should be listed for reference on the "300 page" of the table.

§ 142. **Operations with Negative Characteristics.** When looking up the logarithm of a small number — as already stated — we do not combine the negative characteristic with the positive decimal, but merely indicate the subtraction, in the form, say, $.01514 = 10^{.18013-2}$. This procedure avoids negative mantissas, and also saves labor.

In working with such combination logarithms, there are a few points to be looked out for, as shown in the following examples.

(I) *Raising to a power:* say $x = (.4074)^5$.
By tables: $.4074 = 10^{.61002-1}$. $\therefore \quad x = 10^{3.05010-5}$.

(Observe that we have multiplied the *entire* exponent by 5 — of course.)
The resulting exponent is clearly equal to $.05010 - 2$, simply dropping $3 - 3$, or zero. Looking up the mantissa $.05010$ and pointing off according to the -2, we find $x = .01122^+$.

(II) *Extracting a root:* say $x = \sqrt[3]{.1998}$.
By tables: $.1998 = 10^{.30060-1}$.

Dividing this exponent by 3 would give $.10020 - .33333$, producing a negative mantissa. To avoid this, we may add $2 - 2$ to the original logarithm, making it $2.30060 - 3$, still the same value. Then we can divide evenly:

$$x = \sqrt[3]{10^{2.30060-3}} = 10^{.76687-1} = .5846 \text{ (by tables).}$$

To extract any other root we should likewise make the negative integer exactly divisible by the index of the root. Of course, we must do this without changing the value of the combination, *i.e.*, by adding zero in the form $n - n$.

(III)   *Dividing:*   say $x = \dfrac{.003166}{.06314}.$ [Est., $.05^+$.]

By tables: Modified form (adding $1 - 1$):
$\quad .003166 = 10^{.50051-3}$ $\quad .003166 = 10^{1.50051-4}$
$\quad .06314 \ = 10^{.80030-2}$ $\quad .06314 \ = 10^{.80030-2}$
The subtraction gives finally: $x = 10^{.70021-2} = .05014.$

EXERCISES

1. Estimate the following values roughly, and then calculate to four significant figures:

(a) 37.92×860.9,   (b) $.6835 \div .692$,   (c) $.0594 \div 129.9$,
(d) $.002881 \times .7117$,   (e) $(.396)^5$,   (f) $.08236 \div .00979$,

(g) $\sqrt[3]{.000\,089}$,   (h) $\sqrt[4]{.054}$,   (i) $3\sqrt[5]{.01}$,

(j) $\sqrt[3]{.000\,235} \times .199$,   (k) $(.5816)^9$,   (l) $(.2107)^{12}\,(2.761)^{10}$.

2. Likewise calculate the following:

(a) $7.936 \times .9426 \times .02874$,   (b) $.008897 \times \sqrt{.2409} \times 4.006$,

(c) $\dfrac{5278 \times .0003365}{711.4 \times .259}$,   (d) $\dfrac{\sqrt[3]{41300}}{6.257 \times .0349}$.

3. In certain radio work a wave length (l meters) is found from the formula $l = 1884\sqrt{LC}$. Calculate l if $L = 11.25$ and $C = .0073$.

4. Find the edge of a cube whose volume is .04875 cu. in.

5. Estimate and calculate "Young's modulus" for steel from the formula $Y = mgl/(\pi r^2 s)$, if $m = 1023$, $g = 981$, $l = 85.4$, $r = .0253$, and $s = .02191$.

6. The frequency (f periods per sec.) of a vibrating musical string is given by the formula: $f = \dfrac{1}{2\,rl}\sqrt{\dfrac{T}{\pi\,d}}$. Find f if $r = .025$, $l = 30$, $T = 5 \times 10^7$, $d = 8.02$.

7. In certain studies the weight (W gm.) and sitting height or length of trunk (h cm.) for an average man were found to be related approximately thus: $W = .180\,h^{3.13}$. Calculate W if $h = 65$.

8. The distance (d cm.) between atomic planes in a crystal of rock salt is calculated from $d^3 = 58.46 \times 1.662 \times 10^{-24} \div 4.34$. Find d.

9. A formula for the skin resistance of air upon an airplane (R lb./sq. ft.) is $R = .0000082(V^2A)^{.93}$. Find R if $V = 100$ and $A = 20$.

10. Translate into logarithmic notation in a parallel column each of the equations involving a power of 10 which was used in Ex. 2 (d). Thus:

$$41300 = 10^{4.61595} \qquad\qquad \log 41300 = 4.61595,$$

etc. How was the "log" of the cube root obtained from the "log" of the number? The "log" of the product from the "logs" of the factors? The "log" of the fraction?

§ 143. Tables of Proportional Parts. In the margins of logarithmic tables there are small auxiliary tables which make interpolation easy.

Ex. I.   Find log 1.5146.

The required logarithm lies between .18013 and .18041, which differ by 28 (units of the fifth place). Select the marginal table headed 28. This tells how much to add to the smaller tabulated logarithm [.18013] because of any fifth figure in the given number. In our example the fifth figure is 6: add 16.8 (*i.e.*, 17), making

log 1.5146 = .18013 + .00017 = .18030.

Ex. II.   Find N if log N = .18037.

The next smaller logarithm in the table is .18013, belonging to 1.514.   (This gives the first four figures of the required number N.)

Now log N exceeds .18013 by 24 units. Hence our problem is this: *What fifth figure in N would add 24 to the logarithm, in a total difference of 28?*   The nearest to 24 shown in the marginal table is 25.2 and this is opposite 9 — the required fifth figure of N.   Thus N = 1.5149.

28	
5TH FIG.	ADD TO LOG
1	2.8
2	5.6
3	8.4
4	11.2
5	14.0
6	16.8
7	19.6
8	22.4
9	25.2

Remarks.   (I) In using these auxiliary tables, note carefully which you are finding: how much to *add* to a logarithm, or what fifth figure to *affix* to a number.   With practice the operations can all be performed mentally, and only the final result written.

(II) These auxiliary tables are based upon proportional parts.   If ten units in the fifth place of the number (one unit in fourth place) make a difference of 28 in the logarithm, then 3 units make a difference three tenths as large, or a difference of 8.4.

(III) What if a given number has six figures, say 1.51436?   The 36 units of the *sixth* place will change the logarithm by .36 × 28.   By the little table, .3 × 28 = 8.4 and .06 × 28 = 1.68.   Thus .36 × 28 = 8.4 + 1.68 = 10.08.   Simply add 10.   (There is almost no chance of securing greater accuracy by preserving figures beyond the fifth place.)

§ **144. Laws of Logarithms.**   Since logarithms are exponents, they combine according to the usual laws of exponents. These are already familiar; but in what follows it will be convenient to have them restated in logarithmic form, as follows:

(I) *The logarithm of a product equals the sum of the logarithms of the factors:*

$$\log (ac) = \log a + \log c.$$

(II) *The logarithm of a fraction equals the logarithm of the numerator minus the logarithm of the denominator:* *

$$\log \frac{a}{c} = \log a - \log c.$$

(III) *The logarithm of a power of a number equals the index of the power times the logarithm of the number:*

$$\log a^n = n \log a.$$

(IV) *The logarithm of a root of a number equals the logarithm of the number, divided by the index of the root:*

$$\log \sqrt[n]{a} = \frac{1}{n} \log a.$$

If a formal proof of these laws is desired, it can be given as in the following illustrations:

PROOF OF (I):

If $\qquad \log a = x \qquad$ and $\qquad \log c = y,$

i.e., if $\qquad a = 10^x \qquad$ and $\qquad c = 10^y,$

then $\qquad ac = (10^x)(10^y) = 10^{x+y},$

which shows that $\qquad \log ac = x + y = \log a + \log c.$

PROOF OF (IV):

If $\qquad \log a = x,$

i.e., if $\qquad a = 10^x,$

then $\qquad \sqrt[n]{a} = \sqrt[n]{10^x} = 10^{\frac{x}{n}},$

which shows that $\log \sqrt[n]{a} = \dfrac{x}{n} = \dfrac{1}{n} \log a.$

The proofs of (II) and (III) are similar. (Ex. 8, p. 202.)

§ 145. **Abbreviated Form.** In calculating by combining powers of 10, the actual operations are performed upon the exponents or logarithms. Hence it will suffice to set down the logarithms alone, and work with them. This should, however, be done in an orderly manner and labeled clearly.

The following example shows a calculation worked out

---

* This applies also to a fractional *form* whose value happens to be a whole number not truly a "fraction."

with powers of 10 as heretofore, and the same calculation in the abbreviated form.

Ex. I.   Calculate $x = \sqrt{\dfrac{(25.89)^3\,(.0125)}{927}}$.

Exponential Form

$$25.89 = 10^{1.41313}$$

$$25.89^3 = 10^{4.23939}$$
$$.0125 = 10^{.09691-2}$$

$$\text{product} = 10^{4.33630-2}$$
$$927 = 10^{2.96708}$$

$$\text{fraction} = 10^{1.36922-2}$$
$$x = 10^{.68461-1}$$

$$\therefore\; x = .48373.$$

Logarithmic Form

No.	Log.
25.89	1.41313
25.89³	4.23939
.0125	.09691 − 2
prod.	4.33630 − 2
927	2.96708
frac.	1.36922 − 2
x	.68461 − 1

$$\therefore\; x = .48373.$$

The latter form is the one which we shall use hereafter.*

EXERCISES

Get all results in the following exercises accurate to the nearest unit in the fifth place.

1. Look up the logarithms of:

39.284,   982670,   1.0362,   .0054108.

2. Find the numbers whose logarithms are:

.34213,   6.46230,   7.68837 − 10,   3.99010 − 10.

3. Estimate and calculate:

(a) $\dfrac{(1182)^3\,(.007933)}{32642}$

(b) $\dfrac{\sqrt{485.7}}{8.1576 \times .1088}$,

(c) $\sqrt[3]{\dfrac{(26.813)^2}{2039.7}}$,

(d) $\dfrac{1}{\sqrt{51.094}}$,

(e) $2\,\pi\,(.1346)\,(29.842)$,

(f) $4\,\pi\,(.026917)^2$.

4. The time of swing of a pendulum is $T = 2\,\pi\sqrt{l/g}$. Estimate and calculate T if $l = 2$ and $g = 32.088$.

5. The amount of \$$P$ with 6% compound interest after n years is $A = P(1.06)^n$. Find A if $P = 2750$ and $n = 20$.

6. In Ex. 5 find the principal \$$P$ required to yield an amount of \$15000 after 30 years.

* In using this be careful not to write the = sign between a number and its logarithm. The resulting confusion would sometimes be disastrous.

7. Find the radius of a gold sphere weighing 1 ton, if 1 cu. ft. of water weighs 62.425 lb. and gold is 19.32 times as heavy.

8. Prove: $\log \dfrac{a}{c} = \log a - \log c;$ $\log a^n = n \log a.$

9. Prove: $\log \dfrac{ab^2}{c\sqrt[3]{d}} = \log a + 2 \log b - (\log c + \tfrac{1}{3} \log d).$

§ 146. Arrangement of Work. Before looking up any logarithms for a calculation, it is best to plan the work in full and lay out a "skeleton form," providing a place for each step and labeling it. We can then concentrate attention on the tables and the necessary arithmetic. This will save time and mistakes, and will keep the calculation in a presentable form.

The following example shows an arrangement of work pretty satisfactory for the more complicated calculations.

Ex. I.   Calculate $x = \dfrac{\sqrt{.5212} \;\; (13.953)^{\frac{5}{3}}}{\sqrt{(8.2)^5 \; (45.187) \; \sqrt[3]{.0973}}}.$

Plan: The logarithm of x will be obtained as follows:

$\log x = [\tfrac{1}{2} \log .5212 + \tfrac{5}{3} \log 13.953]$

$\qquad - \tfrac{1}{2} [5 \log 8.2 + \log 45.187 + \tfrac{1}{3} \log .0973].$

The following "skeleton form" (printed in black type) provides for these steps — as explained below:

No.	Log.		Combination
.5212	19.71700 − 20	⎣2	9.85850 − 10
13.953	1.14467	× $\frac{5}{3}$	1.90778
Numer.			11.76628 − 10
8.2	0.91381	× 5	4.56905
45.187			1.65501
.0973	28.98811 − 30	⎣3	9.66270 − 10
Product			5.88676 ⎣2
Denom.			2.94338
x			8.82290 − 10

$$\therefore \;\; x = .066512$$

Here the first column lists the given numbers; the second shows their logarithms as they come from the table; the third shows the modified logarithms and their combinations. Thus the top line indicates that the number .5212 has the logarithm $19.71700 - 20$; and that taking half of this, as called for in the *plan* above, gives $9.85850 - 10$. Adding this to $\frac{5}{3}$ log 13.953, just below, gives the logarithm of the numerator; and subtracting the logarithm of the denominator, similarly obtained, gives log x. (This subtraction is facilitated by temporarily covering the intervening figures. Or, space can be left to copy the logarithm of the denominator in, just under that of the numerator.) For the fourth given number, 45.187, the logarithm is to be combined without previous alteration, and so is entered at once in the "combination" column.

The above form can of course be modified. But we need *some* orderly place to put down the figures and make the combinations.

The negative characteristics above are so written that the subtracted integer is 10, or a multiple of 10. This system is used by computers, for reasons of uniformity and convenience in working with certain tables. (§ 155.) Evidently -1 may be written either $9 \cdots - 10$, or $19 \cdots - 20$, or $29 \cdots - 30$, etc.

§ **147** S. **Cologarithm.** By the cologarithm of a number N is meant the logarithm of the reciprocal, $1/N$:

$$\text{colog } N = \log \frac{1}{N} = \log 1 - \log N = - \log N. \qquad (2)$$

Where a calculation calls for the subtraction of log N, we can instead *add* colog N. The latter can with practice be read easily from the logarithmic table.

We mentally subtract log N from zero, or $10 - 10$. The easiest way is to subtract each significant figure from 9, until the last, which we subtract from 10; and then affix -10 if needed. Thus,

if log $N = 2.88036$,   colog $N = 7.11964 - 10$;

if log $N = 8.11250 - 10$,   colog $N = 1.88750$.

Special care is needed for reading off cologarithms when interpolating.

Cologarithms are especially helpful when we have to divide many different numbers by the same N: after once reading colog N, we add it repeatedly and avoid many subtractions.

In calculating a fraction with several factors in the denominator, the use of cologarithms instead of logarithms requires more subtractions, but these are of the simple type above. The work can be so planned that the final combination is merely the adding of a single column, without obtaining the logarithms of numerator and denominator separately.

In Ex. I, § 146, we would use
$$\log x = \tfrac{1}{2} \log .5212 + \tfrac{5}{3} \log 13.953 + \tfrac{5}{2} \operatorname{colog} 8.2$$
$$+ \tfrac{1}{2} \operatorname{colog} 45.187 + \tfrac{1}{6} \operatorname{colog} .0973.$$

EXERCISES

1. Read off from a logarithmic table the cologarithms of 2, 3, 4, 5; 20; 2320; 6030000; .0614; .000477.

2. Find the result of dividing each following number by 376.5: 19000000; 98.16; π; .02658; .0005108.

3. Calculate $x = \dfrac{100\,\pi}{(32.6)\,(9247)\,(.0652)}$:

   (a) Using cologarithms;   (b) Without cologarithms.

4. Estimate and compute to five figures;

(a) $\dfrac{(3.7325)^3}{(91.56)^2}$,

(b) $\dfrac{(9.1467)^4}{204890}$,

(c) $\dfrac{(6.85)^5 \times .0576}{\sqrt{88036000}}$,

(d) $\dfrac{5.137 \times (.006879)^3}{.9735 \times (.022544)^2}$,

(e) $\sqrt[5]{\dfrac{.62 \times \sqrt{93685}}{\sqrt[3]{.70007}}}$,

(f) $\sqrt{\dfrac{(.043)^3 \times 740.83 \times 7^5}{\sqrt{60} \times .039 \times (300.18)^{\frac{1}{2}}}}$.

5. The best elevation (E in.) for the outer rail of a railway curve of radius R ft. is given by $E = 12\,GV^2/(32.2\,R)$ where G feet is the gauge and V ft. per sec. the greatest speed used. Estimate and calculate E if $G = 4.71$, $V = 79.8$, and $R = 5729$.

6. The volume of an oblate spheroid is $V = \tfrac{4}{3}\pi R^2 r$. Estimate and compute the volume of the earth if $R = 3963.3$ and $r = 3949.8$.

7. The rate (V cc./sec.) at which a liquid will flow through a small tube is often calculated from the formula $V = \pi\,p\,r^4/(8\,le)$. Find V if $p = 980600$, $r = .3217$, $l = 101.42$, $e = .00894$.

8. A formula for the safe working pressure (P lb./sq. in.) in certain flues is $P = 1472600\ T^{2.1}\,L^{-.9}\,D^{-1.16}$. Find P if $T = .25$, $L = 60$, and $D = 35$.

[9.] What steps would you take to calculate logarithmically $V = \tfrac{2}{3}\pi\,r^3 + \tfrac{1}{3}\pi\,r^2 h$, if given values for r and h?

§ 148. Calculations with Negative Numbers. There is no "real" value of x, positive or negative, for which 10^x is a negative number. That is, a negative number cannot have a "real" logarithm.

But calculations involving negative numbers can be made as follows: First decide by the elementary rules of signs whether the final result should be positive or negative. Then find its *numerical value* by logarithms, treating all the given numbers as positive.

Ex. I.   Calculate $x = \sqrt[3]{\dfrac{-3.14\,(-56.8)^2}{(-17.5)^5\,\sqrt[7]{-100}}}.$

The combined effect of all these negative signs is to make x negative.

$$\therefore \; x = -\sqrt[3]{\dfrac{3.14(56.8)^2}{(17.5)^5\,\sqrt[7]{100}}}.$$

By logarithms the value of the radical itself is $R = .14731$.

$$\therefore \; x = -.14731.$$

N.B. It would be correct to write $\log R = \frac{1}{3}\,[\log a + \cdots]$; but not to write a similar equation for $\log x$, since x has no real logarithm.

§ 149. Sums and Differences. Suppose we have to make a calculation which calls for the addition of two quantities, as in

$$x = \sqrt{(1.1825)^{20} + \sqrt[3]{87556}.}$$

The quantities can be expressed as powers of 10, giving say

$$x = \sqrt{10^{1.45600} + 10^{1.64743}},$$

but they cannot be added by merely combining the exponents.

In what sort of calculation would you have to add the exponents or logarithms?

We must evidently look up the numbers which these two powers of 10 equal, and then add those numbers. And similarly in any other calculation involving a sum or difference, we must go from logarithms back to numbers before adding or subtracting.

In the example above, the calculation could be arranged conveniently as follows, using U and V to denote the two quantities:

$U = (1.1825)^{20}$,		$V = \sqrt[3]{87556}$,		$x = \sqrt{U+V}$	
No.	Log.	No.	Log.	No.	Log.
1.1825	.07280	87556	4.94229	$U+V$	1.86321
$(1.1825)^{20}$	1.45600	$\sqrt[3]{87556}$	1.64743	$\sqrt{U+V}$	.93160

$$\therefore\ U = 28.576 \qquad \therefore\ V = 44.405 \qquad \therefore\ x = 8.5428$$
$$U + V = 72.981$$

Thus there are in reality three separate calculations: To find U, to find V, and to find x. The last cannot be started until we have finished the first two and have added the numbers U and V.

§ 150. Short-Cuts. Sometimes by making a preliminary change in the form of the quantity to be computed we can save considerable work.

(A) *If some of the given numbers can be canceled or combined*, mentally, fewer logarithms will need to be handled.

E.g., in $A = \pi (25)^2$, replace $(25)^2$ by 625, and save one operation. Or, in $V = \frac{1}{3}\pi r^2 h$, cancel 3 into the value of h; and one fewer logarithms will be needed.

(B) *By factoring, a sum or difference can sometimes be reduced to a product* of known numbers.

E.g., the total area of a cylinder, $A = 2\pi r^2 + 2\pi rh$, may be written $A = 2\pi r (r + h)$. If given $r = 113.4$ and $h = 246.6$ we have $r + h = 360$; and multiplying by the factor 2:

$$A = (113.4)\ (720)\ \pi.$$

The two separate calculations needed to find A from the first formula are thus replaced by one simple calculation.

Similarly, suppose we wish to find one leg a of a right triangle, having given the hypotenuse and other leg, $c = 983.5$, $b = 726.2$.

Since $a = \sqrt{(983.5)^2 - (726.2)^2}$, the calculation apparently involves going from a logarithm back to the number three times in all. But the difference of two squares is factorable: $c^2 - b^2 = (c + b)\ (c - b)$. Here

$$c + b = 1709.7, \quad c - b = 257.3. \quad \therefore\ a = \sqrt{(1709.7)\ (257.3)}.$$

Thus a is very readily computed.

EXERCISES

1. Estimate and compute to five significant figures:

    (a) $\sqrt{398.4^2 - 217.3^2}$,   (b) $[\sqrt{87.264} - 1.069^2]^{\frac{1}{2}}$.

2. (a) Estimate and compute by logarithms $(\sqrt{6} - \sqrt{.9})^3$.

    (b) Calculate the same value by using tables of roots.

3. Find the total area of a cylinder whose base radius is 64.7 cm. and whose height is 177.9 cm.

4. An iron casting consists of a cone and hemisphere united, the flat side of the latter coinciding with the base of the cone. If the common radius is 3.988 ft. and the height of the conical part is .742 ft., calculate the volume of the casting.

5. The hypotenuse and one leg of a right triangle are respectively 562.84 ft., and 408.77 ft. Find the other leg.

6. If $Q = (u^2 - v^2) \div (2\,uv)$, find Q when $u = 9.8753$ and $v = 2.1647$.

7. Like Ex. 6 if $Q = (a^2 + 2\,ab + b^2 - c^2) \div 2\,ab$, and if $a = 98.69$, $b = 57.48$, and $c = 75.13$.

8. A formula relating to the field strength of a magnet is

$$H = \frac{4\,m\,l\,r}{(r^2 - l^2)^2}.$$

Calculate H if $m = 612.5$, $l = 14.82$, and $r = 36.45$.

9. Compute to five significant figures:

    (a) $\sqrt[3]{\dfrac{-\,.046935}{-\,.29728}}$,   (b) $\pi\sqrt[5]{\dfrac{(-\,366.46)^3}{(-\,.60797)^2}}$.

Exercises involving Calculus

10 C. Find the slope of the curve $y = 1.423\,x^{\frac{7}{5}}$ at $x = 3$.

11 C. Find the area under the curve $y = .656\,x^{\frac{3}{5}}$ from $x = 1$ to $x = 3$.

12 C. Like Ex. 11 for the curve $y = 17.5/x^{\frac{4}{5}}$.

13 C. Find the minimum value of $y = x^3 - 25\,x + 100$.

§ 151. Compound Interest Formula. It is tedious to calculate by elementary arithmetic the amount which would be accumulated by leaving a sum of money at compound interest for a long time. Business men generally use interest tables. But there are problems not readily solvable by the tables. It is well, therefore, to know a general formula, which can be used either to make ordinary calculations quickly or to solve new types of problems.

For simplicity consider first some particular rate of interest, say 6%. Then if the interest is figured annually, the amount accumulated at the end of any year will be 106% of the sum at the beginning of the year. In other words, the sum will be multiplied by 1.06 during each year.

If the original principal is P, the amount after one year will be $P(1.06)$; after two years, $P(1.06)^2$; after three years, $P(1.06)^3$; and so on. The final amount after n years will be

$$A = P(1.06)^n. \tag{3}$$

If the interest is compounded semi-annually, the sum will gain 3% in each half-year, or be multiplied by 1.03. After n years the original principal will have been multiplied by this factor $2n$ times in all, making

$$A = P(1.03)^{2n}.$$

GENERAL FORMULA. From these special cases it appears that the amount of any investment P, after n years, with interest at any annual rate r (r being a fractional value, as .06, say), compounded k times a year, will be

$$A = P\left(1 + \frac{r}{k}\right)^{kn}. \tag{4}$$

This inference is easily proved correct.

Proof: Let S be the sum accumulated at the beginning of any interest period. Then the interest gained during the period (one k-th of a year) will be rS/k; and the amount at the end of the period will be $S + rS/k$, or $S(1 + r/k)$. Thus the sum will be multiplied by $(1 + r/k)$ during each period; and there are kn periods in n years. Hence we have (4).

Remarks. (I) Formula (4) should be memorized carefully, as it covers all cases. For instance, if the interest is compounded annually, simply put $k = 1$, getting $A = P(1 + r)^n$, like (3) above.

(II) The formula is strictly correct, however, only at the *ends* of the interest periods, *i.e.*, for *integral* values of kn. To find A after $10\frac{3}{4}$ periods, say, the exact method would be to find A after 10 periods, and then add simple interest for three fourths of a period. But formula (4) would give a very approximate result by simply putting $n = 10.75$.

(III) When compounding semi-annually, at the rate of 6%, the amount after 1 yr. will be $A = P(1.03)^2 = P(1.0609)$. Thus, due to the frequent compounding, the *effective* rate of increase is 6.09%. 6% is merely the *nominal* rate used in figuring.

§ 152. Typical Problems. We can now solve various typical problems in compound interest by merely substituting the numerical values in formula (4), and using logarithms.

In each of the following examples, set up the formula and logarithmic scheme for yourself. Then compare with the work shown here in fine print.

Ex. I.   What will be the amount after 20 years, on an original investment of $2750 with interest at 5%, compounded quarterly?

Here $P = 2750$, $n = 20$, $k = 4$, $r/k = .05/4 = .0125$.
$$\therefore\ A = 2750\ (1.0125)^{80}.$$

We have merely to add the logarithm of 2750 to 80 times the logarithm of 1.0125, and look up the number A. [*Ans.*, taking log 1.0125 as .0053950, $A = 7429$.] Observe that it is best to reduce r/k to .0125 before substituting it in the formula; also, to use a very accurate logarithm for 1.0125, so that multiplying by 80 will not make the error affect the fifth place. Many tables give a special page of logarithms for interest calculations.

Ex. II.   How much must be invested now to yield $5000 thirty years hence, interest being at $3\frac{1}{2}\%$, compounded annually?

Here $A = 5000$, $n = 30$, $k = 1$, $r/k = .035$.
$$\therefore\ 5000 = P\,(1.035)^{30}, \qquad \text{or} \qquad P = 5000/(1.035)^{30}.$$

We have merely to subtract 30 times the logarithm of 1.035 from log 5000, and look up the number P. [*Ans.*, $P = 1781.40$.]

Ex. III.   At what rate of interest, compounded semi-annually, would an investment of $1750 yield $5000 after 20 years?

Here $A = 5000$, $P = 1750$, $n = 20$, $k = 2$.
$$\therefore\ 5000 = 1750\left(1 + \frac{r}{2}\right)^{40}.$$

Let the unknown quantity $1 + r/2$ be denoted by x. Then

$$5000 = 1750\,x^{40}, \qquad\qquad \therefore\ x = \sqrt[40]{\frac{5000}{1750}}.$$

Subtracting log 1750 from log 5000 and dividing by 40, we find
$$\log x = .01140, \qquad\qquad \text{whence}\ x = 1.0266.$$
This is $1 + r/2$;   that is, $1 + r/2 = 1.0266$.

$$\therefore\ \frac{r}{2} = .0266, \qquad\qquad r = .0532. \qquad [\textit{Ans.},\ 5.32\%.]$$

Ex. IV.   In how many years would \$983.50 amount to \$3875 with interest at 7% compounded semi-annually?

Here $A = 3875$, $P = 983.5$, $k = 2$, $r/k = .07/2 = .035$.
$$\therefore \ 3875 = 983.5 \ (1.035)^{2n}.$$

There is no method in elementary algebra for solving an equation for an *unknown exponent*. This problem will be discussed in § 153.

EXERCISES

In these exercises interest is to be compounded annually unless otherwise specified.

1. What amount would a principal of \$875 yield after 30 yr., with interest at 5%, compounded semi-annually?

2. Like Ex. 1 for \$500, 25 yr., and 6%, compounded quarterly.

3. What sum, deposited now, would yield \$7500 forty years hence, if interest is at 6%, compounded semi-annually?

4. Like Ex. 3 for \$20,000, fifty years, and 4%.

5. At what rate will \$8000 amount to \$25000 in 30 years, compounding semi-annually?

6. At what rate of interest will any sum be quadrupled in 20 years? (Take any convenient sum, say \$1.)

7. In 1626 the Dutch bought Manhattan Island for \$24. To how much would this amount in 1936 if it had been at 7% interest?

8. The enrollment in a certain high school was 850 in 1925, and has since increased 6.7% annually. If this continues, what will it be in 1945?

9. What sum set aside when a boy is 1 year old would provide an education fund of \$3000 when he is 18, if 4% interest is obtained, compounded semi-annually?

10. At what rate will any sum double itself in 12 years?

11. The value of a piece of timber-land increased in 10 years from \$75,000 to \$135,000, despite enough logging to pay taxes. To what rate of interest was this equivalent?

12. Find the amount of \$100 after 1 year with interest at 8%, compounded quarterly. What percentage is actually gained during the year, due to the frequent compounding — *i.e.*, what is the effective rate?

13. A building costing \$9000 must be rebuilt every 15 years. What sum (\$P) set aside when the building is erected will provide for its perpetual replacement, if the cost remains constant and money will always yield $4\frac{1}{2}$%? (Hint: P must produce $P + 9000$ in 15 yr.)

[**14.**] Estimate, and compute by logarithms $\dfrac{.47712}{.00860}$. Also see if you can solve the equation $(1.02)^n = 3$ for n. Can you think of any interest problem which would require the solution of this equation?

§ 153. Finding an Unknown Exponent. Suppose we wish to solve the equation

$$2^x = 25. \tag{5}$$

Since 2^x and 25 are equal, their logarithms must be equal. But the logarithm of 2^x equals x *times* log 2:

$$\therefore \; x \log 2 = \log 25, \qquad \text{or } x \,(.30103) = 1.39794.$$

That is, x *multiplied by* .30103 equals 1.39794; and hence to find x we must *divide* 1.39794 by .30103:

$$x = \frac{1.39794}{.30103} = 4.6439. \tag{6}$$

This result is evidently about right, since $2^4 = 16$ and $2^5 = 32$.

Notice then that this new problem of solving for an unknown exponent calls for the *division of a logarithm by a logarithm* — not a mere subtraction of logarithms.

But we could of course avoid this long division by looking up *further* logarithms — just as if we had been given the fraction to calculate in the first place. Subtracting the logarithm *of* .30103 from the logarithm *of* 1.39794 would give log x.

We can now return to Ex. IV, p. 210, and find n from the equation,

$$3875 = 983.5 \,(1.035)^{2n}.$$

Here $\log 3875 = \log 983.5 + 2\,n \log 1.035.$
By tables: $3.58827 = 2.99277 + 2\,n\,(.01494).$
Transposing 2.99277, and simplifying the coefficient of n:

$$.59550 = n\,(.02988).$$

By division: $n = \dfrac{.59550}{.02988} = 19.93.$ \hfill (7)

(We could avoid division by looking up further logarithms.)

It would be useless to calculate n more accurately, since the interest formula is exact only at the ends of interest periods.

§ 154. Depreciation. In any business it is necessary to allow for depreciation in the value of buildings, machinery, etc., due to wear which cannot be made good by current repairs.

For simplicity it is commonly figured that the value will decrease by a certain fixed sum during each year, until finally reduced to the mere "scrap value." But for some kinds of property it is more accurate to figure the loss during each year as a certain constant fraction of the value at the beginning of that year.

Ex. I. An automobile costing $2000 loses each year 30% of its value at the beginning of that year. What will be its value after 5 years?

At the end of each year the value is 70%, or .7, of the value at the beginning of the year. Multiplying by .7 each year, we get the final value:

$$V = 2000 \ (.7)^5 = 336.14.$$

Remarks. (I) If 15% were deducted every half-year, this would be "figuring the depreciation semi-annually at the yearly rate of 30%." After each half-year the current value would be multiplied by .85, and after each year by $(.85)^2$.

In general, if depreciation is figured k times a year at any nominal annual rate r, the value after n years would be

$$V = P \left(1 - \frac{r}{k} \right)^{kn}. \tag{8}$$

(II) If we wished to know when the above automobile would be worth $500 — say n yr. after purchase — we should put

$$2000 \ (.7)^n = 500, \qquad \text{or} \quad (.7)^n = .25.$$

Hence $n \log .7 = \log .25$, or by tables: $n \ (.84510 - 1) = .39794 - 1$. Multiplying both sides by -1 gives: $n \ (1 - .84510) = 1 - .39794$, or

$$n \ (.15490) = .60206, \qquad \therefore \ n = \frac{.60206}{.15490} = 3.89, \text{ nearly.}$$

EXERCISES

1. Solve for x:

    (a) $2^x = 7$,   (b) $3^x = 13$,   (c) $4^x = 1000$.

2. In how many years would

    (a) $50,000 amount to $120.000 at 6%, compounded quarterly?

(b) Any sum quadruple itself, at 7%, compounded semi-annually?

(c) $250 amount to $1000, at $4\frac{1}{2}\%$, compounded semi-annually?

(d) $2250 amount to $8000, at 8%, compounded quarterly?

(e) Any sum be doubled, at 5%, compounded semi-annually?

3. An investment of $48,000 depreciates so as to lose in each year $3\frac{1}{2}\%$ of its value at the beginning of that year. What will it be worth after 20 years?

4. The same as Ex. 3 if the rate is 6% and the original value $200,000.

5. A man directed in his will that for 20 years his children should receive half the net income of his estate, the rest to be added to the principal. If the estate was originally worth $300,000 and produced 5.5% net each year, what was its value after 20 years? How soon did the value reach $400,000?

6. If the annual birth-rate of a county were always 28 per thousand inhabitants, and the death-rate 20 per thousand, and if migrations balanced, how long would it take the population to double?

7. The length (g hr.) of one generation in bacterial growth is calculated from $N' = N (2^{\frac{t}{g}})$, where N is the original number observed and N' is the number t hr. later. Transform this equation into $g = t \log 2/(\log N' - \log N)$; and find g if $t = 7$, $N = 3300$, and $N' = 28,000$.

8. If depreciation is figured semi-annually at the nominal annual rate of 20%, what is the actual rate of depreciation per year? What if figured quarterly? (See Remark above; also (III), p. 208.)

Exercises involving Calculus

9 *C.* The force (F lb.) driving a piston varied thus with the distance moved (x in.): $F = 135 \, x^{-\frac{7}{5}}$. Find the work done from $x = 1$ to $x = 9$.

10 *C.* How fast does $A = 200 \, (1 + r)^{40}$ change, per unit increase in r, at $r = .1$?

11 *C.* If $A = 1000 \left(1 + \dfrac{r}{4} \right)^{60}$, approximately how much larger is A at $r = .061$ than at $r = .059$?

§ 155 *S.* **Logarithms of Trigonometric Functions.** In solving a triangle, we can use logarithms to perform the multiplications and divisions. To make this very convenient, there are special tables from which we can read directly the logarithm of each sine, cosine, etc., which is used, *without first* *looking up the function itself.*   Part of a typical page is shown here.

12° — Logs of Trigonometric Functions

′	L sin	d	L tan	cd	L ctn	L cos	d	
0	9.31 788	59	9.32 747	63	0.67 253	9.99 040	2	60
1	9.31 847		9.32 810		0.67 190	9.99 038		59
—								—
18	9.32 844	58	9.33 853	60	0.66 147	9.98 991	2	42
19	9.32 902		9.33 913		0.66 087	9.98 989		41
—								—
59	9.35 154	55	9.36 279	57	0.63 721	9.98 875	3	1
60	9.35 209		9.36 336		0.63 664	9.98 872		0
	L cos	d	L ctn	cd	L tan	L sin	d	′

Pro. Pts.

60	58
2 12	11.6
3 18	17.4
4 24	23.2
5 30	29.0
6 36	34.8
7 42	40.6
8 48	46.4
9 54	52.2

Logs of Trigonometric Functions — 77°

Explanation.   With every logarithm in the table -10 is to be understood, except in the third main column headed *L ctn.*   *E.g.,* the first entry opposite 18′ means that

$$\log \sin 12° \ 18' = 9.32844 - 10 = .32844 - 1.*$$

The labels at the bottom and minutes at the right indicate that this same value $9.32844 - 10$ is log cos 77° 42′.

Interpolations can be made rapidly by using the marginal tables of proportional parts, and the narrow columns marked "*d*" or "*cd*" which give the differences between successive logarithms.

Ex. I.   Find log sin 12° 18′.7.   Between 18′ and 19′, the value increases by 58.   By the marginal table seven tenths of 58 is 40.6. Adding 41 to log sin 12° 18′, we find $9.32885 - 10$.

Ex. II.   Find log ctn 12° 18′.1.   Here $d = 60$, and the value is *decreasing.*   From log ctn 12° 18′ we *subtract* one tenth of 60 (which being obviously 6, is not shown in the marginal table), and get 0.66141.   A common-sense check is that this result lies between the values given for 18′ and 19′, and is much nearer the former.

Ex. III.   Given log tan $A = 0.66130$, clearly $A = 77° 41'$+.   Here

---

* Without these tables we should have to look up sin 12° 18′ (= .21303), and then look up log .21303 (.32844 − 1).   Two interpolations would be necessary in finding log sin 12° 18′.4.

$d = 60$, and the given logarithm exceeds log tan 77° 41′ by 43. The question is, how many tenths of a minute will make a difference of 43 in the logarithm? The marginal table headed 60 says .7 approximately. (More accurately, 43 is .72 × 60.) Thus $A = 77° 41′.7$ approx.

Ex. IV. Given log cos $B = 9.32852 - 10$. Clearly $B = 77° 41′+$. Opposite 41′ we read 9.32902, from which the given logarithm differs by 50. The marginal table headed 58 shows 50 opposite .9. Hence $B = 77° 41′.9$.

N.B. We always work from the value shown opposite the *smaller angle*, whether this value is the smaller logarithm or not — for the simple reason that angles are written in the form 77° 41′.9 rather than 77° 42′ − .1′!

§ 156 S. Logarithmic Solution of Triangles. Typical examples.

Ex. I. Given $b = 750$, $A = 40°$, $C = 80°$, find a, c, B. (Estimate, using a protractor: $a = 550$, $c = 850$, $B = 60°$.)

Sine law:
$$\frac{a}{\sin 40°} = \frac{750}{\sin 60°} = \frac{c}{\sin 80°}.$$

We subtract log sin 60° from log 750; then add log sin 40° or log sin 80°.

No.	Log.		No.	Log.
750	2.87506		frac.	2.93753
sin 60°	9.93753		sin 80°	9.99335
frac.	2.93753		c	2.93088
sin 40°	9.80807			
a	2.74560			

$$a = 556.67$$
$$c = 852.86$$

Ex. II. Given $b = 21.75, c = 24.75$, $A = 40°$; find a, B, C. (Graphical estimate: $B = 60°$, $C = 80°$, $a = 16$.)

Cosine Law: $a^2 = (21.75)^2 + (24.75)^2 - 2(21.75)(24.75) \cos 40°$.

The addition and subtraction can be performed only after going back from logarithms to numbers. Thus the Cosine Law is inconvenient for logarithmic work. Better formulas are derived in §§ 157–159.

Ex. III. Given $a = .8273$, $b = .9999$, $C = 90°$; find B. This is a right triangle and *should be solved as such*:

$$\tan B = \frac{b}{a} = \frac{.9999}{.8273}.$$

Subtract log a from log b, and look up B directly. [*Ans.*, $B = 50° 23′.8$.]

EXERCISES

1. Look up the logarithms of sin 24° 7', sin 58° 12'.4, ctn 86° 33'.7. (Check the first by looking up the sine itself and then its logarithm.)

2. Look up log tan 21° 17'.8; log cos 72° 14' 12''.

3. Look up ∠A if log sin A = 9.76966 − 10; log ctn A = 0.48750.

4. Look up ∠B if log cos B = 8.99046 − 10; log tan B = 1.05000.

5. The hypotenuse and one leg of a right triangle are 84.459 and 60.088 inches. Solve the triangle, finding the third side by means of an angle.

6. In Ex. 5, check in part by finding the third side directly from the given sides.

7. Solve graphically and by tables the triangle in which a = 936.2, B = 73° 24' 42'', C = 56° 38'.

8. What is the elevation angle of the sun when a pole 103.5 ft. high casts a shadow 265.8 ft. long on level ground?

9. Solve each of the following oblique triangles for the missing parts:

	a	b	c	A	B	C
i	290.55			83° 27'	70° 12'	
ii		.017453		62 25	3 42	
iii			35.628	32 38	22 13	
iv		4260.3			68 6.2	38° 37'.5
v	38.194	50.082		25 12.8		
vi	68.208	50.082		25 12.8		

10. Find the radius of the inscribed circle, in a regular octagon whose perimeter is 68.68 ft.

11. If the Earth (E) and Venus (V) were 9.28×10⁷ mi. and 6.69×10⁷ mi. from the Sun (S), respectively, when ∠SEV was 28° 17', how far was V from E? (Get two possible answers.)

12. Like Ex. 11 for Mars (M), 1.402 × 10⁸ mi. from S, if ∠SEM = 148° 17'. (Why is there only one solution here?)

13. From O 3 ft. above the vertex V of an erect cone of radius 10 ft. and height 20 ft. a line inclined 75° is drawn meeting the cone at a point P. Find OP.

14. The gravitational acceleration g (cm./sec.²) is given for any latitude L by the equation g = 977.989 [1 + .0052 (sin L)²]. Find g for the latitude L = 45° 29'.

§ 157 S. Area of a Triangle. To find the area of a triangle we may first solve for some one of its altitudes by dropping a perpendicular, and then multiply by one half the corresponding base.

Or if the three sides happen to be known, we can find the area immediately by using a formula from geometry:*

$$S = \sqrt{h\,(h-a)\,(h-b)\,(h-c)}, \qquad (9)$$

where S denotes the area, and h one half the perimeter, *i.e.*,

$$h = \tfrac{1}{2}\,(a+b+c). \qquad (10)$$

Remark. From (9) we can also derive a formula for the radius r of the inscribed circle. For by Fig. 87:

$$S = \tfrac{1}{2}\,ar + \tfrac{1}{2}\,br + \tfrac{1}{2}\,cr = \tfrac{1}{2}\,(a+b+c)r.$$

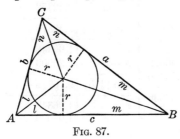

FIG. 87.

That is, $S = hr$, or $r = S/h$. Using here the value of S in (9) above and putting our divisor h also under the radical, we get, on simplifying:

$$r = \sqrt{\frac{(h-a)\,(h-b)\,(h-c)}{h}}. \qquad (11)$$

§ 158 S. Half-Angles. Since the center of the inscribed circle lies on the bisector of each angle, we have from Fig. 87:

$$\tan\,(\tfrac{1}{2}\,A) = \frac{r}{l}, \qquad \tan\,(\tfrac{1}{2}\,B) = \frac{r}{m}, \text{ etc.} \qquad (12)$$

But $l + m + n$ is one half the perimeter, or h.　(§ 157.)

$$\therefore\ l = h - (m+n) = h - a. \qquad (13)$$

Similarly　　$m = h - b$, and　$n = h - c$.

Substituting in (7) above:

$$\tan\,(\tfrac{1}{2}\,A) = \frac{r}{h-a}, \qquad \tan\,(\tfrac{1}{2}\,B) = \frac{r}{h-b}, \text{ etc.} \qquad (14)$$

where r denotes the radical quantity in (11) above.

Formulas (14) can be used instead of the Cosine Law to

* If this formula is unfamiliar, see p. 525, Appendix, for its derivation.

solve a triangle when the three sides are given. They are well suited to logarithmic methods.

Ex. I. Find the angles and area of a triangle in which $a = 275.8$, $b = 361.4$, $c = 446.2$.

The formulas are (14) above, together with

$$h = \frac{a+b+c}{2}, \qquad r = \sqrt{\frac{(h-a)(h-b)(h-c)}{h}}, \qquad S = hr.$$

(What steps are needed to find log r? log tan $\frac{1}{2} A$? log S?)

No.	Log.	No.	Log.	
$h = 541.7$		r	1.96348	
		$h - a$	2.42472	
$h - a = 265.9$	2.42472			$\frac{1}{2} A = 19° 4' 22''$
$h - b = 180.3$	2.25600	tan $(\frac{1}{2} A)$	9.53876 − 10	$A = 38\ \ 8\ \ 44$
$h - c = \ \ 95.5$	1.98000			
		r	1.96348	
(Check*)	6.66072	$h - b$	2.25600	$\frac{1}{2} B = 27\ \ 1\ \ \ 0$
$h = 541.7$	2.73376			$B = 54\ \ 2\ \ \ 0$
	3.92696	tan $(\frac{1}{2} B)$	9.70748 − 10	
r	1.96348	r	1.96348	$\frac{1}{2} C = 43\ 54\ 38$
h	2.73376	$h - c$	1.98000	$C = 87\ 49\ 16$
S	4.69724	tan $(\frac{1}{2} C)$	9.98348 − 10	

Area, $S = 49801$. Final check: $A + B + C = 180°$.

The final check is satisfied closely enough for five-place tables if the discrepancy between 180° and $A + B + C$ is less than $6''$.

To find C from A and B by the relation $A + B + C = 180°$ would be undesirable, as it would leave us no simple check

EXERCISES

1. Find the angles of a triangle in which $a = 61.41$, $b = 132.62$, $c = 124.25$. Find all independently, and check.

2. Derive the formula $tan \frac{1}{2} C = r/(h - c)$.

3. In each of the triangles whose sides are given below find the three angles independently, and check. Also find the area.

	a	b	c		a	b	c
i	389.8	562.6	478.2	iv	.8826	.4151	.6639
ii	504.9	605.5	961.0	v	.00884	.00519	.00945
iii	28.85	19.37	10.23	vi	11640	14962	17538

* A check on $h - a$, $h - b$, and $h - c$, is that their sum, $3\,h - (a + b + c)$, must equal h. (Why?)

4. A ladder 26.65 ft. long is set 11.85 ft. from the foot of a sloping buttress, and reaches 22.48 ft. up its face. Find the inclination of that face.

5. Find the outer radius of the largest circular tank that can be placed on a triangular lot whose sides are 116.8 ft., 172.4 ft. and 181.0 ft. How could the center be located?

6. Like Ex. 5 for a lot with sides 152.5 ft., 167.5 ft., and 170.0 ft.

7. If two forces of 738.6 lb. and 1311.3 lb. have a resultant of 1547.1 lb., what is the angle between them?

8. Like Ex. 7 for 44.25 lb. and 52.75 lb. with a resultant of 63.62 lb.

9. From the Cosine Law get this formula, $1 + \cos A = 2\,h(h - a)/bc$. [Hint: $1 + \cos A$ equals a fraction whose numerator, $b^2 + 2\,bc + c^2 - a^2$, is the difference of two squares.]

10. As in Ex. 9 show that $1 - \cos A = 2\,(h - b)\,(h - c)/bc$.

11. (a) By the formula in Ex. 9 calculate $(1 + \cos A)$ in Ex. I, p. 218, and thence obtain A. (b) Likewise by the formula in Ex. 10.

§ 159 S. Tangent Law. On any side c of a given triangle, as base, construct an isosceles triangle ABF by extending the shorter of the other two sides, say b, and making $\angle ABF = \angle A$. (Fig. 88.)

Then in $\triangle BCF$ two of the angles are $A + B$ and $A - B$, and the opposite sides are, say, x and $x - b$. By § 158,

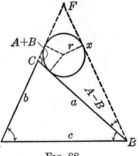

FIG. 88.

$$\tan \tfrac{1}{2}\,(A - B) = \frac{r}{h - (x - b)}, \quad \tan \tfrac{1}{2}\,(A + B) = \frac{r}{h - x}, \quad (15)$$

where r is the radius of the circle inscribed in $\triangle BCF$, and

$$h = \tfrac{1}{2}\,(a + x + \overline{x - b}) = x + \tfrac{1}{2}\,(a - b).$$
$$\therefore\ h - x = \tfrac{1}{2}\,(a - b), \qquad h - (x - b) = \tfrac{1}{2}\,(a + b).$$

From (10), by dividing and substituting these values:

$$\frac{\tan \tfrac{1}{2}\,(A - B)}{\tan \tfrac{1}{2}\,(A + B)} = \frac{h - x}{h - (x - b)} = \frac{a - b}{a + b}. \quad (16)$$

Observe what this means for the original triangle ABC:

The tangent of half the difference of any two angles of a tri-

angle is to the tangent of half the sum as the difference of the opposite sides is to the sum of those sides.*

This "tangent law" is adapted to the logarithmic solution of a triangle, when two sides and their included angle are given, say a, b, and C. For the sum $\frac{1}{2}(A + B)$ is known, and by finding $\frac{1}{2}(A - B)$ from (16), we can combine to obtain A and B separately.†

Ex. I. If $a = 37.485$, $b = 28.392$, $C = 40°$, find A, B, c.

$a - b = 9.093$ $\qquad\qquad A + B = 180° - 40°$
$a + b = 65.877$ $\qquad\qquad \frac{1}{2}(A + B) = 70°$

$$\frac{\tan \frac{1}{2}(A - B)}{\tan 70°} = \frac{9.093}{65.877}.$$

(How would $\tan \frac{1}{2}(A - B)$ be found from this last equation without logarithms? How, therefore, when using logarithms?)

No.	Log.	
9.093	0.95871	$\frac{1}{2}(A + B) = 70°$
tan 70°	0.43893	$\frac{1}{2}(A - B) = 20° \ 46' \ 6''$
Product	1.39764	$A = 90° \ 46' \ 6''$
65.877	1.81873	$B = 49 \ \ 13 \ \ 54$
tan $\frac{1}{2}(A - B)$	9.57891	

To find c use the Sine Law: $\dfrac{c}{\sin C} = \dfrac{b}{\sin B}.$

Remark. Merely adding the three angles would give *no check whatever* upon the logarithmic work done in finding A and B. Suppose, for example, that we had erroneously found in the case above:

$$\frac{1}{2}(A - B) = 10°, \qquad\qquad \therefore \ A = 80°, \ \ B = 60°.$$

Adding: $A + B + C = 180°$, which does not show the error.

Why does this fail to detect the error? [Where did we get the value of $\frac{1}{2}(A - B)$?] What *formula* could be used as a real check upon A and B?

---

* In Fig. 88 we took $\angle A$ as acute. If it happens to be obtuse, simply produce b and BF backwards to meet at some point F'. Two angles in $\triangle BCF'$ will be the *supplements* of $A - B$ and $A + B$. Halving these angles will give the *complements* of $\frac{1}{2}(A - B)$ and $\frac{1}{2}(A + B)$. The proof can then be carried through as above, if we recall that the tangent of the *complement* of $\frac{1}{2}(A - B)$ is ctn $\frac{1}{2}(A - B)$ or $1/\tan \frac{1}{2}(A - B)$; etc.

† The method of § 119, Ex. I, may also be used.

EXERCISES

1. Given $C = 126°\ 44'$, $a = 152.6$, $b = 125.8$.   Find the other parts.

2. Given $a = 31.006$, $b = 58.724$, $C = 58°\ 23'\ 38''$.   Find the other parts.

3. (a), (b). Find the areas of the triangles in Ex. 1, 2.

4. Find the missing parts of the following triangles; and also the areas.

	a	b	c	A	B	C
i	1385.5	2884.3				40° 28'
ii	0.9246	0.6788				98 25.3
iii	82.895		49.497		20° 35'.6	
iv	6.0636		5.3940		122 58	
v		6.4689	3.6261	50° 46'.8		
vi		96.880	114.84	107 58		

5. Two points B, C, located respectively 261.7 ft. and 319.5 ft. from A with $\angle BAC = 92°\ 16'$, are to be connected by a straight underground passage.   Find the length of the latter, and the angle it must make with BA.

6. Like Ex. 5 for a tunnel through a hill if $AB = 1948$ ft., $AC = 2307$ ft., and $\angle BAC = 69°\ 49'$.

7. A sloping mast 38.75 ft. long rests on level ground at A and is supported at the top B by a straight cable 59.25 ft. long anchored on the ground 40.5 ft. behind A.   Find the inclination of the mast.

8. For the mast in Ex. 7 to be inclined $88°\ 30'$ how long a cable would be needed?

9. Find the resultant of two forces of 68.42 lb. and 56.18 lb. whose included angle is $132°\ 44'$.   What angle does it make with the first force?

§ 160. Other Bases.   The logarithms which we have been using are possible because of the fact that every number is some power of 10.   But it is equally true that every positive number is some power of 2, or of 7, or of any other positive number, except 1.   Hence it is possible to have other systems of logarithms, based upon powers of 2, or 7, etc.

For instance, if

$$5 = 2^{2.32193},$$

the exponent 2.32193 is called "the logarithm of 5 to the base **2**," written $\log_2 5$.

And in general, the logarithm of any number to any base is *the exponent of the power to which the base must be raised to produce the number.*

The "common logarithms," to the base 10, which we have been using, are by far the best for most numerical calculations — because of the fact that moving a decimal point in a number merely adds some integer to the characteristic. Only one other base is very generally used for any purpose; this will be discussed in § 171. But it is well to be familiar with the following general principles.

No matter what base B we may be using:

$$\log 1 = 0, \quad \text{and} \quad \log B = 1. \tag{17}$$

For $\qquad\qquad 1 = B^0, \quad \text{and} \qquad B = B^1.$

The logarithm of any positive number to any base is easily found with the help of common logarithms. For instance, suppose we want $\log_2 25$. We simply let this equal x, and write the equivalent exponential equation:

$$\log_2 25 = x, \qquad\qquad 25 = 2^x.$$

Solving the latter equation as in § 153, we find $x = 4.6439$.

§ 161 S. Slide Rule. Logarithmic calculations can be made mechanically by means of a "slide rule." This has a fixed scale F and a sliding scale S (roughly illustrated in Fig. 89), each so ruled that the distance from 1 to any other number x is equal to $\log x$.

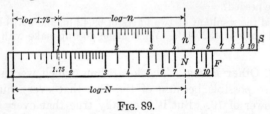

Fig. 89.

When S is moved over to the position shown, its 1 being opposite 1.75 on F, every number (n) on S will have moved a distance equal to $\log 1.75$ and hence will be opposite some number N on F whose logarithm is the sum of $\log 1.75$ and $\log n$. This number N must be the product of 1.75 and n.

Thus to multiply any number n by 1.75, we merely set the slide as in Fig. 89 and then read off the number on F opposite n. (Observe how this works for the simple product $2 \times 1.75 = 3.5$.)

Similarly for other multiplications: moving S adds logarithms mechanically. Divisions may also be performed, square roots extracted, etc. Results accurate to two or three places can be obtained very fast. Full directions are given in handbooks supplied with the rule.

§ 162 S. Nomographic or Alignment Charts. In recent years much use has been made of "nomograms" — *i.e.*, charts of lines ruled with number scales in such a way that various calculations can be made by merely laying a straight-edge across the scales.

Fig. 90 illustrates this. The cost of an automobile tire per mile traveled can be read off from scale B by laying a ruler or stretching a thread across from the original cost of the tire on scale A to the number of miles realized, as shown on scale C.

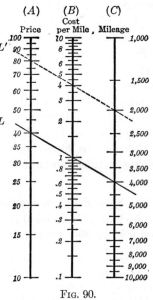

Fig. 90.

Explanation. The scales here are logarithmic, the unit on B being half as long as on A or C. Any line L through 1 on B passes through equal numbers on A and C — as it obviously should.

Raising L a distance equal to log 2 on A would bring it to a parallel position L', passing through a number on A twice as large as formerly — just as with a slide rule. On C, L' will pass through a number half the former value. Hence the ratio A/C will be four times as great as for line L — *i.e.*, it equals 4. But the distance L' was raised, viz. log 2 on scale A equals log 4 on scale B; hence L' will cross B at 4, as it should to give the value of A/C.

But every line which could be laid across the scales would be some line L, raised or lowered; and by a similar argument must cross B at the right point.

§ 163. Summary of Chapter VI. In § 140 we have already summarized the definition and basic properties of common logarithms. We have since observed that any positive num-

ber (except 1) could serve as the base of a system of logarithms.

Logarithms follow the laws of exponents, and are therefore
specially adapted to the calculation of products, quotients,
powers, roots, and unknown exponents. They are continually
used in scientific work of many kinds, as is also their mechanical substitute, the slide rule.

Sums and differences can sometimes be factored into products.
Otherwise we must go from logarithms back to numbers before
adding or subtracting. For this reason, the Cosine Law is
ill-adapted to the solution of triangles where large numbers
are involved. It may then be replaced by the Half-Angle
Formulas or the Law of Tangents.

Calculations involving negative numbers can be made by
taking separate account of the combined effect of the minus
signs.

The tremendous power of the logarithmic method is hard to realize.
Notice how easily we could compute a root such as $\sqrt[2011]{3.1416 \times 10^{817}}$,
and how fearfully complicated such a calculation would be by pure
arithmetic.

Logarithms were invented by Lord Napier, a Scotchman, who
published the first tables in 1614. These were not to the base 10, but
to a base closely related to the one discussed later in § 171.

Our more convenient tables, to the base 10, were calculated soon
afterward by Henry Briggs, an Englishman, and Adrian Vlacq, a
Hollander, who unselfishly gave up several years to the tedious work.

EXERCISES

1. Find the logarithm of 5 to the base 2.

2. Similarly find (a) $\log_3 25$; (b) $\log_{25} 3$; (c) $\log_8 \frac{1}{2}$.

3. Make a nomogram adapted to the relation $V = x^2 y$, by marking
off a certain suitable scale on each of three parallel, equally separated
lines. (Hint: Through the point $x = 1$ on the middle line, first locate
corresponding points for V and y, choosing the scale advisedly.)

4. Show that the nomogram in Ex. 3 could be used also for the
formula $F = m/x^2$. Also for $z = \sqrt{V/u}$.

5. Calculate correct to five significant figures:

(a) $\sqrt{\dfrac{.058074}{9.6236}}$,

(b) $\dfrac{84.563}{.09865\,(.5675)\,(5.7603)}$,

(c) $\sqrt{\dfrac{.68753\,(40.008)}{.000000239}}$,

(d) $\sqrt[3]{\dfrac{704.03\,(-.05703)}{.049523\,(-670.9)^2}}$,

(e) $\sqrt{(85.268)^2 - (60.074)^2}$,

(f) $\sqrt[8]{\dfrac{4.20 \times \sqrt[5]{8.3725}}{(.620)^2 \times \sqrt{228.49}}}$,

(g) $\dfrac{(.3796)^{20} \times (-58.279)^5}{\sqrt[6]{.0001} \times (.067527)^2}$

(h) $\left(\dfrac{-53854}{6.407}\right)^{\frac{3}{7}} \times (.2)^{11}$,

(i) $\dfrac{3\,\sqrt[3]{.7}\,\sqrt[4]{.003}\,\sqrt[5]{553.7}}{92\,(.8)^5\,(4.5673)}$,

(j) $\dfrac{24372\,(.89576)^6\,\sqrt[3]{.0945}}{3.8762 \times \sqrt{.0074635}}$,

(k) $\left(\dfrac{\sqrt{6}}{.807} - \sqrt[3]{2.08}\right)^{\frac{5}{2}}$,

(l) $\sqrt{59000\,\pi + (596)^2}$.

6. Find the amount of $3800 after 30 yr. with interest at 6%, compounded quarterly.

7. What principal will yield $25000 in 25 years, if interest is at 5%, compounded semi-annually?

8. At what rate of interest, compounded annually, will $16250 yield $57500 in 35 years?

9. In how many years will $7500 amount to $27500 if interest is at 4%, compounded quarterly?

10. A wheel originally turning 800 degrees per sec. lost in each second 23.6% of its speed at the beginning of that sec. What was its rotary speed after 10 sec.?

11. The temperature of water in a jar was originally 70° higher than that of the air; 20 min. later, only 60° higher. If the temperature difference decreased by a fixed percentage in each minute, what was it after 15 min. more?

12. A house originally costing $8000 depreciates annually by 8% of its current value. It yields a net annual income of $600 above taxes and repairs. Ignoring interest find the combined value of the house and accumulated income, at the end of 5 yr.; 10 yr.; 15 yr.

13. From the following formula for the quantity of water (Q cu. ft./sec.) flowing over a triangular notch, find Q if $A = 62°$, $g = 32.2$, and $H = 1.08$: $Q = \tfrac{8}{15}\tan\dfrac{A}{2}\sqrt{2g}\,H^{\frac{5}{2}}$.

Solve the following by trigonometry, and check by drawing to scale and measuring the required distances or angles.

14. A flag pole is broken by the wind. Its top strikes the level ground 38.25 ft. from the foot of the pole, and makes an angle of 42° 39′ with the ground. Find the original height.

15. Two lighthouses A and B are 25.37 mi. apart. The direction of A from B is 39° 17' north of west. Observed from a ship, A is 62° 24' north of west, and B is 73° 19' north of east. How far is the ship from each lighthouse?

16. A triangular lot has an area of 538.65 sq. yd., and two of its sides are 57.25 yd. and 24.82 yd. Find its perimeter. (Two solutions.)

17. A circular track $4\frac{1}{2}$ yd. wide is to be laid out in a triangular field whose sides are 248.2 yd., 325.3 yd., and 401.6 yd. If made as large as possible, how much will the length exceed or fall short of 440 yd., the length being measured on the track $\frac{1}{2}$ yd. from the inner edge?

18. Find the area of a parallelogram if two adjacent sides are 93.42 cm. and 106.56 cm., and include an angle of 107° 19'.

19. Two buoys A and B in a lake are observed from C and D on shore: $CD = 648.3$ ft., $\angle ACD = 78° 29'$, $\angle BCD = 61° 37'$, $\angle BDC = 91° 46'$, $\angle ADC = 63° 12'$. How far apart are the buoys?

§ 164. Looking Back.

Let us now recall in brief outline the work of the course up to this point.

We began by noting that a fundamental problem of science, whether in studying the physical world or the social and economic world, is to determine the relations between varying quantities — in other words, to ascertain *precisely how any one quantity will vary with any other on which it depends.* And our aim all along has been to find methods of dealing with this problem — how to calculate rates of increase, maximum and minimum values, etc. Incidentally we have tried to get some idea of how these methods are used in science and in the practical affairs of daily life.

We first saw that approximate results can be obtained by graphical methods, and that we can always fall back upon those methods as a last resort.

Upon attempting to calculate instantaneous rates exactly, we were led to differentiation. To reverse the rate-problem and calculate the size of a growing quantity, we had to take up integration. Our differentiations and integrations were confined to Power Functions, such as $y = x^n$ or $y = u^n$.

Various integrations and numerical calculations which we could not carry out showed the necessity of becoming familiar with further types of functions, especially trigonometric functions and logarithms.

We have now done this, in a measure, and are ready to proceed with the main problem and make a further study of varying quantities. A new type of function will be required to represent the quantities in question — a function closely related to logarithms.

MISCELLANEOUS AND COMBINATION PROBLEMS

Chapters I-VI

1. A concrete pedestal has horizontal sectional areas (A sq. ft.) which vary with the distance (x ft.) above the ground, as in Table I. Find the rate at which A changes with x at $x = 6.4$; also, the volume from $x = 5$ to $x = 13$.

2. Given a table showing the temperature T at two-hour intervals during a day, how could you estimate closely the average temperature for the whole 24-hr. period?

TABLE I

x	A
5	96
7	86
9	64
11	42
13	32

3. Solve $2 x^2 - 3 x - 7 = 0$ graphically. Also, find one root by Proportional Parts; and account for any discrepancy. Check by solving exactly.

4. If y varies inversely as $\sqrt{x}$ and $y = 15$ when $x = 4$, find the formula. Express it in the form of the Power Law.

5. State accurately what is meant by saying: "This spiral bends faster and faster; just at this point it is bending at the rate of exactly 3° per inch."

6. State clearly what is meant by the weight of a cubic foot of air "at any height h ft." Evidently a cubic foot cannot all be at the same height.

7. Can you see any definite interpretation that can be given to this statement: "The amount of $100 with 10% interest for 10 years, compounded *continuously*, would be $271.83"? How could this amount be verified approximately?

8. Explain graphically how it would be possible for $f'(x)$ to have a large value (say 1000) at some point, even if $f(x)$ was everywhere small (say never more than .2 nor less than zero).

9. Differentiate by rule:

(a) $y = \frac{1}{4} x^6 + .3 x^2 (10 x - 4) + 9 x - 5 \sqrt{x} + \sqrt{75}$,

(b) $y = 30 - \dfrac{5}{x} + \dfrac{8}{\sqrt{x^3}}$,   (c) $y = (x^5 + 9)^{20}$,

$$(d) \quad y = \frac{\sqrt{16 - x^2}}{7} + \frac{30 - x}{3}, \qquad\qquad (e) \quad y = \frac{12}{5 (4 - x^3)^2}.$$

10. The horsepower transmitted by a certain machine belt varies thus with the speed: $H = .48 V - .000026 V^3$. Find the best speed.

11. Find the least possible weight for a cylindrical boiler which is to contain 1465 cu. ft., figuring 11.8 lb. per sq. ft. of surface.

12. A cylindrical tank is to contain 10,000 cu. yd. The bottom including foundations will cost $2 per sq. yd., the sides $1 per sq. yd., and there is to be a hemispherical roof costing $1 per sq. yd. Find the least possible cost.

13. The volume of a balloon (V cu. ft.) t hours after sunrise was $V = \dfrac{\pi}{3} \, (100{,}000 + 160 \, t^3 - 10 \, t^4)$. When was V increasing most rapidly? Approximately how much did V change from $t = 3.99$ to $t = 4.01$?

14. If the volume of a spherical balloon varies thus with the absolute temperature: $V = 40{,}000 \, T^{.8}$, and if T is rising at the rate of $2°$ per min., how fast is V increasing when $T = 290$? Also, how fast is the radius increasing?

15. Sand, falling at the rate of 3 cu. ft. per min., forms a conical pile whose vertex angle is constantly $142°$. How fast is the base radius changing at the instant when the radius is 10 ft.?

16. Integrate, and check your result by differentiation:

$$\left(x^5 - 9 \, x^3 + \frac{x^2}{2} + \frac{13 \, x}{4} - \sqrt{x} - 11 + \frac{4}{x^2} - \frac{5}{x^3} \right) dx.$$

17. Along a certain curve the ordinate y varies as the square of the abscissa x, and is 20 when $x = 10$. Calculate the area under the curve from $x = 1$ to $x = 6$; also find the slope at $x = 5$.

18. The frequency of any event (f times per hr.) and the total number of occurrences N have the relation: $dN/dt = f$. If we had a graph exhibiting f as a function of t, what would represent N? (Why?)

19. A solid is hollowed out in the middle, so that every horizontal cross-section is a ring between two concentric circles, whose radii (r in. and R in.) vary thus with the distance (x in.) below the highest point: $r = \sqrt{8 \, x - x^2}$ and $R = \sqrt{12 \, x - x^2}$. Calculate the volume, from $x = 0$ to $x = 4$.

20. In Ex. 19, if the material weighs w lb. per cu. in., and w varies with x (say $w = .08 \, x$), devise some method for calculating exactly the total weight of the solid from $x = 0$ to $x = 4$.

21. Find the force down to a depth of 20 ft. against a vertical dam whose width varies thus: $w = 500 - x^2$.

22. A certain grade of oil exerts against the wall of its container a pressure of 50 x lb. per sq. ft., at a depth of x ft. below the surface. (*A*) Explain precisely what this statement means, in view of the fact that no square foot of wall could be at any one depth x ft. below the surface. (*B*) Express by an integral the total force exerted by the oil against the circular wall of a cylindrical tank of radius 20 ft., down to any depth x ft.

23. An open reservoir has the shape of a hemisphere of radius 30 ft. How much water will it contain when the water is 20 ft. deep in the middle?

24. The electromotive force (E volts) in a thermoelectric circuit increases with the temperature ($T°$) of the hot junction at the rate $R = .9 + .013\, T$. If $E = 1250$ when $T = 400$, what should it be when $T = 500$?

25. Starting with an initial velocity of 100 ft. per sec., a point moves along a straight line; its acceleration (a ft./sec.^{2}) after t sec. varying as in Table II. Discover the formula for the acceleration. Then find the distance traveled at any time.

TABLE II

t	a
0	3.1
1.5	4.1
2.7	4.9
3.9	5.7
6.0	7.1

26. A column of air (x in. long) expanded in a cylinder, under a force F lb. which varied as in Table III. Find graphically the rate at which F was changing when $x = 20$; and the work done while x changed from 10 to 24.

27. The formula for Table III is $F = 9000/x^{1.41}$. Calculate to five figures the rate and work in Ex. 26.

TABLE III

x	F
8	479.6
12	270.8
16	180.5
20	131.8
24	101.9

28. The force (F lb.) required to stretch a certain wire x inches varied as in Table IV. (*a*) Find graphically the total work done in stretching the wire 1 inch. (*b*) Obtain a formula for F in terms of x, and from this calculate the same work exactly.

29. The speed (v ft. per min.) of a moving object t min. after starting was $v = 10\, t^3 (12 - t)$. Find the distance traveled in the first 15 min. Also find when the speed was increasing most rapidly, and the maximum speed attained.

30. Plot a graph showing how the speed v in Ex. 29 varied from $t = 0$ to $t = 12$; and check the several answers.

TABLE IV

x	F
.2	26
.5	65
.7	91
.8	104
1.0	130

31. Water is poured from a cylindrical cup 4 in. in diameter until the surface of the liquid bisects the bottom of the cup, the bottom being then inclined 58°. Find the

volume of water remaining and the area of the surface of water exposed to the air.

32. A ball was thrown straight up from the ground with an initial
speed of 64 ft./sec.   Find its height and speed 3 sec. later.

33. A stone was thrown straight down with an initial speed of
40 ft. per sec. from a balloon 2750 ft. high at the instant when an
auto running 100 ft. per sec. passed straight under it.   (a) Find the
distance of the auto from the stone 10 sec. later.   (b) How fast was
that distance then increasing?   (c) When was the stone nearest to
the auto?

34. If the slope of a line 68 in. long is $\frac{15}{8}$, find its inclination and its
exact horizontal and vertical projections.

35. Calculate to five significant figures:

(a) $\sqrt{96.49^2 - 31.38^2}$;   (b) $\left(\dfrac{\sqrt{62}}{8.5} + \sqrt[3]{.2}\right)^{\frac{3}{2}}$;   (c) $\sqrt[5]{\dfrac{-58.896\sqrt{.088}}{(-261.29)^2}}$.

36. Find the polar coordinates of the point $(-43.25, 68.92)$, θ being
measured from the positive X-axis.

37. Find the largest angle of a triangle whose sides are 9, 11, 17.

38. A monument is 142 ft. high, and stands at the top of a hill.
At a point 294 ft. down the hill the monument subtends an angle
of 12° 30'.   Find the distance from this point to the top of the monument.

39. From one bank of a river the angle of elevation of a tree on
the other bank directly opposite is 22° 42'.   From a point 227.6 ft.
farther away horizontally in a direct line its angle of elevation is
18° 30'.   Find the width of the river.

40. The sides of a triangle are 296.89, 381.46, and 388.26.   Find the
length of the perpendicular from the largest angle upon the opposite side.

41. A cliff rises vertically 350.12 ft. above sea-level.   From its
top the angles of depression of two ships A and B are 18° 24' and
16° 18'.   At the bottom of the cliff the angle subtended by AB is
128° 36'.   How far apart are the ships?

42. In Ex. 45 C, p. 186, change the 47 to 30, and solve.

43. Find the pressure of water against a vertical dam, trapezoidal
in shape, which is 50 ft. wide at the bottom (12 ft. below the surface)
and whose sides are inclined 38°.   Also state clearly how you could
proceed to find the depth below which half of all this pressure is sus-
tained.

44. Find the inclination of the curve $y = 3x^3 - x^4$ at the point
where the slope is increasing most rapidly.   Also state just what
steps would be needed in finding where the slope of this curve
equals -20.

45. An airplane leaves the ground with an initial speed of 80 ft./sec., rising at a constant angle of 7°. If its acceleration after t sec. is $12 - .6\,t$, how far will it be after 10 sec. from a point on the ground 800 ft. straight behind the starting point?

46. A block of ice is drawn up an incline whose grade is 36% by means of a rope passed over a pulley 10 ft. directly above the top of the incline. If the block is to move at the rate of 3 ft./sec., how fast must the rope be drawn in when the block is 20 ft. down the incline?

47. A beam 30 ft. long and weighing 20 lb./ft. rests on piers at its ends A and B. A weight $W = 4000$ lb. moves from A to B at the rate of 2 ft./sec. Find the supporting force F at B when W has gone x ft. How fast is F increasing?

48. A safety-valve stopper is held down by a level rod x in. long, weighing .1382 lb. per in., and pivoted at one end 5 in. from the valve. What force F lb. would blow the stopper out, for any x? About how much larger is F if $x = 20.005$ than if $x = 19.991$?

49. If \$1 had been at 6% interest, compounded annually, from the beginning of the Christian era (say 1935 years), how large a gold ball would be required to pay the amount due? Give the radius in miles. (Regard 1 cu. ft. of gold as worth \$614,000 in 1935.)

50. A nebula had a temperature $T = 7850$ but cooled so that T decreased in each million-year period about one-fourth its value at the beginning of the period. Find the approximate T after 10,000,000 yr.

51. A man bought a piece of property for \$1000, and another piece twenty years later for \$2000. He used the annual income to pay taxes and make improvements; and ten years after the second purchase sold both pieces for \$18,000. To what rate of interest, compounded annually, was this investment equivalent?

52. In how many years would \$1000 with 12% interest, compounded quarterly, amount to the same as \$2000 with 6% interest, compounded semi-annually, plus \$4000 with 3% compounded annually, during the same length of time?

53. Approximately what change in the amount of \$2000 after 27 yr. at any rate r, compounded semi-annually, would result from increasing r from .059 to .061?

54. The base of a solid is a circle of radius 30 in., and every vertical section perpendicular to one diameter is an isosceles triangle whose base angles are 75°. Find the volume.

55. Find the total load on a circular floor of radius 20 ft., if the loading (y lb. per sq./ft.) varies thus with the distance (x ft.) from the center: $y = 100 + 6\,x$.

56. In Fig. 90, p. 223, suppose the (B) scale were equal to the

232   MISCELLANEOUS PROBLEMS

others but increased downward, with its number 50 where 1 now
stands. Show that the new nomogram could
be used for the formula $B = 5\sqrt{C/A}$, if we
employ the printed values of C and A.

57. Like Ex. 56, with the new B-scale increasing upward, for the formula $B = 500\sqrt{A/C}$.

58. The point of maximum stability in
operating a vacuum tube was located by
drawing a tangent from the origin to the
graph of Table V. Find E and I at the point
of tangency.

TABLE V		TABLE VI	
E	I	t	N
0	0	0	0
20	0.5	2	18
40	1.5	4	48
60	3.9	6	83
70	5.6	8	114
80	6.5	10	130
90	6.8	12	138

59. The number of bacteria (N million) that had died in t hr. after
exposure to a disinfectant is shown in Table VI. Plot the graph, also
the derived curve showing the death rate per hour. Measure areas
under the latter and check against the given table.

CHAPTER VII

EXPONENTIAL AND LOGARITHMIC FUNCTIONS

CONSTANT PERCENTAGE RATES OF GROWTH

§ 165. Growing Like Compound Interest. Many quantities in nature grow in the same way as a sum of money at compound interest — or rather, as such a sum would grow, if the interest were compounded *exceedingly often* or *continuously.*

That is to say: Money at interest grows faster and faster. The *percentage rate* remains constant, as 6%, or $3\frac{1}{2}$%, etc., but the *total rate* of growth (or number of dollars per year) increases — being proportional to the amount accumulated at the beginning of the interest-period in question.

Thus, if we compound annually at 40%, the rate of growth at any instant (as at P in Fig. 91) will be 40% of the value at the beginning of the year. If we compound semi-annually, the rate will be 40% of the value at the beginning of the half-year in which P lies. And so on.

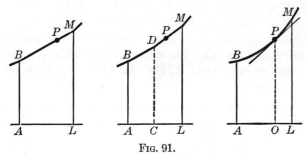

FIG. 91.

In each case AL represents 1 yr.

If the interest were compounded exceedingly often, say a trillion or more times a year, the periods would be so short that the rate at any instant would be practically *proportional to the amount at that same instant.* Just so for many quantities in nature: the larger they become, the faster they increase — *proportionately* — until stopped by modified physical conditions.

Many other quantities *decrease* in a similar way — like an investment depreciating at a constant percentage rate, figured almost continuously.

§ 166. Effect of Compounding Continuously.

To arrive at a formula for quantities of the kind just mentioned, let us see how the value of an investment will be affected if the interest is compounded exceedingly often.

Compounding k times a year, the amount is (by § 151):

$$A = P\left(1 + \frac{r}{k}\right)^{kn}. \tag{1}$$

How will this be affected if k is indefinitely increased?

Consider first a special case: The amount on $1 after 1 year with interest at 100%. Then $P = 1$, $n = 1$, $r = 1$. and

$$A = \left(1 + \frac{1}{k}\right)^{k}. \tag{2}$$

Taking successively $k = 1$, $k = 10$, $k = 100$, etc., we find the values of A shown in the following table. (Eight-place logarithms are needed to get the last two values accurately.)

Notice that, although we are increasing k faster and faster, A is increasing less and less rapidly, apparently *approaching some limiting value* near 2.718. In higher analysis this is definitely proved.

k	A	k	A
1	2	1000	2.717
10	2.594	10,000	2.718
100	2.704		

Remark. This limiting value of A is called the result of compounding *continuously*. The original dollar gains about $1.718 during the year, or 171.8%. Hence compounding continuously at 100% is about equivalent to compounding annually at 171.8%.

§ 167. The Number *e*. The limit approached by the quantity $(1 + 1/k)^k$ in (2) above, as k increases indefinitely (written $k \to \infty$), is denoted by e:

$$e = \operatorname*{L}_{k \to \infty} \left(1 + \frac{1}{k}\right)^k. \tag{3}$$

This number is very important in what follows. Approximately:

$$e = 2.7183, \qquad \log e = .43429.$$

Remark. $1 with 100% interest, compounded continuously for one year, would amount to precisely e dollars.

§ 168. General Formula. Now consider the effect of compounding interest continuously for any number of years at any rate.

Returning to the standard formula

$$A = P\left(1 + \frac{r}{k}\right)^{kn}, \tag{4}$$

we are to let $k \to \infty$ without giving special values to P, r, and n. The problem is, however, reducible to the special case above. Denoting the reciprocal of the fraction r/k by z, we may write:

$$\frac{r}{k} = \frac{1}{z}, \qquad k = zr.$$

$$\therefore \qquad A = P\left(1 + \frac{1}{z}\right)^{zrn} = P\left[\left(1 + \frac{1}{z}\right)^{z}\right]^{rn} \tag{5}$$

Now, as k increases without limit, so must z. Hence the bracketed quantity in (5) varies in the same way as the k-quantity in (3), approaching e. Thus the limiting value of A in (5) is

$$A = Pe^{rn}. \tag{6}$$

This is the amount of any principal P after n years with interest *compounded continuously* at any annual rate r.[*]

Similarly, if a physical quantity Q grows at a constant per-

---

[*] Since formula (4) is strictly correct at the ends of all interest periods, (6) is correct at all times, and not merely for integral values of n.

centage rate r (per year, hour, or other unit of time), its value after t units must be

$$Q = Pe^{rt}. \tag{7}$$

Ex. I. As the number of bacteria in a culture increased, the instantaneous rate of growth (per hr.) was always 6% of the number then present. If the original number was 1000, how many were there after t hr.?

By (7), $\qquad N = 1000\, e^{.06t}.$

The value of N at any time is easily calculated by logarithms, since $\log N = \log 1000 + .06\, t \log e$, and $\log e = .43429$.

Ex. II. What rate of interest, compounded annually, will yield the same amount as 6% interest compounded continuously?

$$P(1+r)^n = Pe^{.06n}$$
$$\therefore\ 1 + r = e^{.06}$$

By logarithms this gives $1 + r = 1.0618$; whence $r = 6.18\%$.

Remark. Similarly in Ex. I, the number of bacteria is multiplied by $e^{.06}$ or 1.0618, in each hour. Thus the actual gain is 6.18% of the number at the beginning of the hour, though the instantaneous rate of gain is but 6% of the growing number then present.

Likewise, in (7), r always denotes the *instantaneous* percentage rate, not the average percentage rate during a whole unit. And, in (6), r is the *nominal* rate used in compounding continuously, not the effective rate actually realized.

§ 169. Depreciation. For negative values of r, formula (4) above represents a depreciating investment. When r is negative, so is z in (5). But by Ex. 13 below, the quantity $\left(1 + \dfrac{1}{z}\right)^z$ still approaches e if $k \to \infty$.

Hence formula (6) gives the value of an investment which depreciates at the nominal percentage rate r, *figured continuously*. If the rate is 8%, merely put $r = -.08$, getting $A = Pe^{-.08n}$.

The corresponding formula (7) evidently holds for any physical quantity Q which decreases in an analogous manner.

EXERCISES

1. (a) Express the amount of $2500 after t years with interest at 4%, compounded continuously. How much is this after ten years? (b) What rate compounded annually would yield the same amount? (c) When would the amount be $6000?

2. If the population of a state increases by 5% each year and is now 1,000,000, write a formula for the population t years hence. To what rate, figured continuously, would this be equivalent?

3. An estate originally worth $250,000 depreciated so that the instantaneous rate was continually 3% of the current value. What was its value after t yr.? After 100 yr.? What percentage was actually lost in any year?

4. In 1870 the population of a certain city (Portland, Ore.) was 8300, and this grew until 1910 almost like an investment with interest at 8%, compounded continuously. Write a formula for the population at any time (t years after 1870), on this basis. If the formula had remained valid, what would the 1930 population have been?

5. The number of bacteria N in a culture increased at an instantaneous rate (per hour) continually equal to 25% of N. How many were there at any time from an original 1000? How many after 10 hours? When had the original number doubled?

6. The speed (V) of a chemical reaction increases with the temperature (T) at an instantaneous rate constantly equal to 7% of V. If $V = 20$ when $T = 0$, write a formula for V at any temperature. Find T for which $V = 60$. What percentage does V actually gain in a 1° rise in T?

7. Radium decomposes at a rate (per century) which at every instant equals 3.8% of the quantity Q remaining. How much will be left after 5000 years from a present quantity of 200 mg.?

8. The speed (V) of a rotating wheel after the power was cut off decreased at a rate (per sec.) which at every instant was 15% of V itself. If V was originally 1000, what was its value after 10 sec.? When was the speed reduced to one tenth its original value?

9. As the temperature ($T°$) rises, the viscosity V of olive oil decreases at an instantaneous rate per degree which is continually 2.3% of V. At $T = 0$, $V = 3.265$. Find V at $T = 40$.

10. The quantity (Q gm.) of sugar remaining from an original 1000 gm., after being subjected to an acid for t hr., decreased at an instantaneous rate always 8.4% of Q. Find Q at $t = 25$.

11. Express as powers of 10: e, e^2, $e^{.4}$, $e^{.5t}$.

12. Calculate the value of the quantity $(1 + 1/z)^z$ for $z = 1$, 10, 100, 1000, 10000 — using 7 or 8 place tables if accessible.

13. The same as Ex. 12 for $z = -10, -100, -1000, -10000$.

§ 170. Equivalent Forms. Any such quantity as $Q = Pe^{.02t}$ can be expressed also as a power of 10. For $e = 10^{.43429}$ (§ 167);

$$\therefore \ Q = Pe^{.02t} = P \ (10^{.43429})^{.02t} = P \ 10^{.0086858t}.$$

That is, the forms $e^{.02t}$ and $10^{.0086858t}$ are equivalent. But the 2% rate which is clearly exhibited in the e form is entirely hidden in the 10 form. Thus the e form is the more natural, if we wish to recognize the percentage rate readily.

§ 171. Natural Logarithms. Common logarithms are based upon the fact that every positive number is some power of 10. (§ 135.) But it is equally true that every such number is some power of e. For instance

$$5 = e^{1.6094}.$$

We call this exponent 1.6094 the logarithm of 5 "to the base e." This is often written $\log_e 5$, when necessary to distinguish it from the common logarithm or $\log_{10} 5$. (Cf. § 160.)

Logarithms to the base e, being exponents, follow the same four rules of combination as logarithms to the base 10. (§ 144.) Thus, the logarithm of a product equals the sum of the logarithms of the factors; etc.

The base e is naturally suited to calculations concerning the continuous compounding of interest.

E.g., in calculating q from $q = 30\,e^{.02t}$ we should have, for any base:

$$\log q = \log 30 + .02\,t \log e.$$

If the base is 10, $\log e = .43429$; but if the base is e, $\log e = 1$ simply.

Similarly to find t if q were given, the base e would be the simpler.

The chief reason for introducing the base e, and regarding it as the "natural base," will, however, appear later.

N.B. Another notation for a logarithm to the base e, or "natural logarithm" is *ln*. Thus ln 5 means the same as $\log_e 5$.

§ 172. Use of Table. In the Appendix (pp. 536–37) there is a table of natural or "Napierian" logarithms, referred to the base e or $2.71828\cdots$. A few lines are reproduced here.

N		0	1	2	3	4	5	6	7	8	9
5.0	1.6	094	114	134	154	174	194	214	233	253	273
5.1		292	312	332	351	371	390	409	429	448	467
—	—	—	—	—	—	—	—	—	—	—	—
10.0	2.3	026	036	046	056	066	076	086	096	106	115

This means, for example:

$$\log 5.14 = 1.6371; \qquad \therefore\ 5.14 = e^{1.6371}.$$
$$\log 10 = 2.3026; \qquad \therefore\ 10 = e^{2.3026}$$

To find the logarithm of a number which lies beyond the limits of the table, we use the idea of Scientific Notation.

For instance, $514 = 5.14 \times 10^2$.

Hence, to get log 514, we would look up log 5.14 and add twice log 10:

$$\log 514 = 1.6371 + 4.6052 = 6.2423.$$

We do this, in fact, with the base 10; but then twice log 10 is simply 2.

Conversely, if given log $N = 6.2423$, we would subtract log 10 twice, or 2 log 10, getting down to 1.6371. Then N must be the number which corresponds to 1.6371, multiplied by 10^2: $\qquad N = 5.14 \times 10^2 = 514.$

Remark. In solving an equation like $749 = 135\,e^{.06t}$ for t, it would simplify matters to divide through by 100, and have only the small numbers 7.49 and 1.35 to deal with. The division would have no effect on the value of t.

EXERCISES

1. Look up the natural logarithms of:

$\qquad$ 5.62 $\qquad$ 88.7, $\qquad$ 925, $\qquad$ 309000, $\qquad$ .0593, $\qquad$ .00076.

Check each roughly by inspection, thinking of e as nearly 3.

2. The same as Ex. 1, interpolating for each given fourth figure:

$\qquad$ (*a*) 3.286, $\qquad\qquad$ (*b*) 7142, $\qquad\qquad$ (*c*) .006483.

3. Look up the numbers (to 3 figures) whose natural logarithms are:

$\qquad$ 2.0057, $\qquad$ 5.4188, $\qquad$ 9.4763, $\qquad$ 9.3316 − 10. $\qquad$ 6.9095 − 10.

4. The same as Ex. 3, interpolating to get a fourth figure, for

$\qquad$ (*a*) 0.4675, $\qquad\qquad$ (*b*) 4.6936, $\qquad\qquad$ (*c*) 12.6129,

$\qquad$ (*d*) 8.4167 − 10, $\qquad$ (*e*) 4.1275 − 10, $\qquad$ (*f*) 7.6181 − 10.

5. Calculate the following, using natural logarithms:

$\qquad$ (*a*) $A = 64\,e^{-2.6751}$, $\qquad$ (*b*) $y = 9200\,e^{1.3165}$, $\qquad$ (*c*) $Q = .35\,e^{2.7168}$.

6. Solve for the unknown n or r, after making any possible preliminary simplifications:

$\qquad$ (*a*) $879 = 265\,e^{20r}$, $\qquad$ (*b*) $12.8 = 85\,e^{-10r}$, $\qquad$ (*c*) $.0168 = .095\,e^{-.05n}$.

7. The tension (T lb.) in a belt increased with the distance (x ft.) along a pulley at an instantaneous rate always 4.2% of T. At $x = 0$, $T = 40.5$. Find x where $T = 52.2$.

8. Penetrating x ft. below the surface of a lake, daylight loses its brightness y at a rate (per foot) instantaneously equal to 0.86% of y. At what x will y be one-tenth of the original surface brightness?

9. Express as powers of e: 2^x, $(1.06)^{4n}$, $3^{.1t}$, $10^{-.3x}$.

10. By means of common logarithms calculate for yourself $\ln 5$, and compare with the table. [See §§ 160, 171.]

§ 173. Compound Interest Law. If any quantity y varies with another, x, in such a way that its *rate* of increase or decrease is constantly *proportional to its value*, it is strictly analogous to an investment whose interest or depreciation is figured continuously at a fixed percentage rate. (Cf. § 165.)

Such quantities are said to vary "according to the *Compound Interest Law*" (abbreviated *C. I. L.*).*

Clearly, any such quantity is given by the formula

$$y = P e^{rx}, \qquad (8)$$

where P is the value of y at $x = 0$, and r is the fixed percentage rate.

E.g., if y decreases at a rate always equal to 15 per cent of y, then $r = -.15$, and $y = P e^{-.15x}$.

Conversely, any quantity given by a formula of type (8) must vary according to the *C. I. L.* For instance, if given

$$y = P e^{.09x},$$

Graph of $i = 10\, e^{-300t}$

Fig. 92.

we would recognize this as the formula for a quantity which increases at a rate constantly equal to 9% of its value.

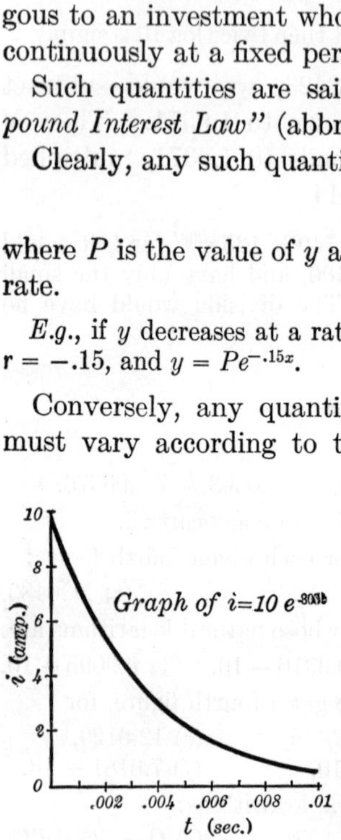

Ex. I. An electric current does not instantly vanish when the *"EMF"* is cut off; but it falls off rapidly, as in Fig. 92, decreasing at a constant percentage rate which is very great. If this rate is, say, 30000% per sec., then $r = -300$; and if the original intensity is 10 amperes, then, after t sec., it will be

$$i = 10\, e^{-300t}.$$

§ 174. Exponential Functions. As we saw in § 34, the functions x^2 and 2^x vary in radically different ways, and are functions of entirely different kinds.

A variable raised to a fixed power (like x^n) is called a Power

* Also called the Law of Organic Growth, or the Snowball Law.

Function. A constant raised to a variable power is called an *Exponential Function*. (The constant, however, is to be positive and not equal to 1.)

E.g., 2^x, 1.06^x, $10^{.3t}$, $e^{-.08x}$, and in general, b^{kx} are exponential functions.

Any quantity represented by an exponential function, or by such a function times some constant, must vary according to the *C. I. L.* — provided the exponent is of the first degree, as in the illustrations just given. For the constant base which is raised to the variable power is itself some power of e, and the given exponential function must therefore be reducible to a power of e in the type form (8), p. 240. An example will make this clear.

Ex. I. The speed v of a certain chemical reaction doubles with every $10°$ rise in the temperature. Obtain a formula for v at any temperature.

If $v = P$ at $T = 0$, we have the following table. As the final item indicates, when T has made x increases of $10°$ each, v has doubled x times, and hence equals 2^x times P. Or, since $x = .1\,T$, we may write:

T	v
0	P
10	$2\,P$
20	$4\,P$
30	$8\,P$
$10\,x$	$2^x\,P$

$$v = P2^x = P\,(2)^{.1T}.$$

But by the table of natural logarithms: $2 = e^{.6931}$.

$$\therefore\ v = P\,(e^{.6931})^{.1T} = Pe^{.06931T}$$

which falls under (7) or (8) and is a case of the *C. I. L.*[*]

Any quantity which doubles, or gains a fixed percentage, at any regular intervals must increase according to the *C. I. L.*

It is therefore a characteristic feature of the Compound Interest Law, and of the corresponding formula $y = Pe^{rx}$, that *adding* a fixed amount to x will *multiply* y by a fixed amount.

On pp. 536–37 there are small marginal tables, from which values of e^x and e^{-x} can be read off directly. Where these are not sufficiently accurate, logarithms can be used.

§ 175. Graphs. Exponential functions are so important that we should be thoroughly familiar with their graphs. Consider the following standard forms.

(I) $y = e^x$, (II) $y = ae^x$,

(III) $y = ae^{kx}$, (IV) $y = ab^{kx}$.

[*] For some purposes the first formula. $v = P\,(2)^{.1T}$, is more convenient than the final e form.

By § 174 these all vary according to the *C. I. L.*, and their *rates* of increase are constantly proportional to their *values*.

The graph for (I) runs as in Fig. 93. The higher the curve, the faster it rises. Toward the left the curve approaches

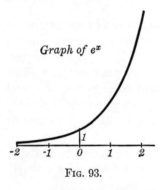

Graph of e^x

FIG. 93.

the base line indefinitely, never reaching it. (At $x = -100$, $y = e^{-100}$. What does e^{-100} mean?)

The graph for (II) is the same, except that every ordinate is *a* times as great. With a change of scale, Fig. 93 would do, provided *a* were positive. (What if *a* were negative?)

In (III) the values of y at $x = 1, 2, 3, \cdots$, are the same as those in (II) at $x = k, 2k, 3k, \cdots$.

If k is positive the graph is the same as for (II), with a change in the horizontal scale. If k is negative, the graph is reversed as regards positive and negative values of x. It then falls toward the right, and is the typical "die-away curve." (Cf. Fig. 92, p. 240.)

The form (IV) is reducible to one of the preceding forms, and thus has the same graph, to some scales.

The graph, however, is very different when the exponent involves anything beyond the first power of x. *E.g.*, the function $y = e^{-x^2}$, which is very important in statistical studies, varies very nearly as in Fig. 4, p. 4.

EXERCISES

1. Using the marginal tables, pp. 536–37 — or logarithms where interpolation would be needed — read off: $e^{.15}$, $e^{1.5}$, $e^{2.16}$, $e^{-.45}$, $e^{-2.4}$.

[2.] Plot the graph of $y = e^x$, taking $x = 0$, 0.5, etc., to $x = 2.5$. Over the same base line plot $y = log \, x$ from $x = 1$ to 10. Explain any similarity between the two curves.

3. Solve for r or t, roughly by the e^x or e^{-x} tables, and then more accurately by logarithms:

(a) $30 \, e^{6r} = 75$, $\quad$ (b) $20 \, e^{10r} = 14$, $\quad$ (c) $100 \, e^{-.2t} = 16.5$.

4. The number of bacteria in a culture increased at a constant percentage rate of 20%, the unit of time being 1 hr. If $N = 1000$ at $t = 0$, write a formula for N at any time. When was $N = 6000$?

[5.] In Ex. 4 plot a graph showing how N increased from $t = 0$ to $t = 10$. Also plot another graph showing how log N varied. Can you explain the peculiarity of the latter?

6. Draw the graphs of the following functions roughly by inspec‣ tion, merely showing the general shape and location:

$$(a)\ y = 20\ e^{.2x}, \qquad\qquad (b)\ y = .055\ e^{6x},$$
$$(c)\ y = 900\ e^{-3t}, \qquad\qquad (d)\ y = .4\ e^{-.006t}.$$

7. Write a formula for a quantity Q which equals 30 at $t = 0$ and (a) increases at the constant percentage rate of 14%, 65%, 250%; (b) decreases at the constant percentage rate of 45%, 106%, 2000%.

8. Express as a power of e: $y = P3^{.2t}$. What percentage rate?

9. For uniform strength the horizontal sectional area of a pier (A sq. ft.) should decrease according to the $C. I. L.$ as the elevation (E ft.) increases. Express this by a formula, if $A = P$ at $E = 0$.

10. The percentage of pneumococci surviving t sec. after treatment with an antiseptic decreased thus: $p = 100\,(2^{-\frac{t}{g}})$, where g is a certain constant. Calculate p at $t = 0$, g, $2g$, $\cdots$, $7g$; and plot. Is this a case of the $C. I. L.$? Reason?

11. In washing out a tank, the remaining volume of sediment (V cu. ft.) decreased according to the $C. I. L.$, diminishing by 60% in any five-minute interval. Find the instantaneous percentage rate, also the percentage removed in any minute.

12. The velocity of propagation of a nerve impulse increases by 80% with every 10° rise in the temperature $T°$. If $V = k$ when $T = 0$, find the formula. What is the instantaneous percentage rate r?

§ 176. Semi-logarithmic Graphs. In study-ing the variation of a given quantity y, it is sometimes desirable to plot a graph showing how the logarithm of y varies with the independ-ent variable x. (Fig. 94.)

Such a "semi-logarithmic graph," as it is called, will always be a straight line when y varies according to the $C. I. L.$,

FIG. 94.

$$y = Pe^{rx}. \qquad\qquad (9)$$

For, taking logarithms to any base, we must have

$$\log y = \log P + rx \log e. \qquad\qquad (10)$$

And as this equation is of the first degree in terms of log y and x, the two quantities plotted, the graph must be straight. (§ 26.)

Conversely, if that graph is straight, y must obey a *C. I. L.* (Why?)

§ 177. Use in Statistical Problems. The characteristic feature of the *C. I. L.* is that y varies at a constant percentage rate. Hence we may say that whenever a quantity increases or decreases at a constant percentage rate, *its semi-logarithmic graph will be straight*. And conversely.

For this reason such graphs are much used by statisticians in studying the growth of populations, bank clearings, bonded indebtedness, etc. If the semi-logarithmic graph of a population is straight, the population has increased at a constant percentage rate. If not, we can see at a glance where the largest percentage gains were made, by simply noting where the graph is steepest. By comparing such graphs for various different populations — *e.g.*, for the native and foreign-born populations of Portland, Oregon, in Fig. 95 — we can see which made the largest percentage gain in any interval.

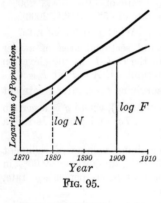

Fig. 95.

This same idea is used by large business houses in comparing the gains made by different departments of the business, or in comparing the growth of their business with the volume of postal receipts or other indications of general business conditions.

§ 178. Semi-logarithmic Paper. To make it easy to plot semi-logarithmic graphs, a specially ruled paper has been devised. Horizontally it has a uniform scale, to represent values of x; vertically, a logarithmic scale (like a slide rule), to represent values of log y. (See Fig. 96.)

The number on the vertical scale at any point is a value of y, but the height of that point above the base line is log y. Thus the distance up to the point marked "10" is log 10 — or 1 unit, using the base 10. The distance up to "100" is

log 100, or 2 units. And so on. To erect an ordinate equal
to log 20, we have merely to run it up to the cross-line marked
"20," etc.

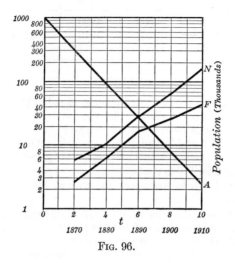

FIG. 96.

Hence if we plot a given table of values (x and y), without
looking up any logarithms, the paper will automatically plot
log y as a function of x — *i.e.*, will plot the semi-logarithmic
graph. Similarly, if given a *formula*, we have simply to calculate a table by substituting in the formula, and then plot.
In case the formula is a *C. I. L.* two points will be enough,
as the graph must be straight.

Ex. I. Plot the semi-logarithmic graph of $y = 1000\, e^{-.6t}$.
When $t = 0$, $y = 1000$. When $t = 10$, $y = 1000\, e^{-6} = 2.5$, approx.
Plotting these two values of y, and joining by a straight line gives
the required graph. (Fig. 96, A.) Observe that further values of y
satisfying the given formula can now be read off directly. *E.g.*, $y = 91$
when $t = 4$.

Ex. II. From 1870 to 1910 the native and foreign-born populations
of Portland, Oregon, increased as shown in the table below. Plot
the semi-logarithmic graphs.

Taking the numbers of the vertical scale as thousands rather than
units, we get Fig. 96, F, N — the same graphs as in Fig. 95, but obtained now without looking up logarithms.

These graphs do not give intermediate values correctly, unless the percentage rate of growth was constant during the interval considered.

Year	Native	Foreign	Year	Native	Foreign
1870	5700	2600	1900	64600	25900
1880	11300	6300	1910	163400	43800
1890	29100	17300			

EXERCISES *

1. Table 1 shows the estimated number of radios (N million) in the United States in various years. Plot the ordinary and semi-logarithmic graphs. Judge from these the intervals in which N made the largest actual gain and largest percentage gain. Verify by the table. Likewise for the smallest actual and percentage gains.

2. Like Ex. 1 for Table 2 which shows the approximate distance (D million miles) flown by transport airplanes in the United States in several years.

3. Table 3 shows the number of survivors expected at various ages (x yr.) from a typical group of 100,000 persons at age 10. Plot the ordinary and semi-logarithmic graphs from $x = 10$ to $x = 90$. Does the percentage rate of decrease become continually greater? The total rate? Estimate from both graphs the number surviving at age 85; at age 55.

4. Table 4 shows (in millions) the assets of a certain life insurance company at the end of various years, and also the amount of insurance

TABLE 1		TABLE 2		TABLE 3		TABLE 4		
Year	N	Year	D	x	N	Year	A	I
1921	0.05	1926	4.61	20	92,637	1864	0.3	6
1923	0.6	1927	5.24	30	85,441	1874	16	65
1925	4.0	1928	10.47	40	78,106	1884	23	99
1927	7.0	1929	20.24	50	69,804	1894	73	341
1929	12.0	1930	28.83	60	57,917	1904	195	709
1931	15.5	1931	43.40	70	38,569	1914	328	1365
1933	18.5	1932	48.34	80	14,474	1924	632	2879
		1933	50.80	90	847	1934	1018	3705

* The scales printed on the paper usually run from 1 to 10 and repeat. We re-label them to fit the problem. Thus the first "1" might be taken as 100, the next as 1000, etc., making the first "2" mean 200, etc. Evidently "200" should come just as far above "100" on the scale as "2" above "1." For log 200 − log 100 = log (200/100) = log 2.

Accurately ruled paper can be obtained from dealers in scientific supplies But paper good enough for rough practice can be run off on a mimeograph.

in force. Plot the semi-logarithmic graphs on the same sheet. In which decades did A gain a noticeably greater percentage than I? Noticeably smaller?

5. Plot on the same sheet the semi-logarithmic graphs of N and V in Table 8, p. 10. Does the percentage rate for N grow continually smaller? For V? Estimate N and V at age 75.

6. The population of Miami, Florida, was 29,571 in 1920, and 110,637 in 1930. Assuming a constant percentage rate of growth, estimate the population in 1925. When did it reach 50,000?

7. Plot the semi-logarithmic graph of the formula $y = 5\,e^{.6x}$, from $x = 0$ to $x = 10$. Read off y when $x = 2.5$, likewise x when $y = 1000$.

8. The quantity of radium remaining after t years from an original 1000 mg. is given approximately by the formula $Q = 1000\,e^{-.00038t}$. Plot the semi-logarithmic graph, using $t = 0$ and $t = 5000$. Read off intermediate values, and compare Table 3, p. 14.

9 For a decade the annual use of petroleum (Q bbl.) t yr. after 1910 was approximately $Q = 188,000,000\,(1.1)^t$. Express this in the standard $C.I.L.$ form. Also plot the semi-logarithmic graph from $t = 0$ to $t = 10$. If this formula and graph had continued valid, what would Q have been in 1925; 1930; 1935?

10. Table 5 shows the population P of the United States since 1790, and the savings bank deposits D since 1830, both in millions. Plot semi-logarithmic graphs on the same sheet. In which, if any, decades did P make a larger percentage gain than D? (Notice the nearly constant percentage rate for P prior to 1860.)

TABLE 5

YEAR	P	D	YEAR	P	D
1790	3.9		1870	38.6	550
1800	5.3		1880	50.2	819
1810	7.2		1890	62.9	1 525
1820	9.6		1900	76.0	2 450
1830	12.9	7	1910	92.0	4 070
1840	17.1	14	1920	105.7	6 538
1850	23.2	43	1930	122.8	10 605
1860	31.4	149			

[11.] Determine P and r in the formula $y = P\,e^{rx}$, if this is to be satisfied by the values $x = 3$, $y = 4$ and $x = 8$, $y = 7$. (Hint: After substituting, write the equivalent logarithmic equations, and combine. Cf. § 30.)

[12.] In the formula $y = .2\,x^2$ plot a graph showing how log y varies with log x from $x = 5$ to $x = 25$. Explain the peculiar result.

[13.] Like Ex. 11 for the formula $y = kx^n$, and the values $x = 20$, $y = 6$ and $x = 45$, $y = 9$.

§ 179. Logarithmic Graphs. In some statistical work where it is necessary to handle very large and very small values of y and x, it is customary to plot the logarithms of *both* variables — *i.e.*, to plot a graph *showing how log y varies with log x.* This greatly tones down the contrasts. *E.g.*, log 100 000 is only 5, and log .001 is -3.

Such "logarithmic graphs" are, however, mainly useful in scientific work in studying *Power Laws*:

$$y = k\,x^n. \tag{11}$$

For any such law, the logarithmic graph is straight. For

$$\log y = \log k + n \log x; \tag{12}$$

or, writing Y and X in place of log y and log x, the two quantities plotted:

$$Y = \log k + nX. \tag{13}$$

This equation is of the first degree, and the graph must be

Values of y

Values of x

FIG. 97.

straight. Incidentally, the slope must equal the exponent n in (11). For, by (13), $dY/dX = n$.

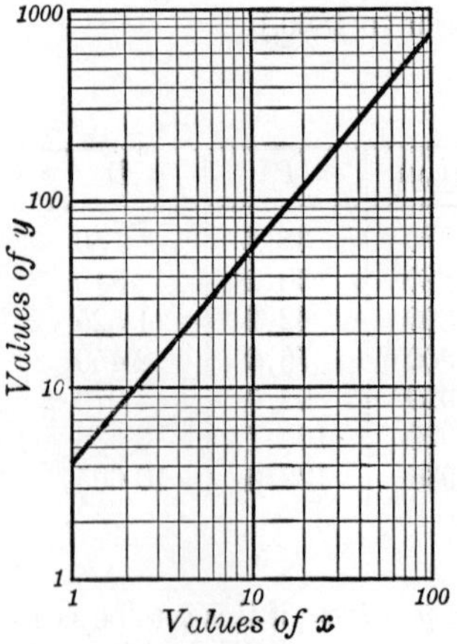

Conversely, whenever the logarithmic graph is straight, y must vary according to the *Power Law*. For by § 30 the relation between log y and log x must be linear — say $\log y = a \log x + b$. And as this is of the form (12), equation (11) must hold, for some values of k and n.

Logarithmic graphs can be plotted without looking up any logarithms, by using a special "logarithmic paper." This is ruled with logarithmic scales both horizontally and vertically. (Fig. 97.) A point for which

$x = 20$ and $y = 8$ has its actual distances from the reference lines equal to log 20 and log 8.

Ex. I. Plot the logarithmic graph of the Power Law, $y = 4\,x^{1.13}$.
When $x = 1$, $y = 4$. When $x = 100$, $y = 4\,(100)^{1.13} = 728$, approx.
Plotting these values and drawing a straight line through the resulting points gives the required graph. (Fig. 97.)

§ 180. Discovering Scientific Laws.

As noted in § 30 many scientific laws are discovered experimentally. A table of values (of x and y, say) is obtained by observation; and various mathematical tests are then applied to ascertain what formula or formulas are satisfied by the tabulated values.

A simple test for the three most common types of law (§§ 30, 33, 173) can be made by plotting certain graphs:

(I)   *Ordinary graph straight*:   *Linear Law*, $y = ax + b$,

(II) *Logarithmic graph straight*: *Power Law*, $y = kx^n$,

(III) *Semi-logarithmic graph straight*: *C. I. L.*, $y = Pe^{rx}$.

If none of these graphs is straight, the law is not one of these types. Tests for some other types will be discussed in §§ 282, 347.

If the test shows a given table to satisfy one of these laws, the required constants (k, n) or (P, r), etc., can be found by merely substituting two pairs of values in the proper formula, and solving algebraically. (Cf. § 30.)

For the Power Law it is also possible to find n approximately by measuring the slope of the logarithmic graph. The value of k (or that of P in the *C. I. L.*) can be read off from the graph as the value of y where $x = 1$ (or $x = 0$ for the *C. I. L.*).

Ex. I. Discover the formula for the following table.

x	1	2	4	6	8	10
y	3.3	5.4	14.8	40.2	109.2	296.8

The semi-logarithmic graph turns out to be straight. Hence the required formula is a *C. I. L.*:

$$y = Pe^{rx}.$$

Substituting the first and last values of the table:

$$3.3 = Pe^r,$$
$$296.8 = Pe^{10r}.$$

Taking logarithms:

$$\log 296.8 = \log P + 10\, r \log e,$$
$$\log 3.3 = \log P + r \log e. \qquad (14)$$

Looking up the logarithms of 296.8 and 3.3 (either to the base e, with $\log e = 1$, or to the base 10, with $\log e = .43429$), and subtracting, we find $r = .5$, approx. Substituting this in either equation of (14) gives $P = 2$. Hence the required formula is finally

$$y = 2\, e^{.5x}.$$

N.B. When $\log P$ happens to come out negative, we add $10 - 10$. Thus $\log P = -1.75000$ would be the same as $\log P = 8.25000 - 10$, which could easily be looked up.

§ 181. **Inverse Functions.** If y is any function of x, then x is also some function of y. Either function is called the *inverse* of the other.

E.g., if $y = x^3$, then $x = \sqrt[3]{y}$. Thus the cube and cube root are mutually inverse functions. Likewise,

$$\text{if} \quad y = e^x, \qquad\qquad \text{then} \quad x = \log y. \qquad (15)$$

Hence the exponential and the logarithm are mutually inverse.

To test whether a given table fits the *C. I. L.*, we sometimes have to plot two semi-logarithmic graphs: one with y vertical, and the other with x. Either variable might be an exponential function; the other would not.

Such double plotting is unnecessary in testing for a Power Law; for the inverse of a power is some other power. If y varies as a power of x, then also x varies as a power of y.

EXERCISES

1. Plot the logarithmic graph of $y = 2\, x^{\frac{3}{2}}$ from $x = 1$ to $x = 25$. Read off y when $x = 10$; also x when $y = 100$.

2. Plot the logarithmic graph of each of the following from $x = 1$ to $x = 100$:

(a) $y = 1/x$. Read off the reciprocals of 6.2; 35; 89.8.

(b) $y = \sqrt{x}$. Read off the square roots of 8 and 60.

3. For dogs, on the average, the heart weight (H gm.) varies as the .8 power of the body weight (B gm.); and $H = 100$ when $B = 30\,000$.

Write the formula; also draw the logarithmic graph from $B = 2000$ to $B = 40\ 000$. Read off H when $B = 8000$.

4. For many mammals and birds the pulse rate varies thus with the body weight: $R = k/B^{.23}$. On what kind of paper would this formula give a straight graph, and with what slope?

5. On a standard railway curve having the maximum desirable elevation of the outer rail, the degree of curvature D and the intended speed (V mi./hr.) are related thus: $DV^2 = 14490$. Plot the logarithmic graph. Read off D for $V = 20, 30, \cdots, 60$.

6. Determine what kind of formula is satisfied by the values in each of the Tables 1 and 2.

7. The attraction (f dynes) between two electric charges was found to vary with the distance (x cm.) apart as in Table 3 below. Find the formula and check.

8. A cold plate was taken into a warm tunnel. The difference between the temperatures of the air and the plate decreased as in Table 4 after t hours. Find the formula for D at any time.

9. The rate of rotation of a wheel under water decreased as in Table 5 after the power was cut off. Find a formula for R at any time.

TABLE 1		TABLE 2		TABLE 3		TABLE 4		TABLE 5	
x	y	x	y	x	f	t	D	t	R
1	3	1	3	0.5	256	0	29.4	0	3000
20	22.1	40	3.7	1.0	64	0.5	22.1	10	1221
90	60.3	200	8.2	8.0	1	1.0	16.6	20	495
300	134.5	600	60.3	16.0	0.25	1.5	12.5	30	202
1000	300	1000	445	20.0	0.16	2.0	9.4	40	82

10. The speed of a certain chemical reaction doubles every time the temperature is raised 10° C. Calling the speed 1 at 30°, make a table of its values at several other temperatures and find a formula which will represent the Table.

11. The distance of the planets from the sun and their periods of revolution (T yr.) are given below. Discover the law. ("Kepler's Third Law.")

	MERC.	VENUS	EARTH	MARS	JUP.	SAT.	UR.	NEP.	PLUTO
D	.387	.723	1.00	1.52	5.20	9.54	19.2	30.1	41.3
T	.241	.615	1.00	1.88	11.9	29.5	84.0	165	265

12. The oxygen consumption (x units) of a low form of life in t hours after a certain treatment varied as tabulated below. Find an approximate formula.

t	2	3	4	5	6	7	8	9
x	.234	.290	.343	.385	.417	.447	.472	.500

13. In treating some sugar with an acid, the amount (x gm.) remaining after t min. varied as shown below.   Discover an approximate formula.

t	0	30	60	90	120	150
x	46	39.4	33.7	28.8	24.6	21.1

§ 182. Derivative of log x.

In many problems it is necessary to know just how the logarithm of a number changes with the number — in other words, how the function $\log x$ varies with x.

To find a formula for the derivative or *rate* of increase at any instant we resort to the increment process.   (§ 55.)

Let $\qquad y = \log x, \qquad\qquad$ to any base.

Then $\qquad y + \Delta y = \log (x + \Delta x).$

$$\therefore \frac{\Delta y}{\Delta x} = \frac{\log (x + \Delta x) - \log x}{\Delta x}. \tag{16}$$

The final step is to find the limit of this fraction as $\Delta x \to 0$. The numerator approaches $\log x - \log x$, or zero.   Thus we have a quantity which is becoming very small, divided by another, also becoming very small.   Without more information no one can tell what limit the fraction will approach.

But we can simplify the numerator.   Subtracting one logarithm from another gives the logarithm of a fraction:

$$\therefore \frac{\Delta y}{\Delta x} = \frac{\log \left(\dfrac{x + \Delta x}{x} \right)}{\Delta x} = \frac{\log \left(1 + \dfrac{\Delta x}{x} \right)}{\Delta x}. \tag{17}$$

To simplify this further make the substitution:

$$\frac{\Delta x}{x} = \frac{1}{z}, \quad \text{or} \quad \Delta x = \frac{x}{z}. \tag{18}$$

Then equation (17) becomes

$$\frac{\Delta y}{\Delta x} = \frac{\log \left(1 + \dfrac{1}{z} \right)}{\dfrac{x}{z}} = \frac{z \log \left(1 + \dfrac{1}{z} \right)}{x}.$$

But multiplying a logarithm by z gives the logarithm of the zth power.

$$\therefore \quad \frac{\Delta y}{\Delta x} = \frac{\log\left(1 + \frac{1}{z}\right)^z}{x}.$$

We can now see what happens as $\Delta x \to 0$. By (18), z must increase indefinitely. And by § 167, the quantity $\left(1 + \frac{1}{z}\right)^z$ approaches e, so that the limit approached by $\Delta y/\Delta x$ is

$$\frac{dy}{dx} = \frac{\log e}{x}. \tag{19}$$

This is the derivative of $y = \log x$, no matter what base of logarithms is used.

If the base is e, $\log e = 1$ simply. Hence

$$\text{if } y = \log_e x, \quad \frac{dy}{dx} = \frac{1}{x}. \tag{20}$$

But if the base is 10, $\log e = .43429$, approx. The exact $\log e$ is denoted by M. Thus,

$$\text{if } y = \log_{10} x, \quad \frac{dy}{dx} = \frac{M}{x}. \tag{21}$$

Remarks. (I) These formulas show that the rate at which a logarithm increases with the number is inversely proportional to the size of the number. Geometrically stated: The graph of $\log_e x$ has a slope of 1 at $x = 1$, a slope of $\frac{1}{2}$ at $x = 2$, $\frac{1}{3}$ at $x = 3$, etc.

(II) Formulas (19)–(21) rest ultimately on the existence of the limit e — proved in higher analysis, but assumed in this course. Compare (18) above with the substitution used in § 168.

(III) Observe that e is the *natural* base to use in problems requiring the differentiation of a logarithm — because of the simplicity of formula (20) as compared with (21). In calculus, when no base is specified, e is always understood, not 10.

§ 183. Log u. To differentiate the logarithm of a *quantity*, say

$$y = \log u, \tag{22}$$

we use the same principle as in differentiating a power of a quantity, $y = u^n$. That is, we multiply dy/du by du/dx. (§ 77.) Here

$$\frac{dy}{du} = \frac{1}{u}.$$

$$\therefore \frac{dy}{dx} = \frac{1}{u}\frac{du}{dx}.\tag{23}$$

Thus, *the derivative of the logarithm of any quantity equals one divided by that same quantity, times the derivative of that quantity.* (Memorize.)

    Ex. I. $y = \log (x^3 - 1).$

$$\frac{dy}{dx} = \frac{1}{x^3 - 1} \cdot 3\,x^2.$$

    Remark. It is instructive to compare this with a *power* case, say

$$y = (x^3 - 1)^{100},$$

$$\frac{dy}{dx} = 100\,(x^3 - 1)^{99} \cdot 3\,x^2.$$

Note the final factor $3\,x^2$ in each case.

    Ex. II. $y = \log x^3.$

$$\frac{dy}{dx} = \frac{1}{x^3} \cdot 3\,x^2 = \frac{3}{x}.$$

This result could have been foreseen, $\log x^3$ being the same as $3 \log x$.

    Ex. III. $y = \log \sqrt{\dfrac{x^4 - 1}{x^4 + 1}}.$

This can be simplified greatly *before differentiating.* By § 144, the logarithm of the radical equals one half the logarithm of the fraction. And the latter equals what?

$$\therefore y = \tfrac{1}{2} \left[\log (x^4 - 1) - \log (x^4 + 1)\right].$$

Each of these logarithms is easily differentiated.

$$\frac{dy}{dx} = \frac{1}{2}\left[\frac{1}{x^4 - 1} \cdot 4\,x^3 - \frac{1}{x^4 + 1} \cdot 4\,x^3\right] = \frac{4\,x^3}{(x^4 - 1)\,(x^4 + 1)}.$$

    N.B. We have as yet no rule for differentiating the fraction $(x^4 - 1)/(x^4 + 1)$, without dividing out or resorting to the Δ process. (§ 55.) But, curiously, we have just differentiated the logarithm of the square root of that fraction!

EXERCISES

1. Find the instantaneous rate of increase of $y = \log x$ at $x = 3$, 5, and 7. Check the first value by finding from the tables the average rate of increase of $\log x$ from $x = 2.99$ to 3.01.

2. Plot $y = \log x$ from $x = 1$ to $x = 10$, and check the results in Ex. 1.

3. Approximately how much does $\log x$ increase while x increases from 4 to 4.0006? If $\log 4 = 1.38629$, find $\log 4.0006$.

4-6. Proceed as in Exs. 1, 2, 3, using the base 10, and $\log 4 = .60206$.

7. Simplify and differentiate the following natural logarithms:

(a) $y = \log x^{10}$, $z = 3 \log x^{-5}$; (b) $y = \log x^{\frac{7}{2}} + \log x^{-3}$;

(c) $y = \log 9\, x + \log 400\, x$; (d) $y = \log 3\, x^3 + \log .1\, x^{-2}$;

(e) $y = \log \sqrt[3]{x^8} - 4 \log \sqrt{x}$; (f) $y = \log (10/x^2) + \log (7\, x^4)$;

(g) $y = \log 2\, x^6 + 12 \log \sqrt{x} + 3 \log \dfrac{x}{20} - 9 \log \dfrac{20}{x^2}$.

8. Like Ex. 7 for the following, the base being 10:

$y = 5 \log 8\, x^4$, $z = 12 \log (\sqrt{x}/25)$, $w = \log (40/x)$.

9. The elevation (E ft.) above sea-level corresponding to any atmospheric pressure (p in.) is given by the formula:

$$E = 88630 - 60000 \log p. \qquad \text{(Base 10)}$$

Approximately what change in elevation corresponds to an increase of p from 25 to 25.1?

10. How fast is a balloon rising if the pressure recorded is decreasing at the rate of .2 in./min. when $p = 25$? (See Ex. 9.)

11. Find dy/dx for each of the following functions:

(a) Base e: $y = \log (x^6 + 1)$, $z = \log (12 - 4\, x - x^2)$;

(b) Base 10: $y = \log (x^2 - 16)$, $z = \log (1 - x^2)$.

N.B. In the following differentiations the base is e.

12. Differentiate in two ways and check:

$y = \log x^{400}$, $z = \log (300\, x)$, $w = \log (60\, x^5)$.

13. Simplify each of the following and then differentiate:

(a) $y = \log \dfrac{x}{x^2 + 4}$, (b) $y = \log \dfrac{x^3}{x^6 + 1}$,

(c) $y = \log (x \sqrt{x^2 + 1})$, (d) $y = \log \sqrt{\dfrac{x^2 - 9}{x^2 + 9}}$.

14. Differentiate and simplify the results:

(a) $y = x^4 - \log (x^4 + 1)$, (b) $y = \log (\log x)$.

15. The time required for a certain biological change is

$$T = \frac{a}{k} \log \frac{x}{k-x} - k,$$

where a and k are constants, and x is the number of bacteria present. Find dT/dx.

16. In studying the diffusion of water through membranes this formula was used:

$$T = a - b - v + a \log \frac{b}{a-v},$$

where a and b are constants. Show that $dv/dT = (a-v)/v$. (First find dT/dv.)

17. What is the derivative *with respect to x* of:

$$y = \log u, \qquad y = \log z, \qquad q = \log r, \qquad w = \log y?$$

§ 184. Differentiating Logarithmically. Numerous non-logarithmic functions which we cannot yet differentiate directly are easily handled by *introducing* logarithms.

Ex. I. $\qquad y = \sqrt{\dfrac{x^4 - 1}{x^4 + 1}}$

Taking the logarithms of both sides, and simplifying as in § 183:

$$\log y = \tfrac{1}{2} [\log (x^4 - 1) - \log (x^4 + 1)].$$

Differentiating each term *with respect to x* gives:

$$\frac{1}{y} \frac{dy}{dx} = \frac{1}{2} \left[\frac{4\,x^3}{x^4 - 1} - \frac{4\,x^3}{x^4 + 1} \right] = \frac{4\,x^3}{(x^4 - 1)\,(x^4 + 1)}.$$

Now dy/dx is what we are after; so we multiply through by y, and then substitute the value of y as originally given in terms of x.

$$\therefore \frac{dy}{dx} = \frac{4\,x^3}{(x^4 - 1)\,(x^4 + 1)} \cdot y = \frac{4\,x^3}{(x^4 - 1)\,(x^4 + 1)} \sqrt{\frac{x^4 - 1}{x^4 + 1}},$$

or, simplified,

$$\frac{dy}{dx} = \frac{4\,x^3}{(x^4 - 1)^{\frac{1}{2}}\,(x^4 + 1)^{\frac{3}{2}}}.$$

N.B. It is desirable to simplify the logarithms as much as possible before differentiating, also to *combine the fractions* obtained in differentiating the right member, *before multiplying across by the given function.* Compare this example with Ex. III, § 183.

§ **185.** $\int \frac{1}{x}\, dx.$ In Chapter IV we could not find this integral, because there is no *power* of x whose derivative is $1/x$, or x^{-1}. But we now see that

$$\int \frac{1}{x}\, dx = \log_e x + C.$$ (24)

Hence we can now integrate *every* power of x: namely, x^{-1} by (24) and any other power x^n by (8), § 92.

Remark. It is also true that

$$\int \frac{1}{x}\, dx = \frac{1}{M} \log_{10} x + C.$$ (25)

But this formula is not used if tables of natural logarithms are at hand.

Ex. I.   The force (F lb.) driving a piston varied thus with the distance (x in.): $F = 6000/x$.   Find the work done from $x = 10$ to $x = 20$.

Always $W = \int F\, dx.$ (§ 96.)   In the present case,

$$W = \int \frac{6000}{x}\, dx = 6000 \int \frac{1}{x}\, dx.$$

∴ $W = 6000 \log x + C.$

Now the work starts (*i.e.*, $W = 0$) when $x = 10$.

∴ $C = -6000 \log 10,$

∴ $W = 6000 \log x - 6000 \log 10.$

This is the work done from $x = 10$ to any other x.   To $x = 20$:

$$W = 6000\,(\log 20 - \log 10) = 6000 \log 2.$$

By the table of natural logarithms, $W = 4159$ (in.-lb.).

§ **186** *S.* $\int \frac{du}{u} \cdot$ In general we may write

$$\int \frac{du}{u} = \log u + C,$$ (26)

where u denotes any quantity.   Thus if u is $(x^4 + 1)$ whose differential du is $4\,x^3\,dx$, this formula states that

$$\int \frac{4\,x^3\,dx}{x^4 + 1} = \log(x^4 + 1) + C.$$

Differentiating the result will show this to be correct.

Observe that the formula does not deal with $\dfrac{dx}{u}$, but with $\dfrac{du}{u}$.
It will not apply unless the numerator is the differential of the entire denominator u.

Ex. I.   Find the integral $F = \displaystyle\int \frac{(2\,x + 13)\,dx}{x^2 + 13\,x + 25}$.

If we let $u = x^2 + 13\,x + 25$, then $du = (2\,x + 13)\,dx$.   Hence the given fraction is of precisely the form du/u.

$$\therefore\ F = \log(x^2 + 13\,x + 25) + C. \qquad \text{(Check?)}$$

Ex. II. Find the integral $G = \displaystyle\int \frac{x^2\,dx}{x^3 - 8}$.

If we call the denominator u, then $du = 3\,x^2\,dx$.   The numerator lacks the factor 3; but we supply this, with a compensating factor $\frac{1}{3}$ before the integral sign:*

$$G = \tfrac{1}{3} \int \frac{3\,x^2\,dx}{x^3 - 8} = \tfrac{1}{3} \log(x^3 - 8) + C.$$

N.B.   If the given numerator had been $3\,x\,dx$, we could not have supplied the missing *variable* factor x; and could not have integrated.

Ex. III. Find the integral $H = \displaystyle\int \frac{3\,x^2\,dx}{\sqrt{x^3 - 8}}$.

If we let $u = \sqrt{x^3 - 8}$, du will also involve a radical.   As none is present in the numerator, this will not work: (26) does not apply. But if we let $u = x^3 - 8$, we see that H is of the form

$$H = \int \frac{du}{\sqrt{u}} = \int u^{-\frac{1}{2}}\,du.$$

This gives $H = 2\,u^{\frac{1}{2}} + C$, or $H = 2\,\sqrt{x^3 - 8} + C$.   [Check.]   Cf. § 101.

* This step is permissible since the derivative of *a constant times* a variable is equal to the constant times the derivative of the variable — a statement not true for the product of two variables.   (Cf. § 61.)

EXERCISES

1. Differentiate logarithmically:

(a) $y = \dfrac{x}{x^2 + 1}$,

(b) $z = \dfrac{x^4}{x^8 - 9}$,

(c) $w = 2\,x^3\,(x^2 - 1)^5$,

(d) $q = 3\,x^6\,\sqrt{x^2 + 4}$,

(e) $r = \sqrt{\dfrac{x^6 - 1}{x^6 + 1}}$,

(f) $s = \dfrac{(x + 4)^{\frac{2}{3}}}{x - 6}$,

(g) $y = 15\,e^{x^2}$,

(h) $z = 10^{x^3}$.

2. As in Ex. 1 (g) prove that if $y = e^u$, then $dy/dx = e^u\,du/dx$.

3. (a) Calculate the area under the curve $y = 1/x$ from $x = 1$ to $x = 10$. (b) Check by plotting and measuring the area.

4. A rough table of logarithms could be constructed by measuring areas under the curve in Ex. 3. Explain briefly.

5. The force used in driving a piston varied thus: $F = 1000/x$. Find the work done from $x = 20$ to $x = 50$.

6. In each of these forms see whether the numerator is the exact differential of the denominator. If so, find the integral by (26):

(a) $\displaystyle\int \frac{5\,x^4\,dx}{x^5 + 8}$,

(b) $\displaystyle\int \frac{(2\,x + 4)\,dx}{x^2 + 4\,x + 10}$,

(c) $\displaystyle\int \frac{5\,dx}{5\,x - 6}$.

Check by differentiating each result.

7. Reduce $\displaystyle\int \frac{x^3\,dx}{x^4 + 1}$ to the form $\dfrac{du}{u}$ by supplying a suitable numerical factor and compensating. Integrate and check.

8. Like Ex. 7 for the following:

(a) $\displaystyle\int \frac{x\,dx}{x^2 + 25}$,

(b) $\displaystyle\int \frac{x^3\,dx}{16 - x^4}$,

(c) $\displaystyle\int \frac{dx}{9 - 2\,x}$

9. Find the following integrals (Cf. § 101):

(a) $\displaystyle\int \frac{2\,x\,dx}{(x^2 + 1)^{10}}$,

(b) $\displaystyle\int \frac{x^2\,dx}{(x^3 - 1)^4}$,

(c) $\displaystyle\int \frac{x^2\,dx}{\sqrt{x^3 - 1}}$.

§ 187. Derivative of e^u. Differentiating $y = e^u$ logarithmically gives

$$\frac{dy}{dx} = e^u\,\frac{du}{dx}. \qquad (27)$$

That is, *the derivative of any power of e is that very same power, times the derivative of the exponent.* (Memorize.)

Formula (27) bears no resemblance whatever to the formula $d(u^n) = nu^{n-1} du$. The reason is that an exponential function e^u and a power function u^n vary in entirely different ways. (§ 174.)

To differentiate an exponential function in any modified form, as a^u, first express it as a power of e.

Ex. I. $y = e^{-x^2}$.   Here $\dfrac{dy}{dx} = e^{-x^2}(-2x)$.

Ex. II. $y = 100\, e^{.4t}$.   Here $\dfrac{dy}{dt} = 100\, e^{.4t}\,(.4)$.

This result is the same as $.4\,y$. Thus the rate is proportional to y itself. In fact the given formula is evidently a case of the *C. I. L.*

Ex. III. $v = P \cdot 2^{.1T}$.

This is an e form in disguise. In fact by Ex. I, § 174:

$$v = P \cdot e^{.06931T}.$$

$$\therefore \quad \frac{dv}{dT} = P \cdot e^{.06931T}\,(.06931).$$

That is, $dv/dT = .06931\,v$, which shows again that this v varies according to the *C. I. L.* Observe that the coefficient .06931 in the exponent (kT) refers to the instantaneous rate of increase, rather than the average rate during an entire unit.

§ 188 *S.* **C. I. L. by Integration.** The general formula for the *C. I. L.*,

$$y = Pe^{rx}, \tag{28}$$

was obtained in § 173 by considering the analogy to an investment whose interest is compounded continuously. The formula can now be derived without any thought of that analogy. The method is precisely the same as in the following numerical illustration.

Ex. I. A quantity y increases with x at a rate constantly equal to $.04\,y$. If $y = 100$ at $x = 0$, find the formula.

Solution. We are given $\dfrac{dy}{dx} = .04\,y$.

The problem, then, is simply to integrate this, and get y in terms of x.

There is one difficulty: as the equation stands, the derivative on the left side is taken with respect to x, whereas the right member is expressed in terms of y. But let us divide through by y:

$$\frac{1}{y}\frac{dy}{dx} = .04. \tag{29}$$

Or, in differential notation:

$$\frac{dy}{y} = .04\,dx. \tag{30}$$

$$\therefore \int \frac{dy}{y} = \int .04\,dx + C.$$

$$\log y = .04\,x + C.$$

But $y = 100$ when $x = 0$, whence $C = \log 100$.

$$\log y = .04\,x + \log 100.$$

Transposing log 100, and remembering that the difference $\log y - \log 100$ is the same as the logarithm of the fraction $y/100$ (§ 144), we have

$$\log \frac{y}{100} = .04\,x.$$

This means that $.04\,x$ is the *exponent* of the power to which the base e must be raised to equal the fraction $y/100$.

$$\therefore \quad \frac{y}{100} = e^{.04x}, \qquad \text{or} \quad y = 100\,e^{.04x}. \tag{31}$$

Remarks. (I) This formula is the same as would be obtained by thinking of the analogy to compound interest, the given quantity y growing at the rate of 4% compounded continuously.

(II) The formula can also be checked directly. Substituting $x = 0$ gives $y = 100$; and differentiating gives

$$\frac{dy}{dx} = 100\,e^{.04x}\,(.04) = .04\,y$$

as required.

§ 189 S. Natural Laws and Differential Equations. Our derivation of equation (31) above, from a given fact concerning the derivative dy/dx, is typical of the mathematical study of natural phenomena.

The complex relations between varying quantities x and y are often not recognizable directly; but frequently we can discover how the rate at which y changes is determined by the instantaneous values of x and y. That is, we can see that dy/dx is some particular function of x and y. Symbolically expressed,

$$\frac{dy}{dx} = f(x, y). \tag{32}$$

Any equation involving one or more derivatives can be written in differential notation, as in (30) above, and hence is called a *differential equation*.

Thus, a law of nature may be basically expressed by a differential equation. The problem then is to deduce, by integration and other suitable steps, the common statement of the law — in the form of a relation between the variables alone (*i.e.*, without derivatives). In many complicated cases, considerable manipulation is needed to get the differential equation ready for integration.*

In Ex. I above, the necessary preparation was made by simply dividing through by y, and multiplying through by dx. This gave (30) in which the variables are separated: with dy there was no term involving x, and vice versa.

EXERCISES

1. Differentiate each of the following functions:

(a) $y = 25\, e^{.03x}$, (b) $i = 60\, e^{-10t}$,

(c) $z = \frac{1}{2}(e^{\frac{x}{5}} - e^{-\frac{x}{5}})$, (d) $q = 9\, e^{-8t^2}$,

(e) $w = \dfrac{.25}{e^{4x}}$, (f) $s = \dfrac{1}{\sqrt{2\,\pi}}\, e^{-\frac{1}{2}t^2}$.

2. Differentiate $y = (e^{3x} + 10)^2$ in two ways:
  (a) Directly, regarding y as a power of a quantity (§ 77);
  (b) By first squaring the binomial. Compare results.

* See *Higher Course*, Chapter VIII, or any text on Differential Equations.

3. Like Ex. 2 for $y = (e^{7x} + e^{-7x})^2$.

4. Differentiate in the most convenient way: $y = (e^{\frac{x}{5}} + 1)^{10}$.

5. Differentiate each of the following by taking logarithms, also by expressing y as a power of e:

(a) $y = 3^{x^2}$, (b) $y = 10^{t^4}$, (c) $y = 2^{-10x}$.

[6.] By differentiating logarithmically prove the following formulas, where u and v are functions of x:

(a) If $y = uv$, then $\dfrac{dy}{dx} = u\dfrac{dv}{dx} + v\dfrac{du}{dx}$;

(b) If $y = \dfrac{u}{v}$, then $\dfrac{dy}{dx} = \left(v\dfrac{du}{dx} - u\dfrac{dv}{dx}\right) \div v^2$.

7. The amount of dye in a frog's capillaries t min. after injection was $A = 7.63\,e^{-.24t}$. How fast was A decreasing at $t = 5$?

8. The strength of an electric current t sec. after starting was $i = 10\,(1 - e^{-150t})$. How large was i at $t = .02$, and how fast was it then increasing?

9. To what interest problem is this equivalent: If $y = 2000$ at $t = 0$ and grows at a rate always equal to $.05\,y$, what will be the value of y at any time? Write the formula by inspection, and check. (See § 188, Remarks I, II.)

10. In Ex. 9 obtain the required formula also by integration.

11. The difference D between the temperature of a hot wire and that of the air decreased thus: $dD/dt = -.2\,D$. To what sort of depreciation is this analogous? What formula if $D = 40$ at $t = 0$? Check.

12. In Ex. 11, derive the formula for D by integration.

N.B. In Exs. 13–17, obtain each required formula by integration.

13. The number of bacteria in a culture increased thus: $dN/dt = .15\,N$. At the start, $N = 200$. Derive the formula.

14. In Ex. 13 draw by inspection a rough graph showing how N increased from $t = 0$ to $t = 10$.

15. (a), (b). Like Ex. 13, 14 for an electric current which died out thus: $di/dt = -50\,i$, and $i = 12$ at $t = 0$.

16. When an iron rod is heated its length increases thus:

$$dL/dT = .00001\,L.$$

Express L as a function of T, if $L = 80$ when $T = 0$.

17. Passing through dark glass the intensity of light varied thus with the distance (x in.): $di/dx = .25\,i$. If i was originally 100, derive a formula for i at any distance.

18. Each quantity mentioned below varies at a rate constantly proportional to the value of the quantity. In certain cases the constant of proportionality has the value shown. Express these facts in calculus notation, and write by inspection the result of each integration. Check each result by differentiating.

(a) Rotary speed, with the time elapsed since the power was cut off: $k = -.025$, and $R = 75$ at $t = 0$.

(b) The length of a glass rod, with the temperature: $k = .0000083$; $L = 120$ when $T = 0$.

(c) Viscosity of olive oil, with temperature: $k = -.023$ and $V = 3.265$ when $T = 0$.

(d) Tension in a pulley belt, with the distance along the pulley. $k = .03$ and $T = 40$ when $D = 0$.

19. The number of negative "ions" passing between two charged plates is given by the relation: $dn = kn\,dx$, where k is the gas constant, and x is the distance from the negative plate. Derive a formula for n at any x, if $n = N$ at $x = 0$.

20. In studying the specific gravity of bacteria the equation $dx/dt = k(x + a)$ was used, k and a denoting given constants. Show that this is equivalent to $x = be^{kt} - a$, where b is any constant.

21. Solve the differential equation $dy = 2xy\,dx$, if $y = 5$ when $x = 0$. Check the result by differentiating.

§ 190 *S*. Derivative of a Product.   Any product can be differentiated logarithmically. But often it is more conveniently differentiated directly, by using the formula derived in Ex. 6 (*a*), p. 263, viz.:

$$\frac{d}{dx}(uv) = u\frac{dv}{dx} + v\frac{du}{dx}. \tag{33}$$

That is, *the derivative of the product of two variables is equal to the first variable times the derivative of the second, plus the second variable times the derivative of the first.*   (Memorize.)

Ex. I.   Differentiate $y = x^2 \log x$.
Here the first variable is x^2 and the second is $\log x$.

$$\therefore \frac{dy}{dx} = x^2\left(\frac{1}{x}\right) + (\log x)\,2\,x;$$

i.e., $$\frac{dy}{dx} = x(1 + 2\log x),$$ simplified.

§ 191 *S*.   A Typical Application.   Suppose that, under pressure, the height of a rectangular plate is decreasing at the rate of .05 in./min. and the base increasing .02 in./min. How fast is the area changing when $h = 20$ and $b = 15$?

$$A = bh.$$

$$\therefore \quad \frac{dA}{dt} = b\frac{dh}{dt} + h\frac{db}{dt}. \tag{34}$$

Substituting given values for b, dh/dt, etc.,

$$\frac{dA}{dt} = 15\,(-\,.05) + 20\,(.02) = -\,.35.$$

The area is *decreasing* at the rate of .35 sq. in. per min.

§ 192 S. Derivative of a Fraction. Differentiating $y = u/v$ logarithmically as in Ex. 6 (b), p. 263, we find that

$$\frac{dy}{dx} = \frac{v\dfrac{du}{dx} - u\dfrac{dv}{dx}}{v^2}. \tag{35}$$

That is, *the derivative of a fraction equals the denominator times the derivative of the numerator, minus the numerator times the derivative of the denominator, all divided by the square of the denominator.* (Memorize.)

Ex. I. Find the maximum value of $\qquad y = \dfrac{\log x}{x^4}$.

By (35) $\qquad \dfrac{dy}{dx} = \dfrac{x^4\left(\dfrac{1}{x}\right) - (\log x)\,4\,x^3}{x^8}$;

i.e., $\qquad \dfrac{dy}{dx} = \dfrac{1 - 4\log x}{x^5}$.

To find the maximum value of y, we set $dy/dx = 0$:

$$\frac{1 - 4\log x}{x^5} = 0.$$

Multiplying through by x^5 gives $1 - 4\log x = 0$, or $\log x = \frac{1}{4}$. Since the base is e, this means that

$$x = e^{\frac{1}{4}} = \sqrt[4]{e}, \qquad = 1.284 \text{ approx.}$$

Substituting for x and $\log x$ in the original equation: $y = \dfrac{\frac{1}{4}}{e} = \dfrac{1}{4\,e}$.

Test: At $x = 1$, $dy/dx = +$. At $x = 2$, $dy/dx = -$. Hence a maximum.

EXERCISES

1. Differentiate and simplify the results:

(a) $y = (x^4 - 1)(x^3 + 2)$, (b) $z = x^3 e^{2x}$,

(c) $u = 4 x^4 \log x - x^4$, (d) $v = x \log x$,

(e) $w = \dfrac{x^3}{x^6 + 1}$, (f) $p = \dfrac{x^2 - 1}{x^4 + 9}$,

(g) $q = \dfrac{\log x}{x^{10}}$, (h) $r = \dfrac{e^{2t} - e^{-2t}}{e^{2t} + e^{-2t}}$,

(i) $s = 7 x \sqrt{x^2 + 100}$, (j) $y = r^2 \sqrt{16 - r^4}$,

(k) $z = \dfrac{x}{\sqrt{x^2 + 25}}$, (l) $w = \dfrac{t^2}{\sqrt{t^4 + 1}}$.

2. Differentiate $y = (x^4 + 1)^7$ logarithmically and compare (22), p. 104. The same for $y = u^n$.

3. Test for maxima and minima:

(a) $y = \dfrac{x}{x^2 + 25}$, (b) $z = \dfrac{\log x}{x^5}$,

(c) $u = x \sqrt{400 - x^2}$, (d) $v = x^2 e^{-6x}$.

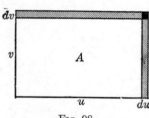

FIG. 98.

4. Approximately how much will the area of a rectangle change if the base and height increase slightly as in Fig. 98? Cf. § 191.

5. If the radius of a cylinder is increasing at the rate of .1 in./min. and the height is decreasing at the rate of .2 in./min., how fast is the volume changing when $r = 10$ and $h = 30$?

6. A rectangular metal block has a square base whose edge (x in.) increases at the rate of .02 in./min. The height is increasing at the rate of .06 in./min. How fast is the volume changing when $x = 10$ and $h = 30$?

7. For a certain quantity of a gas $PV = 500\ T$. If P increases at the rate of .04 units per min., and V decreases at the rate of 2 units per min., how fast will T increase when $P = 60$ and $V = 5000$?

8. In studying the physiology of the blood this formula has been used: $S = kx^n/(1 + kx^n)$, where k and n are constants. Find dS/dx.

9. The strength of electric current needed to excite a nerve x units long was found to be $S = ke^x/(e^x - 1)$, where k is constant. Find dS/dx.

10. The speed of signals through an oceanic cable is proportional to the function $S = (log\ x)/x^2$, where x is the ratio of the thickness of the covering to the radius of the core. Find the maximum value of S.

11. Find how high a wall-light L should be placed to secure the maximum illumination I of a level surface at S, 2 ft. from the wall, if I varies as the sine of $\angle S$, and inversely as the square of the distance LS. [First show that the function to be tested is $x/(4 + x^2)^{\frac{3}{2}}$.

12. For an output of x units the efficiency of an electric generator is $E = x/(a + bx + cx^2)$. What value of x, in terms of the constants a, b, c, will maximize E?

§ 193. Summary of Chapter VII.
A quantity which varies according to the $C.\ I.\ L.$ (§ 173) is strictly analogous to an investment whose interest is compounded continuously. Its value is expressible as an exponential function — *i.e.*, as a varying power of e (§ 167) or of some other constant. These formulas for the $C.\ I.\ L.$ can be obtained either from this analogy or by integration.

Logarithms to the base e are the simplest and most natural in studying the $C.\ I.\ L.$, and also in differentiating and integrating.

The differentiation formulas for e^u, uv, u/v, and u^n have all been derived from the formula for $log\ u$, which assumes the existence of the limiting value e. Thus all of our differentiation and integration formulas to date rest upon this assumption — except that the formula for $d(u^n)$ had already been derived independently in the case of an integral or fractional value of n. The (uv) and (u/v) formulas are also easily derived independently by the Δ process.

The logarithmic method is the best for differentiating complicated products, roots, etc.

Logarithmic and semi-logarithmic plotting are useful in statistical work, and in discovering or studying Power Laws and Compound Interest Laws.

The functions and differentiation formulas of this chapter find many applications in other connections. For some of these we need further ideas relating to geometry and motion. The latter, themselves major concerns of mathematical analysis, will next be studied.

EXERCISES

1. What differentiation formulas have been covered so far in the course? Under which of these does each of the following forms come *primarily*:

$y = \log(x^{20})$, $y = (\log x)^{20}$, $y = (\log x)/x$, $y = e^{x^5}$, $y = (e^x + 1)^6$?

2. (*a*)–(*e*). Differentiate each of the functions in Ex. 1.

3. Differentiate each of the following functions:

(*a*) $y = (\log_{10} x)^2$,

(*b*) $y = \log(x^3/\sqrt{x-4})$,

(*c*) $y = (\log x)/x^{50}$,

(*d*) $y = x^2/(\log x)$,

(*e*) $z = x^5 \sqrt{x^{10}+25}$,

(*f*) $z = x^4 e^{-20x}$,

(*g*) $w = \dfrac{t^3}{t^6-1}$,

(*h*) $w = \dfrac{e^{3t}+e^{-3t}}{e^{3t}-e^{-3t}}$,

(*i*) $y = x^4 [(\log x)^2 - \frac{1}{2}\log x + \frac{1}{8}]$,   (*j*) $y = e^{3x}(x^3 - x^2 + \frac{2}{3}x - \frac{2}{9})$.

4. Approximately how much should $\log x$ increase while x runs from 1 to 1.000125? Hence $\log 1.000125 = \ldots$?

5. Find where the slope of the curve $y = e^{-\frac{1}{2}x^2}$ is a maximum or minimum.

6. The intensity of light needed to produce x units of a certain chemical in the retina is $i = kx^2/(a-x)$, where a and k are constants. Find di/dx.

7. In studying the vitality of certain cells this formula was used: $R = 93.1 e^{-.018t} - 3.1 e^{-.540t} + 10$. Calculate R and dR/dt at $t = 10$.

8. Another equation used in studying cells is: $x = k(1 - e^{-at})$, where a and k are constants. Find dx/dt in terms of x.

9. The speed of a point on a rotating wheel (v ft./sec.) varied thus: $v = 200 e^{-4t}$. Find a formula for the distance (x ft.) covered in any length of time.

10. In how many years will any sum double, drawing 5% interest, compounded continuously?

11. A sum of money, drawing interest compounded continuously, doubles in 8 years. What is the nominal rate r?

12. If a weight is to be suspended by a vertical rod, and the stress on every horizontal section of the rod is to be the same, the sectional area (A sq. in.) should vary thus with the elevation (x in.) above the bottom: $dA/dx = kA$. If $A = 10$ when $x = 0$, find the formula for A. If $k = .00002$, will the change in A from $x = 0$ to $x = 100$ be appreciable?

13. The speed V of a certain chemical reaction increases thus with the temperature: $dV/dT = .07 V$. If $V = 100$ when $T = 0$ write by inspection the formula for V at any temperature. Check, both as to the initial value and the rate. Also find T when $V = 500$. Draw by inspection a graph showing the general way in which V increased from 100 to 500.

14. In Ex. 13 derive the required formula by integration.

15. (a) Prove that the natural and common logarithms of any number are related thus: $\log_e N = 2.30259 \log N$, approx. [*Hint:* Let $\log N = x$, and proceed to exponential forms.] (b) From this relation find $\log_e 23.985$ correct to five decimals. (c) The same for $\log_e .23985$.

16. The population of Los Angeles Jan. 1, 1920, was 576,673; and Apr. 1, 1930, was 1,238,048. Assuming a constant percentage rate of growth, estimate graphically the population Jan. 1, 1925; also the date when the population reached 1,000,000.

17. In an experiment with light passed through a pinhole the intensity was found to vary as in Table I with the distance (x in.) from the hole. Find the formula for I.

(I)

x	2	4	10	20	50
I	600	150	24	6	.96

(II)

D	0	1	5	10	15
I	100	81.9	36.8	13.5	5.0

18. In an experiment with X-rays, the intensity i varied inversely as the 2.1th power of a certain distance x. Write the formula if $i = 10$ when $x = 1$. Draw the logarithmic graph from $x = 1$ to $x = 100$. What slope has it?

19. The intensity of light passing through a solution of copper chloride varied with the depth (D cm.) as in Table II. Find the law.

20. The area (A sq. cm.) of a deep wound treated by Dr. Carrel's method * decreased after t days, as in Table III. Show that this roughly follows a $C. I. L.$

(III)

t	0	2	4	5	7	10	12
A	6.2	4.7	3.5	3.0	2.2	1.3	1.0

21. The following table shows the reading of a vacuum gauge t hours after the pump broke down. (One value is grossly incorrect.) Discover the law. Also correct the error in the table.

t	0	1	2	3	4	5
R	29.2	15.6	9.40	4.48	2.40	1.28

* Cf. Ex. 10, p. 15.

CHAPTER VIII

RECTANGULAR COORDINATES

MOTION AND ANALYTIC GEOMETRY

§ 194. Our Object. We have seen that coordinates are useful in mapping and in facilitating general definitions of the trigonometric functions. Even more important, they provide a basis for the scientific investigation of motion, and for a very powerful and systematic method of studying geometry. In this chapter we deal with rectangular coordinates, leaving polar coordinates until later. We begin by indicating the basic procedure in analyzing the movements of a particle or material point.

The exercises will cover also some ideas which will be useful presently in studying geometry — together with some mapping for review.

(A) THE STUDY OF MOTION

§ 195. Path of a Moving Point. The motion of a point in any plane is conveniently studied *by means of its varying coordinates* (x, y), referred to axes in the plane. If we have a table giving the values of x and y at various instants, we can map each successive position and draw the approximate path.

Still better, if we have a pair of equations giving the values of x and y *at any time*, we can calculate as many positions as we please, and study the motion in detail. Such "equations of motion" are used in studying the motions of projectiles, airplanes, parts of machines, points on the vibrating strings of musical instruments, etc.

Ex. I. The position of a projectile t sec. after firing was
$$x = 1000\,t, \qquad\qquad y = 500\,t - 16\,t^2,$$
x and y being in feet. Plot the path.

At $t = 5$; $\qquad x = 5000, \qquad\qquad y = 2500 - 400 = 2100$;

and similarly for the other values in the following table.

t	x	y	t	x	y
0	0	0	20	20000	3600
5	5000	2100	25	25000	2500
10	10000	3400	30	30000	600
15	15000	3900			

Plotting these points (x, y), we draw the path smoothly. (Fig. 99.) Of course t is not plotted: it merely shows when the projectile reached each point (x, y).

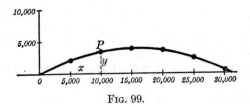

Fig. 99.

Remark. The projectile was highest when y was a maximum, or $dy/dt = 0$:

$$500 - 32\,t = 0, \qquad t = \tfrac{500}{32} = 15\tfrac{5}{8}.$$

It struck the ground when its height y became zero:

$$500\,t - 16\,t^2 = 0, \qquad \text{or } t = 500/16 = 31\tfrac{1}{4}.$$

The projectile struck at a point where $x = 1000\,(31\tfrac{1}{4}) = 31{,}250$.

EXERCISES

1. Plot the points $(0, 0)$ and $(16, 12)$, and join. Calculate the slope of the line; also its inclination angle, and its length.

2. A city is laid out in squares, 10 to the mile. Map the following points: A $(0, 0)$; B $(9, 23)$; C $(-15, 20)$; D $(22, -12)$; E $(-5, -12)$; F $(-22, -4)$. (The X-axis points east, and the Y-axis north.) How long a wire would be needed to reach from A to E? Which plotted points are inside the $2\tfrac{1}{2}$ mile circle about A? What direction is F from A? How far is C from F by a straight subway?

3. Referred to X- and Y-axes pointing east and north from Soissons, the coordinates of several cities and towns (in miles) are: Rheims $(32, -8)$; Cantigny $(-37, 19)$; Paris $(-44, -36)$; Château-Thierry $(4, -23)$. Map these points. Calculate the direct distance of Paris from Château-Thierry.

4. The positions (x, y) of a moving point after various intervals (t sec.) are shown in Table I. Plot these, and draw the path.

5. A point P moved thus: $x = 5t$, $y = 3t$. Calculate its position at various instants from $t = 0$ to $t = 5$. Draw the path. Did P travel the same distance in each unit of time?

6. Like Ex. 5, if $x = 3t^2$, $y = 2t^2$.

7. Like Ex. 5, from $t = -5$ to $t = 5$, if $x = t^2 - 9$, $y = t(t^2 - 9)$.

TABLE I

t	x	y
0	0	0
1	0.6	1.5
2	4.8	6.0
3	16.2	13.5
4	38.4	24.0
5	75.0	37.5

8. A batted ball traveled thus: $x = 60t$, $y = 80t - 16t^2$, the X-axis being horizontal and the Y-axis vertical. Calculate its position at various instants from $t = 0$ to $t = 5$. Plot the path, using the same scale both ways. By rolling a ruler along the curve, measure the distance traveled through the air.

9. In Ex. 8 find when the ball was highest. Where did it strike the ground?

10. The cross-section of a ship's hull at a bulkhead is a curve passing through the points shown in Table II. (All the abscissas are to be taken both positive and negative.) Draw the curve. Find the approximate area of the bulkhead, from the flat bottom up to the 30 ft.-level.

[11.] In Ex. 8 find dx/dt, and dy/dt. What meaning can you attach to these? Hence devise a way to find the actual speed of the ball at $t = 2$. (Cf. § 116.)

TABLE II

x	y
0.6	0
2.0	5
3.2	10
5.2	15
8.7	20
13.8	25
18.3	30
20.1	33.5

§ 196. Speed and Direction of Motion.

From a pair of "equations of motion," we can find not only where the moving point will be at any time, but also *how fast it will be moving,* and *in what direction.*

Consider, for instance, the projectile P in Ex. I, § 195:

$$x = 1000t, \qquad y = 500t - 16t^2.$$

The rate at which its height y is increasing at any time is the rate at which P is then rising. That is,

$$\text{vertical speed} = \frac{dy}{dt} = 500 - 32t.$$

E.g., at $t = 10$, P will be rising at the rate of $500 - 320$, or 180, ft./sec.

Similarly, since $dx/dt = 1000$, P will be moving horizontally at the rate of 1000 ft./sec.   (Fig. 100.)

In reality the motion of P will be neither horizontal nor vertical. But it is convenient to regard the *actual* motion as composed of two independent motions, in the X and Y directions.

If we draw directed lines or "vectors" to represent on some scale these two rates of motion, or "component speeds," then the *actual* speed and direction

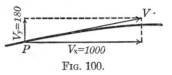

FIG. 100.

of motion will be represented by the diagonal of the rectangle:

$$\therefore \; v = \sqrt{1000^2 + 180^2} = 1016^+, \quad \tan A = \tfrac{180}{1000} = .18.$$

By tables, $A = 10° 12'$. Thus at $t = 10$, P was moving with a speed of 1016 ft./sec., in a direction $10° 12'$ above horizontal.

If the two component speeds were maintained for one second, the point P would move as just calculated, throughout the second.

§ 197. General Formulas.   Let v_x and v_y denote the speeds of any moving point (x, y) in the X and Y directions, respectively, at any instant.   Then, reasoning as in § 196, the actual speed and direction of motion are given by

$$v = \sqrt{v_x^{\,2} + v_y^{\,2}}, \tag{1}$$
$$\tan A = v_y/v_x. \tag{2}$$

That is, the actual speed and direction are represented by the diagonal of a rectangle whose sides, drawn from the same vertex, represent v_x and v_y.*

§ 198 S. Distance Traveled.   Knowing the speed v of a moving object at every instant, we can find by integration the distance s traveled during any interval of time.   For by (B), § 99:

$$s = \int v \, dt. \tag{3}$$

---

* A formal mathematical proof of formulas (1) and (2) is given in the Appendix, p. 524.

To illustrate, suppose that an object moves thus:
$$x = t^2, \qquad\qquad y = \tfrac{1}{3}\, t^3 - t.$$
Then
$$v_x = 2\, t, \qquad\qquad v_y = t^2 - 1,$$
and by (1) above the speed at any time is
$$v = \sqrt{(2\, t)^2 + (t^2 - 1)^2} = \sqrt{t^4 + 2\, t^2 + 1} = t^2 + 1.$$
Hence the distance traveled is
$$s = \int v\, dt = \int (t^2 + 1)\, dt = \tfrac{1}{3}\, t^3 + t.$$

The constant of integration is zero since $s = 0$ at $t = 0$.

N.B. The value of v which we must integrate in any case is the *general value in terms of t*, and not the numerical value at some one instant.

EXERCISES

1. At a certain instant a moving point P was at $(8, 15)$; and its horizontal and vertical speeds were $v_x = 4$, $v_y = 3$. Plotting P and drawing vectors as in Fig. 100, find the actual speed and direction of motion.

2. Like Ex. 1 if $v_x = 24$ and $v_y = -7$.

3. A point P moved thus: $x = 5\, t$, $y = 3\, t^2$. Plot the path, $t = 0$ to $t = 5$. Find the actual speed and direction of motion at $t = 2$; and draw the vectors representing v_x, v_y, and v.

4. Like Ex. 3 if $x = 15\, t$, $y = 50 - 2\, t^2$.

5. A bullet traveled thus: $x = 300\, t$, $y = 400\, t - 16\, t^2$. Find its position, speed, and direction of motion at $t = 25$. What do the results mean? Plot the point, and show the vectors.

6. A thrown ball traveled thus: $x = 64\, t$, $y = 5 + 48\, t - 16\, t^2$. With what speed and inclination did it start? Where was it highest, and with what speed was it then moving?

7. A stone thrown from an airplane traveled thus: $x = 140\, t$, $y = 3600 - 16\, t^2$, where y is the height above ground. With what speed and inclination did the stone (*a*) begin its flight, and (*b*) strike the ground?

8. A point moved thus: $x = 3\, t^2$, $y = 3\, t - t^3$. Plot its path from $t = -4$ to $t = 4$. Calculate v_x, v_y, at $t = 2$; also the actual speed and direction then. Illustrate by vectors.

9. In Ex. 8 find v at *any* time. Also find the exact distance traveled from $t = 0$ to $t = 4$; and check roughly by measurement.

10. A point moved thus: $x = 3\,t^2$, $y = 2\,t^3$. Find the distance traveled in the first t sec. (*Hint*: Show that $v = 6\,t\sqrt{t^2 + 1}$, and integrate as in § 101.)

11. As in Ex. 10 find the distance traveled from $t = 0$ to $t = 4$ in each following case:

(a) $x = t^3$, $y = 9\,t^2$;   (b) $x = \frac{16}{3}\,t^{\frac{3}{2}}$, $y = t^2 - 8\,t$.

12. (a), (b). Plot each path in Ex. 11a, b; and measure it.

[13.] If P starts at $(0, 0)$ and moves so that $v_x = 40$ continually, and $v_y = 60 - 32\,t$, find its coordinates (x, y) as functions of t. Also find the horizontal and vertical accelerations.

§ 199 S. Deriving the Equations of Motion.

The foregoing methods of studying motion exactly can be used only when we know the "equations of motion," which give x and y in terms of t. The question therefore arises as to how such equations are obtained in the first place.

The method is different in different cases. Sometimes the equations are discovered experimentally, the position of the moving object being observed at various times, and a formula being devised to fit the resulting table. But usually the equations are deduced mathematically from some physical or mechanical principle which governs the motion. A good example is the motion of a projectile, or other object, fired or thrown in any way.

If we ignore air resistance, there is no horizontal acceleration, and the vertical acceleration is -32 (ft./sec.^{2}).* That is,

$$\frac{d^2x}{dt^2} = 0, \qquad \frac{d^2y}{dt^2} = -32. \qquad (4)$$

Integrating both of these twice gives the desired equations, the constants of integration being determined by the way the projectile is fired, and by the choice of the origin of coordinates and the zero instant of time.

Some further types of motion, equally important, will be discussed later.

Ex. I. Find the equations of motion for a projectile fired with a speed of 1000 ft./sec. at an inclination of 30°.

* See §§ 91, 23.

Integrating (4):

$$\frac{dx}{dt} = c, \qquad \frac{dy}{dt} = -32\,t + c', \qquad (5)$$

$$x = ct + k, \qquad y = -16\,t^2 + c't + k'.$$

If we have chosen our axes so as to pass through the firing point, then $x = 0$ and $y = 0$ at $t = 0$. Hence $k = 0$, $k' = 0$. To

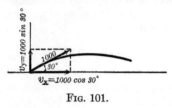

FIG. 101.

determine the values of c and c', observe in (5) that these constants are simply the values of dx/dt and dy/dt (*i.e.*, the component speeds v_x and v_y) at $t = 0$. By Fig. 101 these are simply:

$$v_x = 1000 \cos 30° = 866.03,$$

$$v_y = 1000 \sin 30° = 500.$$

Substituting these values of c and c' gives finally

$$x = 866.03\,t, \qquad y = 500\,t - 16\,t^2. \qquad (6)$$

Remarks. (I) These equations could now be used to study the motion in detail. The general shape of the path could be seen by plotting, as in § 195. Its precise geometrical character can be determined later.

(II) If the projectile were fired from an airplane 2000 ft. high, directly above our origin $(0, 0)$, we should still have $k = 0$, but $k' = 2000$.

EXERCISES

1. A stone was thrown with an initial speed of 80 ft./sec. at an inclination of 60°. What component speeds v_x and v_y had it originally?

2. Like Ex. 1 if thrown with a speed of 40 ft./sec. with a negative inclination of $-20°$.

3. Ignoring air resistance find the equations of motion for a ball, thrown from $(0, 100)$ with an initial speed of 70 ft./sec., at an inclination of 25°.

4. Like Ex. 3 for an initial speed of 50 ft./sec., and each following initial inclination:

(*a*) $-15°$; (*b*) The angle whose tangent is 3/4.

5. (*a*) Derive the equations of motion for a ball, thrown from $(0, 0)$ with a speed of 64 ft./sec., at an inclination of 30°. (*b*) Find the highest point in the path. (c) Regarding the given origin as at the ground, find how far away the ball struck the ground, and with what speed.

6. $(a) - (c)$. Like Ex. 5 $(a) - (c)$, if the initial speed is 96 ft./sec.

7. A golf ball, driven with a speed of 150 ft./sec. and an inclination of 39° 47'.5, over level ground, rolled 50 ft. after striking. Find the equations of motion through the air, and the total length of the "drive."

[8.] Plot the points (5, 2) and (13, 8). Calculate their distance apart. Can you derive a formula for the distance from (5, 2) to any other point (x, y)? From (x, y) to (x', y')?

[9.] Is the quadrilateral whose vertices are (2, 18), (24, 1), (89, 33), (67, 51) a parallelogram? Plot, but also make a sure test by calculating slopes.

(B) ANALYTIC GEOMETRY

§ 200. Formulas Needed. Coordinates are useful not only in mapping points and studying motion, but also in studying geometry. The first step in this direction is to derive certain standard formulas for distances, slopes, etc., by which those quantities can be calculated immediately without the necessity of drawing a figure. These formulas should be carefully memorized.

In deriving the formulas we shall denote any two given fixed points by (x_1, y_1) and (x_2, y_2). Here x_2 (read "x two") means simply the x of the second point. Do not confuse it with x^2.

§ 201. Distance Formula. The distance between any two points (x_1, y_1) and (x_2, y_2) is seen from Fig. 102 to be

$$d = \sqrt{(x_2 - x_1)^2 + (y_2 - y_1)^2}. \tag{7}$$

For d is the hypotenuse of a right triangle, whose legs are the difference of the x's and the difference of the y's.*

Ex. I. The distance between (2, 3) and (8, 15) is by (7):

$$d = \sqrt{(8 - 2)^2 + (15 - 3)^2} = \sqrt{180}.$$

Remarks. (I) It makes no difference which point is considered as (x_1, y_1) and which as (x_2, y_2). *E.g.*, $(2 - 8)^2$ equals $(8 - 2)^2$.

---

* The formula may also be written $d = \sqrt{\Delta x^2 + \Delta y^2}$.

(II) Formula (7) is correct even when some of the coordinates **are** negative. *E.g.*, for the points $(-4, -10)$ and $(-24, 6)$, (7) gives

$$d = \sqrt{(-24+4)^2 + (6+10)^2} = \sqrt{20^2 + 16^2},$$

which agrees with Fig. 102 where the legs of the right triangle are 20 and 16.

(III) Formula (7) holds also if the two points are on a common horizontal or vertical line. *E.g.*, if $y_2 = y_1$, (7) gives $d =$ the numerical value of $(x_2 - x_1)$, which is correct whether x_1 or x_2 is the greater.

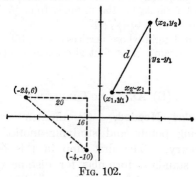

Fig. 102.

§ 202. Slope Formula. The slope of the line joining (x_1, y_1) and (x_2, y_2) is

$$l = \frac{y_2 - y_1}{x_2 - x_1}. \tag{8}$$

For the line rises $(y_2 - y_1)$ units in $(x_2 - x_1)$ horizontal units.

Ex. I. The slope of the line through $(3, 4)$ and $(8, 10)$ is

$$l = \frac{10 - 4}{8 - 3} = \frac{6}{5}.$$

(This is simply the difference of the y's divided by the difference of the x's, or $\Delta y / \Delta x$.)

Remarks. (I) The order of subtraction must not be reversed for x or y alone.

(II) Formula (8) is correct even when the line *descends* toward the right. For instance, for the line from $(-24, 6)$ to $(-4, -10)$ in Fig. 102, the formula gives $l = (-10 - 6) \div (-4 + 24)$ or $-\frac{16}{20}$, which agrees with the figure.

(III) If the given points lie on a horizontal line, (8) holds since, with $y_1 = y_2$, it gives $l = 0$. But for two points on a vertical line, $x_1 = x_2$ and (8) calls for an impossible division by zero. This corresponds to the fact that there is no possible slope for a vertical line.

DIRECTION. The direction of a line may be described by giving its *inclination* measured from the positive X-axis, upward or downward. This can be calculated from the *slope*, as in § 113.

The angle between two lines can be found from the two inclinations.

A sure test whether two lines are parallel is to see whether their slopes are equal. (Why?)

§ 203. Midpoint Formula. The point $(\bar{x}, \bar{y})$ midway between (x_1, y_1) and (x_2, y_2) is:

$$\bar{x} = \tfrac{1}{2}(x_1 + x_2), \quad \bar{y} = \tfrac{1}{2}(y_1 + y_2). \quad (9)$$

For the vertical line-segment through $(\bar{x}, \bar{y})$ in Fig. 103 bisects the base, and equals half the height, of the large right triangle. (Why?) That is,

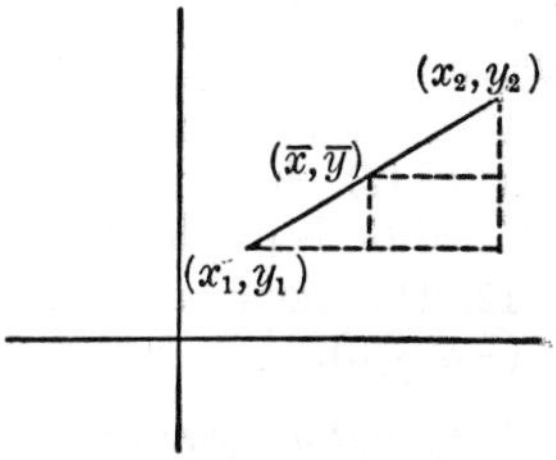

FIG. 103.

$$\bar{x} - x_1 = \tfrac{1}{2}(x_2 - x_1), \quad \bar{y} - y_1 = \tfrac{1}{2}(y_2 - y_1),$$

which, simplified, reduce to the formulas in (9).

The best way to remember (9) is to observe that $\bar{x}$ and $\bar{y}$ are simply the *averages* of the x's and y's of the given end points.

Ex. 1. The point midway between $(1, 14)$ and $(9, 8)$ is
$$\bar{x} = \tfrac{1}{2}(10) = 5, \qquad\qquad \bar{y} = \tfrac{1}{2}(22) = 11.$$

Ex. II. The point midway between $(1, 14)$ and $(-16, -6)$ is
$$\bar{x} = \tfrac{1}{2}(-15) = -\tfrac{15}{2}, \qquad\qquad \bar{y} = \tfrac{1}{2}(8) = 4.$$

EXERCISES

1. Calculate the distance from $(8, 16)$ to $(3, 4)$. From $(13, -5)$ to $(-2, 15)$. From $(0, 0)$ to $(8, -15)$. From $(-7, -3)$ to $(95, 133)$.

2. Show by the distance formula that the diagonals of the rectangle whose vertices are $(0, 0)$, $(15, 0)$, $(15, 8)$, $(0, 8)$ are equal.

3. In the triangle whose vertices are $A(8, 1)$, $B(11, -5)$, and $C(9, -2)$, which is the longest side?

4. Which of the points $(13, 14)$, $(14, 13)$, $(7, 19)$, $(2, -11)$, $(1, -9)$, $(9, 18)$ are on the circle with center at $(6, 3)$ and radius 13; and which are inside? Try to tell by plotting; but check by exact calculation.

5. Find the slopes and inclinations of the lines joining: $(8, 1)$ and $(13, 6)$; also $(-10, -12)$ and $(9, 7)$. Are these lines parallel?

6. Like Ex. 5 for $(0, 0)$ and $(6, -8)$; $(1, 10)$ and $(4, 4)$.

7. Find the length and slope of each side of the quadrilateral with vertices A $(13, 2)$, B $(5, 8)$, C $(-5, 4)$, D $(3, -2)$. What sort of figure?

8. Find the midpoint between $(9, 12)$ and $(3, 4)$. Between $(4, -5)$ and $(-2, 9)$.

9. How far is $(9, 6)$ from the midpoint of $(1, 4)$ and $(5, -8)$?

10. Find the midpoint of the hypotenuse of the triangle whose vertices are $(0, 0)$, $(30, 0)$, and $(0, 40)$; and show that this point is equidistant from all three vertices.

11. In the triangle whose vertices are A $(11, 2)$, B $(19, 8)$, and C $(13, 12)$ show that the line-segment joining the midpoints of AC and BC is parallel to AB, and equal to half of it.

12. The same as Ex. 11 for the triangle: A $(1, 7)$, B $(7, -1)$, C $(-3, -3)$.

N.B. Draw figures in the following exercises, but also use some sure test.

13. What sort of triangle is it whose vertices are $(14, 33)$, $(29, 13)$, and $(77, 49)$? Can you find the area of this triangle?

14. What sort of quadrilateral has the vertices $(-17, 33)$, $(3, 3)$, $(36, 25)$, and $(16, 55)$? Find the lengths of the diagonals.

15. A triangle has vertices $(3, 50)$, $(39, 14)$, and $(52, 63)$. What is its perimeter? Is it equilateral?

16. A triangle has vertices A $(8, 4)$, B $(22, 2)$, and C $(16, 10)$. Is it isosceles? Equilateral? A right triangle?

17. In the triangle A $(1, 6)$, B $(11, -4)$, C $(7, 12)$, find the length of the median from A to the midpoint of BC.

18. In Ex. 17 find the lengths of the other medians.

19. A quadrilateral has vertices $(11, -4)$, $(35, 12)$, $(31, 18)$, and $(7, 2)$. Is it a parallelogram? A rectangle? (Test the diagonals.)

20. Certain buildings in a city are located as follows: City Hall, A $(0, 0)$; Post Office, B $(3, 2)$; Court House, C $(0, -2)$; railroad stations, D $(-5, 4)$ and E $(9, 10)$. Plot. A garage is to be built midway between D and E, and a law library midway between A and C. What locations? How far is B from C and E in air lines?

21. A boulevard joins the points $(4, 1)$ and $(14, 7)$. What is its direction, if the X-axis points east?

22. At what angle is the boulevard in Ex. 21 crossed by a straight railroad connecting $(6, -5)$ and $(10, 15)$?

23. In Fig. 103 if $(\bar{x}, \bar{y})$ were taken as the point three fifths of the way from (x_1, y_1) to (x_2, y_2), derive formulas for $\bar{x}$ and $\bar{y}$.

24. The line from (x_1, y_1) to (x_2, y_2) is divided by a point $P\ (x', y')$ into two segments having any ratio $m_1 : m_2$. Prove that

$$x' = \frac{m_1\,x_2 + m_2\,x_1}{m_1 + m_2}, \qquad y' = \frac{m_1\,y_2 + m_2\,y_1}{m_1 + m_2}, \qquad (10)$$

25. Using (10) as formulas find on the line from $A\ (7, 2)$ to $B\ (28, 14)$ the point of trisection nearer A. [What are m_1 and m_2 in this case?] Check by plotting.

26. Find both points of trisection on the line from $A\ (-1, 9)$ to $B\ (17, 3)$.

27. In the triangle $A\ (4, 1)$, $B\ (10, 11)$, $C\ (-2, 5)$, find the midpoints P, Q, R on the sides opposite A, B, C respectively. Then find on each median AP, BQ, CR, the point of trisection nearer P, Q, R. Interpret the result.

[28.] Find the inclinations of lines having these slopes: $\frac{3}{5}$, $-\frac{5}{3}$, $2, -\frac{1}{2}$. Are some of the lines perpendicular? What is the rule, apparently?

[29.] Show that, for any point (x, y) on a circle with center $(0, 0)$ and radius 5: $x^2 + y^2 = 25$.

§ 204. Test for Perpendicularity.

Suppose that two lines are perpendicular, and that one rises at an angle of 40°. Then the other must fall at an angle of 50°. (Fig. 104.) Hence by § 113 the two slopes are

$$l_1 = \tan 40°, \quad l_2 = -\tan 50°.$$

But $\tan 50° = \operatorname{ctn} 40°$; hence $l_2 = -\operatorname{ctn} 40°$, $= -1/\tan 40°$. (§ 109.) That is,

$$l_2 = -\frac{1}{l_1}. \qquad (11)$$

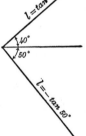

Hence, for these two perpendicular lines, *the slope of one is the negative reciprocal of the slope of the other.*

Fig. 104.

Moreover, this is true for *any* pair of perpendicular lines.* No matter at what angle A_1 one line ascends, the other must descend at an angle A_2 which is the *complement* of A_1. Thus the same reasoning applies as above:

$$l_1 = \tan A_1, l_2 = -\tan A_2 = -\operatorname{ctn} A_1 = -1/l_1.$$

* Except a horizontal and a vertical line. The latter has no such thing as a "slope," strictly speaking. See § 46.

Hence if one of two perpendicular lines has the slope 3, the other must have the slope $-\frac{1}{3}$. If one has the slope $-\frac{2}{5}$, the other must have the slope $+\frac{5}{2}$.

Conversely: if $l_2 = -1/l_1$, the lines must be perpendicular. For the perpendicular to the first line at the common point would have its slope equal to $-1/l_1$, and would have to coincide with the second line, since there can be only one line through a given point with a given slope.

§ 205. Equation and Locus. A sure test whether a point (x, y) is on the circle with center $(0, 0)$ and radius 10 (Fig. 105) is to see whether

$$x^2 + y^2 = 100. \qquad (12)$$

This equation holds for any point on the circle, no matter where taken. But it does not hold for points inside or outside the circle.

Similarly, a sure test whether a point lies on any other curve or line, say an ellipse or spiral or straight line, is to see whether some other definite equation is satisfied by the coordinates x and y of the point in question. Along any graph, for instance, there is some definite relation $y = f(x)$.

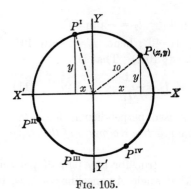

Fig. 105.

Definition. An equation which is satisfied by the coordinates of any point on a curve, but not by the coordinates of any other point, is called *the equation of the curve.* And the curve is called the *locus* of the equation.

E.g., (12) is the equation of the circle in Fig. 105. And that circle is the locus of equation (12). We have already plotted the loci of many other equations — such as $y = x^2$, $y = x^3 - 12\,x + 5$, etc.

§ 206. Descartes' Great Invention.

The fact that any one equation *belongs exclusively to some particular curve* makes possible the solution of many geometrical problems by means of coordinates.

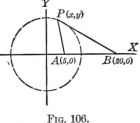

ILLUSTRATION. If a point (x, y) moves in such a way that its distance from $(20, 0)$ is always twice its distance from $(5, 0)$, along what curve will it move?

FIG. 106.

By hypothesis we have continually, in Fig. 106,

$$BP = 2\,AP.$$

Expressing BP and AP in terms of coordinates by the standard distance formula (7), p. 277,

$$\sqrt{(x - 20)^2 + (y - 0)^2} = 2\sqrt{(x - 5)^2 + (y - 0)^2}.$$

Simplifying by squaring and collecting terms:

$$x^2 - 40\,x + 400 + y^2 = 4\,(x^2 - 10\,x + 25 + y^2)$$
$$3\,x^2 + 3\,y^2 = 300.$$

That is, P must move in such a way that $x^2 + y^2 = 100$ continually. But by (12), p. 282, all points for which this is true lie on a certain circle. (Fig. 105.) *Hence P must move along that circle.*

This fact can also be proved by elementary geometry; but some ingenuity is required to know what construction lines to introduce. (Do you see what lines?)

Observe that in solving this problem by the coordinate method, we had only to express by a standard formula the given fact that $BP = 2\,AP$, and then simplify according to the standard rules of algebra. Much more difficult problems can be handled easily by this method as soon as we are familiar with the standard equations of certain curves, and can recognize the equations at sight.

Coordinates were invented by René Descartes, a Frenchman, who published in 1637 a systematic treatment of geometry by means of coordinates and equations. This was a great step in advance, for the method is so systematic and powerful that it permitted a tremendous extension of higher geometry. In particular, the problem at once arose of finding the direction of any curve at any point; and this soon led to the invention of calculus by Newton and Leibnitz. (Cf. § 103.)

Geometry thus studied is called "analytic" or "coordinate" or "Cartesian" geometry — Cartesius being the Latin form of Descartes' name.

EXERCISES

1. What is the slope of the line joining A $(2, -3)$ and B $(8, 7)$? Of any line perpendicular to AB?

2. List any pairs of the following slopes that would give perpendicular lines: $l_1 = .4$, $l_2 = -8$, $l_3 = -.25$, $l_4 = \tan 20°$, $l_5 = -2.5$, $l_6 = -1$, $l_7 = .125$, $l_8 = \tan 45°$, $l_9 = -\tan 20°$, $l_{10} = -\tan 70°$.

3. In the triangle A $(-2, 4)$, B $(12, -4)$, C $(8, 6)$ is the median from C perpendicular to AB?

4. The vertices of a quadrilateral are $(8, 4)$, $(12, -2)$, $(36, 14)$, and $(32, 20)$. Is it a rectangle? Are the diagonals perpendicular?

5. The vertices of a quadrilateral are $(4, 7)$, $(8, -7)$, $(40, -1)$, and $(10, 13)$. Show that the lines joining the midpoints of its four sides form a parallelogram. Is it a rectangle?

6. What is the equation of a circle with center $(0, 0)$ and radius 9? What is the locus of the equation $x^2 + y^2 = 9$?

7. What is the locus of $x^2 + y^2 = 625$?   Which of the points A $(20, 15)$, B $(24, -7)$, C $(-21, 14)$ are on it?   At which of its points is $x = 15$?   At which is $y = -10$?

8. (a) What is the locus of the equation $y = x$? Check by plotting the points where $x = -10$, -5, 0, 5, 10.   (b) Likewise for the locus of $y = -x$?

9. What is the equation of the X-axis?   Of a line 4 units above it? Of one 6 units below?   Of the Y-axis?   Of a vertical line 10 units to the left?   Of a vertical line through the point $(7, -2)$?

10. What value must r have if the curve $x^2 + y^2 = r^2$ is to pass through the point $(3, -4)$?   Through $(-5, -12)$?

11. Where does the curve $x^2 + y^2 = 25$ cross the **horizontal** line 4 units below the X-axis?   Where does it cross the line which bisects the angle between the negative X- and Y-axes?

12. Is the point $(12, 16)$ on the circle $x^2 + y^2 = 400$? Find the slopes of the lines joining it to the ends of the horizontal diameter What theorem of geometry is illustrated?

13. A point (x, y) moves so that the sum of the squares of its distances from $(-4, 0)$ and $(4, 0)$ is always 50. Find its path. Check by seeing whether its intersections with the X-axis meet the stated requirement.

14. Like Ex. 13 for $(0, 3)$, $(0, -3)$, and the sum of the squares equal to 90.

15. A square has its vertices at $(5, 5)$, $(5, -5)$, $(-5, -5)$, and $(-5, 5)$. A point (x, y) moves so that the sum of the squares of its distances from these vertices is always 600. Find its path. Show its position with respect to the given points, and check.

16. A point (x, y) moves so that the lines joining it to $(8, 0)$ and $(-8, 0)$ are always perpendicular. Find the path.

17. A point (x, y) moves so that its distance from $(0, 50)$ is always 5 times its distance from $(0, 2)$. Find its path. Check the points where it crosses the Y-axis; also the X-axis.

18. Express by an equation the fact that a point (x, y) is on the circle with center $(6, 1)$ and radius 15.

19. Calculate several points on the locus of each following equation and plot the general form:

(a) $y = \frac{1}{2} x + 5$,   (b) $2 x + 3 y = 10$,   (c) $2 y = x^2$.

Which of these loci have a constant slope dy/dx?

§ 207. Linear Equations.

If an equation is of the first degree — *i.e.*, of the form

$$ax + by + c = 0, \tag{13}$$

where a, b, and c are constants, a and b not both zero, its locus is a straight line.

PROOF. (I) If b is not zero, so that y is actually present, we can solve for y, getting an equation of the form

$$y = lx + k, \tag{14}$$

where l and k are some constants (viz. $l = -a/b$, $k = -c/b$). Differentiating this:

$$\frac{dy}{dx} = l, \text{ constant.}$$

That is, y increases at a constant rate, and its graph (or the required locus) must be straight (§ 5). In other words the locus has a constant slope; and all points for which the equation is satisfied lie along a straight line. Conversely, by § 30 the coordinates of all points on the line satisfy one and the same linear equation.

(II) If b happens to be zero, so that y is missing, then by hypothesis $a \neq 0$ and hence equation (13) gives simply $x = - c/a$. All points at which x has this constant value lie on a certain straight line parallel to the Y-axis. And, for all points on that line, x has the value $- c/a$.

Hence, whether $b = 0$ or $b \neq 0$, the locus of (13) is a straight line.

To find the slope of a line whose equation is given, we simply think of the equation as thrown into the form (14). The coefficient of x will then be l, the slope.

To draw a line from its equation, we simply calculate two points, well separated, and join them. A third point should be calculated as a check.

Ex. I. $2x + 3y + 5 = 0$. Here $y = -\frac{2}{3}x - \frac{5}{3}$. $\therefore$ Slope $= -\frac{2}{3}$.

Ex. II. $4x - 7y = 8$. Here $y = \frac{4}{7}x - \frac{8}{7}$. $\therefore$ Slope $= \frac{4}{7}$.

The directed distances which a line or curve cuts off on the X- and Y-axes — measured *from* the origin and regarded as positive or negative according to the direction — are called the *intercepts* of the line or curve. To find them, simply let $y = 0$ and solve for x; or vice versa. Thus, in (13), the intercepts are $- c/a$ and $- c/b$, provided a and b are not zero.

EXERCISES

1. Draw the line $3x + 2y - 24 = 0$, getting three points. What is its slope, according to your points; also by differentiation?

2. Like Ex. 1 for each of the following:

(a) $2x - 5y = 20$,   (b) $x + 3y = 12$,   (c) $3x - 2y = 0$.

3. What is the complete locus of $4x^2 - y^2 = 0$? How about slopes?

4. Draw the lines: $x = 7$; $y = -8$; $2x + 11 = 0$; $y^2 = 4$.

5. Draw the following lines, on a single pair of axes, checking each: $y = \frac{1}{3}x + 7$, $y = -2x + 7$, $y = \frac{3}{2}x + 7$, $y = \frac{3}{2}x + 1$, $y = \frac{3}{2}x - 4$. Observe how the constants 7 and $\frac{3}{2}$ appear in these lines.

6. What is the geometric significance of a and b in the equation $y = ax + b$? Compare Ex. 5.

7. Find by inspection the slope of each of these lines: $x - y - 10 = 0$, $2x - 3y + 1 = 0$, $5x + 4y - 3 = 0$.

8. What is the slope of any line parallel to $x + 8y = 100$? Of any line perpendicular to this?

9. Find such values for a and b that the line $y = ax + b$ will be parallel to $2x - y = 7$ and pass through $(1, 4)$.

10. Like Ex. 9 for a perpendicular line through $(1, 4)$.

11. Is the line $4x - 3y = 7$ perpendicular to the line joining $A(2, 9)$ and $B(6, -3)$? Does it pass through the midpoint of AB?

12. A point (x, y) moves so that its distances from $(2, 3)$ and $(8, -1)$ are always equal. (A) Find the equation of its path, in simple form. (B) Show from this that the path is perpendicular to, and bisects, the line joining the given points.

13. Show analytically that the locus of a point equidistant from $(3, 6)$ and $(9, -4)$ is the perpendicular bisector of the line joining these points.

14. Like Ex. 13 if the given points are $(3, 6)$ and $(3, -4)$.

15. How far is the point $(11, -7)$ from the line $x = -5$? Likewise the point $(6, 4)$? Likewise any point (x, y)? How far is (x, y) from the lines $x = -8$, $y = -4$, $y = 0$?

16. A point moves so that the sum of its distances from the X- and Y-axes is constantly 10. Draw its path. (Is this properly an unlimited line? Discuss.)

17. The total cost of publishing x copies of a book is: $T = ax + b$. What do a and b mean in this case? How would they show in the graph of T?

18. The pressure on a turbine is 2.8 tons when the water surface behind the dam is at "zero" level. It increases by .52 ton for each extra foot of depth. Express this relation. How would the values 2.8 and .52 appear in the graph?

19. A formula used in hydraulics may be written: $Q = 3.34\,H^{1.47} + 1.8704\,H^{3.47}\,x$. With H constant, but Q and x varying, what sort of graph? What slope? What vertical intercept? Plot the line for $H = 1$.

20. A point Q travels along the X-axis. Prove that the point $P(x, y)$ midway between Q and $A(4, 12)$ travels in a straight line. [Take Q as $(X, 0)$; consider $(\bar{x}, \bar{y})$.]

21. Like Ex. 20 if $AP = \frac{1}{3} QP$. [Use (10), p. 281]

22. Like Ex. 20 if Q travels along the Y-axis.

§ 208. Type Equation of a Circle.

Let (h, k) denote the center and r the radius of any circle. Then for any point (x, y) on the circle, and for no other points, we have by the distance formula:

$$(x - h)^2 + (y - k)^2 = r^2. \tag{15}$$

This is therefore the general equation for any circle. Observe that the coordinates of the center are *subtracted* from x and y — not added to them.

Ex. I. For a circle with center (5, 2) and radius 7, the equation is

$$(x - 5)^2 + (y - 2)^2 = 49.$$

Ex. II. Find the equation of the circle having (8, 3) and (4, − 5) as ends of a diameter.

The center is the midpoint (6, − 1); and the radius is the distance from (6, − 1) to (8, 3) or (4, − 5), viz. $\sqrt{20}$. The equation is

$$(x - 6)^2 + (y + 1)^2 = 20.$$

§ 209. Drawing a Circle from its Equation. In case a given equation represents a circle, we can easily recognize

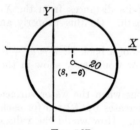

that fact, and determine the center and radius, by comparing the given equation with the type equation (15). The circle can then be drawn with the compasses.

Ex. I. Draw the locus of

$$(x - 8)^2 + (y + 6)^2 = 400.$$

This is a case of

FIG. 107.

$$(x - h)^2 + (y - k)^2 = r^2,$$

in which $h = 8$, $k = − 6$, $r = 20$. Hence, the locus is the circle with center (8, − 6) and radius 20. (Fig. 107.)

Ex. II. Find the locus of

$$2\,x^2 + 2\,y^2 + 10\,x + 7\,y - 10 = 0.$$

Dividing through by 2 and completing both squares gives

$$(x^2 + 5\,x + \tfrac{25}{4}) + (y^2 + \tfrac{7}{2}\,y + \tfrac{49}{16}) = 5 + \tfrac{25}{4} + \tfrac{49}{16};$$

i.e.,

$$(x + \tfrac{5}{2})^2 + (y + \tfrac{7}{4})^2 = \tfrac{229}{16}.$$

This represents a circle: center $(-\tfrac{5}{2}, -\tfrac{7}{4})$; radius, $\sqrt{229}/4$.

Ex. III. Is the locus of $2\,x^2 + 3\,y^2 - 5\,x = 7$ a circle?

No; for this equation cannot be reduced to the type equation (15) — in which the coefficients of x^2 and y^2 are both 1. (At present we could plot the locus only by calculating points; later we shall be able to recognize precisely what curve it is.)

Remark. The only terms which can appear in the type equation (15) when multiplied out are: $x^2 + y^2$, with a common coefficient; x and y, with any coefficients, and a constant term. (The product xy cannot occur, nor $x^2 - y^2$, nor higher powers.) Thus we can tell at a glance whether any given equation represents some circle.

EXERCISES

1. Write the equations of the circles which have the following centers and radii: $(8, 4)$, $r = 15$; $(-2, -7)$, $r = 9$; $(0, 4)$, $r = 2$.

2. Find the equations of the following circles:

(a) With center $(1, -2)$, and passing through the point $(6, -14)$;

(b) With center midway between $(4, 9)$ and $(8, -3)$, and passing through $(-1, -1)$;

(c) Having the line joining $(4, 4)$ and $(-8, 20)$ as a diameter.

3. Find where the line $y = 12$ meets the circle with center $(-3, 15)$ and radius 5.

4. What are the centers and radii of: $(x - 2)^2 + (y + 1)^2 = 9$; $(x + 8)^2 + y^2 = 16$; $x^2 + (y - 7)^2 = 4$? Draw each circle by compasses.

5. Find the centers and radii of the circles $x^2 + y^2 + 10x - 24y = 0$; $x^2 + y^2 = 6x$. Draw the circles.

6. The same as Ex. 5 for the circles $2x^2 + 2y^2 - 4x + 3y = 0$, and $3x^2 + 3y^2 + 8x = 1$.

7. A point (x, y) moves so that the sum of the squares of its distances from $(0, 8)$ and $(0, -8)$ is 200. Find the equation, and draw the path. Select some special point on the curve and verify that it fulfills the specified requirement.

8. A point moves so that the sum of the squares of its distances from $(5, 0)$ and $(-5, 0)$ is any constant k. Find the character of its path. Draw the path when $k = 58$ and when $k = 148$. In each case check for some point.

9. A point moves so that its distance from $(9, 12)$ is always twice its distance from $(0, 0)$. Find the equation of its path; plot, and check for some point.

10. Like Ex. 9 for $(0, -9)$ and $(0, 0)$, respectively.

11. In an "addition" to a certain city a boulevard is to run east to $(22, 9)$, then swing around a quarter-circle and run south from $(27, 4)$. By inspection, what center and radius must the curved arc have? What equation? Where will the curve meet a street on which $x = 26$?

12. The same as Ex. 11 if the curve starts at $(21, 18)$ and ends at $(34, 5)$.

13. Draw circles with centers $(0, 0)$ and $(6, 8)$ and passing through $(15, 20)$. Find their equations. How much higher is the first at $x = 0$ than the second at $x = 18$? Are they tangent? Reason?

14. The curve of the under side of a bridge consists of three circular arcs, as follows: (I) Center $(0, 0)$, connecting $(56, 192)$ and $(-56, 192)$; (II) Center $(14, 48)$, running from $(56, 192)$ as far as $x = 104$; (III) Symmetrical with (II), on the left. Draw this compound curve. Show that the intersection $(56, 192)$ is on the line of centers, making the arcs tangent.

15. In Ex. 14, calculate the radius of each circle and write each equation. Calculate the height of the arch at the middle, above the ends. Compare with your drawing.

16. Find by differentiation the slope of the tangent to the circle $x^2 + y^2 = 25$, at the point $(3, 4)$. Find independently the slope of the radius drawn to $(3, 4)$ and compare. What theorem is illustrated?

17. Let t be the length of a tangent to the circle $(x - h)^2 + (y - k)^2 - r^2 = 0$ from an external point (X, Y). By using a simple right triangle relation, prove that t^2 equals the left member of this equation, with (X, Y) substituted for (x, y).

18. By Ex. 17, what is the length of the tangent from $(9, 4)$ to the circle $(x - 2)^2 + (y + 3)^2 - 25 = 0$?

19. Draw the circle $x^2 + (y - 10)^2 = 25$. How high above the X-axis are the two points at which $x = 3$?

20. If the circle in Ex. 19 were revolved about the X-axis, what form of surface would be generated? How far would the center travel? Also the two points just mentioned?

21. A line-segment 10 units long moves with its ends on the X- and Y-axes. Find the path of the midpoint P (x, y).

22. Find the path of P if the lines joining it to $(0, 0)$ and $(8, 6)$ are always mutually perpendicular.

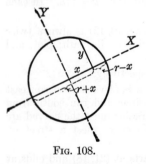

FIG. 108.

§ 210. Choosing Axes. In proving a geometrical theorem analytically we must first introduce axes. We select these, of course, in such a way as to make the equations and coordinates considered as simple as possible. When we wish to be general we use letters rather than special numbers for the coordinates of the given points. Two illustrations follow.

(I) THEOREM: *The perpendicular dropped from any point*

*of a circle upon any diameter is a mean proportional between
the segments of the diameter.*

PROOF.   Choose the diameter in question as the X-axis,
and the center of the circle as origin.   Then the equation of
the circle is simply $x^2 + y^2 = r^2$.   The proposed perpendicular
is simply y.   (Fig. 108.)   Hence we are to prove y a mean
proportional between the segments of the diameter $(r + x)$
and $(r - x)$.

Now from the equation of the circle we have at once

$$y^2 = r^2 - x^2,$$

or $$y^2 = (r + x)\,(r - x).$$

$$\therefore\ \frac{r + x}{y} = \frac{y}{r - x}.$$ (Q. E. D.)

(II) PROBLEM: *A point P (x, y)
moves in such a way that the sum
of the squares of its distances from
two fixed points F and F' is constant.   Along what curve does it
move?*

SOLUTION.   Choose the line FF'
as the X-axis, and the midpoint
as the origin.   Let c denote one
half the distance between F and
F', whose coordinates are then
simply $(c, 0)$ and $(- c, 0)$. (Fig. 109.)

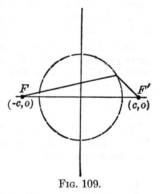

FIG. 109.

Let k denote the constant sum of the squares: $FP^2 + F'P^2$.
Then

$$\left[\sqrt{(x - c)^2 + y^2}\right]^2 + \left[\sqrt{(x + c)^2 + y^2}\right]^2 = k.$$

The radicals disappear, and the equation reduces to

$$x^2 + y^2 = (k/2) - c^2.$$

The path is a circle with center midway between F and F'.

EXERCISES

Use analytic methods of proof or investigation

1. Prove that the middle point of the hypotenuse of any right
triangle is equidistant from the three vertices.

2. Prove that the diagonals of any rectangle are equal, but that they are perpendicular only if the rectangle is a square.

3. In Fig. 109, if the *difference* of the squares were constant instead of the sum, what would the path be?

4. A point moves in such a way that the sum of the squares of its distances from the three vertices of a triangle is constant. Prove that its path is some circle.

5. A point moves so that its distances from two fixed points have a constant ratio. What kind of curve is the path in general? Is there any exception?

6. A point moves so that the sum of the squares of its distances from the four sides of a square is constant. What sort of path?

7. Find the locus or possible path of a point P if the lines joining P to two fixed points A and B are always mutually perpendicular.

8. Find the locus of the midpoint P of a turning and varying line-segment which joins a fixed point A to a fixed line L.

9. A line-segment of constant length moves with its ends on two mutually perpendicular lines. Determine the locus of its midpoint.

10. A point P moves so that the tangent from it to a fixed circle C has a constant length. Prove that the locus of P is a circle concentric with C. Cf. Ex. 17, p. 290.

[11.] A point (x, y) moves so that its distance from $(6, 0)$ equals its distance from the line $x = -6$. (Cf. Ex. 15, p. 287.) Find the equation of its path.

[12.] From the answer to Ex. 11 calculate several points and plot. Then select several points on the curve and test by measurement whether they meet the requirement stated in Ex. 11.

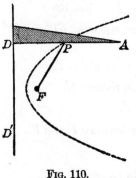

FIG. 110.

§ 211. The Parabola. We proceed now to study a few plane curves other than circles, which are used frequently in scientific work.*

Definition: A parabola is the locus of a point which is equidistant from a fixed straight line and a fixed point not on this line.

This means (Fig. 110) that any point P on the parabola is equidistant from the line DD' and the point F; and also that every point

* We shall deal further with the geometry of lines and circles; but may get a clearer idea of the power of the analytic method by seeing it at work now on unfamiliar material.

thus equidistant is to be considered as part of the parabola. The fixed line DD' is called the *directrix*; and the fixed point F the *focus*.

Any number of points on a parabola can be found by simply drawing lines parallel to DD', and cutting them by arcs described from F with the proper radii.

Or the parabola can be drawn *by continuous motion*. A triangular ruler (Fig. 110) slides along DD', the edge DP being perpendicular to DD'. A string just long enough to reach from A to D has one end fastened to the ruler at A; and the other end fastened at F. The pencil point P keeps the string taut — that is, keeps $FP = DP$, while the ruler moves. Hence P travels along a parabola.

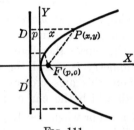

Fᴵɢ. 111.

§ 212. Type Equation. Denote by $2\,p$ the distance from F to DD'; and choose axes as in Fig. 111, so that F has the coordinates $(p, 0)$ and DD' is p units to the left of the Y-axis. Then for any point $P\,(x, y)$:

$$DP = x + p,$$
$$FP = \sqrt{(x - p)^2 + (y + 0)^2}.$$

At every point of the parabola, and at no others: $DP = FP$.

I.e., $x + p = \sqrt{(x - p)^2 + y^2}.$

Simplified, this gives as the type equation of a parabola:

$$y^2 = 4\,px. \tag{16}$$

E.g., $y^2 = 15\,x$ is the equation of a parabola in which $p = \frac{15}{4}$. That is, the distance from directrix to focus is $\frac{15}{2}$.

§ 213. Nature of a Parabola. The general character of a parabola can be seen from its equation

$$y^2 = 4\,px.$$

(1) It *does not extend to the left* of $(0, 0)$. For substituting negative values for x in the equation gives imaginary values for y. (2) It extends *indefinitely far toward the right*. For y is real at all positive values of x. (3) It is *symmetrical with*

respect to the X-axis. For there are always two values of y, $\pm$, numerically equal. Consider, then, only the upper half of the curve. (4) It has *no highest point* but rises continually. For y continually increases with x. (5) *Its slope,* however, *continually decreases.* For, differentiating gives

$$2\,y\,\frac{dy}{dx} = 4\,p, \qquad \text{or } \frac{dy}{dx} = \frac{2\,p}{y}, \tag{17}$$

which shows that dy/dx grows smaller as y increases. That is, although the curve continues to rise, it rises less and less rapidly. (6) It *makes no undulations.* For the slope reaches no maximum or minimum value.

The curve therefore appears as in Fig. 111. The axis of symmetry is called the *axis* of the parabola; and the point where this axis crosses the curve, the *vertex.* The rapidity with which the curve spreads apart depends upon the value of p. For when $x = 1$, $y = \pm \sqrt{4\,p}$.

When $x = p$, $y = \pm 2\,p$. Thus the width of the parabola, measured through the focus F along a chord perpendicular to the axis, is $4\,p$. This chord is called the *latus rectum.* (The fact that its length is $4\,p$ is a useful check in drawing a parabola and marking its focus.)

N.B. A curve may *look* very much like a parabola and yet not be one. It may even have all six of the properties above; and still it will not be a true parabola, unless all points on it are exactly equidistant from some fixed point and fixed line.

§ **214. Applications.** The parabola is a frequently encountered and much used curve.

An ideal cable of a suspension bridge, provided it is loaded uniformly per horizontal foot, will hang in a parabola (the axis of which is vertical). The arches of a bridge, or high ceiling, are often made parabolic — likewise the "crown" of a pavement.

The hollow upper surface of a rotating fluid in equilibrium is parabolic. (Fig. 43, p. 120.) So are the reflecting surfaces used in searchlights and telescopes.

The orbits of some comets, the paths of projectiles in a vacuum, and the graphs of many scientific formulas are parabolas.

§ 215. Parabola with Axis Vertical. If the axis of a parabola is turned straight upward, the focus being at $(0, p)$ on the Y-axis, and the directrix p units below the X-axis, the only change in the equation (16) will be that x and y will be interchanged. [Draw a rough figure to illustrate this.] The equation, then, will be

$$x^2 = 4\,py. \tag{18}$$

Ex. I. A parabolic suspension cable is to have its ends 200 ft. apart and 40 ft. higher than the middle. Required, the equation of the curve, and the height 50 ft. from the center.

With the origin taken at the lowest point the equation is of the form (18). But we are to have $y = 40$ when $x = 100$, at the end. Substituting gives $4\,p = 250$.

$$\therefore\ x^2 = 250\,y. \tag{Check?}$$

At $x = 50$, this equation gives $y = 10$. The cable will be 10 ft. above its lowest point 50 ft. from the middle; and a vertical strand to reach from the cable to the bridge should be cut accordingly.

EXERCISES

1. Draw $y^2 = 6\,x$ by inspection after calculating two or three points. What focus and directrix? How long is the latus rectum?

2. Like Ex. 1 for the following, drawing each pair on common axes:

    (a) $x^2 = 16\,y,\qquad x^2 = y;$ (b) $y^2 = x,\qquad y^2 = 9\,x.$

3. Write by inspection the equation of a parabola having:
(a) focus $(3, 0)$, directrix $x = -3$;   (b) focus $(0, 5)$ directrix $y = -5$.

4. Test without plotting which of the following points are on the parabola $y^2 = 24\,x$: $(6, -12)$, $(4, 9)$, $(9, 16)$, $(\frac{2}{3}, -4)$, $(0, 0)$, $(-6, 12)$, $(-24, -24)$, $(15000, -600)$.

5. For what value of p will the parabola $y^2 = 4\,px$ pass through $(10, 40)$? Find the point on that parabola at which $y = 8$.

6. Find the equation of a parabola whose axis is vertical, whose vertex is at the origin, and which passes through $(20, 4)$.

7. The hollow upper surface of a rotating fluid is parabolic: 4 in. deep and 20 in. across. Find the equation of the curve, taking the lowest point as $(0, 0)$. Find y at $x = 5$.

8. Going toward the bow, a ship's deck rises in a parabolic curve to a height of 8 ft. in a horizontal distance of 240 ft. Find the equation of the curve and the height at $x = 60$.

9. A suspension cable is so loaded as to hang in a parabola. Its ends are 1200 feet apart and 90 feet above the lowest point. Find its simplest equation; also its height at $x = 200$ and $x = 400$.

10. A level foot-bridge of span 200 ft. is supported by a parabolic suspension cable from towers 53 ft. above the floor, the center of the cable being 3 ft. above the floor. How long a wire is necessary to reach vertically from the cable to the floor 50 ft. from the center?

11. A circle moves and changes size so as to be always tangent to a fixed line and pass through a fixed point not on the line. Mark several positions of the center. Apparently what locus? Proof?

12. Finish deriving the equation $y^2 = 4\,px$ in § 212.

13. A reflecting telescope has a parabolic mirror 60 in. across. The distance from vertex to focus is 300 in. (a) Write by inspection the equation of the parabola, with its axis vertically upward. (b) How deep is the mirror at the center? (c) What is its slope at the edge?

14. (a–c) Like Ex. 13 (a–c) for the new telescope whose mirror will be 200 in. across with the focus 660 in. above the vertex.

15. (a–c) The same for another mirror 100.4 in. across, with the focus 508 in. above the vertex.

16. Prove that the area under the parabola $y = x^2$ from $x = 0$ to $x = 10$ is one third of the circumscribed rectangle having the same base. (Use the calculus method for finding the area under a curve. Archimedes obtained the result by other methods — a real achievement.)

17. State what kind of curve each following equation represents:

(a) $x^2 = 10\,y$,   (b) $x^2 + y^2 = 10$,   (c) $x^2 + y^2 = 10\,y$.

18. Find the height and slope of $x^2 = 5\,y$ at the point P where $x = 10$. Show that joining P to $(0, -20)$ would give the exact tangent line at P.

19. Prove that the latus rectum of any parabola subtends a right angle at the intersection of the directrix with the axis produced.

20. Prove that the angle subtended by the latus rectum at the vertex is the same for all parabolas — about 126° 52′.

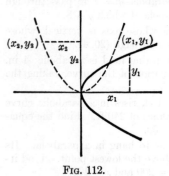

FIG. 112.

§ 216. Rotating a Curve 90°. It is important to know how the equation of any curve will be modified when the curve is moved to some new position without changing its shape or size.

Let us first consider the effect of merely turning a curve 90° about the origin, counter-clockwise. (Fig. 112.)

If (x_1, y_1) is a point on the original curve, and (x_2, y_2) the corresponding point on the new curve, then

$$x_1 = y_2, \qquad\qquad y_1 = -x_2. \qquad (19)$$

That is, each x in the original equation will be replaced by y and each y by $-x$.

E.g., if the parabola $y^2 = 4\,px$ is rotated 90°, its equation will be

$$(-x)^2 = 4\,p(y), \quad i.e., \quad x^2 = 4\,py. \qquad \text{[Cf. 18.]}$$

If rotated another 90°, so that its axis extends to the *left*, along the negative X-axis, its equation changes to $y^2 = -4\,px$. And, if rotated still another 90°, $x^2 = -4\,py$. (Verify this. Also see what effect a *fourth* rotation would have.)

Hence each of the equations

$$y^2 = \pm\,4\,px, \qquad x^2 = \pm\,4\,py \qquad (20)$$

represents some parabola. We need not memorize how the curve is turned for each of these equations; but in any given case simply make a substitution or two. Or notice which variable, x or y, may have both positive and negative values.

Ex. I. Locate the parabola $x^2 = -12\,y$.

Clearly x can be either positive or negative; but y cannot be positive. Hence no part of this parabola is above the X-axis; and the curve must extend along the negative Y-axis. (Draw the figure.)

Of course the focus and directrix are carried along with a parabola in its rotation. Hence the focus here is $(0, -3)$ on the Y-axis, and the directrix is $y = 3$.

EXERCISES

1. Draw by inspection $x^2 = -20\,y$ and $y^2 = -8\,x$. Also mark each focus and directrix; and find the length of each latus rectum.

2. Like Ex. 1 for the curves $3\,x^2 = -4\,y$ and $x + 5\,y^2 = 0$.

3. Write the equation of a parabola with focus $(-10, 0)$ and directrix $x = 10$; likewise of a parabola with focus $(0, -9)$ and directrix $y = 9$.

4. (*a*) Find the equation of a parabola through $(-12, -9)$, with vertex $(0, 0)$ and axis vertically downward. (*b*) Find y when $x = 8$.

5. A stone thrown from a cliff fell along the curve $x^2 = -100\,y$: (*a*) How far did it descend in going 50 ft. horizontally? 100 ft.? 200 ft.? (*b*) Find the slope and inclination of the path at $x = 200$. (*c*) Locate the vertex and directrix of the path.

6. A porch roof slopes away from the building in a parabolic curve with the axis downward and the vertex at the building. It descends 2 ft. in a horizontal distance of 8 ft. (*a*) Find an equation for the parabola. (*b*) How much does the roof descend in the first 2 ft. horizontally? 4 ft.? 6 ft.?

7. A roadway 20 ft. wide is 6 in. lower at the sides than in the middle. If the curve of the "crown" is a parabola, find its equation. What is the drop in 8 ft. from the middle? What slope at a side?

8. The curve of a ship's deck athwartship is a parabola which, in a horizontal distance of 30 ft. from the center, falls 1.5 ft. (*a*) Find its equation. (*b*) How much does the deck fall in the first 20 ft.? (*c*) What is the inclination at either edge?

9. The arch of a bridge is parabolic with a horizontal span of 400 ft., and with the ends 80 ft. lower than the middle. (*a*) Find the equation of the arch with the origin at the vertex V. (*b*) How much does the arch descend in a horizontal distance of 100 ft. from V?

10. In Ex. 9, a level road-bed, 10 ft. above the vertex, is supported by vertical columns from the arch, 20 ft. apart. Find the lengths of the columns at $x = 40$ and $x = 120$.

11. A hall 40 ft. wide has a parabolic arched ceiling 30 ft. high along the middle line and 25 ft. high at either side wall. Find the height and inclination of the ceiling 10 ft. either side of the middle.

[12.] (*a*) Square the binomial $\sqrt{x} - \sqrt{y}$. Also show that rationalizing the equation $\sqrt{x} - \sqrt{y} = \sqrt{x + y + 6}$ will ultimately give $xy = 9$. (*b*) If $\sqrt{(x-4)^2 + y^2} = 10 - \sqrt{(x+4)^2 + y^2}$, show that squaring gives $20\sqrt{(x+4)^2 + y^2} = 16x + 100$. Reduce finally to $9\,x^2 + 25\,y^2 = 225$.

[13.] A point (x, y) moves so that the sum of its distances from $(-16, 0)$ and $(16, 0)$ is always 40. Find the equation of its path, simplified. (Transpose one radical before squaring.) Locate several points by compasses and draw.

14. Prove this theorem: Any tangent to a parabola makes equal angles with the axis (produced) and with the radius from the focus to

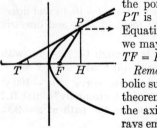

the point of tangency. [Hint: The slope of PT is y_1/TH, but by § 213 it is also $2\,p/y_1$. Equating, and remembering that $y_1{}^2 = 4\,px_1$, we may show that $TH = 2\,x_1$ and hence that $TF = FP$. Carry out the details of the proof.]

Remark. The reflection property of parabolic surfaces may be proved by the use of this theorem. Rays of light entering parallel to the axis will be focussed at F. Conversely, rays emanating from a source at F will emerge parallel to TF as a non-scattering beam.

Fig. 113.

§ 217. The Ellipse. *Definition: An ellipse is the locus of a point whose distances from two fixed points have a constant sum.* The two fixed points F and F' are called the foci.

Any number of points on an ellipse can be found by describing arcs from F and F' with various radii, FP and $F'P$, whose sum is constant. (Fig. 114.)

Or the ellipse may be drawn *by continuous motion.* Take a string longer than the distance FF', and fasten its ends at F and F'. Then, if a pencil point P keeps the string taut, it will move in such a way that $FP + F'P$ is constant — *i.e.*, along an ellipse. (A loop of string passed around two pins at F and F', and drawn taut, accomplishes the same result more conveniently.)

Evidently an ellipse must be a smooth symmetrical oval, as in Fig. 114. But not every such oval is an ellipse. In a true ellipse, the sum of FP and $F'P$ must be absolutely constant for all points. (Contrast this with Ex. II, § 210.)

§ 218. Type Equation. Denote by $2\,c$ the distance between the foci; and by $2\,a$ the constant sum $FP + F'P$. (Fig. 114.) Clearly $2\,a$ must be greater than $2\,c$.

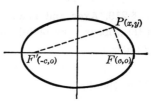

Fig. 114.

Choose axes as in the figure, making the coordinates of the foci $(c, 0)$ and $(-c, 0)$. Then by the distance formula:

$$FP = \sqrt{(x - c)^2 + y^2}, \qquad F'P = \sqrt{(x + c)^2 + y^2}.$$

At every point of the ellipse, and at no others:

$$FP + F'P = 2\,a.$$
$$\sqrt{(x - c)^2 + y^2} + \sqrt{(x + c)^2 + y^2} = 2\,a.$$

Transposing one radical, squaring, and simplifying:

$$a\sqrt{(x + c)^2 + y^2} = cx + a^2.$$

Squaring again and simplifying:

$$\frac{x^2}{a^2} + \frac{y^2}{a^2 - c^2} = 1.$$

Since $a>c$, as noted above, $a^2 - c^2$ is positive and may be regarded as the square of some real number b. Substituting b^2 for $a^2 - c^2$:

$$\frac{x^2}{a^2} + \frac{y^2}{b^2} = 1. \tag{21}$$

This is the type equation of the ellipse, when the X- and Y-axes are chosen as above.

Ex. I. What will equation (21) be if the ellipse is drawn with a string 10 in. long whose ends are 8 in. apart?

Here $2a = 10$, $2c = 8$. Hence $b^2 = a^2 - c^2 = 9$, and the equation is

$$\frac{x^2}{25} + \frac{y^2}{9} = 1.$$

Remark. To draw this ellipse roughly by inspection of its equation, simply find where it crosses the X- and Y-axes:

$$y = 0, \quad x = \pm 5; \qquad\qquad x = 0, \quad y = \pm 3.$$

Then draw a smooth symmetrical oval through these four points.

§ 219. Axes and Foci. The constants a and b of equation (21) appear very plainly in the ellipse. For the curve crosses its axes of symmetry at the points

$$y = 0, \; x = \pm a; \qquad\qquad x = 0, \; y = \pm b.$$

Thus the diameters AA' and BB' are $2a$ and $2b$.

Observe that the major axis $2a$ equals the "constant sum" mentioned in the definition — *i.e.*, equals the length of string required to draw the ellipse.

Observe also in Fig. 115 that FB and $F'B$, whose sum is $2a$ by the definition, must each equal a. That is, *the distance from either end of the minor axis to either focus is equal to half the major axis.* By using this fact, we can construct the foci geometrically, when a and b are known. Knowing the foci, we can draw the ellipse with a string, if desirable.

Moreover, if we get this triangular relation clearly in mind, we need not memorize the equation $b^2 = a^2 - c^2$, for the triangle will supply it.

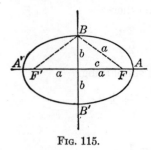

Fig. 115.

How flat an ellipse will be is determined by the relative magnitude of the distance $2\,c$ between the foci and the "constant sum" $2\,a$. The ratio c/a is called the *eccentricity*: it is less than 1. The chord through F or F' perpendicular to the axis is called a *latus rectum*.* The ends of the major axis are called the *vertices* of the ellipse.

Remark. If the ellipse is rotated through 90°, so that the major axis is vertical and the foci are on the Y-axis instead of the X-axis, the equation (by § 216) will be simply

$$\frac{y^2}{a^2} + \frac{x^2}{b^2} = 1.$$

The only change is that y now has the larger denominator. But no rule is necessary as to this; for *inspection of the equation at $x = 0$ and at $y = 0$ will show the lengths of the two axes.*

§ 220. Applications.

Many ellipses are encountered in studying nature: the orbits of the earth and other planets; the meridians on the earth's surface; any oblique section of a circular cylinder; the intersection of two equal circular cylinders or tunnels.

Ellipses are also much used in practical work: In making machine-gears, man-holes in ships' decks, the arches of many artistic bridges, and, in general, wherever a shapely oval is needed, as in a flower-bed, or an eye-glass, etc. The roofs of "whispering galleries" are elliptical in shape: faint sounds originating at one focus are reflected to the other, and can be heard there though inaudible between.

EXERCISES

1. Draw by inspection and find the foci of each following ellipse:

(a) $\dfrac{x^2}{169} + \dfrac{y^2}{25} = 1,$ (b) $\dfrac{x^2}{4} + \dfrac{y^2}{\frac{25}{4}} = 1,$

(c) $25\,x^2 + 9\,y^2 = 900.$ (d) $4\,x^2 + 25\,y^2 = 100,$

(e) $4\,x^2 + y^2 = 1,$ (f) $16\,x^2 + 25\,y^2 = 1.$

2. $(a$–$c)$ Find the eccentricity and the length L of either latus rectum for each ellipse in Ex. 1 $(a$–$c)$.

(d) From equation (21) show that for the general ellipse, $L = 2\,b^2/a$. By this check your results in $(a$–$c)$.

* The Latin plural is used: *latera recta.*

3. Write the equation of an ellipse with center $(0, 0)$ and axes along OX and OY, for which

(a) Longest diameter (horizontal) = 11, shortest diameter = 5;

(b) Longest diameter (vertical) = 9, shortest diameter = 2;

(c) Foci are $(-5, 0)$ and $(5, 0)$, longest diameter = 26;

(d) Foci are $(0, 7)$ and $(0, -7)$, shortest diameter = 48.

4. (a–c) How far apart should pins be placed and how long a string should be fastened to them, to draw each ellipse in Ex. 1 (a–c)? Or, how long a loop of string should be used around the pins?

5. An ellipse is drawn with a string 40 cm. long, whose ends are 24 cm. apart. Find its simplest equation.

6. Using pins 8 in. apart, and a loop of string whose total length is 28 in., what a and b will the resulting ellipse have? What equation?

7. The arch of a bridge is elliptical (a half-ellipse), 16 ft. high at the middle M, and having a horizontal span of 40 ft. Write its equation. How high is it 9 ft. to the right or left of M? How high 16 ft. from M? 10 ft. from M?

8. A hall 20 ft. wide has an elliptical ceiling 12 ft. high at the side walls and 18 ft. high in the middle. Find the height 4 ft. from either wall.

9. A bridge has an elliptical arch, of span 50 ft. and height 15 ft. Find the equation and draw the curve. The level roadway is 5 ft. above the arch at $x = 0$. How far is it above the arch at $x = 15$ and at $x = 20$?

10. The arches of London Bridge are semi-ellipses, the central one having a span of 152 ft. and a height of 37.8 ft. Draw the arch to scale. Also find its equation.

11. In the ellipse $9\,x^2 + 25\,y^2 = 225$, inscribe a rectangle having two sides in the lines $x = 4$ and $x = -4$. Find its area A. Repeat with the lines $x = 3$ and $x = -3$. Express A for *any* such inscribed rectangle.

12. In Ex. 11 find the area of the largest rectangle that can be inscribed in this ellipse.

13. Recognize and draw, showing the centers and foci, if any:

(a) $25\,x^2 + 16\,y^2 = 1600$, (b) $x^2 + 32\,y = 0$,

(c) $4\,x^2 + 9\,y^2 = 144$, (d) $4\,x + 9\,y^2 = 0$,

(e) $2\,x^2 + 2\,y^2 = 49$, (f) $x^2 + y^2 = 8\,x$.

14. The ellipse in which the earth travels around the sun has its longest diameter = 186 000 000 mi., and the distance between foci = 3 000 000 mi. Calculate the shortest diameter.

15. A point (x, y) moves so that its distance from $(-32, 0)$ is always $\frac{4}{5}$ of its distance from the line $x = -50$. Derive the equation of the path. Draw the figure, and check for some special point.

16. If every ordinate of a circle of radius 10 inches is reduced to half its value, show that the resulting curve is a true ellipse. [Hint: If (x, y) is on the new curve, then $(x, 2\,y)$ is on the circle.]

§ **221** *S.* **Further Properties.** An ellipse has numerous interesting geometrical properties, two or three of which may be mentioned here.

(I) *Relation to the Major Circle.* Let a circle be circum‑scribed about an ellipse, its diameter being the major axis. Erect any ordinate y of the ellipse, and prolong it until it meets the circle. Call its length up to the circle Y. Then from the equations of the circle and ellipse,

$$x^2 + Y^2 = a^2, \qquad\qquad \therefore\ Y = \pm\,\sqrt{a^2 - x^2}.$$

$$\frac{x^2}{a^2} + \frac{y^2}{b^2} = 1, \qquad\qquad \therefore\ y = \pm\,\frac{b}{a}\,\sqrt{a^2 - x^2}.$$

Hence $y = (b/a)\,Y$. That is, any ordinate of the ellipse equals b/a times the corresponding ordinate of the major circle.

E.g., in an ellipse having $a = 10$ and $b = 6$, every ordinate is three fifths of the corresponding ordinate of the circumscribed circle.

(II) *Converse of* (I). If in any curve every ordinate y equals some constant k times the corresponding ordinate Y of a circle, the curve must be an ellipse.

For, calling the radius of the circle a, we have

$$Y = \pm\,\sqrt{a^2 - x^2}, \quad y = \pm\,k\,\sqrt{a^2 - x^2}.$$

Simplifying the latter equation by squaring, transposing, etc., gives

$$\frac{x^2}{a^2} + \frac{y^2}{(ka)^2} = 1. \qquad (22)$$

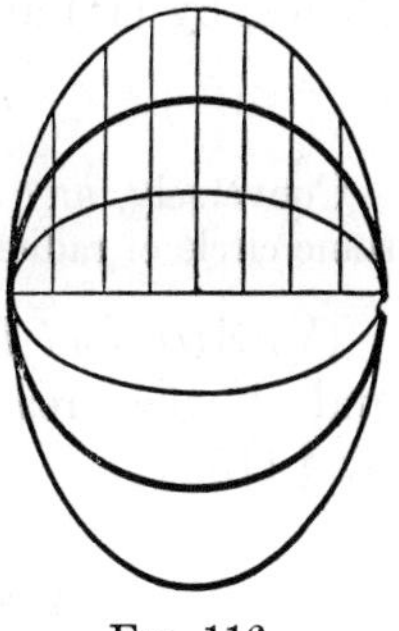

If $k < 1$, this represents an ellipse whose vertical axis (ka) is the shorter; and if

Fig. 116.

$k > 1$, an ellipse whose vertical axis is the longer. (Fig. 116.)

E.g., if we take a circle and reduce every ordinate to one half or two thirds of its original length, we get a true ellipse. Or if we lengthen every ordinate, say by 50%, we obtain an ellipse, with its major axis vertical.

(III) *Construction by Auxiliary Circles.* From the common center of two concentric circles, of radii a and b ($a > b$), draw

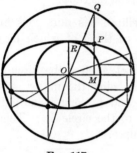

FIG. 117.

any radius meeting the outer circle at Q and the inner at R. Drop an ordinate QM from Q, and draw a horizontal line from R meeting QM at P. (Fig. 117.) Then the ordinates of P and Q have the same ratio as the radii. Hence this construction reduces each ordinate of the larger circle in the constant ratio b/a; and by (II) the locus of P is an ellipse. We can construct accurately in this way as many points of an ellipse as we wish, with any desired semi-axes a, b.

(IV) *Projection of a Circle upon Another Plane.* Let a semicircle of radius r be turned about its diameter until it makes some angle C with its former plane. (Fig. 67, p. 161.) Its projection on the former plane is some semi-oval, whose precise shape we wish to know.

Every ordinate (y) of the semi-oval is the projection of some ordinate (Y) of the semi-circle. By § 115, $y = Y \cos C$. Hence, by (II) above, the projection is a true ellipse, in which

$$a = r, \qquad b = r \cos C.$$

Conversely, any ellipse, of semi-axes a and b, is the projection of some circle of radius a, inclined at an angle C whose cosine is b/a.

(V) *Area and Perimeter.* Let A be the area of any ellipse, and A' the area of the circle whose projection it is. Then by § 115,

$$A = A' \cos C = A' \left(\frac{b}{a}\right) = (\pi a^2) \left(\frac{b}{a}\right).$$

$$\therefore \ A = \pi ab. \tag{23}$$

If an ellipse is nearly circular, its perimeter or circumference is given closely by the formula

$$P = \pi (a + b). \tag{24}$$

If there is much flattening, however, more elaborate formulas are needed.

Reasonably close results can be obtained by adding to the value given by (24) a percentage thereof, which runs as indicated in the following table.

b/a	0	.1	.2	.3	.4	.5	.6	.7	.8	.9
Add (%)	27.3	17.6	11.5	7.4	4.6	2.8	1.6	.8	.3	.1

Graphical interpolation can be used for other ratios. This table and (24) are found by more advanced methods.

Ex. I. Find the area and perimeter of an ellipse having $a = 10$, $b = 6$.

$A = \pi\, ab = 60\, \pi = 186.5$, approx.

$P = 16\, \pi +$ correction of $1.6\% = 51.07$, approx.

Ex. II. A damper in a circular stove pipe turned 60° from the position of complete obstruction cuts off an elliptic area in which $a = r$, $b = r \cos 60° = .5\, r$, and hence $A = .5\, \pi r^2$.

EXERCISES

1. Find the area of an ellipse having $a = 20$, $b = 6$. Also find the perimeter, applying a suitable correction to the rough formula.

2. Like Ex. 1 if $a = 10$ and $b = 7$; also if $a = 10$ and $b = 2$.

3. Find the volume of a cone whose height is 60 in. and whose base is an ellipse having longest and shortest diameters of 50 in. and 40 in.

4. The same as Ex. 3 for a height of 20 in. and diameters of 12 in. and 6 in.

5. Every ordinate of a circle of diameter 30 in. was reduced in the ratio 3:5. What axes had the resulting ellipse? What area? What perimeter? Write the equation in a simple form.

6. Like Ex. 5 for a diameter of 40 in., and a ratio of 4:5.

7. How long a loop of string should be used to lay out an elliptical flower bed 20 ft. long and 16 ft. wide; and how far apart should the fixed pins or stakes be? What area would the bed have?

8. Like Ex. 7 for beds (a) 25 ft. by 15 ft.; (b) 26 ft. by 10 ft.

9. Find the ground area covered by the Roman amphitheatre at Nîmes: an ellipse 133 meters long and 101 meters wide. What perimeter?

10. Like Ex. 9 for the ellipses covered by the following:

(a) The Colosseum at Rome: $a = 94$, $b = 78$ (meters),
(b) The arena of the Colosseum: $a = 43$, $b = 27$ (meters).

11. (*a*) The arch of a bridge is a semi-ellipse, 40 ft. high and having a horizontal span of 120 ft. Find the area of the opening under the bridge. (*b*) How would you solve this problem if the arch were parabolic?

12. In a photograph, the circular rim of a cup appeared as an ellipse. Explain this. Why do circular wheels, rings, lampshades, etc., appear elliptical when viewed obliquely? What shape, generally, is the shadow of a circular plate?

13. The circular damper of a pipe is turned 55° from the position of complete obstruction. What axes has the obstructed elliptical area?

14. In a photograph of a new moon, the crescent is always bounded by a semi-circle and semi-ellipse. (Why?) Supposing you had measured *a* and *b* for the latter (say 5 cm. and 4 cm., respectively), how could you proceed to calculate the actual illuminated area of the moon shown in the crescent? (The moon's radius is 2163 mi.)

15. A straight line 40 cm. long moves with its ends on the *X*- and *Y*-axes. Find the path of a point *P* 25 cm. from one end. (First mark several positions of *P* as the line turns, and draw the path.* Then derive the equation.)

16. Carry out the construction of Fig. 117, using two circles of radii 5 cm. and 3 cm. approximately.

[17.] A point moves so that the *difference* of its distances from (− 25, 0) and (25, 0) is always 40. Find the equation of the locus. Construct enough points to determine the general character of the curve.

18. The same as Ex. 15, p. 302, but using the point (− 16, 0) and the line *x* = − 25.

§ 222. Hyperbola. The locus of a point whose distances from two fixed points have a *constant difference* is called an

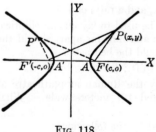

FIG. 118.

hyperbola.

We can construct geometrically as many of its points as we wish, by describing arcs with centers at the fixed points *F*, *F'*, and with radii *FP* and *F'P* which differ by a fixed amount. (Fig. 118.) Two separate curves are obtained, according as we choose *FP* or *F'P* the larger.

* Large ellipses are often drawn with a "trammel," using this principle.

(The two curves together are called the hyperbola.) These curves can also be drawn by continuous motion.

An hyperbola is clearly symmetrical with respect to the line through the *foci* F, F', and also with respect to the perpendicular bisector of FF'. A and A' are called the *vertices* and the distance AA' the transverse axis.

§ 223. **Type Equation.** Let the foci F, F' be denoted by $(c, 0)$, $(-c, 0)$; and the constant difference between FP and $F'P$ by $2\,a$. (Clearly $2\,a$ must be less than $2\,c$.)

Then at every point of the hyperbola, and at no others

$$\sqrt{(x+c)^2 + y^2} - \sqrt{(x-c)^2 + y^2} = 2\,a, \text{ or } -2\,a.$$

Transposing, squaring, and finally putting $c^2 - a^2 = b^2$:

$$\frac{x^2}{a^2} - \frac{y^2}{b^2} = 1. \tag{25}$$

(Since $a < c$, $c^2 - a^2$ is positive and may properly be called b^2.)

E.g., $\dfrac{x^2}{36} - \dfrac{y^2}{64} = 1$ is an hyperbola with $a = 6$, $b = 8$, and hence $c = 10$.

That is, FF' is 20 units and the "constant difference" $2\,a$ is 12.

Similarly, $\dfrac{x^2}{64} - \dfrac{y^2}{36} = 1$ is an hyperbola with $a = 8$, $b = 6$, $c = 10$.

That is, FF' is 20 units, and the constant difference $2\,a$ is 16.

Observe that in an hyperbola, a may be either larger or smaller than b. But c is greater than either.

§ 224. **Nature of an Hyperbola.** Because of the symmetry of the curve, we need to discuss only that quarter in which x and y are both positive.

Solving (25) for y gives

$$y = \frac{b}{a} \sqrt{x^2 - a^2}. \tag{26}$$

When $x < a$, y is imaginary; when $x = a$, $y = 0$. Thereafter as x increases, so does y, and the curve continually rises.

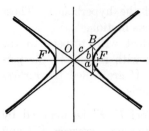

FIG. 119.

But y is always less than $b/a\ \sqrt{x^2}$. Hence the curve remains always below the line $y = (b/a)\,x$. This line is easily drawn; and will help in sketching the curve if we can tell how closely the latter will approach the line. (Fig. 119.)

The difference between the ordinate of the line, Y, and that of the hyperbola, y, is

$$Y - y = \frac{b}{a}\,(x - \sqrt{x^2 - a^2}). \tag{27}$$

When x becomes large, so will $\sqrt{x^2 - a^2}$. Will the *difference* become large or small? To find out, we multiply and divide by the *sum* $x + \sqrt{x^2 - a^2}$, getting

$$Y - y = \frac{b}{a}\,\frac{(x - \sqrt{x^2 - a^2})\,(x + \sqrt{x^2 - a^2})}{x + \sqrt{x^2 - a^2}} = \frac{b}{a}\cdot\frac{a^2}{x + \sqrt{x^2 - a^2}}.$$

It is now clear that $Y - y$ approaches zero, as x becomes very great. Hence the hyperbola will come as close as we please to the line if we draw it far enough. The lower half of the curve must approach a similar descending line.

These two lines approached by the hyperbola, but not reached by it, are called *asymptotes*. Their equations are

$$y = \pm\frac{b}{a}\,x. \tag{28}$$

Hence they pass through $(0, 0)$ and through the points where $x = a$ and $y = \pm b$.

Ex. I. Draw by inspection the hyperbola $\dfrac{x^2}{4} - \dfrac{y^2}{16} = 1$.

When $y = 0$, $x = \pm 2$. (Vertices.) At each vertex we erect an ordinate $b = 4$. Through $(0, 0)$ and the ends of these ordinates we draw straight lines, the asymptotes. Starting at $(\pm 2, 0)$ we draw the curve, approaching an asymptote as it recedes. (Draw the figure.)

Remarks. (I) Although the constant b of equation (25) does not show itself in the *curve*, it appears in the height of the asymptotes above the vertices.

(II) In Fig. 119, $OB = \sqrt{a^2 + b^2}$. That is, by § 223, OB is c, half the distance between the foci F and F'. Hence to locate F and F' geometrically, we need only describe a circle with center O and radius OB. Fix this picture in mind, and you need not remember the formula $c^2 = a^2 + b^2$, nor the equations $y = \pm\, (b/a)\, x$.

(III) The *latera recta* are defined as for the ellipse. Also, c/a is again called the eccentricity; but here it exceeds 1.

EXERCISES

1. Draw the hyperbola

$$\frac{x^2}{9} - \frac{y^2}{16} = 1,$$

showing foci and asymptotes. Also list the values of a, b, c, and the eccentricity.

2. Like Ex. 1 for each of the following:

(a) $\dfrac{x^2}{16} - \dfrac{y^2}{9} = 1$,   (b) $\dfrac{x^2}{25} - \dfrac{y^2}{144} = 1$,   (c) $\dfrac{x^2}{144} - \dfrac{y^2}{25} = 1$.

3. (a) In Ex. 1, find the length L of either latus rectum. (b) From equation (25) show that in general $L = 2\,b^2/a$.

4. (a–c) Use the formula obtained in Ex. 3 (b) to read off the length of a latus rectum for each hyperbola in Ex. 2 (a–c).

5. Write the equation of an hyperbola whose foci are $(\pm 10, 0)$, and whose constant difference $2\,a$ is 12; also of another with foci $(\pm 6, 0)$ and $2\,a = 10$.

6. As in § 224, express the difference $D = x - \sqrt{x^2 - 16}$ in a form to prove conclusively that $D \to 0$ as $x \to \infty$.

7. A circle moves and changes size so as to remain always tangent to two fixed unequal circles which are external to one another. (a) Mark several positions of the moving center C and state what its locus is. (b) Give a proof by considering the distances of C from the fixed centers F and F', in relation to the constant radii R and R'.

8. Like Ex. 7 if one fixed circle contains the other.

9. The same if the fixed circles intersect.

10. Like Ex. 7 but using a fixed straight line and circle instead of two fixed circles.

11. A point moves in such a way that its distance from $(-25, 0)$ is always $\frac{5}{4}$ of its distance from the line $x = -16$. Find the equation and draw the path. Check some particular point.

12. The same as Ex. 11 for $(-50, 0)$ and the line $x = -32$.

13. Draw a circle of some radius r with $(5, 0)$ as center; and another of radius $(r + 8)$, with $(-5, 0)$ as center, cutting the first at P and P'. Show that the locus of P and P' as r varies is one branch of an hyperbola. Write the equation.

14. How could numerous points on the hyperbola (25) be constructed geometrically?

15. Two stations A, B for airplane forest patrols are 50 mi. apart. What is the locus of points P that can be reached simultaneously from A and B, if the plane from B must start 6 minutes later than that from A, and each plane makes 140 mi./hr.? Likewise starting 6 min. earlier. Write an equation covering the locus in both cases.

[16.] If the hyperbola in Ex. 1 were rotated 90°, what would its new equation be? What foci then?

[17.] A point P (x, y) moves so that the difference of its distances from A $(10, 10)$ and B $(-10, -10)$ is always 20. Derive the equation of its path. Calculate a few points and plot.

18. As in Ex. 17 derive the equation if the difference of the distances is $2\,a$, and the given points are (a, a) and $(-a, -a)$.

§ 225. Hyperbola with Axis Vertical.

If the hyperbola $(x^2/a^2) - (y^2/b^2) = 1$ is rotated 90°, its new equation, found by replacing x by y and y by $-x$ (§ 216), will be

$$\frac{y^2}{a^2} - \frac{x^2}{b^2} = 1. \tag{29}$$

Thus the y^2 term will be positive and the x^2 term negative. Either x^2 or y^2 may have the larger denominator.

No rule is needed to tell whether an hyperbola has a horizontal or vertical position: simply try $x = 0$ and $y = 0$ in the equation.

Ex. I. $\qquad \dfrac{y^2}{9} - \dfrac{x^2}{25} = 1.$

If $x = 0$, $y = \pm 3$;   if $y = 0$, $x =$ imaginary.

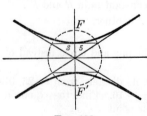

FIG. 120.

The curve meets the Y-axis 3 units above and below $(0, 0)$, but does not meet the X-axis at all. It is turned vertically.

The geometrical relation of the foci, asymptotes, etc., to the curve must be the same, no matter how the curve may be turned with respect to the X- and Y-axes. *The entire figure of auxiliary lines is rotated with the curve.* (Fig. 120.)

Hence to draw this hyperbola, we start at $(0, 3)$ and $(0, -3)$, where the curve meets the Y-axis, lay off *horizontal* lines 5 units long, draw the asymptotes, and fill in the curve.

§ 226. Rectangular Hyperbolas. If an hyperbola of a constant difference $2\,a$ has its foci at (a, a) and $(-a, -a)$, on the line through $(0, 0)$ inclined $45°$ to the axes, its equation is, by Ex. 18, p. 310,

$$xy = a^2/2. \tag{30}$$

By giving a different values, a set of such hyperbolas is obtained whose equations are all of this form, or

$$\boldsymbol{xy = k.} \tag{31}$$

Moreover, for every positive value of the constant k, this equation represents such an hyperbola — viz. one in which

$$a = \sqrt{2\,k}. \tag{32}$$

For negative values of k, (31) represents such hyperbolas, with $a = \sqrt{-2\,k}$, and with foci $(a, -a)$ and $(-a, a)$.

The asymptotes of all these hyperbolas are simply the X- and Y-axes. For, by (31), when x becomes very great, $y \to 0$; and *vice versa*. (Cf. Fig. 121.)

To draw the locus of (31) by inspection for a given value of k, first calculate the vertex by letting $y = x$, (or $-x$ if $k < 0$).

Because of the fact that the asymptotes are mutually perpendicular, these hyperbolas are called *rectangular*. Such hyperbolas, with the axes for asymptotes, are often used in making calculations concerning rectangular areas.

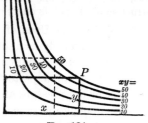

FIG. 121.

For instance, engravers use a chart like Fig. 121 to read off the price of a half-tone or zinc etching. Any desired rectangular plate is simply placed on the chart, with two of its edges along the X- and Y-axes. If its fourth corner P falls, say, anywhere along the curve $xy = 50$, then its area is 50 sq. in. The price to quote for a plate of that area is marked on the hyperbola, and similar prices on the other curves — which come at frequent intervals — so that no calculation is necessary.

EXERCISES

1. Draw these hyperbolas, showing foci and asymptotes:

(a) $\dfrac{y^2}{36} - \dfrac{x^2}{64} = 1,$ (b) $\dfrac{y^2}{64} - \dfrac{x^2}{36} = 1,$

(c) $9\,y^2 - 16\,x^2 = 3600,$ (d) $16\,y^2 - 9\,x^2 = 3600.$

2. (a–d) For each curve in Ex. 1 (a–d), find the eccentricity and the length of a latus rectum.

3. Write the equation of each hyperbola determined thus:
(a) foci $(0, \pm 5)$, vertices $(0, \pm 3)$;   (b) foci $(0, \pm 13)$, vertices $(0, \pm 12)$;   (c) vertices $(0, \pm 15)$, $b = 8$;   (d) vertices $(0, \pm 2)$, $b = 5$.

4. By (30) what is the equation of a rectangular hyperbola with the foci $(3, 3)$ and $(-3, -3)$? $(5, 5)$ and $(-5, -5)$? $(4, -4)$ and $(-4, 4)$?

5. Draw by inspection after calculating one vertex and some other point:

(a) $xy = 100$;   (b) $xy = -16$;   (c) $xy = 20$;   (d) $xy = -4.$

6. (a–c) In each case of Ex. 5 find the foci by comparison with (32). Check by the construction in Fig. 119, rotated $45°$.

7. Draw a chart of hyperbolas $xy = k$, for $k = 20, 30, 40$. If zinc etchings cost 24¢ per sq. in., label each of your curves with the cost of any plate which would fit it as in Fig. 121.

8. Steel weighs 7.83 gm. per cc. State how you could make a chart for reading off the weights of rectangular steel plates 1 cm. thick.

9. Through $P(5, 2)$ draw any line, meeting the X-axis at A and the Y-axis at B. From B lay off toward P on BA a distance $BQ = PA$. By considering equal lines and similar triangles, show that the coordinates (x, y) of Q satisfy the equation $xy = 10$. Hence what is the locus of Q as the line BA turns? How would you proceed to construct similarly points on $xy = 30$?

§ 227. Further Uses of Hyperbolas.

Whenever a quantity (y) varies inversely as another (x), $y = k/x$, or $xy = k$. Hence the graph is a rectangular hyperbola. A common example is Boyle's Law for a perfect gas at constant temperature: The product of the pressure and volume is constant, $pv = k$.

Other examples in science relate to electromagnetic field strength, capacity of a plate condenser, potential due to a charge at any distance r, pressure due to surface tension on a drop of liquid, Ohm's law for electric currents [Ex. 2 (h) below], etc.

Economists in discussing "demand curves" like D in Fig. 3, p. 4, use the rectangular hyperbola as a basis of comparison. For reasons indicated in Ex. 3 below this hyperbola is called the "curve of constant return."

In Economics also, ordinary hyperbolas are encountered in considering the boundary of the natural market area for one of two manufacturing centers, under conditions similar to those in Ex. 5 below.

In the World War, hyperbolas were much used in "sound ranging," to locate distant, invisible enemy guns and the bursts of shells fired at those guns. The principle is the same as that in Ex. 7–8 below.

Hyperbolic reflecting surfaces are sometimes used effectively in conjunction with parabolic reflectors.*

§ 228 S. Parabolic and Hyperbolic Formulas. As already noted, it is very common for one quantity to vary as a power of another:

$$y = k\,x^n. \tag{33}$$

Let us now summarize concerning the graphs of such formulas. And let us first confine our attention to the part of the plane in which x and y are both positive.

When $n = -1$, (33) becomes $y = k/x$ or $xy = k$. The graph is then a *rectangular hyperbola*. For any other negative value

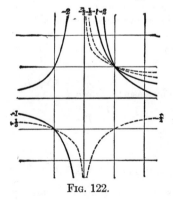

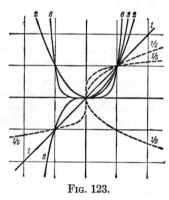

Fig. 122.   Fig. 123.

of n, the graph will be somewhat similar, approaching the axes asymptotically. (Fig. 122.)

When $n = +2$, the graph is the *parabola* $y = kx^2$ with its axis *vertical*. In fact, whenever $n > 1$, the graph is similar, rising slowly at first and then rapidly. (Fig. 123.)

* See *Higher Course*, p. 417.

When $n = \frac{1}{2}$, the graph is the *parabola* $y^2 = (k^2)\, x$, with its axis *horizontal*; and for other positive values of n less than 1 the graph is of similar form.

The lower half of the parabola for $n = \frac{1}{2}$ is obtained only if $x^{\frac{1}{2}}$ be interpreted to mean $\pm \sqrt{x}$.

For negative values of x, y may assume imaginary, or $\pm$ real, values — according to the nature of n. Figs. 122, 123 show several possibilities.

A discussion for irrational values of n would lead too far afield.

For any positive value of n, (33) is called a *parabolic formula* and the graph a *parabolic curve*. Similarly for negative values of n the formula and curve are called *hyperbolic*. For several illustrations of each, see Ex. 2 below, also pp. 51, 54.

EXERCISES

1. (a) Re-draw freely, with separate axes, the curves in Fig. 122 for which $n = -2, -\frac{1}{2}, -\frac{1}{3}$.

(b) Likewise those in Fig. 123 for which $n = 3, 2, \frac{1}{2}$.

2. In the following scientific laws, k and g denote constants. Show the general form of each graph — for positive values of the variables — and classify as parabolic or hyperbolic.

(a) Falling bodies (distance, speed, time): $s = \frac{1}{2} g t^2, \; v = g t.$

(b) Speed after falling h ft.: $v = \sqrt{2\, gh}.$

(c) Time of a pendulum, length l: $T = 2\, \pi \sqrt{l/g}.$

(d) Boyle's Law, volume and pressure for gases: $pv = k.$

(e) Adiabatic expansion of gases: $pv^{1.41} = k.$

(f) Magnetic repulsion, any distance: $F = k/d^2.$

(g) Heat produced by electric current i: $H = ki^2.$

(h) Current for resistance R (with E. M. F. constant): $i = k/R.$

(i) Volume flowing through fine tube, radius r: $V = kr^4.$

3. For a certain commodity suppose that the number of units (y) that could be sold monthly is inversely proportional to the price ($\$x$ each), within broad limits. If $y = 600$ when $x = 10$, make a table showing y when $x = 1, 3, 15, 40, 100$. Write a formula for y, and draw the graph by inspection. What would the total monthly receipts be at *any* price?

4. Like Ex. 3 if y varies inversely as x^2. Compare the total receipts merely for $x = 1, 10, 100$.

5. An article G can be made for \$6 less at A (0, 50) than at B (0, − 50), the coordinates here being in miles. If delivery at any point P could be made in a straight line, with the cost of delivery 10¢ per mile, find the locus of points at which G could be supplied from either A or B at the same total cost.

6. Like Ex. 5 if G can be made \$8 cheaper at B than at A.

7. The sound of an explosion at some unknown point P reached A (500, 0) and B (− 500, 0) at different times, indicating that P was 600 ft. closer to A. (The given coordinates also are in feet.) Show that this restricts the possible locations of P to a single curve. Precisely what?

8. The sound in Ex. 7 was similarly recorded at other points, indicating how much closer P was to A than to each of them. Explain how these observations would jointly locate P definitely.

[9.] Draw the ellipse $16\,x^2 + 25\,y^2 = 400$, and the same curve moved 9 units to the right and 10 units upward, without rotation. What should the new equation be? [Hint: If $(X,\ Y)$ is on the new curve then $(X − 9,\ Y − 10)$ was on the old one; and these values must satisfy the old equation.] Compare the new equation with that of a circle whose center has been moved from (0, 0) to (9, 10).

§ 229. Translating a Curve. Let us now see how the equation of a curve will be affected if we move the curve horizontally or vertically, without rotating it or changing its shape or size.

Let $x,\ y$ be the coordinates of any point on the original curve; and $X,\ Y$ be the coordinates of the same point after the curve has been moved, say *h units to the right and k units upward.* (Fig. 124.) Then

FIG. 124.

$$x = X - h, \qquad y = Y - k. \tag{34}$$

That is, the old coordinates equal the new ones diminished by h and k. Hence the equation of the curve in its new position is obtainable by *replacing each x in the original equation by $(x - h)$ and each y by $(y - k)$.*

Similarly, moving a curve h units to the left and k units downward will replace x by $x + h$, and y by $y + k$. Such constants h and k, which have the effect of sliding the curve along bodily, we shall call "translaters" or "sliders."

Ex. I.   If the circle $x^2 + y^2 = 100$ is moved 4 units to the right and 3 units upward, what will its new equation be?

Answer: $(x - 4)^2 + (y - 3)^2 = 100$.

(This agrees with § 208 for a circle with center (4, 3) and radius 10.)

Ex. II.   Recognize $(y - 2)^2 = 10 (x - 7)$.

This is the parabola $y^2 = 10\,x$, but moved 7 units to the right and 2 units upward.   To draw it, start from (7, 2) as vertex instead of (0, 0); and run the axis horizontally to the right, just as if you were drawing $y^2 = 10\,x$.

Ex. III.   Recognize

$$9\,x^2 + 72\,x - 25\,y^2 - 100\,y + 269 = 0.$$

Completing the squares for both the x and y terms:

$$9\,(x^2 + 8x + 16) - 25\,(y^2 + 4y + 4) = -269 + 144 - 100 = -225.$$

$$\therefore \frac{(y + 2)^2}{9} - \frac{(x + 4)^2}{25} = 1.$$

This is the same curve as $(y^2/9) - (x^2/25) = 1$ (Fig. 120, p. 310), but moved 4 units to the left and 2 units downward.   Hence we merely draw the curve represented by the latter equation, but starting from $(-4, -2)$ as the center instead of (0, 0).

Remark.   Observe that in translating a curve we replace each x by $x \pm h$ and y by $y \pm k$; never by $y^2 - k$ nor $ax + h$, nor any other expression.   Hence to recognize $y^2 + 12\,x - 7 = 0$ we must write it in the form $y^2 = -12\,(x - \frac{7}{12})$, rather than $y^2 - 7 = 12\,x$ or otherwise.

§ 230. Conics.   It can be proved that the parabola, ellipse, and hyperbola, though defined independently in what precedes, are all in reality special cases of a single kind of curve called a *conic*, which is defined thus:

A conic is the locus of a point whose distances from a fixed point and a fixed line have a constant ratio.

Ex. 15–16 below, also Ex. 15, p. 302, and Ex. 11–12, p. 309, illustrate this.   (What must the "constant ratio" be for a parabola?)

EXERCISES

1. If we shift each following curve as indicated, what new equation will it have:

(a) $x^2 = 10\,y$, right 4, up 2;   (b) $xy = 20$, left 4, down 5;

(c) $x^2 + 4\,y^2 = 100$, left 1, up 3;   (d) $xy = -1$, right 10?

2. Recognize the "translaters" and draw the curves:

(a) $\dfrac{(x+2)^2}{25} + \dfrac{(y-3)^2}{9} = 1$,   (b) $(y+4)^2 = 12\,(x-6)$,

(c) $x^2 + y^2 - 6\,x + 8\,y - 24 = 0$,   (d) $x^2 + 2\,x = 10\,y + 19$,

(e) $16\,x^2 - 64\,x + 25\,y^2 + 50\,y = 311$,   (f) $x^2 + 4\,y^2 - 48\,y - 52 = 0$,

(g) $(x-2)\,(y+11) = 10$,   (h) $xy + 3\,y - 4\,x = 0$.

3. Draw by inspection, showing the asymptotes and the foci:

(a) $\dfrac{(x-7)^2}{36} - \dfrac{(y+8)^2}{64} = 1$,   (b) $\dfrac{y^2}{16} - \dfrac{(x+15)^2}{9} = 1$,

(c) $16\,x^2 + 96\,x - 9\,y^2 + 180\,y = 612$,

(d) $9\,x^2 - 90\,x - 16\,y^2 - 256\,y = 223$.

4. An ellipse has its center at $(-5, -3)$, and is tangent to the X- and Y-axes. Write its equation by inspection. What are the foci?

5. An ellipse has the foci $(3, 1)$ and $(3, 9)$ and is tangent to the Y-axis. What is its equation?

6. A parabola has the point $(-3, -4)$ as focus and the line $y = 6$ as directrix. Write its equation by inspection.

7. A point (x, y) moves so that the sum of its distances from $(1, -2)$ and $(9, -2)$ is always 10. Express these distances, derive the equation of the path, and check by your knowledge of the ellipse.

8. An hyperbola has the foci $(3, 2)$ and $(3, 12)$, and one vertex is $(3, 4)$. Write its equation.

9. A point (x, y) moves so that its distance from $(0, -6)$ is twice its distance from $(0, 0)$. Find the equation of the path. What curve?

10. A ball moved along the curve $y = x - .01\,x^2$. Locate the highest point by differentiation. Check by completing the square and recognizing the sliders.

11. A ball traveled thus: $x = 20\,t$, $y = 32\,t - 16\,t^2$. Show that the path was a parabola; and draw it by inspection. [Hint: Since $t = x/20$, we can find y in terms of x.]

12. If a point moves so that $x = at$, $y = bt - 16\,t^2$, show that it travels along the parabola $\left(x - \dfrac{ab}{32}\right)^2 = -\dfrac{a^2}{16}\left(y - \dfrac{b^2}{64}\right)$. [Cf. § 199.]

318 RECTANGULAR COORDINATES

13. Draw by inspection: $(x + 100\,000)\, y = 15\,000\,000$. [This formula and curve are used by a telephone company in insulation tests.]

14. In studying red blood cells during a treatment of anemia, this formula was encountered: $y = (.73 - .2\,x)/(.73 + .8\,x)$. Reduce this to the form $(x + .91)\,(y + .25) = 1.14$, in round numbers. What is the graph?

15. A point moves so that its distance from $(c, 0)$ equals a constant e times its distance from the Y-axis. Derive the equation of the path.

16. In the equation of Ex. 15 put $c = 15$, and give e each following value. Reduce to a standard form and recognize the curve:

(a) $e = \frac{1}{2}$,   (b) $e = 1$,   (c) $e = 2$.

[**17.**] Test by slopes whether $(19, 35)$, $(28, 45)$, and $(-17, -25)$ are on the straight line through $(10, 20)$ whose slope is $\frac{5}{3}$. Express by an equation the fact that a point (x, y) is on this line.

§ 231. Point-Slope Equation of a Line.

Various geometrical properties of triangles relate to the intersections of certain straight lines. In studying such properties algebraically, the first step is to be able to write the equation of any specified line. This is easy *if we know the slope l and some point (x_1, y_1)* through which the line passes.

If (x, y) is any point whatever along the line, then

$$\frac{y - y_1}{x - x_1} = l. \tag{35}$$

For by § 202 this fraction is the slope of the line joining (x, y) and (x_1, y_1) which is the line under consideration. Moreover, (35) is not true if (x, y) is any point off this line. Hence (35) is the equation of the line. Or, more simply,

$$y - y_1 = l\,(x - x_1). \tag{36}$$

E.g., the line through $(4, 5)$ with slope 2 is

$$y - 5 = 2\,(x - 4), \qquad i.e., 2\,x - y = 3.$$

Note the distinction between (x, y) and (x_1, y_1); also that (36) cannot be applied to a vertical line, as there is then no such thing as a "slope." Along such a line, however, the value of x must remain constant, and hence the equation can be written at sight, in the form

$$x = \text{some constant.}$$

Ex. I. Find the equation of the perpendicular bisector of the line joining (5, 6) and (11, 14).

Slope of given line: $l_1 = \dfrac{14 - 6}{11 - 5} = \dfrac{4}{3}$.

Slope of required line: $l_2 = -\frac{3}{4}$. (§ 204)

The midpoint through which the required line passes is

$$x_1 = \tfrac{1}{2}(11 + 5) = 8, \qquad\qquad y_1 = \tfrac{1}{2}(14 + 6) = 10.$$

Hence the equation of the required line through (8, 10) with slope $-\frac{3}{4}$ is

$$y - 10 = -\tfrac{3}{4}(x - 8), \qquad \text{or} \quad 3x + 4y = 64.$$

§ 232 S. Tangents and Normals. The slope of a curve or of its tangent line PT at any point P is dy/dx.

The line PN perpendicular to the tangent line at P is called the *normal* to the curve at that point. Its slope is the negative reciprocal of dy/dx.

By using these slopes in (36), we can write the equations of the tangent and normal.

Ex. I. Find the equations of the tangent and normal to the ellipse $4x^2 + 9y^2 = 100$ at $(4, -2)$.

We could first solve for y, getting $y = -\frac{1}{3}\sqrt{100 - 4x^2}$, and then differentiate this under u^n (§ 77). Rather, we differentiate implicitly as in § 80 S.

$$8x + 18y\,\frac{dy}{dx} = 0,$$

$$\frac{dy}{dx} = \frac{-4x}{9y}.$$

Substituting $(4, -2)$ gives $dy/dx = \frac{8}{9}$, the slope of the tangent. Hence the normal has the slope $-\frac{9}{8}$. Thus the required equations are

Tangent: $y + 2 = \frac{8}{9}(x - 4)$, or $8x - 9y - 50 = 0$. (37)

Normal: $y + 2 = -\frac{9}{8}(x - 4)$, or $9x + 8y - 20 = 0$. (38)

A partial check is that $(4, -2)$ satisfies each final equation. A rough drawing would supply further verification.

Ex. II. Find the area of the triangle formed by the above normal with the X- and Y-axes.

Putting $y = 0$ in (38) gives $x = \frac{20}{9}$; while $x = 0$ gives $y = \frac{5}{2}$. These intercepts of the normal are legs of the right triangle in question.

$$A = \tfrac{1}{2}\left(\tfrac{20}{9}\right)\left(\tfrac{5}{2}\right) = \tfrac{25}{9},$$

EXERCISES

1. Write the equations of the following straight lines:

(*a*) Passing through (6, 2) with the slope 5;

(*b*) Perpendicular to the line in (*a*) from $(2, -10)$;

(*c*) Passing through $(-3, -2)$ parallel to the line in (*a*);

(*d*) Passing through $(-6, 9)$ and (12, 15);

(*e*) Through $(6, -5)$ and bisecting the line from $(2, -3)$ to (8, 11);

(*f*) Perpendicular to and bisecting the line from $(-6, 1)$ to $(2, -7)$;

(*g*) Through (0, 0) perpendicular to the line $3x - 7y = 15$;

(*h*) Through the midpoint of $(18, -1)$ and (6, 5) parallel to the line $5x - 2y = 9$.

2. The vertices of a triangle are $(8, -1)$, (14, 11), and $(-2, 17)$. Find the equations of the sides. Does any side pass through (0, 0)?

3. Find the equations of the medians in Ex. 2. Is any one of them perpendicular to the opposite side?

4. In the triangle A (2, 7), B (10, 1), C (8,15), which if any median is perpendicular to the opposite side?

5. A point moves so as to be equidistant from $(7, -3)$ and (17, 9). Show analytically that its path is the perpendicular bisector of the line joining those points.

6. The same as Ex. 5 for the points (5, 2) and $(-3, 14)$.

7. Find the equations of the tangent and normal to the parabola $y = x^2$ at the point where $x = 3$.

8. Like Ex. 7 for each following case, with y positive in (*c*):

    (*a*) $6y = x^2$,   (*b*) $xy = 12$,   (*c*) $y^2 = 12x$.

9. (*a*) Find the slope of $3x^2 + 4y^2 = 144$ at (6, 3) by first solving for y. (*b*) Check by differentiating implicitly and showing that the slope at any point is $-3x/4y$. (*c*) Write the equations of the tangent and normal at (6, 3).

10. Find the equations of the tangent and normal to each following curve at the point indicated:

(*a*) $4x^2 + \quad y^2 = \quad 25$, $(-2, -3)$;   (*b*) $x^2 - y^2 = \quad 16$, $(5, -3)$;

(*c*) $25x^2 - 16y^2 = 900$, $(-10, 10)$;   (*d*) $x^2 + y^2 = 169$, (5, 12).

11. At what point on the parabola $y^2 = 12x$ is the slope equal to 3? Write the equation of the tangent at that point.

12. Find the equation of the normal N to $y^2 = 12x$ at any point P (x_1, y_1). Show that N meets the X-axis at $x = x_1 + 6$. Hence state how a normal and tangent could be drawn to this parabola at any point. (Cf. Ex. 14, p. 298).

[**13.**] Draw $2x - 5y = 11$ and $2x + y = 5$, and find the intersection. How could you find this without plotting? If given the equations of three lines, how could you determine without plotting whether all the lines pass through a common point?

§ 233. Intersections of Loci. If any point is common to two lines or curves, its coordinates must satisfy both equations at once. Thus the problem of finding the intersection of two curves is equivalent to the algebraic problem of solving a pair of simultaneous equations. This is easy in the case of straight lines, whose equations are always of the first degree.

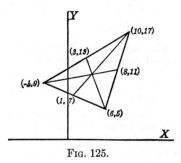

Fɪɢ. 125.

To see whether *three* lines are *concurrent* (*i.e.*, pass through a common point), we may solve for the intersection of two, and, by substituting in the third equation, test whether this intersection lies on the third line.

Ex. I. Prove analytically that the medians of the triangle whose vertices are $(-4, 9)$, $(6, 5)$, and $(10, 17)$ are concurrent.

On each median we know a point — viz. a vertex — and we can find the slope after getting the opposite midpoint.

Vertices:	$(-4, 9)$	$(6, 5)$	$(10, 17)$
Opposite midpoints:	$(8, 11)$	$(3, 13)$	$(1, 7)$
Medians' slopes:	$\frac{1}{6}$	$-\frac{8}{3}$	$\frac{10}{9}$

Equations: $\quad \dfrac{y - 9}{x + 4} = \dfrac{1}{6}, \quad \dfrac{y - 5}{x - 6} = -\dfrac{8}{3}, \quad \dfrac{y - 17}{x - 10} = \dfrac{10}{9}.$

Simplified: $\quad x - 6y = -58, \quad 8x + 3y = 63, \quad 10x - 9y = -53.$

To find the intersection of the first two medians, we solve the first two equations. Eliminating y gives $x = 4$; whence $y = 10\frac{1}{3}$. Testing $(4, 10\frac{1}{3})$ in the third equation shows that this point lies on the third median also. (*Q.E.D.*)

§ **234** *S.* **Pencils of Lines and Curves.** The lines through a fixed point A in all directions are said to form a *pencil* of lines. Similarly, the total set of circles through two points A and B is called a pencil of circles. It is convenient to consider pencils in solving many geometric problems.

Ex. 1. Find the equation of a circle which passes through $(1, 2)$ and also through the intersections of the circles C_1: $x^2 + y^2 - 5x + 7y + 16 = 0$ and C_2: $x^2 + y^2 - 25 = 0$.

Consider the equation:

$$(x^2 + y^2 - 5x + 7y + 16) + k(x^2 + y^2 - 25) = 0, \quad (39)$$

where k is an unspecified constant.

If we assign k a value, say $k = 5$ — in fact, any value except $k = -1$, which will be discussed presently — (39) will represent a circle, since the coefficients of x^2 and y^2 when collected will be equal and distinct from zero. Moreover, that circle must pass through the intersections A and B of the given circles C_1 and C_2. For, at A and B, the equations of C_1 and C_2 are both satisfied — *i.e.*, the quantities in parentheses in (39) are both zero — and hence (39) is satisfied.

Conversely, it can be proved that every circle (except C_2) through A and B is given by (39) for some value of k. (C_1 is obtained for $k = 0$; and C_2 can be obtained if we permit $k = \infty$.)

To find that circle of the pencil (39) which passes also through $(1, 2)$, simply substitute these coordinates in (39) and solve for k. We get

$$(30) + k(-20) = 0, \qquad k = \tfrac{3}{2}.$$

Using this value of k in (39) and reducing gives

$$5x^2 + 5y^2 - 10x + 14y - 43 = 0. \quad (40)$$

This is the required equation. Other ways of getting it would be much more laborious. Ordinarily it would be tedious to solve for the intersections A and B, and to use those directly. In the present example one intersection happens to be simple, $(4, -3)$. This can be used as a check in (40) and in the two given equations. Also the given point $(1, 2)$ can be used to check (40).

If $k = -1$, (39) reduces to a linear equation representing some straight line. But this must pass through A and B. Hence it is the line containing the *common chord* of the circles. This line is called the "radical axis" of the two circles. (Its points external to the circles can be proved to form the locus of a point P from which equal tangents can be drawn to the two circles. The latter property holds even when two given circles do not intersect.

Ex. II. Find the equation of that straight line through the intersection of $7x + 9y - 25 = 0$, and $8x - 3y + 31 = 0$; which has the slope $\frac{3}{5}$.

The equation of the pencil through the intersection A is

$$7x + 9y - 25 + k(8x - 3y + 31) = 0. \tag{41}$$

Collecting terms:

$$(7 + 8k)x + (9 - 3k)y - (25 - 31k) = 0.$$

This has the slope $l = -(7 + 8k) \div (9 - 3k)$, which is required to equal $\frac{3}{5}$.

$$-\frac{7 + 8k}{9 - 3k} = \frac{3}{5}, \qquad \therefore \ k = -2.$$

Using this value of k in (41) gives the required equation:

$$-9x + 15y - 87 = 0, \quad \text{or} \quad 3x - 5y + 29 = 0.$$

Check: The slope here is $\frac{3}{5}$. We could also get A as a check, if desired.

EXERCISES

1. Find the intersection of the lines $3x - 4y = 7$ and $x + 2y = 15$. Plot the lines and check your result.

2. The same as Ex. 1 for the lines $3x + y = 10$ and $3x - 2y = 6$.

3. Find the intersection of two medians of the triangle whose vertices are $A(5, 4)$, $B(1, -4)$, and $C(-9, 6)$. Test whether the third median passes through the same point.

4. Like Ex. 3 for the triangle $D(0, 0)$, $E(2, -4)$, $F(10, 10)$.

5. For the triangle $J(-1, -4)$, $K(11, -6)$, $L(5, 4)$, find the equations of the perpendicular bisectors of the sides, and show that these bisectors are concurrent.

6. Like Ex. 5 for the triangle $P(0, -3)$, $Q(12, 3)$, $R(0, 9)$.

7. In triangle JKL above, prove that the three altitudes are concurrent.

8. (a, b) Likewise prove the altitudes concurrent in the above triangles ABC and DEF, respectively.

9. Find the equation of the circle circumscribed about the triangle whose vertices are $(9, 4)$, $(-5, -10)$, and $(9, -8)$. (Hint: On what lines must the center lie?)

10. Like Ex. 9 for the triangle $(0, 0)$, $(6, 8)$, $(10, -2)$.

11. The vertices of a trapezoid are $(-6, 0)$, $(6, 0)$, $(-2, 2)$ and $(4, 2)$. Show that the non-parallel sides and the line joining the midpoints of the parallel sides are concurrent.

12. The same as Ex. 11 for the vertices $(-8, 0)$, $(8, 0)$, $(-4, 3)$, and $(2, 3)$.

13. Write the equation of a pencil of lines through the intersection of $2x + 3y - 9 = 0$ and $5x + y - 11 = 0$. Determine the line of the pencil which

(a) Passes through $(3, 1)$;   (b) Passes through $(0, 0)$;

(c) Has the slope $-\frac{12}{5}$;   (d) Has the slope $\frac{3}{2}$;

(e) Is vertical;   (f) Is horizontal;

(g) Is parallel to the line $2x - y = 0$;

(h) Is perpendicular to $x - y = 12$;

(i) Passes through the center of $(x + 2)^2 + y^2 = 25$;

(j) Meets $xy = -4$ at the vertex where x is positive;

(k) Passes through the focus of $y^2 = 12(x + 2)$.

14. (a–k) In Ex. 13 (a–k) check by finding the intersection of the given lines and using this to solve the problem.

15. Write the equation of a pencil of circles through the intersections of C_1: $x^2 + y^2 + 2x - 10y + 12 = 0$ and C_2: $x^2 + y^2 - 6x - 8y = 0$. Determine the circle of the pencil which

(a) Passes through $(0, 10)$;   (b) Passes through $(-3, 0)$;

(c) Reduces to a straight line (the radical axis of C_1 and C_2);

(d) Has its center on the X-axis;

(e) Has its center on the line $y = -x$.

16. Find the equation of the common chord of $x^2 + y^2 - 100 = 0$ and $x^2 + y^2 - 4x + 5y - 91 = 0$.

§ 235. Summary of Chapter VIII.

Coordinates are useful in following a moving point. The speed and direction of motion at any time can be found from v_x and v_y, which are merely the rates of change of x and y. The distance traveled during any interval can be found by integration. From the physical law of acceleration, ignoring air resistance, equations of motion can be found for projectiles by repeated integrations. Also the precise geometrical nature of the path can be found. Thus in the study of motion, coordinates are almost indispensable.

Coordinates are also helpful in studying geometry. The test as to whether a point lies on a given curve is to see whether its coordinates satisfy a certain equation. This connection between curves and equations permits the study of geometrical properties of curves by means of their equations.   Various theorems of Elementary Geometry relating to loci and inter-sections of lines are also easily proved analytically.

In the next chapter we shall study some algebraic techniques, which, besides having their own important uses, will provide us with further methods in Analytic Geometry.   We shall see, too, that the connection between curves and equations may be helpful in solving equations.   In some later chapters various higher curves are mentioned; and in more advanced courses a vast number of properties of the foregoing curves, and others, are worked out.   One interesting fact is that the ellipse, pa-rabola, and hyperbola can all be obtained by cutting a right circular cone by a plane.*

Remark.   The work of this chapter is closely connected with our central problem of studying functions.   For along any curve y varies with x in some definite way and is therefore a function of x.

There is, however, an important new element in the recent work. The equation of a curve is generally in the form of a *relation between the two variables* x and y, rather than a formula giving y explicitly in terms of x, as $y = f(x)$.   The equation implies that y is a function of x, but it defines y as such only *implicitly*.   Thus we may be said to be studying "implicit functions" now rather than "explicit functions."

EXERCISES

1. Draw by inspection: (a) $2x - 5y = 20$;   (b) $x^2 + y^2 = 169$;

(c) $(x + 8)^2 + (y - 2)^2 = 81$;   (d) $y^2 = 44x$;   (e) $x^2 = 60y$;
(f) $xy = -20$.

2. A railway easement curve, joining a straight track to a curved track of constant radius, has the form indicated by the following table.   Draw it.

x	0	300	600	900	1200	1350
y	0	3.9	31.7	109.4	282.2	443.4

3. A point moves so that its distance from $(-9, 6)$ is always twice its distance from $(0, 0)$.   Find the equation of the path and draw it.

4. Write by inspection the equation of a parabola whose focus is $(0, -6)$ and whose directrix is the line $y = 6$.

---

* The geometrical properties of these conic sections are of interest historically. By utilizing them modern Astronomy has explained the motions of the heav-enly bodies, and has freed mankind from the superstitions formerly excited by unusual celestial phenomena.

5. The same as Ex. 4 if the focus is $(7, -9)$ and the directrix is the line $x = -3$.

6. To draw an ellipse whose longest and shortest diameters are 50 in. and 48 in., how long a string would you use and how far apart would you fix the ends? How long a loop could be used?

7. Find the area and approximate perimeter of the ellipse in Ex. 6.

8. If the foci of an ellipse are $(-11, 8)$ and $(13, 8)$ and one end of the minor axis is $(1, 3)$, what is the equation?

9. The arched ceiling of a tunnel 24 ft. wide has the form of a half-ellipse. The height at the side walls is 12 ft.; at the center line, 20 ft. Find the height 6 ft. from the middle.

10. Derive the equation of the locus of a point (x, y) whose distance from the X-axis constantly equals its distance from $(0, 16)$. Draw the curve roughly by inspection.

11. The same as Ex. 10, if the distance from $(0, 16)$ is always $\frac{5}{3}$ times the distance from the X-axis.

12. Recognize and draw the curve $y^2 - 6y + 9x = 0$. What are the vertex and focus?

13. Find the center and foci, and draw each of the following curves: (a) $4x^2 - 64x + 25y^2 = 144$; (b) $9x^2 - 36x - 25y^2 + 100y = 39$.

14. An ellipse has foci $(15, 10)$ and $(15, -6)$, and is tangent to the Y-axis. Write its equation by inspection.

15. A point moves so that its distance from $(-14, 0)$ is always 12 units greater or less than its distance from $(6, 0)$. Find its path.

16. An hyperbola has the foci $(8, 7)$, and $(18, 7)$, and one vertex is $(10, 7)$. Draw it roughly. Also write its equation by inspection.

17. A point moved thus: $x = 40t$, $y = 144 - 16t^2$. Plot the path from $t = 0$ to $t = 3$. Find the speed and direction of motion at $t = 1$; and represent these on the graph.

18. In Ex. 17 prove that the path was a parabola. Find the vertex, focus, and length of the latus rectum.

19. A ball was thrown horizontally from a roof, 400 ft. high, with a speed of 80 ft./sec. (a) Find its equations of motion and prove the path a parabola. (b) How far did the ball move horizontally to reach the ground, and with what speed and inclination did it strike?

20. A triangle has the vertices $(0, 0)$, $(3, 2)$, $(2, 4)$. Show that the three altitudes are concurrent.

21. Find the equation of the circle which passes through $(10, 10)$ and through the intersections of $x^2 + y^2 - 6x = 0$ and $x^2 + y^2 + 8y = 0$.

22. Find the equations of the tangent and normal to $xy = 30$ at $(-5, -6)$.

23. If a point $P(x, y)$ moves on the curve $y^2 = 10x$, and if $Q(X, Y)$

is the midpoint of the chord joining P to the origin, find the equation of the curve in which Q moves.   Draw the two curves roughly.

24. If there are x complete heart beats per min., and each beat occupies y sec., express the relation between x and y.   What kind of graph?

25. A point P moves in such a way that the tangent to its path is always perpendicular to a line joining P to a moving point on the Y-axis 20 units higher than P.   Find the equation of the path.   Draw by inspection.

26. The force (F lb.) driving an object varied thus with the distance (x in.) from a certain point: $F = 5 + 20/x$.   What sort of graph? Find the work done from $x = 3$ to $x = 24$.

27. The air resistance to an airplane (P lb./sq. in.) varied as the square of the speed (V mi./hr.), P being 420 when $V = 100$.   Write the formula.   What sort of graph?   About what change in P between $V = 99.8$ and $V = 100.1$?

28. If a beam has one end embedded in a wall, and carries a load at the free end, its slope will vary as the distance (x ft.) from the wall.   What sort of a curve will it form?

29. In the main span of the Golden Gate bridge, each suspension cable forms a parabolic arc, whose ends are 4200 ft. apart and 475 ft. higher than the midpoint M.   (*a*) Find an equation for the curve. (*b*) How high above M are the cables 882 ft. either side of M?

30. Like Ex. 29 (*a*) for the George Washington bridge, with the ends 3500 ft. apart and 325 ft. higher than M.

31. In a span of the San Francisco-Oakland bridge, the parabolic cables rise 160 ft. in a horizontal distance of 960 ft. from the lowest point L.   How much have they risen at $x = -1100$?   At $x = 1210$?

CHAPTER IX

SOLUTION OF EQUATIONS

DETERMINANTS; ANALYTIC GEOMETRY

§ 236. Our Aim. In pure and applied mathematics many equations have to be solved. Various methods are covered in elementary algebra, and a few have been mentioned in earlier parts of this course. (§§ 17–21, 64.)

We now proceed to study systematically the best methods for solving certain types of equations that are important. Two main categories will be considered: (1) sets or systems of simultaneous linear equations; (2) single equations of higher degree. In both cases there will be important applications to analytic geometry.

(A) SYSTEMS OF LINEAR EQUATIONS: DETERMINANTS

§ 237 S. Simplest Case. Any two equations which are linear in two unknowns, x and y, can be written

$$a_1x + b_1y = r_1, \tag{1}$$
$$a_2x + b_2y = r_2, \tag{2}$$

where a_1, b_1, r_1, etc., denote numbers, or else quantities free from x and y. The problem is to find what, if any, values of x and y satisfy these equations simultaneously.

To eliminate y multiply equation (1) by b_2, and (2) by $- b_1$; and add. This gives:

$$(a_1b_2 - a_2b_1)\, x = r_1b_2 - r_2b_1. \tag{3}$$

Likewise multiplying (1) by $- a_2$ and (2) by a_1, and adding:

$$(a_1b_2 - a_2b_1)\, y = a_1r_2 - a_2r_1. \tag{4}$$

If $a_1b_2 - a_2b_1 \neq 0$, we may divide it out, getting *

$$x = \frac{r_1b_2 - r_2b_1}{a_1b_2 - a_2b_1}, \qquad\qquad y = \frac{a_1r_2 - a_2r_1}{a_1b_2 - a_2b_1}. \tag{5}$$

These, and similar results for three or more equations, can be conveniently expressed in a symbolic form.

---

* What happens if $a_1b_2 - a_2b_1 = 0$ will be discussed later. (§ 239.)

§ 238 S. Determinant Notation. Let the symbol

$$\begin{vmatrix} a_1 & b_1 \\ a_2 & b_2 \end{vmatrix} = a_1b_2 - a_2b_1. \tag{6}$$

That is, let it denote the product of the "elements," a_1 and b_2, in the "principal diagonal" (running down to the right from the "leading element" a_1), minus the product for the other diagonal.

E.g.,
$$\begin{vmatrix} 3 & 4 \\ 2 & 5 \end{vmatrix} = 15 - 8 = 7; \quad \begin{vmatrix} 3 & -4 \\ 2 & -5 \end{vmatrix} = (-15) - (-8) = -7.$$

The symbol in (6), called a *determinant of order 2*, is precisely the common denominator for x and y in (5). The numerator for x differs from the denominator only in having the a's replaced by the r's, or right members of (1) and (2). Similarly in the numerator for y, the b's are replaced by the r's. Hence (5) may be written:

$$x = \frac{\begin{vmatrix} r_1 & b_1 \\ r_2 & b_2 \end{vmatrix}}{\begin{vmatrix} a_1 & b_1 \\ a_2 & b_2 \end{vmatrix}}, \quad y = \frac{\begin{vmatrix} a_1 & r_1 \\ a_2 & r_2 \end{vmatrix}}{\begin{vmatrix} a_1 & b_1 \\ a_2 & b_2 \end{vmatrix}}. \tag{7}$$

Note, again, that (5) and (7) cannot be used if the denominator $(a_1b_2 - a_2b_1)$ *is zero.*

Ex. I. Solve by determinants $\begin{cases} 11x + 17y = 4, \\ 13x + 29y = 5. \end{cases}$

By (7) $x = \dfrac{\begin{vmatrix} 4 & 17 \\ 5 & 29 \end{vmatrix}}{\begin{vmatrix} 11 & 17 \\ 13 & 29 \end{vmatrix}}, \quad y = \dfrac{\begin{vmatrix} 11 & 4 \\ 13 & 5 \end{vmatrix}}{\begin{vmatrix} 11 & 17 \\ 13 & 29 \end{vmatrix}}.$

Multiplied out, the denominator gives 98, and the numerators 31 and 3 respectively. (Verify.) Hence

$$x = \frac{31}{98}, \quad y = \frac{3}{98}. \tag{8}$$

Check: $11\left(\frac{31}{98}\right) + 17\left(\frac{3}{98}\right) = 4, \quad 13\left(\frac{31}{98}\right) + 29\left(\frac{3}{98}\right) = 5.$

Definition. In any determinant the numbers or elements in any horizontal line form a "row"; those in a vertical line, a "column."

§ 239 S. Geometric Interpretation. If we regard the unknowns x and y in (1) and (2), p. 328, as coordinates of a point, allowed to vary, either equation alone represents a straight line. The two lines represented by the two equations may *intersect*, or be *parallel*, or *coincide*. If they intersect, their common point is given by (7) — likewise by (8) in Ex. I above.

If the two lines are parallel, they have no common point, and equations (1) and (2) have no simultaneous solution. If the lines coincide (as would be the case for such equations as $2x + 3y = 7$ and $4x + 6y = 14$), there is no unique solution: every pair of values x, y which satisfies one equation must satisfy the other.

For either parallel or coinciding lines (non-vertical), the slopes must be equal. Thus, from (1) and (2):

$$l = -\frac{a_1}{b_1} = -\frac{a_2}{b_2}; \qquad \therefore \; a_1b_2 - a_2b_1 = 0.* \qquad (9)$$

It can be shown conversely that whenever (9) holds, the lines either are parallel or coincide. This explains geometrically why the solution of (1) and (2) by formulas (5) or (7) must break down if $a_1b_2 - a_2b_1 = 0$.

EXERCISES

1. Find the value of each of the determinants:

$$\begin{vmatrix} 2 & 10 \\ 3 & 32 \end{vmatrix}, \qquad \begin{vmatrix} 5 & 9 \\ -1 & 4 \end{vmatrix}, \qquad \begin{vmatrix} 6 & 7 \\ -8 & 0 \end{vmatrix}, \qquad \begin{vmatrix} p & q \\ r & s \end{vmatrix}, \qquad \begin{vmatrix} p & q \\ -q & p \end{vmatrix}.$$

2. Like Ex. 1 for the following:

$$\begin{vmatrix} 6 & 30 \\ 3 & 32 \end{vmatrix}, \qquad \begin{vmatrix} 15 & 27 \\ -1 & 4 \end{vmatrix}, \qquad \begin{vmatrix} 0 & a \\ -a & 0 \end{vmatrix}, \qquad \begin{vmatrix} r+s & r-s \\ r-s & r+s \end{vmatrix}.$$

3. Find the values of the following determinants and compare:

$$D = \begin{vmatrix} a_1 & b_1 \\ a_2 & b_2 \end{vmatrix}; \qquad\qquad D' = \begin{vmatrix} a_1 & b_1 \\ a_2 + ka_1 & b_2 + kb_1 \end{vmatrix}.$$

4. In Ex. 3 prove that D would be unaltered in value if, in place of its first column, we put the elements of that column plus any multiple of the elements of column 2.

---

* For vertical lines, y does not appear in (1) or (2). Hence $b_1 = b_2 = 0$, and equation (9) still holds.

5. From $D = \begin{vmatrix} 9 & 2 \\ 11 & 3 \end{vmatrix}$ form a new determinant D' as follows:

Keep the second row unchanged, but replace the first by itself plus twice the second. Multiply out D and D', and compare.

6. For any determinant D of order 2 prove that:

(*a*) Interchanging two rows changes the sign of D — and likewise for columns;

(*b*) Writing rows as columns and vice versa does not affect the value of D;

(*c*) If two rows (or columns) are equal, $D = 0$.

7. Solve the following pairs of equations by determinants; and interpret the equations and results geometrically:

(*a*) $4 x + 3 y = 9,$ (*b*) $15 x - 8 y = 12,$
      $7 x + 8 y = 11.$ $11 x + 5 y = -9.$
(*c*) $10 x - 13 y = 19,$ (*d*) $203 x - 113 y = 400,$
      $11 x - 4 y = 5.$ $141 x + 97 y = 200.$

8. Are the following pairs of equations satisfied by any simultaneous values of x and y? How about the lines in each case?

(*a*) $6 x + 9 y = -25,$ (*b*) $26 x + 91 y = 247,$
      $4 x + 6 y = -15.$ $8 x + 28 y = 76.$

9. Find the intersection of each following pair of lines; and check by substituting back in each equation:

(*a*) $5 x - 6 y = 19,$ (*b*) $27 x - 5 y = 10,$
      $3 x + 8 y = -6.$ $16 x + 3 y = -6.$

10. For what values of p will the following equations not have a unique solution: $2 x + py = 15$, $px + 8 y = 20$? For each case will there be no solution or indefinitely many?

11. If (x, y) are rectangular coordinates, what locus is represented by the equation, $\begin{vmatrix} x & y \\ 4 & 7 \end{vmatrix} = 0$? Does the locus pass through $(4, 7)$?

12. Without actually multiplying out show why the equation $\begin{vmatrix} x & y \\ 9 & -2 \end{vmatrix} = 0$ necessarily represents a straight line through $(0, 0)$ and $(9, -2)$. [Cf. Ex. 6 *c*.]

[**13.**] Multiply both sides of the following three equations by 15, 17, and -7, respectively; add results and thus obtain x:

$4 x + y + 3 z = 11,$ $5 x + 2 y - z = 14,$ $6 x + 7 y + 4 z = 2.$

[**14.**] In Ex. 13 try each of these sets of multipliers:

(*a*) 23, -22, 3;   (*b*) -26, -2, 19.

[15.] For the equations $a_1x + b_1y + c_1z = r_1$, $a_2x + b_2y + c_2z = r_2$, and $a_3x + b_3y + c_3z = r_3$, use each following set of multipliers, and add to obtain x, y, or z, respectively, as in Ex. 13–14:

(I) $b_2c_3 - b_3c_2$, $b_3c_1 - b_1c_3$, $b_1c_2 - b_2c_1$;

(II) $a_3c_2 - a_2c_3$, $a_1c_3 - a_3c_1$, $a_2c_1 - a_1c_2$;

(III) $a_2b_3 - a_3b_2$, $a_3b_1 - a_1b_3$, $a_1b_2 - a_2b_1$.

§ 240 *S*. Determinant of Order 3.

To define a determinant of three rows, say

$$\Delta = \begin{vmatrix} a_1 & b_1 & c_1 \\ a_2 & b_2 & c_2 \\ a_3 & b_3 & c_3 \end{vmatrix} \tag{10}$$

we introduce the idea of a "minor."

If from Δ we *omit the row and column* in which the element a_2 occurs, there remains a determinant $\begin{vmatrix} b_1 & c_1 \\ b_3 & c_3 \end{vmatrix}$, which is called the *minor* of a_2 in Δ, and is denoted by A_2. Similarly for any other element.

Definition. Let the determinant Δ denote this sum:

$$a_1A_1 - a_2A_2 + a_3A_3, \tag{11}$$

that is, the sum of the elements of its first column, each multiplied by its minor, the sign of the second being changed.

Written out in full, the value of Δ is then:

$$\Delta = a_1 \begin{vmatrix} b_2 & c_2 \\ b_3 & c_3 \end{vmatrix} - a_2 \begin{vmatrix} b_1 & c_1 \\ b_3 & c_3 \end{vmatrix} + a_3 \begin{vmatrix} b_1 & c_1 \\ b_2 & c_2 \end{vmatrix}$$

$$= a_1b_2c_3 - a_1b_3c_2 - a_2b_1c_3 + a_2b_3c_1 + a_3b_1c_2 - a_3b_2c_1. \tag{12}$$

§ 241 *S*. Alternative Expansions.

The six terms (12) can also be obtained from the determinant (10) by using minors along any other column or row, provided proper signs are taken.

Each of the nine elements occurs in two terms of (12). *E.g.*, c_2 occurs in

$$- a_1b_3c_2 + a_3b_1c_2, \quad = - (a_1b_3 - a_3b_1)c_2 \quad = (-C_2c_2).$$

Similarly, inspection shows that *every* element, as it occurs in (12), is multiplied by its minor or else by its minor with the sign changed — as indicated in the following tabulation.

$$\begin{array}{ccc} a_1A_1 & - b_1B_1 & c_1C_1 \\ - a_2A_2 & b_2B_2 & - c_2C_2 \\ a_3A_3 & - b_3B_3 & c_3C_3 \end{array} \quad \begin{vmatrix} + & - & + \\ - & + & - \\ + & - & + \end{vmatrix}.$$

The − signs in the array at the right show at a glance for which positions in the determinant an element times its minor should have the sign changed. Observe that the + and − alternate along any row or column.

Suppose, in a numerical case, that we prefer to expand Δ along the second row. By the above tabulation, the six terms of (12) will be obtained if we write

$$- a_2A_2 + b_2B_2 - c_2C_2. \tag{13}$$

Similarly for any other row or column, taking account of the positional signs + or −.

Ex. I. Expand the adjacent determinant: (1) by minors of the second row; (2) by minors of the third column.
$$\Delta = \begin{vmatrix} 4 & -3 & 2 \\ 5 & 6 & 9 \\ 1 & 8 & -1 \end{vmatrix}.$$

$$(1) \quad \Delta = -5 \begin{vmatrix} -3 & 2 \\ 8 & -1 \end{vmatrix} + 6 \begin{vmatrix} 4 & 2 \\ 1 & -1 \end{vmatrix} - 9 \begin{vmatrix} 4 & -3 \\ 1 & 8 \end{vmatrix}$$
$$= -5 \, (-13) \quad + 6 \, (-6) \quad - 9 \, (35) \ = \ -286.$$

$$(2) \quad \Delta = \quad 2 \begin{vmatrix} 5 & 6 \\ 1 & 8 \end{vmatrix} \quad - 9 \begin{vmatrix} 4 & -3 \\ 1 & 8 \end{vmatrix} - 1 \begin{vmatrix} 4 & -3 \\ 5 & 6 \end{vmatrix}$$
$$= \quad 2 \, (34) \quad - 9 \, (35) \quad - 1 \, (39) \ = \ -286.$$

N.B. In the last term of (2), the positional sign of the final element would be +, but the element itself is (-1). If the positional sign had been −, we should have changed this term to a $(+1)$ times its minor.

§ 242 S. Three Equations.   If from the equations

$$a_1x + b_1y + c_1z = r_1,$$
$$a_2x + b_2y + c_2z = r_2, \tag{14}$$
$$a_3x + b_3y + c_3z = r_3,$$

we eliminate y and z as in Ex. 15 (I), p. 332, and solve for x, we get *

$$x = \frac{r_1b_2c_3 - r_1b_3c_2 - r_2b_1c_3 + r_2b_3c_1 + r_3b_1c_2 - r_3b_2c_1}{a_1b_2c_3 - a_1b_3c_2 - a_2b_1c_3 + a_2b_3c_1 + a_3b_1c_2 - a_3b_2c_1}, \tag{15}$$

provided the denominator is not zero.

This denominator is precisely the value of Δ in (12), above. The numerator differs from it only in having r's in place of

* This will be explained theoretically in § 248.

the a's. That is, the right members of (14) replace the coefficients of x, in the numerator.

$$\therefore x = \frac{\begin{vmatrix} r_1 & b_1 & c_1 \\ r_2 & b_2 & c_2 \\ r_3 & b_3 & c_3 \end{vmatrix}}{\begin{vmatrix} a_1 & b_1 & c_1 \\ a_2 & b_2 & c_2 \\ a_3 & b_3 & c_3 \end{vmatrix}}. \tag{16}$$

The values for y and z have the same denominator Δ. The numerator for y has r's in place of b's; that for z has r's in place of c's. [Ex. 15 (II), (III), p. 332.]

$$y = \frac{\begin{vmatrix} a_1 & r_1 & c_1 \\ a_2 & r_2 & c_2 \\ a_3 & r_3 & c_3 \end{vmatrix}}{\Delta}, \qquad z = \frac{\begin{vmatrix} a_1 & b_1 & r_1 \\ a_2 & b_2 & r_2 \\ a_3 & b_3 & r_3 \end{vmatrix}}{\Delta}. \tag{17}$$

We may use (16) and (17) as formulas for the solution of (14) provided $\Delta \neq 0$.

The possible cases that may arise when $\Delta = 0$ are discussed in texts on Determinants or Theory of Equations. In any particular case where $\Delta = 0$ the essential facts can usually be seen readily by first combining the equations in pairs, or by employing the multipliers indicated in Ex. 15, p. 332.

Ex. I.   Solve the system $\begin{cases} 2x + 5y - 4z = -7, \\ 3x - 2y + 5z = 21, \\ 8x + 7y - 3z = 11. \end{cases}$

The common denominator, formed from the coefficients, is

$$\Delta = \begin{vmatrix} 2 & 5 & -4 \\ 3 & -2 & 5 \\ 8 & 7 & -3 \end{vmatrix} = 2(-29) - 3(13) + 8(17) = 39.$$

The numerators for x, y, z in equations (16) and (17) are:

$$N_x = \begin{vmatrix} -7 & 5 & -4 \\ 21 & -2 & 5 \\ 11 & 7 & -3 \end{vmatrix}, \qquad N_y = \begin{vmatrix} 2 & -7 & -4 \\ 3 & 21 & 5 \\ 8 & 11 & -3 \end{vmatrix},$$

$$N_z = \begin{vmatrix} 2 & 5 & -7 \\ 3 & -2 & 21 \\ 8 & 7 & 11 \end{vmatrix}.$$

These reduce to $N_x = 117,\quad N_y = -39,\quad N_z = 78.$ Hence

$$x = \frac{117}{39} = 3, \qquad y = \frac{-39}{39} = -1, \qquad z = \frac{78}{39} = 2.$$

Check: Substituting in the given system: $2(3) + 5(-1) - 4(2)$ gives -7; etc.

EXERCISES

1. Evaluate the determinant Δ_1 below by minors of
(a) column 2,   (b) row 1,   (c) row 3.

2. Similarly evaluate Δ_2 by minors of
(a) row 2,   (b) column 1,   (c) column 3.

$$\Delta_1 = \begin{vmatrix} 3 & 2 & -5 \\ 4 & 7 & 6 \\ 9 & 1 & 0 \end{vmatrix}. \qquad \Delta_2 = \begin{vmatrix} 8 & 11 & 0 \\ 3 & -2 & 4 \\ 7 & 1 & -5 \end{vmatrix}.$$

3. Evaluate the following determinants using any row or column:

$$(a)\begin{vmatrix} 0 & 3 & 8 \\ 3 & 0 & 13 \\ 8 & 13 & 0 \end{vmatrix} \qquad (b)\begin{vmatrix} 2 & 3 & -5 \\ 6 & -1 & 7 \\ -4 & 2 & 9 \end{vmatrix} \qquad (c)\begin{vmatrix} 6 & -4 & 2 \\ 9 & -6 & 3 \\ 5 & -8 & 1 \end{vmatrix}.$$

4. From the adjacent determinant Δ form a new determinant Δ' as follows: Without changing rows 2 and 3, replace row 1 by its own elements minus three times the corresponding elements of row 2. Expand Δ and Δ' along any convenient row or column and compare their values.

$$\Delta = \begin{vmatrix} 8 & 9 & 12 \\ 1 & 3 & 4 \\ 2 & -6 & 1 \end{vmatrix}$$

5. Solve each following system of equations and check:

(a) $2x + 3y + 5z = 4,$
$7x - 2y + 4z = 37,$
$4x + 5y + 8z = 8.$

(b) $9x + 5y - 2z = 4,$
$4x + 2y + 3z = 13,$
$7x - 11y + 7z = -1.$

(c) $7x - 2y - 5z = 2,$
$3x + 5y + 2z = 1,$
$8x + y + 2z = 0.$

(d) $3x + 4y + 2z = 2,$
$6x + 3y + 5z = 1,$
$4x - 5y + 8z = 3.$

6. See whether formula (16) can be used for the following system. Also, by using the multipliers listed in Ex. 15 (I), p. 332, show that the assumption that the system can be satisfied by a set of values x, y, z, leads to a contradiction:

$$x + 3y + 7z = 1, \qquad 4x - y + 2z = 3, \qquad 9x - 2y + 5z = 2.$$

7. (a) In the following system solve two equations for x and y in terms of z; and show that the results satisfy the other equation, irrespective of the value of z. (b) Find solutions of the system, for which

$z = 1, 3, -5.$ (c) Ascertain why the system cannot be solved by (16) and (17).

$$x + 3y - 4z = 1, \quad 2x - y + 5z = 4, \quad 14x + 7y + 9z = 24.$$

[**8.**] Without multiplying out, use Ex. 6 (c), p. 331, to show that the adjacent determinant must equal zero. (Think of expanding by minors of column 3.)

$$\begin{vmatrix} 6 & 6 & 2 \\ 11 & 11 & 3 \\ 19 & 19 & -8 \end{vmatrix}$$

§ 243 S. Some Properties of Determinants.

To save labor and avoid erroneous steps in working with determinants, we establish the following theorems. Here Δ denotes the general determinant of order 3 (§ 240); and Δ' denotes the new determinant obtained by any of the operations below. Our arguments can be extended directly to determinants of higher order.

(I) *If rows are changed to columns in the same order, and vice versa, Δ is unaltered in value.* For, the methods of expanding Δ along any row, and the Δ' along the corresponding column, are identical. Corresponding minors would be determinants of order 2, with rows and columns interchanged. By Ex. 6b, p. 331, these minors would be equal; hence also Δ and Δ'.

From this it follows that *any theorem proved for rows will be true for columns also.*

(II) *If two rows be interchanged, $\Delta' = -\Delta$.* To show this, expand Δ' and Δ along the row not involved in the interchange. The minors will be of order 2 with two rows interchanged. By Ex. 6a, p. 331, the minors in Δ' are the negative of those in Δ; hence also the sums which constitute Δ' and Δ.

This indicates the importance of writing rows in their proper order to avoid possible errors in sign.

(III) *Multiplying any row by k multiplies the entire determinant by k.* For, expanding by minors of that row, k occurs precisely once as a factor in each term of Δ.

If any factor k occurs in all the elements of a row, it may be removed and placed before the determinant as a multiplier.

(IV) *If two rows are identical, $\Delta = 0$.* Expanding along the other row gives minors with two identical rows, which are all zero. (Ex. 6c, p. 331).

Likewise if one row is k times another, $\Delta = 0$. For on factoring out k, there are two identical rows.

(V) Δ *is unaltered if a row be replaced by itself plus a* (positive or negative) *multiple of another row.* For, if we expand Δ' and Δ along the row not involved in the combination, we get minors in Δ' which are formed from those of Δ by the replacement in question. By expanding as in Ex. 3-4, p. 330, these latter minors are unaltered by such a replacement. Hence $\Delta' = \Delta$.

This property (V) is particularly useful in evaluating determinants of high order. By a series of replacements of rows, keeping $\Delta = \Delta' = \Delta''$, etc., we can get a column composed of zeros, except for one element. Expanding down that column is then simple.

Ex. I. Evaluate the determinant

$$\Delta = \begin{vmatrix} 3 & 5 & 13 \\ -8 & 1 & -39 \\ 4 & 12 & 26 \end{vmatrix}.$$

Replacing row 2 by itself plus 3 times row 1, and then row 3 by itself minus twice row 1, we have

$$\Delta = \begin{vmatrix} 3 & 5 & 13 \\ 1 & 16 & 0 \\ -2 & 2 & 0 \end{vmatrix} = +13 \begin{vmatrix} 1 & 16 \\ -2 & 2 \end{vmatrix} = 442.$$

§ 244 S. **Loci through Given Points.** When a set of given points determines a locus of a specified type, we can find the equation of the locus. Often this can be written at sight in determinant notation.

Ex. I. Write the equation of the straight line through A (8, 7) and B (5, 2).

In the top row write: x, y, 1. In other rows replace x, y, by the coordinates of A and B. Let the determinant equal zero:

$$\begin{vmatrix} x & y & 1 \\ 8 & 7 & 1 \\ 5 & 2 & 1 \end{vmatrix} = 0. \tag{18}$$

This is the required equation.

Proof. Expanding, preferably along the top row, gives a linear equation, which must represent *some* straight line. If for x and y in the top row we substitute the coordinates of A (8, 7), two rows become identical, making the determinant zero and satisfying the equation. Hence the line passes through A. Likewise through B. This can be checked by expanding (18) to read $5x - 3y - 19 = 0$.

Remark. The 1 in the top row makes provision for the constant term in the equation. Any other number could be used, say 5. But, from a column of 5's, we could remove the common factor, getting back to our column of 1's.

To apply the same idea to other loci, we have to consider *what types of terms* must be provided for in the equation. For a circle, $(x - h)^2 + (y - k)^2 = r^2$, we need

$$(x^2 + y^2), \quad x, \quad y, \quad \text{constant.}$$

For a parabola with its axis horizontal $(y - k)^2 = 4p(x - h)$, we must provide for

$$y^2, \quad y, \quad x, \quad \text{constant.}$$

However, if the axis lies in the X-axis, $k = 0$. Then we need only

$$y^2, \quad x, \quad \text{constant.}$$

And so on.

Ex. II. Write the equation of the parabola through $(8, 7)$ and $(5, 2)$, whose axis lies in the X-axis.

Providing for y^2, x, and a constant, we write:

$$\begin{vmatrix} y^2 & x & 1 \\ 49 & 8 & 1 \\ 4 & 5 & 1 \end{vmatrix} = 0, \quad \text{or,} \quad 3y^2 - 45x + 213 = 0.$$

§ 245 S. Area of a Triangle. Consider the area A of the triangle in Fig. 126, whose vertices are $P_1 (x_1, y_1)$, $P_2 (x_2, y_2)$, $P_3 (x_3 y_3)$. We can find A by adding the areas of the two

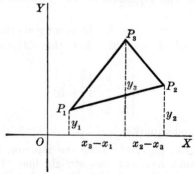

FIG. 126.

trapezoids which have a common base y_3, and subtracting that of the trapezoid whose bases are y_1 and y_2. The latter area is

$$\tfrac{1}{2}\,(y_1 + y_2)\,(x_2 - x_1),$$
$$= \tfrac{1}{2}\,(x_2y_1 - x_1y_2 + x_2y_2 - x_1y_1).$$

Expressing likewise the sum of the other two areas, and subtracting (as in Ex. 10 below), we find

$$A = \tfrac{1}{2}\,[x_1\,(y_2 - y_3) - x_2\,(y_1 - y_3) + x_3\,(y_1 - y_2)]. \quad (19)$$

The quantity in brackets is, however, the expansion of the following simple determinant:

$$A = \tfrac{1}{2}\begin{vmatrix} x_1 & y_1 & 1 \\ x_2 & y_2 & 1 \\ x_3 & y_3 & 1 \end{vmatrix}. \quad (20)$$

The same formula holds for triangles in other positions, provided the counter-clockwise numbering of vertices is followed.

This easily remembered formula (20) will give at once the area of a triangle whose vertices are known. It gives the negative of the area, however, if the vertices are taken in a clockwise order.

If the three points lie in a straight line, $A = 0$. Thus (20) yields a simple *test for collinear points*.

EXERCISES

1. Evaluate after combining rows or columns to get zeros:

$$(a)\ \begin{vmatrix} 1 & 9 & 11 \\ 5 & 50 & 48 \\ 3 & 30 & 25 \end{vmatrix}, \qquad (b)\ \begin{vmatrix} -2 & 1 & 3 \\ -9 & 7 & 25 \\ -6 & 13 & 45 \end{vmatrix}, \qquad (c)\ \begin{vmatrix} 5 & 2 & 6 \\ 12 & 6 & 25 \\ -9 & -8 & 6 \end{vmatrix}.$$

2. For what value of k would each following determinant be obviously zero?

$$(a)\ \begin{vmatrix} 7 & 6 & 7 \\ 13 & 11 & 13 \\ -4 & 2 & k \end{vmatrix}, \qquad (b)\ \begin{vmatrix} 2 & 4 & 9 \\ 5 & k & -1 \\ 8 & 16 & 3 \end{vmatrix}, \qquad (c)\ \begin{vmatrix} 90 & -27 & 6 \\ 60 & -18 & k \\ 17 & 3 & 5 \end{vmatrix}.$$

3. Reduce some numbers by factoring, and evaluate:

$$(a)\ \begin{vmatrix} 3 & -4 & 50 \\ 4 & 5 & 75 \\ 2 & 1 & 125 \end{vmatrix}, \qquad (b)\ \begin{vmatrix} 45 & 28 & 9 \\ 75 & 12 & -15 \\ 90 & -16 & 21 \end{vmatrix}, \qquad (c)\ \begin{vmatrix} -6 & -8 & 2 \\ -9 & -14 & 5 \\ -15 & -18 & 3 \end{vmatrix}.$$

340 SOLUTION OF EQUATIONS

4. Write in determinant form the equation of the straight line through each following pair of points, and check:
(a) $(6, 4)$, $(1, 2)$;   (b) $(3, 4)$, $(0, -2)$;   (c) $(2, 7)$, $(-2, -1)$.

5. $(a\text{–}c)$ Similarly obtain and check the equation of the parabola with its axis in the X-axis and passing through each pair of points in Ex. 4.

6. $(a\text{–}c)$ Like Ex. 5 $(a\text{–}c)$ if the axis of the parabola is to lie in the Y-axis.

7. If a parabola is to pass through the origin, and to have its axis horizontal, what types of terms may appear in its equation? Find such a parabola which passes also through $(2, 4)$ and $(5, -1)$.

8. Like Ex. 7 for these pairs of points
(a) $(3, 5)$, $(0, 4)$;   (b) $(2, 4)$, $(-2, 8)$;   (c) $(3, -2)$, $(0, -4)$.

9. Find the area of the triangle with vertices as follows:
(a) $A(1, 3)$, $B(5, -1)$, $C(4, 8)$;   (b) $D(-6, 1)$, $E(-3, -7)$, $F(2, 0)$.

10. Derive (19) in detail: (a) for Fig. 126; (b) for a modified figure obtained by moving P_3 horizontally to the right so that x_3 exceeds x_2.

11. A survey gave the following coordinates in feet for the corners of a triangular park: $(100, 0)$, $(400, 100)$, $(300, 250)$. Find the area.

12. Like Ex. 11 for the corners: $(0, 200)$, $(100, 300)$, $(400, 100)$.

13. Find the area of the quadrilateral whose vertices are: $A(2, 2)$, $B(10, 6)$, $C(7, 8)$, and $D(3, 5)$.

14. (a) Show by (20) that the points $(3, -1)$, $(6, 3)$, and $(12, 11)$ are collinear. (b) Also by (20) show that (18), p. 337, is the correct equation for the line there in question.

15. Solve the following systems of equations and check:
(a) $4x - y + 5z = 21$,
$3x + 7y - 2z = -17$,
$2x + 6y + 9z = 17$.

(b) $5x + 2y + 4z = 0$,
$6x - 7y + z = 0$,
$8x - 3y + 5z = 0$.

§ 246 S. Concurrent Lines. If there is any point (X, Y) common to the three lines

$$\left. \begin{array}{l} a_1x + b_1y + c_1 = 0 \\ a_2x + b_2y + c_2 = 0 \\ a_3x + b_3y + c_3 = 0 \end{array} \right\}, \quad \text{then} \quad \begin{vmatrix} a_1 & b_1 & c_1 \\ a_2 & b_2 & c_2 \\ a_3 & b_3 & c_3 \end{vmatrix} = 0.$$

Proof: Suppose we multiplied each c by z, some unknown value. The new equations must be satisfied by $x = X$, $y = Y$, $z = 1$. But, if the above determinant Δ were not zero, we should have

$$z = \frac{\begin{vmatrix} a_1 & b_1 & 0 \\ a_2 & b_2 & 0 \\ a_3 & b_3 & 0 \end{vmatrix}}{\Delta} = 0.$$

Hence Δ must vanish if the given equations are to have any solution $x = X$, $y = Y$.

Conversely, it can be shown that if $\Delta = 0$, any solution of two of the equations satisfies the third. If two of the lines meet, all three do. If no two meet, the three are all parallel. Parallel lines are sometimes said to be "concurrent at infinity." In this generalized sense, $\Delta = 0$ always means concurrence, and $\Delta \neq 0$ means non-concurrence.

§ 247 S. Determinants of Higher Order n. We may define these, as for the third order, in terms of the minors of elements in the first column. Thus, for $n = 4$, with four rows and columns:

$$\Delta = a_1 A_1 - a_2 A_2 + a_3 A_3 - a_4 A_4. \tag{21}$$

The minors here, A_1, etc., obtained by striking out a row and a column from Δ, are themselves of order 3. By considering the terms, like $a_1 b_2 c_3 d_4$, etc., involved in (21), we can show that they are obtainable also by expanding Δ along any other column or any row, provided positional signs $+$ and $-$ are used as formerly.

The properties I–V, proved in § 243 for $n = 3$, then follow for $n = 4$ by extending the same reasoning.

And so on, for $n = 5, 6, \cdots$.

Ex. I. Find the equation of the circle through $(3, 2)$, $(4, 0)$, and $(0, 5)$.

By § 244, we provide for: $(x^2 + y^2)$, x, y, constant. Using $(3, 2)$ gives in the second row $3^2 + 2^2$ $(= 13)$, etc., as shown:

$$\begin{vmatrix} x^2 + y^2 & x & y & 1 \\ 13 & 3 & 2 & 1 \\ 16 & 4 & 0 & 1 \\ 25 & 0 & 5 & 1 \end{vmatrix} = 0.$$

Before expanding, combine rows, subtracting the last, say, from each of the others:

$$\begin{vmatrix} x^2 + y^2 - 25 & x & y - 5 & 0 \\ -12 & 3 & -3 & 0 \\ -9 & 4 & -5 & 0 \\ 25 & 0 & 5 & 1 \end{vmatrix} = 0.$$

Dividing out a factor 3 and expanding, first along column 4; and then along the top row:

$$(x^2 + y^2 - 25)(-1) - x(11) + (y - 5)(-7) = 0,$$

or

$$x^2 + y^2 + 11x + 7y - 60 = 0. \qquad \text{(Check?)}$$

§ 248 $S.$ **n Linear Equations.** From n equations linear in n unknowns, we can eliminate in a single step $(n-1)$ of the unknowns. The expressions will be written here only for the case $n = 3$, but the argument is general.

Consider the following system of equations and its determinant Δ:

$$\left.\begin{array}{l} a_1x + b_1y + c_1z = r_1 \\ a_2x + b_2y + c_2z = r_2 \\ a_3x + b_3y + c_3z = r_3 \end{array}\right\}, \qquad \Delta = \begin{vmatrix} a_1 & b_1 & c_1 \\ a_2 & b_2 & c_2 \\ a_3 & b_3 & c_3 \end{vmatrix}.$$

To eliminate all unknowns except z, multiply the first equation by C_1, the next by $-C_2$, and so on, where C_1 is the minor of c_1 in Δ, etc. Adding results:

$$(a_1C_1 - a_2C_2 + a_3C_3)x + (b_1C_1 - b_2C_2 + b_3C_3)y$$
$$+ (c_1C_1 - c_2C_2 + c_3C_3)z = r_1C_1 - r_2C_2 + r_3C_3. \qquad (22)$$

The coefficient of z is Δ, expanded along the c column. The right member of (22) differs from Δ only in having r's in place of c's, its minors C_1, etc., indicating no change in the other columns. The coefficient of x, viz.

$$a_1C_1 - a_2C_2 + a_3C_3,$$

likewise differs from Δ only in having a's where Δ has c's. This makes two identical columns of a's, there being such a column involved in the minors, C_1, C_2, C_3. Hence the coefficient of x in (22) vanishes. Likewise that of y. If $\Delta \neq 0$, we divide through by it, and obtain z. [Equation (17), p. 334.] The procedure is similar in solving for x or y.

EXERCISES

1. Evaluate each of these determinants:

$$(a)\ \begin{vmatrix} 3 & 2 & 1 & -4 \\ 11 & 8 & 5 & -9 \\ 2 & -5 & -3 & 10 \\ 18 & 19 & 7 & 2 \end{vmatrix}; \qquad (b)\ \begin{vmatrix} 4 & 3 & 2 & 1 \\ 16 & 9 & 4 & 1 \\ -3 & 5 & 7 & -1 \\ 9 & 0 & 5 & 1 \end{vmatrix}.$$

2. Determine precisely what curve is represented by each following equation, finding the vertex and focus:

$$(a)\ \begin{vmatrix} y^2 & x & y & 1 \\ 4 & 5 & -2 & 1 \\ 64 & 9 & 8 & 1 \\ 0 & 2 & 0 & 1 \end{vmatrix} = 0; \qquad (b)\ \begin{vmatrix} x^2 & x & y & 1 \\ 49 & -7 & 2 & 1 \\ 25 & 5 & 6 & 1 \\ 1 & -1 & 0 & 1 \end{vmatrix} = 0.$$

3. Find and check the equation of the circle through each following set of three points:

(*a*) $A(2, -1)$, $B(-2, 3)$, $C(4, 1)$; (*b*) $D(-1, 2)$, $E(3, 0)$, $F(0, 4)$.

4. Find the equation of the circle circumscribed about the triangle whose vertices are: $A(0, 0)$, $B(1, -1)$, $C(7, 7)$.

5. Solve Ex. 4 by first finding the equations of the perpendicular bisectors of the sides, and using these to obtain the center of the circle.

6. See whether the method of Ex. 4 or that of Ex. 5 is the easier if the given triangle has the vertices $(3, 1)$, $(1, 2)$, $(2, -4)$.

7. Find the equation of the parabola which passes through $(0, 4)$, $(2, 6)$, and $(6, 0)$, and has a vertical axis.

8. Like Ex. 7 if the axis is to be horizontal.

9. The sides of a triangle are $x - y + 4 = 0$, $x + y - 2 = 0$, and $7x + y - 20 = 0$. Find the equation of the circumscribed circle.

10. Test the lines $2x + 7y - 3 = 0$, $5x - 2y + 1 = 0$, and $4x - 9y + 4 = 0$ for concurrence.

11. Write the equations of the altitudes of the triangle in Ex. 6. Show that they meet the test for concurrence.

12. Show how the procedure in § 248 would run to derive the formula for y, eliminating x and z. Note the positional signs.

13. Solve the following systems of equations, and check:

(*a*) $3x - 2y + 5z - 2w = 12$, (*b*) $5x - 2y + 8z + 3w = 13$,
  $2x + 4y - 8z + w = 5$, $x + 3y - 9z - w = -4$,
  $7x - y + z + 3w = 17$, $4x + y + 7z + 2w = 7$,
  $x + 11z - 4w = 20$. $3x - 4y + z = 7$.

(B) Non-Linear Equations: Exact Methods

We now turn our attention to equations of the second and higher degrees. Usually we shall consider the solution of a single equation.

§ 249. Formula for the Roots of a Quadratic.

The most general equation of the second degree involving a single unknown has the form

$$ax^2 + bx + c = 0, \qquad a \neq 0. \tag{23}$$

By completing the square the roots of this are found to be

$$x = \frac{-b \pm \sqrt{b^2 - 4ac}}{2a}. \tag{24}$$

This result should be carefully memorized. It can be used as a formula to write at sight the roots of any quadratic equation.

Ex. I.   Find the roots of $5x^2 + 4x - 3 = 0$.
Here $a = 5$, $b = 4$, $c = -3$;

$$\therefore \ x = \frac{-4 \pm \sqrt{76}}{10} = \frac{-2 \pm \sqrt{19}}{5}.$$

Ex. II.   Solve $x^6 - 19x^3 - 216 = 0$.
This is really a quadratic in terms of x^3. (We could let $x^3 = z$, say.)

$$\therefore \ x^3 = \frac{19 \pm \sqrt{19^2 - 4(-216)}}{2} = 27, \ -8.$$

There are six values for x. For, when $x^3 - 27 = 0$, factoring gives
$$(x - 3)(x^2 + 3x + 9) = 0.$$

Hence one of these factors must be zero: $x - 3 = 0$, or $x^2 + 3x + 9 = 0$.

$$\therefore \ x = 3, \ \text{or} \ x = \frac{-3 \pm \sqrt{-27}}{2}.$$

Similarly $x^3 = -8$ gives $x = -2$, and two imaginary values.

§ 250. The Discriminant, $b^2 - 4ac$.   The nature of the roots of the equation $ax^2 + bx + c = 0$ is determined by the quantity $b^2 - 4ac$ which appears under the radical in (24). We assume here and in § 251 that a, b, c, are themselves real and rational numbers.

The roots are *imaginary* if $b^2 - 4ac$ is negative.   Otherwise they are real.

The roots are *rational* if $b^2 - 4ac$ is a perfect square.   [They are free from radicals.]   Otherwise, if real, they are irrational.

The roots are *equal* if $b^2 - 4ac$ is zero.   [For $(-b+0)/2a$ is the same as $(-b-0)/2a$.]   Otherwise they are unequal.

E.g., in the equation $121x^2 - 176x + 64 = 0$ we have
$$b^2 - 4ac = (176)^2 - 4(121)(64) = 0.$$

Hence the roots are *real*, *rational*, and *equal*.

These criteria are often useful in determining quickly whether two given lines or curves intersect.   *E.g.*, to find whether the line $y = x + 10$ meets the circle $x^2 + y^2 = 25$, we need only see whether the two equations have a real simultaneous solution. Eliminating y gives

$$x^2 + (x + 10)^2 = 25,$$

i.e., $\qquad\qquad 2\,x^2 + 20\,x + 75 = 0 \qquad\qquad$ simplified.

Here $\qquad\qquad b^2 - 4\,ac = 20^2 - 4\,(2)\,(75) = -\,200.$

The values of x are imaginary: the loci do not meet.

EXERCISES

1. Using formula (24) write by inspection the roots of:

(a) $5\,x^2 + 12\,x + 11 = 0,$ (b) $5\,x^2 - 12\,x + 4 = 0,$

(c) $11\,x^2 - 6\,x - 5 = 0,$ (d) $3.6\,x^2 + .35\,x - .0125 = 0,$

(e) $kx^2 - x + 3 = 0,$ (f) $2\,x^2 - 5\,kx + 3\,k^2 = 0.$

2. Solve $ax^2 + bx + c = 0$ by completing the square, and verify formula (24).

3. Solve each of these equations for y:

(a) $y^4 - 13\,y^2 + 36 = 0,$ (b) $y^6 - 7\,y^3 - 8 = 0,$

(c) $8\,y^6 - 65\,y^3 + 8 = 0,$ (d) $y^8 - 17\,y^4 + 16 = 0.$

4. If a wooden column (x in. square) is to carry a certain load the smallest safe value of x is a root of $x^4 - 125\,x^2 - 10368 = 0.$ Find that root.

5. Determine the nature of the roots of the following:

(a) $6\,x^2 + 11\,x + 5 = 0,$ (b) $6\,x^2 + 13\,x + 20 = 0,$

(c) $x^2 - 2\,x - 5 = 0,$ (d) $x^2 - 2\,x + 5 = 0,$

(e) $32\,x^2 + 40\,x + 12.5 = 0,$ (f) $36\,x^2 - 51\,x - 120 = 0.$

6. Without actually solving for the intersections determine:

(a) whether the circle $x^2 + y^2 - 10\,x - 6\,y + 21 = 0$ meets the line $y = 3\,x$;

(b) whether this circle meets the X- and Y-axes.

7. Find the intersections of $y = x - 2$ and $x^2 + y^2 = 100.$

8. In how many points does $y = 2\,x$ meet $x^2 + y^2 + 4\,x + 13\,y + 45 = 0$? What does this mean?

9. For what value or values of k would the equation $kx^2 - 10\,x + 4 = 0$ have equal roots?

10. Like Ex. 9 for the equation $x^2 - 2\,kx + 6 - k = 0.$

[11.] Find the intersections of $y = 3\,x + k$ and $y^2 - 20\,x = 0,$ in terms of k. For what value of k will the intersections come together, making the line tangent?

[12.] As in Ex. 11 determine the values of l for which the line $y = lx$ will be tangent to $x^2 + y^2 - 4\,x - 6\,y + 4 = 0.$

13. The deflection of a loaded beam x ft. from one end is, under certain conditions, $y = k\,(3\,x^5 - 1000\,x^3 + 70000\,x)$. At what value of x is y a maximum?

14. The same as Ex. 13 if $y = k\,(3\,x^5 - 10\,l^2x^3 + 7\,l^4x)$ where l is the length of the beam.

15. Show that the curve $y = x^3 + px^2 + qx + r$ can have no turning points (maxima or minima) if $p^2 < 3\,q$.

16. Show that the curve $y = x^5 + 10\,x^3 + 15\,x$ has no turning points.

17. Show that $399\,x^2 - 1000\,x + 629$ is positive for every value of x.

§ 251. Factorability of a Quadratic.

If we subtract from x each of the roots in (24), multiply the resulting expressions, and simplify, we find

$$\left(x - \frac{-b+\sqrt{b^2-4\,ac}}{2\,a}\right)\left(x - \frac{-b-\sqrt{b^2-4\,ac}}{2\,a}\right) = \frac{1}{a}\,(ax^2 + bx + c).$$

That is, x *minus each root* is a factor of $ax^2 + bx + c$, the left member.

E.g., if a quadratic has the roots $3 + \sqrt{5}$, $3 - \sqrt{5}$, it has the factors $(x - 3 - \sqrt{5})$, $(x - 3 + \sqrt{5})$.

Thus every quadratic is factorable into linear factors of some kind. These will be rational if the roots are, but not otherwise. Hence a sure test whether any quadratic is *rationally* factorable is to see whether $(b^2 - 4\,ac)$ *is a perfect square*.

Ex. I. Test $99\,x^2 - 42\,x - 16$.

Here $b^2 - 4\,ac = 8100$. Hence the factors are rational. They can be found by inspection, or by writing x minus each root, by formula.

§ 252 S. Tangents Found by Discriminants.

The equation of a tangent line can be found by § 232, if the point of tangency is given. We may need, however, to find a tangent from a given external point, or perhaps a tangent having some specified slope. Cases like these are readily handled by using a discriminant, if the equation of the curve is of the second degree.

Ex. I. Find the equations of the tangents to the parabola $y^2 = 8\,x - 24$ from the point $(0, 1)$.

A line through $(0, 1)$ with any slope l has the equation:
$$y - 1 = l (x - 0). \tag{25}$$

At its intersections with the parabola:
$$x = \frac{y^2 + 24}{8} \quad \text{and} \quad x = \frac{y - 1}{l}. \tag{26}$$

Equating these values of x; and simplifying:
$$ly^2 - 8 y + 24 l + 8 = 0. \tag{27}$$

For most values of l this equation gives two intersections. For a tangent line the two points come together, giving equal roots in (27). Hence $b^2 - 4 ac = 0$; that is,
$$(-8)^2 - 4 l (24 l + 8) = 0,$$
or, $\qquad\qquad 3 l^2 + l - 2 = 0.$

Solving by formula (24): $l = \frac{2}{3}$ or -1. Then (25) gives
$$y = \tfrac{2}{3} x + 1, \qquad y = -x + 1, \tag{28}$$
the equations of the required tangents.

Ex. II. Find the equations of the tangents to the ellipse $4 x^2 + 9 y^2 = 36$, which have the slope 2.

Any line of slope 2 has the equation $y = 2 x + k$, and cuts the ellipse where $4 x^2 + 9 (2 x + k)^2 = 36$, or
$$40 x^2 + 36 kx + 9 k^2 - 36 = 0.$$

Putting $b^2 - 4 ac = 0$ and simplifying:
$$1440 - 36 k^2 = 0, \qquad k = \pm \sqrt{40}. \tag{29}$$

The required tangents are $y = 2 x \pm \sqrt{40}$.

EXERCISES

1. Test the rational factorability of the following quadratic expressions. (The actual factors, if any, are not required.)

(a) $11 x^2 - 7 x - 4$,   (b) $8 x^2 - 13 x - 108$,
(c) $416 x^2 - 1066 x + 721$,   (d) $10 x^2 - 89 x - 120$,
(e) $42 x^2 + 215 kx - 48 k^2$,   (f) $x^2 - (y + 1) x - (2 y^2 - 5 y + 2)$

2. By either of the methods suggested in Ex. I of § 251, find the factors of:

(a) $4 x^2 - 29 x - 180$,   (b) $12 x^2 - 715 x - 300$,
(c) $128\,000 x^2 - 142\,303 x - 279\,936$.

3. Find the equations of those tangents to $x^2 + y^2 = 100$, which have the slope 3. Check roughly by drawing the curve and the lines.

4. Like Ex. 3 for the following curves and slopes:

(a) $9 x^2 + 25 y^2 = 900$, $l = 3$;   (b) $xy = 50$, $l = -2$;
(c) $9 x^2 - 16 y^2 = 144$, $l = -1$;   (d) $y^2 = 40 x$, $l = \frac{1}{2}$;
(e) $x^2 + y^2 - 4 x - 8 y + 11 = 0$, $l = 2$.

5. Find the equations of the tangents to $x^2 = 12 y$ from the point $(0, -3)$. Check roughly by drawing the curve and lines.

6. Like Ex. 5 for the following curves and points:

(a) $x^2 + 4 y^2 = 32$, $(0, 4)$;   (b) $xy = 12$, $(3, 3)$;
(c) $x^2 + y^2 = 25$, $(-1, 7)$;   (d) $x^2 - y^2 = 8$, $(0, -8)$.

7. What type of curve is represented by the equation

$$(1 + l^2) x^2 - 16 lx + 16 y = 0 \qquad (30)$$

for any value of l? (a) Find the values of l for which such curves pass through $(2, \frac{11}{4})$. (b) Using these values reduce (30) numerically, and plot the two curves from $x = 0$ to $x = 4$.

8. Do any curves of the "pencil" (30) pass through $(2, 4)$? How many through $(4, 3)$?

9. Find the locus of points (X, Y) through which there passes but one curve of the "pencil" (30).

[10.] Divide $2 x^4 - 3 x^3 + 5 x^2 - 121 x + 86$ by $x - 3$. Also substitute $x = 3$ synthetically in the given polynomial. (§ 21.) Compare the synthetic substitution with your quotient and remainder.

§ 253. Synthetic Division.

Before proceeding to solve equations of the third degree and above, we need to become familiar with a certain easy method of dividing out factors.

To see the underlying principle, divide the polynomial

$$f(x) = 4 x^3 - x^2 - 19 x + 10$$

by $(x - 3)$, and compare with the synthetic substitution of 3 for x in the same $f(x)$.

```
                4 x² + 11 x + 14
    x - 3 ) 4 x³ -     x² - 19 x + 10        4   - 1   - 19   + 10   | 3
            4 x³ - 12 x²                              12      33      42
            ───────────                        ──────────────────────────
                 11 x² - 19 x                   4   + 11   + 14   + 52
                 11 x² - 33 x
                 ───────────
                       14 x + 10
                       14 x - 42
                       ─────────
                             52
```

By § 21 we know that the final sum in the substitution process (+ 52) is the value of $f(x)$ when $x = 3$. But observe that it is also the *remainder* resulting from the division by $(x - 3)$. Further, the other sums in the substitution (4, 11, 14) are precisely the *coefficients in the quotient*. Hence this synthetic substitution could have been used as a quick and easy method of performing the division by $(x - 3)$.

The reason the process works is simply this: In the substitution, we at each step multiply by 3, and *add*; whereas in the division, we multiply by − 3 and subtract.

Synthetic Substitution is also called "Synthetic Division," since it builds up the result of a division.

§ 254. Integral Roots by Trial.
It will now be easy to find all the integral roots of an equation of any degree whatever. We have merely to test a few numbers as roots, and at the same time factor the given polynomial by Synthetic Division.

Ex. I. Solve $4 x^3 - x^2 - 19 x + 10 = 0$.

Substituting 2 synthetically	4	− 1	− 19	+ 10	⌊2
gives zero as the final sum.		8	14	− 10	
Hence 2 is a root.	4	+ 7	− 5		

This substitution also shows that the remainder after dividing out $(x - 2)$ would be zero; and that the quotient would be $4 x^2 + 7 x - 5$. Hence the original equation factored, is
$$(x - 2)(4 x^2 + 7 x - 5) = 0.$$
Setting the factor $4 x^2 + 7 x - 5$ equal to zero gives two more roots:
$$x = \frac{- 7 \pm \sqrt{129}}{8}.$$

There can be no further roots; for any value of x that reduces the original polynomial to zero must make one of the factors zero.

In this example we could have told in advance that any integer, such as 3, which is not a factor of 10, could not be a root of this equation. For multiplying the next to the last sum (an integer) by 3 could not furnish the − 10 necessary to produce the final zero.

Likewise, in any other case, *the only possibilities for integral roots will be the divisors of the final term* — providing the equation has been cleared of fractions.

Ex. II.   Factor $x^4 - 17\,x^2 - 34\,x - 30.$

The only possible integral roots are $\pm\,1, \pm\,2, \pm\,3, \pm\,5, \pm\,6, \pm\,10, \pm\,15, \pm\,30.$ And the test of 5 shows there can be no root above 5.   (§ 21.)

Since 5 is a root, we divide out $(x - 5)$, and test the quotient. Similarly, we divide out $(x + 3)$ and solve the remaining quadratic.

$$
\begin{array}{rrrrr|l}
1 & +0 & -17 & -34 & -30 & \underline{5} \\
  & 5 & 25 & 40 & 30 & \\
\hline
1 & +5 & +8 & +6 & & \underline{-3} \\
  & -3 & -6 & -6 & & \\
\hline
1 & +2 & +2 & & &
\end{array}
$$

$$x^2 + 2\,x + 2 = 0 \ \text{ gives } \ x = \frac{-2 \pm \sqrt{-4}}{2} = -1 \pm \sqrt{-1}.$$

Roots: 5, $-3,$ $-1 + \sqrt{-1},$ $-1 - \sqrt{-1}.$

Factors: $(x - 5),$ $(x + 3),$ $(x + 1 - \sqrt{-1}),$ $(x + 1 + \sqrt{-1}).$

Lowest rational factors: $(x - 5),$ $(x + 3),$ $(x^2 + 2\,x + 2).$

§ 255. Fractional Roots by Trial.

Some equations have fractional roots.   It is easy to tell in any such case what fractions need be tested.

To get the idea let us see, for instance, under what conditions $\tfrac{3}{2}$ might be a root of any equation

$$ax^n + bx^{n-1} + \cdots + k = 0,$$

in which the coefficients $a, b, \cdots, k,$ are all integers.

Substituting synthetically, let S denote the next to the last sum:

$$
\begin{array}{llll|l}
a & +b & \cdots\ (\ ) & +k & \underline{\tfrac{3}{2}} \\
  & +\tfrac{3}{2}\,a & (\ ) & +\tfrac{3}{2}\,S & \\
\hline
a + (b + \tfrac{3}{2}\,a) & \cdots & S + (k + \tfrac{3}{2}\,S) & &
\end{array}.
$$

For $\tfrac{3}{2}$ to be a root, we must have

$$k + \tfrac{3}{2}\,S = 0, \quad \text{or} \quad S = -\tfrac{2}{3}\,k.$$

Now, S cannot be a fraction with the denominator 3; for at no step could this denominator be introduced.   Hence *3 must be a divisor of k.*

Again, the first multiplication introduces a fraction — which will persist and prevent a final zero — *unless 2 is a divisor of a.*

Thus $\frac{3}{2}$ can be a root of an equation only if *the numerator is a divisor of the constant term* (k), *and the denominator is a divisor of the leading coefficient* (a). Similarly for any other fraction p/q.

Ex. I. $\qquad 15\,x^6 - 19\,x^5 + 7\,x^3 - 11\,x^2 + 4 = 0.$

The only possible fractional roots are those whose numerators are factors of 4, and whose denominators are factors of 15:

$$\tfrac{1}{3},\ \tfrac{2}{3},\ \tfrac{4}{3};\quad \tfrac{1}{5},\ \tfrac{2}{5},\ \tfrac{4}{5};\quad \tfrac{1}{15},\ \tfrac{2}{15},\ \tfrac{4}{15};$$

and their negatives. A test shows $\frac{2}{3}$ to be a root:

$$
\begin{array}{rrrrrrr|l}
15 & -19 & +0 & +7 & -11 & +0 & +4 & \;\tfrac{2}{3} \\
   & 10 & -6 & -4 & 2 & -6 & -4 & \\
\hline
15 & -9 & -6 & +3 & -9 & -6 &
\end{array}
$$

The remaining equation is, after canceling a factor 3,
$$5\,x^5 - 3\,x^4 - 2\,x^3 + x^2 - 3\,x - 2 = 0.$$

The only possibilities now are $\pm\frac{1}{5}, \pm\frac{2}{5}, \pm 1, \pm 2.$
None of these is a root. Hence any further roots must be imaginary or irrational.

Ex. II. $\qquad x^3 + 17\,x^2 + 6\,x - 24 = 0.$

The leading coefficient is 1. The only possible "fractional" roots have a denominator 1, and must be *integers*.

EXERCISES

1. Find all the roots of the following equations:

(a) $x^3 - 19\,x + 30 = 0,$ (b) $x^3 - 3\,x^2 - 6\,x + 8 = 0,$
(c) $x^4 + 4\,x^3 - 8\,x^2 - 35\,x - 12 = 0,$ (d) $x^4 + 7\,x^3 - x^2 - 67\,x - 60 = 0,$
(e) $x^5 - 5\,x^2 - 16\,x + 20 = 0,$
(f) $x^5 + 2\,x^3 - 12\,x^2 - 195\,x - 180 = 0,$
(g) $6\,x^4 + x^3 + 4\,x^2 + x - 2 = 0,$ (h) $12\,x^3 + 25\,x^2 + x - 2 = 0,$
(i) $8\,x^4 + 2\,x^3 - 147\,x^2 - 36\,x + 54 = 0,$
(j) $6\,x^4 - 5\,x^3 + x^2 + 60\,x - 20 = 0.$

2. Find all the roots of $3\,x^4 - 2\,x^3 + 14\,x^2 - 10\,x - 5 = 0.$ Also express this polynomial as the product of its lowest rational factors.

3. Find all the roots and the lowest rational factors of:

(a) $2\,x^3 - 29\,x^2 + 20\,x + 102 = 0,$ (b) $2\,x^3 - 7\,x^2 + 18\,x - 24 = 0,$
(c) $36\,x^4 - x^2 - 2\,x - 1 = 0,$ (d) $6\,x^4 + x^3 + 4\,x^2 + x - 2 = 0,$
(e) $6\,x^4 + 7\,x^3 + 23\,x^2 + 2\,x - 8 = 0,$
(f) $x^5 - 5\,x^4 + 3\,x^3 + 13\,x^2 - 8\,x - 12 = 0.$

4. Find the lowest rational factors of $7\,x^4 + 7\,x^3 - 14\,x^2 - x - 2.$

5. Like Ex. 4 for $2\,x^5 - 5\,x^4 + 18\,x^3 - 46\,x^2 + 31\,x - 6.$

6. The rate of rotation of a flywheel (R deg./sec.) t sec. after the power was cut off was $R = t^3 - 192\,t + 1024$. Find when the wheel stopped.

7. The deflection (y ft.) of a loaded beam x ft. from one end was $y = .000001\,(x^4 - 30\,x^3 + 4000\,x)$. For what x was y a maximum?

8. Like Ex. 7 if $y = .0001\,(x^4 - 20\,x^3 + 120\,x^2 - 200\,x)$.

9. It can be proved that if an angle of 120° could be trisected by a Euclidean "ruler and compass" construction the equation $x^3 - 3\,x + 1 = 0$ would have a rational root.* Does it have any? Hence?

10. As in Ex. 9, if a regular heptagon could be drawn by a Euclidean construction, the equations $x^3 + x^2 - 2\,x - 1 = 0$ would have a rational root. Is the construction possible?

[11.] Plot $y = x^3 + 3\,x^2 - 3\,x - 18$, from $x = -4$ to $+5$. What root has the polynomial? What would be the equation of this curve if translated two units to the left? (Multiply out.) What would the former root then become?

§ 256. Further Roots.

When we have found by trial all the rational roots of an equation, any further roots must be *imaginary* or else real and *irrational*.

If imaginary, we cannot find them as yet, unless the equation is in quadratic form or easily factorable into quadratic forms. But if merely irrational, we can at least approximate them — roughly by a graph, and then more closely by successive substitutions near the supposed root.

In treatises on the Theory of Equations it is proved that every polynomial of degree n has precisely n linear factors, real or imaginary — and hence n roots. (Some of the factors may be equal; likewise the roots.)

Also it is proved that, if the given coefficients are real, any imaginary roots must occur in pairs, like $3 + \sqrt{-2}$ and $3 - \sqrt{-2}$, etc.

(C) Methods of Approximate Solution

§ 257 S. Diminishing a Root.

The labor involved in approximating an irrational root closely can be reduced by a simple device.

Suppose, for example, that the unknown root is $2.1768\cdots$, and that we have located it between 2 and 3. If we move

the graph 2 units to the left, the root will be reduced to .1768.
(Fig. 127.) We can easily locate
it between .1 and .2 by testing
these values. If we move the
graph .1 more, the root will be
.0768···. We can locate it by
testing .07 and .08; and the
multiplications involved will be
far simpler than if we were testing 2.17 and 2.18. By continuing

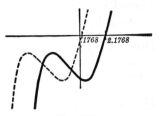

Fig. 127.

to move the graph we can make each successive test by using
a multiplier of a single digit rather than several digits.

To make this device the more effective we shall now find
a very quick method of getting the new equation of the graph
after each successive translation.

§ 258 S. Translating a Graph Synthetically.

THEOREM: If the graph of any polynomial $y = f(x)$ is moved
h units to the left, the coefficients in the new equation will be
simply *the remainders which would result from dividing $f(x)$
synthetically by $(x - h)$, the quotient by $(x - h)$, the new quotient
by $(x - h)$, and so on.*

PROOF: Let the new equation be

$$y = x^n + ax^{n-1} \cdots + bx^2 + cx + d. \tag{31}$$

Now, whatever values the new coefficients $a, \cdots b, c,$ and d may have,
they must be such that, if the graph were moved back h units to the
right, replacing each x by $(x - h)$, we should get back the original
equation $y = f(x)$. Hence

$$f(x) = (x - h)^n + a(x - h)^{n-1} \cdots + b(x - h)^2 + c(x - h) + d.$$

Clearly, then, dividing the original polynomial $f(x)$ by $(x - h)$
would give a remainder equal to d, the quotient being

$$Q = (x - h)^{n-1} + a(x - h)^{n-2} \cdots + b(x - h) + c.$$

Again, dividing Q by $(x - h)$ would give c as the remainder, with

$$Q' = (x - h)^{n-2} + a(x - h)^{n-3} \cdots + b$$

as the next quotient. Dividing this by $(x - h)$ would give b as the
remainder. And so on for the other coefficients.   (*Q.E.D.*)

To illustrate the actual working of the process, let us move
the graph of $y = x^3 + 3x^2 - 3x - 18$ two units to the left:

Dividing $f(x)$ by $(x-2)$:

1	+ 3	− 3	− 18	$\lfloor$2
	+ 2	+ 10	+ 14	
1	+ 5	+ 7	− 4	

quotient, $Q = x^2 + 5x + 7$
remainder, -4

Dividing Q by $(x-2)$:

1	+ 5	+ 7	$\lfloor$2
	+ 2	+ 14	
1	+ 7	+ 21	

quotient, $Q' = x + 7$
remainder, **21**

Dividing Q' by $(x-2)$:

1	+ 7	$\lfloor$2
	+ 2	
1	+ 9	

quotient, $= 1$
remainder, **9**

These remainders, 9, 21, -4, are coefficients in the new equation which results from translating the graph — viz.

$$y = x^3 + 9x^2 + 21x - 4.$$

Remarks. (I) In practice the calculation can be condensed and made rapidly, as shown here.
New function:

$$x^3 + 9x^2 + 21x - 4.$$

1	+ 3	− 3	− 18	$\lfloor$2
	+ 2	+ 10	+ 14	
1	+ 5	+ 7	− 4	
	+ 2	+ 14		
1	+ 7	+ 21		
	+ 2			
1	+ 9			

(II) Another statement of this process is that the new coefficients are found by *substituting 2 for x* in the original $f(x)$ and in the quotients resulting from successive divisions by $(x-2)$.

§ 259 S. Horner's Method, Complete.

Let us now see how the foregoing process works in solving an equation.

ILLUSTRATION: $x^3 + 3x^2 - 3x - 18 = 0.$

I (A) Plot the graph, or find these points:

4 units below at $x = 2$,
27 units above at $x = 3$.
Hence, a root near 2.1.*

After moving the graph, the root will be near .1.

(B) Move graph 2 units (left):

1	+ 3	− 3	− 18	$\lfloor$2
	+ 2	+ 10	+ 14	
1	+ 5	+ 7	− 4	
	+ 2	+ 14		
1	+ 7	+ 21		
	+ 2			
1	+ 9			

New $f(x) = x^3 + 9x^2 + 21x - 4.$

* This estimate is made roughly by inspection: comparing the values 4 and 27 indicates that the crossing is several times as far from $x = 3$ as from $x = 2$.

II (A) Test new $f(x)$ at .1, etc., by substitution:

(B) Move graph .1 unit (left):

1.809 below at $x = .1$.

.568 above at $x = .2$.

Hence, a root near .17.

After moving the graph, the root will be near .07.

$$
\begin{array}{rrrr|r}
1 & +9 & +21 & -4 & \underline{|.1} \\
 & +\ .1 & +\ \ .91 & +2.191 & \\
\hline
1 & +9.1 & +21.91 & -\mathbf{1.809} & \\
 & +\ .1 & +\ \ .92 & & \\
\hline
1 & +9.2 & +\mathbf{22.83} & & \\
 & +\ .1 & & & \\
\hline
1 & +\mathbf{9.3} & & & \\
\end{array}
$$

III (A) New $f(x) = x^3 + 9.3\,x^2 + 22.83\,x - 1.809$.   Testing shows a root between .07 and .08 — near .077.

(B) Moving the graph .07 to the left, the root should be near .007.

IV (A) New $f(x) = x^3 + 9.51\,x^2 + 24.1467\,x - .164\,987$. Testing shows a root between .007 and .006 — near .0068.

(B) Moving the graph .006 to the left, the root should be near .0008.

V New $f(x) = x^3 + 9.528\,x^2 + 24.260928\,x - .019764224$.

Instead of continuing as above we can now get some further figures in the root as follows.   Since x is now very small, the terms x^3 and $9.528\,x^2$ are practically negligible.   Ignoring them, our equation is approximately:

$$24.260928\,x - .019764224 = 0. \tag{32}$$

By ordinary division this gives

$$x = .000\,8146+.$$

Recalling the several translations, the original root is

$$x = 2.1768146+. \tag{33}$$

Remarks.   (I) To test both at $x = 2$ and at $x = 3$ before translating the graph 2 units was very important.   This not only insured us against moving the curve a wrong amount, but also showed about *how many tenths* to test in the next stage.   For similar reasons, at every stage, we make tests until the root is *definitely located*.

Plotting the graph is not essential; but we should determine whether it would rise or fall near the root sought.

(II) To approximate *negative* roots, slide the curve to the *right.*
To do this, use negative substitutions instead of positive.

Another method is to change the sign of x throughout the given
equation, and then seek positive roots of the new equation.

(III) After n figures of a root have been found by testing, and the
next $f(x)$ has been obtained, approximately n more figures can be
obtained by a simple division, as in the last step above.

(IV) This method of approximating irrational roots was invented
about 1820 by W. G. Horner, an Englishman; but the underlying idea
had been used in the sixteenth century by F. Vieta, a Frenchman.
It applies only to equations in the standard polynomial form; but
is often the best method for such equations, and is much used.

EXERCISES

1. Move the curve $y = x^2 - 5x + 8$ three units to the left, using
the synthetic process. Check by "translaters."

2. Solve $x^3 - 10 = 0$ by Horner's method to four decimals and
check directly.

3. Find to 6 decimals the root of $x^3 - 17x + 5 = 0$ which lies
between 3 and 4. (Hint: Get the last three places by division.)

4. In Ex. 3 locate the other roots and approximate each to 4
decimals.

5. Locate graphically the real roots of $x^3 - 9x + 2 = 0$, and approximate one of them to 4 decimals.

6. In Ex. 5 approximate the other roots to two decimals.

7. Show graphically that the equation $x^3 - 3x^2 + 28x - 80 = 0$
has only one real root. Approximate this to six decimals.

8. What are the possibilities as regards the number of real and
imaginary roots for an equation of degree two? three? four? If you
had found one real unrepeated root of a quartic equation could you
draw any conclusion as to the other roots?

9. Approximate to four decimals each of the real roots of
$2x^4 + x^3 + x - 1 = 0$.

10. If a rectangular panel L ft. high and 1 ft. wide is fitted diag-
onally across a door 7 ft. long and 3 ft. wide, prove that L is a root
of $L^4 - 60L^2 + 84L - 57 = 0$. (Hint: Use similar triangles.)

11. From the equation in Ex. 10 find the root in question, accurate
to two decimals.

12. The diameter (d in.) of the bolts needed in certain cylindrical
shafts is a root of the equation $d^4 + 800d^2 - 18d - 360 = 0$. Find d
to two decimal places

13. The greatest and least distances of Jupiter's Fifth Satellite from the center of the planet are approximately roots of the equation $x^3 - 5x^2 + 6.27396x - .060385 = 0$, the unit distance being Jupiter's radius, 45090 miles. Find those roots to 3 decimal places.

14. A magnet placed with its ends in a "magnetic meridian" will neutralize the earth's magnetism at certain points. To calculate the position of these points in a certain case, it was necessary to solve the equation:

$$\frac{20000\,x}{(x^2 - 100)^2} = .2.$$

Simplify and solve. (There are two values — one large and one small.)

15. At what point on the curve $y = x^4 - 7x^2 + 5x + 10$ is the slope equal to 25?

16. Where should an ordinate be erected to the parabola $y = x^2 + 8$ to make the area under the curve between the Y-axis and the ordinate 200 square units?

§ 260. Newton's Method. Another excellent method of approximating irrational roots, which can be used even for equations that involve trigonometric and exponential functions, etc., was invented by Sir Isaac Newton. It does not move the graph, but works throughout with the original $f(x)$ and the derivative $f'(x)$. An example will show the idea.

Ex. I. $x^3 + 3x^2 - 3x - 18 = 0$.

The graph shows a root near 2.2. (Fig. 127, p. 353.) Substituting this value in the given function and in the derivative $3x^2 + 6x - 3$ gives as the height and slope at that point:

$$y = .568, \qquad \text{slope} = 24.72.$$

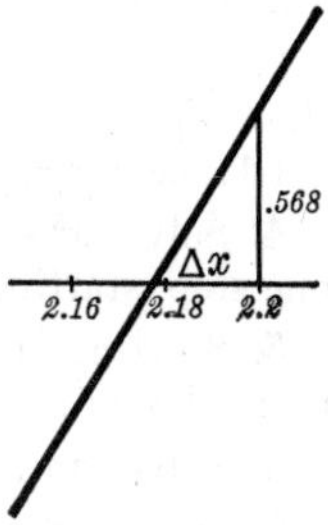

To reach the crossing, we must evidently go back to the left some horizontal distance Δx. Assuming the graph practically straight that far, the slope is approximately $.568/\Delta x$.

FIG. 128.

$$\therefore \; \frac{.568}{\Delta x} = 24.72, \text{ whence } \Delta x = .023, \text{ approx.}$$

Subtracting Δx from 2.2 gives 2.177 as the root.

Repeating the operation with this result as a starting point instead of 2.2 would give a very fine approximation.

§ 261. Isolating the Roots. We can approximate closely the irrational roots of an equation — provided we can first locate them roughly.

Systematic substitutions will usually show any change of sign in $f(x)$. But suppose there were two roots between 2 and 3, so that the graph should cross and recross in this interval, leaving $f(x)$ positive both at $x = 2$ and at $x = 3$. We might not discover that the graph ought to cross at all.

Such double crossings can usually be detected by calculus. For between the crossings there will be a maximum or minimum height — at which $f'(x) = 0$. *If we can solve this "derived equation," $f'(x) = 0$, we can find all the maxima and minima, and thus discover that the curve has crossed and recrossed.*

A sure test in algebraic cases — which was invented about 1830 by J. C. F. Sturm, a Swiss — is given in treatises on the *Theory of Equations.* The methods suggested above suffice, however, for almost all practical problems.

EXERCISES *

1. Verify that the equation $x^3 - 9x - 1 = 0$ has a root near $x = 3$. Approximate it by Newton's method.

2. Check the result in Ex. 1 by Horner's method.

3. Find by Newton's method each root of $2x^3 - 15x + 10 = 0$ shown in Fig. 20, p. 32:
(A) near $x = -3$; (B) near $x = .7$; (C) near $x = 2.3$.

4. Solve $x^5 - 250 = 0$ approximately by Newton's method — in one step, starting from $x = 3$. Check by logarithmic calculation.

5. Starting from the result of Ex. I, § 260, find the crossing still more closely by the same method. (Cf. the value in (33), p. 355.)

6. Solve graphically: $2x^3 - 8x + 1 = 0$.

7. In Ex. 6 approximate each root by Newton's method, in one step, starting from your graphical result.

8. Solve by p. 536 and Newton's method: $2x - \log_e x - 6.5 = 0$.

9. Find the area under the curve $y = 1 + 1/x$, from $x = 1$ to $x = X$. For what X is $A = 4$?

10. Where is the slope of the curve $y = x^2 + e^x$ equal to 8?

11. The rate of interest which a bond will net if purchased at a certain price is known to be roughly 6%, and is given exactly by the

* See also the exercises on pp. 356–57, if previously omitted.

equation $900\,x^{21} - 925\,x^{20} - 1000\,x + 1025 = 0$, where $x = 1 + r/2$. Solve this equation approximately by Newton's method. (Hint: Use compound interest tables giving powers of 1.03 directly — if available.)

12. Like Ex. 11 for the equation $965\,x^{11} - 1000\,x^{10} - 1000\,x + 1035 = 0$, and a rate known to be near 8%.

13. Find graphically the real roots of $3\,x^3 - 27\,x + 31 = 0$. Make a sure test whether the minimum y is positive or negative.

14. Like Ex. 13 for $4\,x^4 - 24\,x^3 - 3\,x^2 + 217\,x - 295 = 0$.

§ 262 S. Plotting a Rotated Conic. In Analytic Geometry it is proved that every equation of the second degree in x and y represents some conic — i.e., ellipse, parabola, hyperbola, or pair of straight lines — unless the locus is imaginary. If the equation contains no product term xy, it can be reduced to a type form with "translaters." But if there is a term xy with other terms, we must in the present course rely mainly on plotting by points.*

Ex. I. Plot the locus of

$$3\,x^2 + 9\,xy + 2\,y^2 = 13.$$

First we solve for y in terms of x by (24), p. 343, noting that

$$a = 2, \quad b = 9\,x, \quad c = 3\,x^2 - 13.$$

$$\therefore\; y = \frac{-\,9\,x \pm \sqrt{57\,x^2 + 104}}{4}.$$

We may now calculate points by substituting values for x.

The curve is clearly real, no matter how large x becomes, either positively or negatively. Hence, as it is some conic, it must be an hyperbola. Its axis is tilted about 42°.

§ 263. Plotting the Locus of Any Equation. Certain curves can be drawn by recognizing their equations. Many others can be plotted by points.

Along any given curve y varies with x in some definite way. If we can solve the equation of the curve for y in terms of x, we have merely to plot the resulting function — just as we did frequently in Chapters I–III.

---

* See *Higher Course*, §§ 221, 250–53.

The amount of calculation required for such plotting can often be greatly reduced by making a preliminary inspection of the equation, and thus learning certain facts in advance.

Ex. 1.   Plot the locus of $xy^2 - 4y^2 + x^3 + 4x^2 = 0$.

Here
$$y = \pm x\sqrt{\frac{4+x}{4-x}}. \tag{34}$$

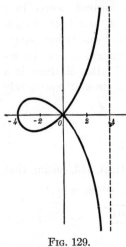

FIG. 129.

(I) *Extent of the curve.*   For any value of x which makes $4 + x$ or $4 - x$ negative, y is imaginary — *i.e.*, if x is below -4 or above $+4$. Hence the curve exists only between $x = -4$ and $x = +4$.

(II) *Symmetry.*   Wherever real, y has two numerically equal but opposite values ($\pm$). Thus the curve is symmetrical with respect to the X-axis. This is not so for the Y-axis.

(III) *Intersections with the axes.* When $x = 0$, $y = 0$. But when $y = 0$, x may be 0 or -4. For one of the factors x^2 and $(4 + x)$ must be zero, and either may be. The curve passes through the origin, and also meets the X-axis four units to the left.

(IV) *Vertical asymptote.*   At $x = 4$ equation (34) gives the form $y^2 = 16(8/0)$ — which is entirely meaningless.   (§ 28). But if we let $x \to 4$, then $y \to \infty$. Thus the curve must rise indefinitely high, approaching the line $x = 4$ asymptotically.

(V) *Table.*   Substituting values for x between -4 and 4, we draw the curve.   (Fig. 129.)

Remark.   Even when the equation of a curve is too complicated to solve for y in terms of x, or vice versa, we may still be able to find its intersections with numerous straight lines, suitably chosen, and by plotting those intersections obtain enough points to draw the curve. (See Ex. 12 below.)

EXERCISES

1. Plot each of the following equations by calculating a table of points. What kind of conic is each locus?

(a) $2x^2 - 2xy + y^2 = 4$, (b) $x^2 - 2xy + y^2 - 12x - 12y + 36 = 0$,
(c) $x^2 + 5xy + 4y^2 = 9$, (d) $2x^2 + xy - y^2 + 7x - 8y - 15 = 0$.

2. Plot $y = x - 4$ and $y = 1/(x - 4)$, using the same axes. Could you have anticipated the character of the latter curve by careful inspection of the former? Explain.

3. Draw the line $y = x$. By considering points on this, obtain several on the rectangular hyperbola $xy = 1$, and so draw the latter freely.

4. Like Ex. 3 for the parabola $y = x^2$ and the curve $y = 1/x^2$.

5. Draw the general form of the following curve, by marking the points where it meets the X-axis and noting whether y is positive or negative in each interval, and beyond all those points:

$$y = (x - 12)(x - 9)(x - 7)(x - 4)^2(x - 1)(x + 2)^2.$$

6. In Ex. 5, change y to y^2, and draw the curve, noting in which intervals y is imaginary, and where real, $+$ and $-$.

7. Similarly draw the following curves roughly:

(a) $y = (x - 10)(x - 7)(x - 3)(x - 1)$,
(b) $y^2 = (x - 10)(x - 7)(x - 3)(x - 1)$,
(c) $y^2 = (x - 8)(x - 5)(x - 2)^2(x + 3)$.

8. Plot the following curve by points, after first noting where $y = 0$ or becomes infinite, and whether y then changes sign:

$$y = \frac{x - 3}{x - 1}.$$

9. In Ex. 8 check by reducing the equation to the "translater" form $(x - 1)(y - 1) = -2$. Precisely what curve?

10. Plot the following by points as in Ex. 8, also testing whether y becomes large or small when x is very great, $+$ or $-$:

(a) $y = \dfrac{(x - 2)}{(x + 1)(x - 5)}$,   (b) $y = \dfrac{(x + 1)(x - 5)}{(x - 2)}$,

(c) $y = \dfrac{(x - 3)(x + 1)}{(x - 1)^2}$,   (d) $y = \dfrac{x}{x^2 + 1}$.

11. Discuss the following as in § 263 and plot:

(a) $y^2 = \dfrac{x^3}{4 - x}$,   (b) $y^2 = x^2\dfrac{x + 4}{x - 4}$.

12. Find where the curve $x^3 + y^3 = 6\,xy$ cuts the lines $y = x$, $2\,x$, $4\,x$, $\frac{1}{2}\,x$, $\frac{1}{4}\,x$, 0, $-\frac{1}{2}\,x$, etc. Plot these intersections and draw the curve.

13. Calculate some points on the curve in Ex. 12 by letting $x = 2$ and solving for y.

14. Like Ex. 12 for $x^3 + y^3 + 12\,xy = 0$.

15. Plot $y = 10 - \sqrt[3]{x}$ from $x = -2$ to $x = 2$. Check your curve at $x = \pm\frac{1}{8}$. Also find dy/dx, and note what happens at $x = 0$. Cf. § 82.

§ 264 *S*. **The Behavior of Algebraic Functions.** Broadly classified, algebraic functions are either rational or irrational; and each of these classes has many subdivisions. We now summarize certain characteristics of important categories.

(I) *Rational Functions*

(*A*) A *polynomial*, or rational integral function,

$$y = a_0\,x^n + a_1\,x^{n-1} + a_2\,x^{n-2} \cdots + a_n, \qquad (35)$$

always varies *continuously* and also *smoothly*, so that its graph is free from breaks and also from abrupt changes in slope. If the coefficients $a_0, \ldots, a_n$ are real, every real finite x gives a real finite unique y. As $x \to \pm \infty$, $y \to \pm \infty$. (The term $a_0\,x^n$ ultimately dominates the sign of y: whether $+$ or $-$ in each direction can be seen by inspection.) When n is odd, the graph intersects the X-axis at least once; but may have no turning point (maximum or minimum). When n is even, there may be no intersection; but there must be at least one turning point. There is no general rule as to the actual number of either.

The following special case illustrates some possible varieties of behavior; other cases are mentioned in Ex. 15–17 below.

Cubic function: $y = ax^3 + bx^2 + cx + d$.

If $a > 0$, $y \to \infty$ when $x \to \infty$; and $y \to -\infty$ when $x \to -\infty$. If $a < 0$, the reverse is true.

The "zeros" of y (*i.e.*, the values x_1, x_2, x_3, for which $y = 0$), if all real, can be approximated by Horner's method or otherwise, or found exactly by trial if rational. Either one or all three must be real: if two coincide, the graph is tangent to the X-axis, making $dy/dx = 0$ also. (More generally, when two zeros of *any* function coalesce, the derivative if continuous also has a zero.)

Since dy/dx is a quadratic, it vanishes for two values of x: real or imaginary. If these zeros of dy/dx are real and distinct, y has two turning values, a maximum and a minimum; if imaginary, no turning value. (When the zeros of dy/dx are equal, the next derivative d^2y/dx^2 has a zero there. The graph has no turning point, but has a horizontal tangent at its point of inflection.) There is sure to be a point of inflection, since d^2y/dx^2 is a linear function and must change sign once.

(B) Rational, non-integral functions. Such a function y is one which can be reduced to a fraction in its lowest terms with a "polynomial" numerator and a similar denominator. If the denominator anywhere becomes zero, then y "becomes infinite," and the graph consists of branches separated by a vertical asymptote. Elsewhere y varies continuously and smoothly.

If the numerator is of higher degree than the denominator, $y \to \pm \infty$ as $x \to \pm \infty$; if of lower degree, $y \to 0$; if of the same degree, $y \to k$ (some constant distinct from zero), as $x \to \pm \infty$. In the last two cases there is a horizontal asymptote, $y = 0$ or $y = k$.

It is possible to have two maxima without a minimum intervening, or *vice versa*.

(II) *Irrational Functions*

Here y is expressed explicitly in terms of x by means of irreducible radicals, such as

$$y = 10 - \sqrt[3]{x^2}, \quad \text{or} \quad y = x\sqrt{\frac{x-4}{x+4}}, \tag{36}$$

or implicitly by means of an equation not solvable for y in rational form, such as

$$x^2 + 4y^2 = 25, \quad \text{or} \quad x^3 + y^3 = 6xy. \tag{37}$$

Such functions are often imaginary for certain ranges of values of x. Where real, y may have only one value for any given x — as in (36) where the positive sign of the radical is intended — or several values, as in (37). In the latter case, we say that y is a two-valued, three-valued, or multiple-valued function of x.

Where a single-valued irrational function changes from real to imaginary as x passes a certain value, the graph has an

end-point and stops abruptly.   Where a multiple-valued function so changes, it is found that two values come together at
the critical point so that the two branches of the graph together
form a smooth curve.

An example of the single-valued type, with end-points, is the upper
half of a circle representing $y = \sqrt{a^2 - x^2}$.   An example of the other
kind is the complete circle, upper and lower halves, representing the
two values of y defined by $x^2 + y^2 = a^2$.

At special points where an irrational function y is itself
continuous, the derivative (or slope) may jump abruptly.
Of course, y also may be discontinuous at certain values of x,
as with rational functions.

§ 265. Summary of Chapter IX.   Systems of linear equations are conveniently handled by means of *determinants*.   For
equations of higher degree our new methods are of two kinds:

(1) *Exact solutions*.   Finding the roots of a quadratic by
formula, and the rational roots of any equation by trial substitutions and removal of factors.

(2) *Approximate solutions*.   Finding the irrational roots
of an equation by Horner's or Newton's method.

By applying some of these methods to geometry, we have
solved problems relating to intersections of lines, collinearity
of points, loci through given points, areas, tangents with given
slopes or drawn from external points, the impossibility of
certain Euclidean constructions, etc.   The algebraic ideas are
also helpful in plotting rotated conics and curves in general;
while the geometry, conversely, sheds light on the nature
of the algebraic procedures, *e.g.*, in Horner's method.

We shall next see how polar coordinates are useful in studying geometry and motion, and in extending our knowledge of
trigonometry.

EXERCISES

1. Find the area of the triangle whose vertices are: A (4, 3),
B (12, 1), C (10, 9).

2. Solve the following system of equations and check:
$11\,x + 2\,y - 3\,z = 23$, $4\,x - 3\,y + 5\,z = -15$, $5\,x + 4\,y + 7\,z = 3$.

3. In Ex. 1 find the equations of the medians and test their concurrence.

4. Like Ex. 3 for the altitudes.

5. Write the equation of the circle through $(-2, 1)$, $(-1, -2)$, and $(0, 5)$. Find the center and radius; and check.

6. What is the nature of the roots of $220\, x^2 + 793\, x - 240 = 0$?

7. For what value of a is $x^2 + y^2 = a^2$ tangent to $y = 2\, x - 10$?

8. Find the equation of the tangent to $y^2 = 10\, x - 20$ which has the slope 4.

9. Solve for x: $e^x + 12\, e^{-x} = 7$. (Hint: Let $e^x = y$.)

10. Factor into their lowest rational factors:

(a) $8\, x^4 - 12\, x^3 - 10\, x^2 + 29\, x - 15$, (b) $x^6 - 9\, x^4 + 16\, x^3 - 9\, x^2 + 1$.

11. Find any rational roots exactly, and approximate any irrational real roots to two decimals:

(a) $2\, x^4 - x^3 + 2\, x^2 + x - 1 = 0$,
(b) $4\, x^5 + 8\, x^4 - 41\, x^3 + 10\, x^2 + 20\, x - 8 = 0$.

12. Solve the simultaneous equations $x^2 + y = 5$, $x + y^2 = 3$:

(a) graphically; (b) algebraically, to 1 decimal.

13. Approximate by Newton's or Horner's method the root of $x^{10} - 5\, x - 1025 = 0$ which lies near $x = 2$.

14. Plot the locus of $2\, x^2 + xy - 6\, y^2 - 4\, x + 27\, y - 30 = 0$.

15. For a quadratic function, $y = ax^2 + bx + c$, make statements corresponding to those in § 264 regarding the cubic, insofar as apropos.

16. Similarly discuss the linear function, $y = ax + b$.

17. For the polynomial of degree n how many intersections can the graph have with the X-axis, *at most*? Turning points? Points of inflection?

18. Draw the graph of $y = x^3/(x - 2)^2$. What minimum? Any maximum?

19. For what values of x is each following curve imaginary? Draw the real locus roughly.

(a) $y^2 = (x - 10)^2 (x - 6) (x - 1) (x + 4)$;
(b) $y^2 = (9 - x) (5 - x) (2 - x) (x + 3)^2$.

CHAPTER X

POLAR COORDINATES AND TRIGONO-METRIC FUNCTIONS

PERIODIC VARIATION

§ 266. Generalized Values of r and θ. As we have previously seen (§ 107), a point P can be located by its polar coordinates (r, θ) — that is, by the length r of its radius vector OP drawn from a chosen origin or "pole" O, and by the polar angle θ measured around to OP from a chosen direction axis or "polar axis" OA. (Fig. 130.)

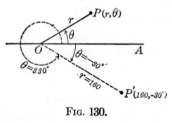

FIG. 130.

$\angle AOP$ is also called the *longitude* or vectorial angle of P.

If measured clockwise, θ is regarded as negative. *E.g.*, in Fig. 130, P' has $\theta = 330°$ or $-30°$, and thus has the coordinates $(160, 330°)$ or $(160, -30°)$.

Moreover, if P moves around O continually, θ will increase up to 360° — and beyond, if we consider the whole angle turned. Thus angles of any size whatever may arise in considering rotary motion. But merely adding 360° to θ will not change the position of P. Thus, any point has innumerable sets of polar coordinates, the θ values differing by multiples of 360°.

To simplify the study of complicated curves, it is important to give a meaning to negative values of r. Such values are laid off from the pole O in a direction *opposite* to that indicated by the value of θ. *E.g.*, the point $r = -10$, $\theta = 90°$, is opposite to the point $r = 10$, $\theta = 90°$; and hence is the same point as $(10, 270°)$. Similarly in Fig. 130, P' could be denoted as $(-160, 150°)$; for if we first lay out $\theta = 150°$ and then run in the opposite direction 160 units, we shall arrive at P'.

Polar coordinates, like rectangular, are used in studying motion and geometry, and are closely linked with trigonometric or circular functions.

§ 267. Circular Motion. Polar coordinates are especially suited to the study of circular motion: r remains constant, and we have only to consider how θ varies.

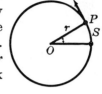

The rate at which θ is increasing — say the number of degrees per sec. — is the rate at which the radius OP is turning. (Fig. 131.) This is called the *angular speed* of P; and is denoted by the Greek letter ω (*omega*).

FIG. 131.

From ω we can find how fast P is moving — say in feet per sec. — in other words, the *linear speed* of P.

Ex. I. A point P moved in a circle of radius 5 ft. so that
$$\theta = .1\,t^3 - .002\,t^4,$$
θ being in degrees, and t in seconds. Find the position and speed of P when $t = 20$.

$$\theta = .1\,(20^3) - .002\,(20^4) = 480 \text{ at } t = 20.$$

That is, the radius OP had then turned 480° since starting.

$$\omega = \frac{d\theta}{dt} = .3\,t^2 - .008\,t^3, \;\; = 56 \text{ at } t = 20.$$

That is, OP was then turning at the rate of 56 deg./sec. Hence P was moving at the rate of $\frac{56}{360}$ of a circumference per sec., *i.e.*, with the speed

$$v = \frac{56}{360}\,(10\,\pi) \text{ ft./sec.}, \;\; = 4.89 \text{ ft./sec.}$$

Remark. When a point moves along a curve with a varying speed, the rate at which the speed changes is called the "tangential acceleration." The term "acceleration" is then used in a different sense.*

EXERCISES

1. Plot the points whose polar coordinates are: $A\,(10, 160°)$, $B\,(-10, 250°)$, $C\,(10, 340°)$, $D\,(10, -110°)$. Describe the figure $ABCD$. How long are its sides? How could B be designated with r positive? Also D with θ positive?

2. Like Ex. 1 for the points $A\,(5, 0°)$, $B\,(-5, 120°)$, $C\,(-5, 60°)$, $D\,(5, -180°)$, $E\,(5, 120°)$, $F\,(5, -300°)$: and for the figure $ABCDEF$

* See *Higher Course*, pp. 443 ff.

3. Halley's comet was nearest the sun in April, 1910. Its position then and after various intervals (t yr.) is shown in Table I. (The sun is at the origin; and the unit distance is the mean distance from the earth to the sun.) Plot these positions and draw the path — a half-ellipse. About what r and θ has the comet now, apparently? Estimate the distance traveled in the ten-year period, $t = 28$ to 38; also in the first year.

TABLE I

t	r	θ
0	0.59	0
$\frac{1}{12}$	0.87	79° 30'
$\frac{1}{2}$	3.08	130°
1	5.01	142° 38'
3	10.4	156° 43'
8	19.0	166° 8'
18	28.9	172° 54'
28	33.8	176° 48'
38	35.4	180°

4. At a certain time the coordinates of several planets were: Venus (.72, 30° 45'), Earth (.98, 100° 30', Jupiter (5.26, 267° 42'), Sat. (9.07, 62° 6'), Ur. (19.8, 303° 14'). Plot these positions. Estimate and calculate the distance from Saturn to Uranus.

5. A point P moved so that $r = 10$ always and $\theta = 2\,t^2$ after t sec. Mark the positions of P at $t = 1, 2, \ldots, 10$. Find the rate of rotation (in degrees per sec.) at $t = 3$.

6. A point moved so that $r = 3\,t$ and $\theta = 50\,t$ after t sec. Plot the path from $t = 0$ to $t = 10$.

7. In Fig. 131 if OP turns at the rate of 8° per sec. and $r = 20$ in., how fast is P moving? Likewise for 90° per hr. and $r = 1000$ ft.

8. A point moved in a circle so that $\theta = 3\,t^2$ (degrees). Find θ and ω when $t = 10$ (seconds).

9. A point moved in a circle of radius 20 in. so that $\theta = 3\,t^2 - .08\,t^3$ (degrees). Find the speed and the distance traveled at $t = 5$.

10. For 30 seconds a wheel turned so that $\theta = .036\,t^3 - .0006\,t^4$ (degrees), after which ω remained constant. Find ω at $t = 30°$. Also find how fast ω was increasing at $t = 10$.

11. A wheel of radius 2 ft. started from rest in such a way that $d^2\theta/dt^2 = 48\,t - 12\,t^2$, where θ is in revolutions and t in minutes. Find θ and ω and the distance traveled by a point on the rim when $t = 4$.

12. In Ex. 11 find the maximum speed of the point.

13. A point moves in a circle of radius 20 in. in such a way that $\theta = 60\,t^2 - t^3$ (degrees). Find the maximum speed of the point.

[14.] How long an arc is intercepted in any circle by a central angle of 1°? Of 1″? How large a central angle will intercept an arc equal to the radius?

§ 268. Radians. An angle which if placed at the center of a circle would intercept an arc equal to the radius in length is called a *radian* — written $1^{(r)}$. (Fig. 132.)

Since the radius is contained precisely π times in a semi-circumference, there are π radians in a central angle of 180°:

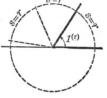

$$\pi^{(r)} = 180°. \qquad (1)$$

Dividing both sides of this by π, or 3.1416 approx.,

$$1^{(r)} = 57° \; 17' \; 44''.8.$$

Since a radian is an angle of perfectly definite size, we can measure any other angle by the number of radians it contains, just as well as by the number of degrees. This greatly simplifies the study of circular motion.

E.g., for every radian through which line *OP* turns (Fig. 131), the point *P* travels a distance equal to the radius. If the angular speed is 4 radians per sec., *P* is moving with a speed of 4 radii per sec.*

§ 269. Tables of Equivalents. By the tables on p. 538 of the Appendix, we can quickly convert any number of radians into degrees, or *vice versa*. The following examples show the reduction of $2.16^{(r)}$ to degrees; and of 7° 42′ to radians.

$2.^{(r)}$	114°	35′	30″		7°	= $.12217^{(r)}$
.1	5	43	46		40′ =	.01164
.06	3	26	16		2′ =	.00058
2.16	123°	45′	32″		7° 42′ =	$.13439^{(r)}$

Any simple fraction of $\pi^{(r)}$ or 180° is best transformed without the tables. *E.g.*,

$$\frac{\pi^{(r)}}{6} = 30°, \qquad\qquad 90° = \frac{\pi^{(r)}}{2}.$$

§ 270. Arc and Central Angle. If a central angle in a circle contains θ radians, its intercepted arc equals θ times the radius:

$$s = r\theta. \qquad (2)$$

This relation is much simpler than if the angle were expressed in degrees.

* Do not confuse a *radian* with a *radius*. A radian is not an arc or line but an *angle*. (Exactly what angle?)

A central angle of 1° intercepts an arc equal to $\frac{1}{360}\,(2\,\pi r)$, or .01745329 r, approx. And for an angle of θ° the arc is

$$s = .01745329\,r\theta. \tag{3}$$

Whatever the units of measure may be, the relation between the arc and the angle is always of this form:

$$\boldsymbol{s = k\,\theta,} \tag{4}$$

k being the length of arc intercepted by a *unit angle* — whatever that may be.

§ 271 S. Estimates Involving Very Small Angles.

By Ex. 14, p. 368, a central angle of θ'' intercepts an arc whose length is

$$s = 4.85 \times 10^{-6}\,r\theta. \tag{5}$$

This formula is useful in making approximations involving very small angles — as illustrated in the following example.

FIG. 133.

Ex. I. A comet subtends at the earth an angle of 2″ at a time when it is known to be one billion miles away. Find its approximate diameter.

Imagine a circle to be drawn with a radius of one billion (= 10^9) miles, and with its center at the earth. (Fig. 133.) The part of its circumference intercepted by a central angle of 2″ is relatively so short an arc as to be practically straight. That is, the arc would approximate the required diameter of the comet.

Substituting $\theta = 2$ and $r = 10^9$ in (5) gives

$$s = (4.85 \times 10^{-6}) \times 10^9 \times 2 = 9700.$$

The diameter of the comet is approximately 9700 miles.

N.B. The value of s in (5) will not approximate closely the distance between two points, unless the line joining them is practically perpendicular to the bisector of the angle.

EXERCISES

1. In a circle of radius 20 in., find the lengths of the arcs intercepted by central angles of $4^{(r)}$, $2.35^{(r)}$, and $.06854^{(r)}$.

2. In the circle of Ex. 1 how large a central angle, in radians, would intercept an arc of 6.5 in.? One of .24 in.?

3. A wheel of radius 6 in. is turning with an angular speed of 12 rad./min. What is the speed of a point P on its rim?

4. If the same wheel turns so that $\theta = .15\,t^2$ (radians), find the speed of P when $t = 10$. How far had P then traveled?

5. A wheel of radius 15 in. turned in such a way that, after t sec., $\theta = .0012\, t^3 - .00002\, t^4$ (radians).   Find the maximum speed attained by a point on the rim.

6. (a) Without tables find the number of degrees in $2^{(r)}$, $.6^{(r)}$, $\dfrac{\pi^{(r)}}{3}$.

(b) Likewise find the number of radians in $1°$; $12°$; $1'$.

7. Using tables, find the equivalents of $6^{(r)}$, $3.89^{(r)}$, $42°\,7'$.

8. The same as Ex. 7 for $\dfrac{\pi^{(r)}}{4}$.   Check without tables.

9. If an auto engine is making 1800 R.P.M. [revolutions per minute] what is its angular speed in rad./sec.?

10. If a flywheel of radius 30 in. makes 6 R.P.M., what is the speed of a point on the rim?

11. If a wheel of radius .8 in. has an angular speed of $825°/\text{sec.}$, what is the speed of a point on the rim?

12. If a watch keeps correct time, what is the angular speed of the hour hand in rad./hr.?   In rad./min.?

13. What is the angular speed of rotation of the earth in rad./sec.?

14. What is the linear speed of a point on the earth's equator, due only to the rotation?   (Take the earth's radius as 3960 mi.)

15. The same as Ex. 14 for a point in latitude $42°$.

16. Find the diameter of a sun-spot which, if viewed perpendicularly, would subtend at the earth (92,500,000 mi. away) an angle of $30''$.

17. A solar prominence was seen to extend $3'$ up from the edge of the sun's disk.   Find its height in miles.

18. Estimate the diameter of a crater on the moon, at the center of the disc, if it subtends at the earth (240,000 mi. away) an angle of $80''$.

19. How far away is Jupiter when its diameter (90,000 mi.) subtends at the earth an angle of $45''$?

20. The distance of the earth from the sun subtends at the nearest fixed star an angle of $0''.76$, approx.   Find the distance to the star.

21. How large an angle would the diameter of a dollar (1.5 in.) subtend at a distance of 6 miles?   (Compare the angle in Ex. 20.)

22. A mountain 12 mi. away has an elevation angle of $.15^{(r)}$.   About how high is its summit above the observer?

23. A mountain rising 7000 ft. above an observer has an elevation angle of $.1^{(r)}$.   How far away is it, roughly?

§ 272. Trigonometric Functions, Resumed.   When any angle, like θ or θ' in Fig. 134, is in "trigonometric position" (§ 122), any point P on the terminal side of θ has definite coordinates:

abscissa, x;   *ordinate, y;*   *radius vector, r.*

(We avoid taking P at the vertex where $r = 0$.) Then, as previously defined, the six trigonometric functions of θ are

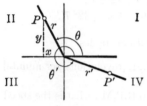

Fig. 134.

$$\sin \theta = y/r, \qquad \csc \theta = r/y.$$
$$\cos \theta = x/r, \qquad \sec \theta = r/x, \qquad (6)$$
$$\tan \theta = y/x, \qquad \operatorname{ctn} \theta = x/y,$$

This tabulation brings each function opposite its reciprocal. Notice these pairs carefully. The order of tabulation here is easily remembered, for on reading down the first column and up the second we have the customary order: sine, cosine; tangent, cotangent; secant, cosecant. These definitions should be carefully fixed in memory, together with their verbal statements in terms of "ordinate of P," etc.

The X- and Y-axes divide the plane into four "quadrants," which we number counter-clockwise I to IV, starting from the positive X-axis. Angles between 90° and 180° are called "angles of the second quadrant." And so on.

Each function is positive in certain quadrants and negative in others. No rule is needed as to this, if we know the definitions (6). We simply picture to ourselves any given angle θ, and note whether x and y are positive or negative: r is always positive on the true terminal line of θ.

Notice, in passing, that the definitions (6) would give the same values, if instead of P on the actual terminal line, we chose a corresponding point P' on the terminal line reversed. (Fig. 135.)

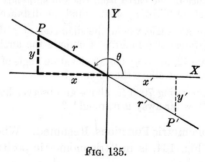

Fig. 135.

For this would simply reverse the signs of x, y, and r; and would have no effect on any of the six ratios above.

§ 273. Finding All from One. Given any one function of an angle, we can find all the others — without tables. We simply draw the angle and read off the desired values. Except for certain extreme cases, there are two possible sets of values, due to the fact that there are two angles in different quadrants, for each of which the given function has the specified value.

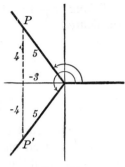

FIG. 136.

Ex. I. $\cos \theta = -3/5$. Find the other functions.

Here $x/r = -3/5$ for every point on the terminal line. Taking $r = 5$ requires $x = -3$. This is satisfied both at P and at P', in Fig. 136. Thus θ may be in either the second or third quadrant.

Quadrant II

$$\sin \theta = 4/5, \quad \csc \theta = 5/4,$$
$$\cos \theta = -3/5, \quad \sec \theta = -5/3,$$
$$\tan \theta = -4/3, \quad \operatorname{ctn} \theta = -3/4.$$

Quadrant III

$$\sin \theta = -4/5, \quad \csc \theta = -5/4,$$
$$\cos \theta = -3/5, \quad \sec \theta = -5/3,$$
$$\tan \theta = 4/3, \quad \operatorname{ctn} \theta = 3/4.$$

Ex. II. $\tan \theta = 3/2$, but $\theta > 90°$ and $< 360°$. Find $\sin \theta$, $\cos \theta$.

Here $y/x = 3/2$ for every point on the terminal line. Since θ is not in Quadrant I, both x and y must be negative. Take $x = -2$, $y = -3$. Then $r = \sqrt{(-2)^2 + (-3)^2} = \sqrt{13}$.

$$\therefore \ \sin \theta = -\frac{3}{\sqrt{13}}, \quad \cos \theta = -\frac{2}{\sqrt{13}}.$$

§ 274. Special Angles. The functions of certain special angles can be calculated exactly by elementary geometry, *e.g.*, of angles which differ from 180° or 360° by 30°, 45°, or 60°.

Ex. I. Functions of 300°.

Taking $r = 10$ gives $x = 5$, $y = -5\sqrt{3}$; for the right triangle formed by x, y, and r is half of an equilateral triangle. (Draw the figure.)

$$\therefore \ \sin \theta = \frac{-5\sqrt{3}}{10} = -\frac{\sqrt{3}}{2},$$

$$\cos \theta = \frac{5}{10} = \frac{1}{2}, \quad \text{etc.}$$

Ex. II.   Functions of 225°.

Taking $r = 10$ gives $x = y = -\sqrt{50} = -5\sqrt{2}$.   (Draw the figure.)

$$\therefore \ \sin 225° = \frac{-5\sqrt{2}}{10} = -\frac{\sqrt{2}}{2},$$

$$\cos 225° = \frac{-5\sqrt{2}}{10} = -\frac{\sqrt{2}}{2}, \quad \text{etc.}$$

§ 275. Quadrantal Angles.   The functions of 0°, 90°, 180°, etc., can be read off directly from a figure.   This should be done often, until their values are fixed in mind.

Ex. I.   Functions of 270°, or $\frac{3}{2}\pi$ radians.
Taking $r = 10$ gives $x = 0$, $y = -10$.   Hence

$$\begin{array}{ll} \sin 270° = y/r = -1, & \csc 270° = r/y = -1, \\ \cos 270° = x/r = 0, & \sec 270° = \cdots, \\ \tan 270° = \cdots, & \operatorname{ctn} 270° = x/y = 0. \end{array}$$

The tangent and secant do not exist for 270°; for it is impossible to divide by x when $x = 0$.   They exist, however, for angles as near 270° as we please.   (See § 276.)

EXERCISES

1. Draw angles of 140°, 220°, and 320°.   By measuring lines calculate the approximate values of the six functions for each.   List separately, noting + and − signs carefully.

2. How do the sine and cosine of − 80° compare with the same functions of + 80°, numerically and as to sign?   Is the same thing true for − 130° and + 130°?   For any − θ and θ?

3. Draw and measure an angle θ between 90° and 270°, for which ctn θ = − .50.

4. Like Ex. 3 for each following positive angle θ:
(a) Less than 180°, having cos θ = − .75;
(b) Between 90° and 270°, having sin θ = − .25;
(c) Less than 270°, with csc θ = − 1.25;
(d) Between 180° and 360°, with sec θ = 2;
(e) In Quadrant II or III, having tan θ = − .60.

5. Find the exact values of all the functions of:
(a) 225°,   (b) 330°,   (c) 300°,   (d) 150°,
(e) 240°,   (f) 315°,   (g) 120°,   (h) 135°.

6. Without tables find the sine and cosine of 90° and 360°.

7. Find the exact values of all the functions of 180° and 270° which exist. Note the sign in each case.

8. What can you say about the value of tan θ when θ is just a little less than 90°? A little more than 90°?

9. What are all the positive angles less than 360°, for which sin θ = -1? Cos θ = 0? Tan θ = -1?

10. The same as Ex. 9, if ctn θ = 0; sec θ = -1; csc θ = 1.

11. Given each following function, draw both possible angles $(0° < \theta < 360°)$; and write by inspection the values of the five remaining functions — in two separate lists, with the Quadrant indicated:

(a) cos θ = $-12/13$,   (b) csc θ = $-5/3$,
(c) tan θ = $-8/15$,   (d) sin θ = $4/9$,
(e) sec θ = $\sqrt{5}$,   (f) ctn θ = 3.

12. Express in radians all angles less than $2\pi^{(r)}$ for which cos θ = -1; ctn θ = 1; csc θ = -1.

§ 276. Graphs. Let us now see how the functions vary as the angle θ increases from 0° to 360° and beyond.

If we keep r fixed, we need only consider what happens to x and y. With r fixed, the point P (Fig. 134, p. 372) moves in a circle. Hence y starts from zero, increases to $+r$, decreases to $-r$ and increases again. Thus sin θ $(= y/r)$ takes the values:

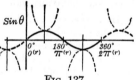

FIG. 137.

θ	0	90	180	270	360
sin θ	0	1	0	-1	0

The graph is the wavy curve in Fig. 137, reaching a maximum height of 1 unit at 90° and a minimum of -1 at 270°. (Note the radian equivalents.)

Similarly the graph of cos θ $(= x/r)$ is seen to run as in Fig. 138.

The graph of tan θ $(= y/x)$ is less simple. As θ approaches 90°, y becomes nearly equal to r. Dividing by x, which is almost zero, makes tan θ exceedingly large. As soon as θ passes 90°, there is a startling change: tan θ jumps to an

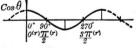

FIG. 138.

exceedingly large *negative* value — for x is now negative. The graph, therefore, is discontinuous. It approaches as-ymptotically the vertical line drawn at $\theta = 90°$. Similarly at $\theta = 270°$.* (Fig. 139.)

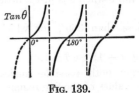

FIG. 139.

The graphs of the cotangent, secant, and cosecant can be drawn by inspection of the foregoing graphs. That of csc θ is shown dotted in Fig. 137.

The sine, cosine, and tangent curves are extremely important. They should be thoroughly fixed in mind — together with the radian equivalents of the angles.

§ 277. Some Important Observations.

(I) *Limitations on size.* Since sin θ and cos θ can never exceed 1 numerically, their reciprocals csc θ and sec θ are never numerically less than 1. There is, however, no limitation upon tan θ and ctn θ. These may have any value whatever, positive or negative.

(II) *Periodicity.* Adding 360° to θ leaves the values of x, y, r unchanged, and hence also the values of the functions. Thus all the graphs repeat themselves every 360° or $2\,\pi^{(r)}$. In fact, the graphs of *tan θ and ctn θ repeat every 180°* or $\pi^{(r)}$. For changing θ by 180° affects x and y only by changing their signs, and does not affect y/x.

(III) *Relation of the sine and cosine curves.* Rotating the line OP (Fig. 134, p. 372) through 90° would replace x by y and y by $-x$. (§ 216.) That is,

$$x \text{ for } \angle \theta = y \text{ for } \angle (\theta + 90°)$$
$$x/r \text{ for } \angle \theta = y/r \text{ for } \angle (\theta + 90°)$$
$$\therefore \; \cos \theta = \sin (\theta + 90°). \tag{7}$$

Hence the graph of cos θ is the same as that of sin $(\theta + 90°)$ — *i.e.*, the same as the graph of sin θ, but moved 90° to the left. This may also be written

$$\cos (A - 90°) = \sin A. \tag{8}$$

§ 278. Reducing to Acute Angles.
Trigonometric tables run only to 90°; but they can be used to find the functions of any angle whatever.

---

* It is customary to say that the tangent of 90° is *infinite*, written tan 90° = ∞. But this is intended merely as a short way of stating that while tan 90° does not exist, tan θ increases without limit as $\theta \rightarrow 90°$. Similarly for 270°. (Cf. Appendix, p. 528.)

For instance, as is clear from Fig. 140, cos 160° is numerically equal to cos 20°, since 160° is just as far from 180°
as 20° is from 0°. Similarly for

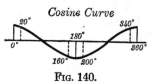

Cosine Curve

Fig. 140.

cos 200° — and for cos 340°, with
respect to 360°. Hence cos 160°,
cos 200°, and cos 340° can all be
found by looking up cos 20°, and
prefixing the proper sign, + or −.

In general, to find any function of any large angle,* we
have simply to take *the difference between the given angle and
180° or 360°*, whichever gives an acute angle, *look up the required function and prefix the + or − sign*, according to the
quadrant. No rule is necessary as to signs. Simply visualize
the angle and note whether x and y are positive or negative.

This method is easily seen to be correct by examining the
graphs of sin θ, cos θ, tan θ, etc. Or it can be proved in detail
by geometry, using the definitions in § 272.

Ex. I. Find sin 190°.
This angle differs from 180° by 10°. By tables,

$$\sin 10° = .17365.$$

But for 190°, y/r is negative. Hence

$$\sin 190° = - .17365.$$

Ex. II. Find ctn 275°.
This angle differs from 360° by 85°. By tables,

$$\text{ctn } 85° = .08749.$$

But for 275°, x/y is negative. Hence,

$$\text{ctn } 275° = - .08749.$$

§ 279. The Reverse Operation. To find an angle of any
size when given one of its functions, we have simply to look
up the acute angle which has the same function numerically;
and combine this acute angle with 180° or 360°, according to
the given sign.

Ex. I. sin $\theta = - .17365$: find θ (between 0° and 360°).
By tables: $.17365 = \sin 10°.$

---

* Of course, an angle larger than 360° is first reduced by a multiple of 360° —
or a negative angle is similarly raised — until between 0° and 360°.

Now sin θ is negative when y is. Hence we must combine 10° with 180° or 360° *in such a way as to get an angle θ in Quadrant III or IV*:

$$\therefore \ \theta = 180° + 10° = 190°, \qquad \text{or } \theta = 360° - 10° = 350°.$$

Ex. II. $\tan \theta = -5.6713$.

By tables: $5.7613 = \tan 80°$.

Since $\tan \theta \ (= y/x)$ is negative when x and y have opposite signs, we combine 80° with 180° or 360° so as to get into Quadrant II or IV:

$$\theta = 180° - 80° = 100°, \qquad \text{or } \theta = 360° - 80° = 280°.$$

Ex. III. $\sec \theta = -1.30541$.

The reciprocal is $\cos \theta = -.76604$; and θ must be in Quadrant II or III, where x is negative.

By tables: $.76604 = \cos 40°$.

$$\therefore \ \theta = 180° - 40° = 140°, \qquad \text{or } \theta = 180° + 40° = 220°.$$

EXERCISES

1. Find from tables the sine, cosine, tangent, and cotangent of:

(*a*) 208°,   (*b*) 301°,   (*c*) 93°,   (*d*) 258° 25′.

2. (*a–c*) How would you look up the secant and cosecant of each angle in Ex. 1 (*a–c*)?

3. Find both positive values of $\theta < 360°$ for which

(*a*) $\sin \theta = -.6561$;   (*b*) $\cos \theta = .2924$;   (*c*) $\tan \theta = 5.6713$;

(*d*) $\operatorname{ctn} \theta = 1.6003$;   (*e*) $\sec \theta = -2.000$;   (*f*) $\tan \theta = -.7002$.

4. Interpolate on p. 539 to find θ if $\operatorname{ctn} \theta = -1.85$.

5. Using five-place tables find to the nearest tenth of 1° all positive angles less than 360° for which

(*a*) $\sin A = .88912$;   (*b*) $\cos B = -.49893$;   (*c*) $\operatorname{ctn} C = 2.8675$.

6. Find the sine, cosine, and tangent of $2.5^{(r)}$. (See table, p. 538.)

7. Like Ex. 6 for each following angle, changing to degrees:

(*a*) $\dfrac{2\,\pi^{(r)}}{3}$,   (*b*) $\dfrac{7\,\pi^{(r)}}{12}$,   (*c*) $\dfrac{7\,\pi^{(r)}}{4}$,   (*d*) $4.3110^{(r)}$,   (*e*) $1.75^{(r)}$.

8. Find in radians (p. 538) both positive angles $< 2\,\pi^{(r)}$ for which

(*a*) $\sin A = -.351$;   (*b*) $\cos B = .765$;   (*c*) $\tan C = -.747$.

9. Find first in degrees and then in radians both positive angles $< 360°$ or $2\,\pi^{(r)}$ for which

(*a*) $\sin A = .9397$;   (*b*) $\cos B = -.9397$;   (*c*) $\tan C = -.1763$.

10. (*a*) Make a table for $\sin \theta$ taking $\theta = 0, \dfrac{\pi}{4}, \dfrac{\pi}{2}, \dfrac{3\,\pi}{4}$, to $2\,\pi^{(r)}$; plot the graph; and compare Fig. 137.

(*b*) Likewise for $\cos \theta$ and Fig. 138.

11. According to the graphs in Figs. 137–39 what are the angles (between $0^{(r)}$ and $2\pi^{(r)}$ inclusive), for which $\sin\theta = 0$? $\cos\theta = 0$? $\tan\theta = 1$?

12. How often does the sine curve repeat?   The tangent curve?

13. (a) By inspection of the graph of $\cos\theta$, draw a rough graph for $\sec\theta$.   (b) The same for $\sin\theta$ and $\csc\theta$.   (c) The same for $\tan\theta$ and $\operatorname{ctn}\theta$.

§ 280. Simple Harmonic Motion.

If a point Q moves in a circle with a constant speed, its projection P upon any diameter will oscillate back and forth in a certain way. (Fig. 141.)   This type of oscillating motion is called Simple Harmonic Motion, often abbreviated *S.H.M.*

To study the nature of an *S.H.M.*, we need an equation giving the distance x from the center of oscillation at any time.

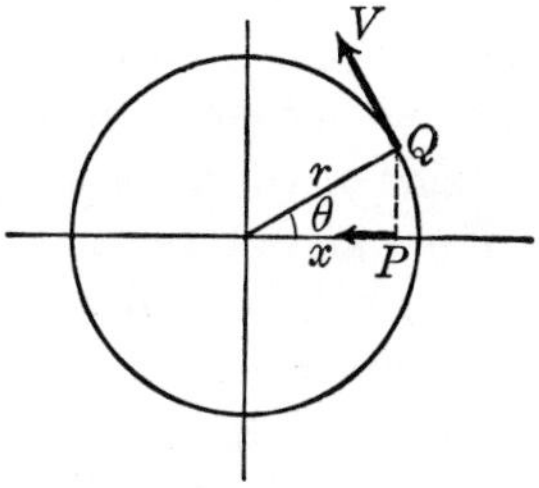

Now

$$x = r\cos\theta.$$

And by hypothesis the angular speed of Q is some constant $d\theta/dt = k$, whence

FIG. 141.

$$\theta = kt + C,$$

C being the value of θ when we begin to count time.

$$\therefore\ x = r\cos(kt + C). \tag{9}$$

This is a general formula, true for any *S.H.M.*, and giving x, the "displacement" from the center, at any time.

If $\theta = 0$ at $t = 0$, making $C = 0$, (9) becomes simply

$$x = r\cos kt. \tag{10}$$

If $\theta = -\dfrac{\pi}{2}$ at $t = 0$, (9) becomes $x = r\cos(kt - \dfrac{\pi}{2})$.   But by (III), § 277, this is the same as

$$x = r\sin kt. \tag{11}$$

The speed and acceleration of P can be found easily from (9) as soon as we have seen how to differentiate sine and cosine functions (§ 285).   We shall then find

$$\frac{d^2x}{dt^2} = -k^2x. \tag{12}$$

That is, *the acceleration is constantly proportional to the dis-placement x* — negatively proportional — which is the char-acteristic physical feature of every *S.H.M.*

The acceleration is zero at the center, where the speed is numerically a maximum. It is greatest at the left extreme, when $x = -r$. The speed is then passing rapidly through zero from negative to positive.

S.H.M.'s occur frequently in machinery. Also many motions which are not simple harmonic may be regarded as the result of combining several or many such motions.

§ 281. Oscillating Quantities. Many physical and other quantities oscillate in value in much the same way as the varying displacement in an *S.H.M.* That is, they vary like the sine or cosine of a growing angle.

E.g., an alternating electric current rises to a maximum intensity in one direction, sinks to zero and on down to a minimum (*i.e.*, a maximum in the opposite or negative direc-tion), rises again, etc. The varying intensity is represented by some such formula as

$$i = 10 \sin (120\ \pi t), \tag{13}$$

where t is the number of seconds elapsed, and $120\ \pi t$ is the number of radians in the "phase angle." *

The graph, on some scale, is the sine curve. (Fig. 137, p. 375.) The greatest value of a sine being 1, the maximum i in (13) is 10 units, represented by the greatest height of the sine curve.

Of course, the oscillations occur very rapidly. Thus in (13) i completes a "cycle" or period when the angle $120\ \pi t$ reaches the value $2\ \pi$:

$$120\ \pi t = 2\ \pi, \qquad t = \tfrac{1}{60}.$$

That is, a cycle takes $\tfrac{1}{60}$ sec.; or the current alternates 120 times a second. The base of each arch of the sine curve here represents $\tfrac{1}{60}$ sec. of time.

§ 282. Finding Sine Formulas. If observed values of a variable y suggest that its graph may be a sine curve on some

---

* That the formula involves a trigonometric function is not strange — inasmuch as the current is generated by *circular revolutions* of an "armature."

scale, we can easily settle the question. Assuming a formula of the type

$$y = a \sin kt, \tag{14}$$

we find a and k to fit the observed maximum value and cycle length. We can then substitute other values from the table, and see whether they actually fit.

Ex. I. Find a and k in (14) if the maximum $y = 25$, and if there are 200 cycles per sec.

Since the greatest value of a sine is $+1$, the greatest y in (14) is $y = a$. Hence a is 25 in our case.

At the end of one cycle we must have the angle $kt = 2\pi$; but also, as given, must have $t = \frac{1}{200}$:

$$k\left(\tfrac{1}{200}\right) = 2\pi. \tag{15}$$

Thus $k = 400\pi$, and the formula is

$$y = 25 \sin 400\pi t. \tag{16}$$

If the graph resembles a sine curve, raised or lowered, we can consider the fluctuations Y above and below the average level of y, say $y = b$. Obtaining a formula for Y as above, we can take $y = b + Y$; and test against the table.

EXERCISES

The angles here are in radians.

1. Plot $y = 10 \sin \frac{1}{2} t$, taking $t = 0, 1, 2, \ldots, 12$ and using the table on p. 538. When would the first cycle end? What is the maximum y and when first attained?

2. Plot $x = 10 \cos \dfrac{\pi t}{3}$, taking $t = 0, 1, 2, \ldots, 6$; and using p. 539. When did x become zero? What minimum x, and when?

3. A quantity varied thus: $y = 8 \sin \pi t$. Draw its graph during one cycle by inspection. Show clearly the value of t at the end of the cycle; also the maximum y.

4. Like Ex. 3 for the following cases:

(a) $y = 20 \sin 100\pi t$,   (b) $y = 5 \sin \dfrac{\pi t}{6}$,

(c) $Q = .3 \sin 100 t$,   (d) $S = .06 \sin 3 t$.

5. Similarly draw the graph by inspection in each following case:

(a) $x = 10 \cos \dfrac{\pi t}{2}$,   (b) $x = .05 \cos 40\pi t$,

(c) $R = 3 \cos 60 t$,   (d) $V = .4 \cos 100 t$.

6. How many cycles per sec. in Ex. 4 a, b and Ex. 5 a, b?

7. As a tuning fork vibrated, its displacement (x cm.) from the position of rest varied thus with the time (t sec.): $x = .06 \cos 1024 \pi t$. How many complete vibrations or cycles per sec.? Draw the graph by inspection.

8. Like Ex. 7 for a pendulum whose angular displacement varies thus: $\theta = .04 \sin 6 \pi t$.

9. What values should a and k have in the formula $y = a \sin kt$, if there are

(*a*) 5 cycles per sec., with the maximum $y = 65$;

(*b*) 700 000 cycles per sec., with the maximum $y = .002$;

(*c*) 1 cycle in 10 sec., with the maximum $y = 15$?

10. A 60-cycle alternating current has a maximum strength $i = 45.$ Find a formula for i, assuming a sine graph.

11. A tuning fork makes 256 complete vibrations per second (middle C). The maximum displacement (x cm.) is $x = .12$, at $t = 0$. Write a sine or cosine formula, as may be appropriate.

12. During several winter days the temperature ($T°$) fluctuated from $6° C.$ at 3 P.M. to $- 6° C.$ at 3 A.M. Counting time (t hr.) from 3 P.M., and assuming a pure sine or cosine graph, express T in terms of t.

13. An economic variable y fluctuates with a period of 12 mo., between a minimum of $- 20$ and a maximum of $+ 20$. Assuming a sine curve as the graph, starting with $y = 0$ at $t = 0$, find a formula for y at the end of t mo. What value does this give when $t = 2$?

14. What were the maximum and minimum values, and when reached, if y varied thus: $y = 100 + 25 \sin 8 \pi t$? Likewise if x varied thus: $x = 250 + 70 \cos \dfrac{\pi t}{20}$?

15. Plot; and find a formula which appears likely to fit the following table approximately. Check when $t = 1$; $t = 5$.

t	0	1	2	3	4	5	6	7	8
y	0	71	100	71	0	$- 71$	$- 100$	$- 71$	0

16. The population of a health resort t mo. after Jan. 1 runs about as shown in the following table. Discover an approximate formula and check all items.

t	0	1	2	3	4	5	6	7	8	9	10	11	12
P	500	485	450	400	350	315	300	315	350	400	450	485	500

17. In Fig. 141, if $r = 10$ and Q makes a revolution in 12 sec., and if we begin to count time when $x = 10$, write the formula for x at any time. In the *S.H.M.* represented by this formula, find the positions of P at $t = 0, 1, 2, \cdots, 6$. Mark these positions on the line of motion, labeling each with its value of t.

§ 283 *S*. **Combining Sine Curves.** If a piano string vibrated with a single frequency, say 256 times per sec., it would produce a pure tone — in this case, middle *C*. Actually, overtones are also produced because the motion of any particle *P* in the string is a combination of vibrations of different frequencies. For a pure tone the varying displacement of *P* could be represented by a sine curve: for a composite tone a combination of two or more such curves is needed.

In studying the flow of heat also, and many other phenomena, it is necessary to combine sine curves.

Ex. I. Draw by inspection the graph of

$$y = 10 \sin t + 6 \sin 2 t. \tag{17}$$

We first draw, with a common base line, the graphs of $y = 10 \sin t$ and $y = 6 \sin 2 t$, viz. (I) and (II) in Fig. 142. In doing this we note the maximum height of each, 10 or 6; and that (II) completes a cycle when $t = \pi$.

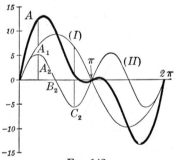

Fig. 142.

Next, we select any point on (II) say A_2, note the height of (II), and lay this off from the corresponding point A_1 of (I) — upward if positive, downward if negative. We thus get A, whose ordinate is the sum of the ordinates at A_1 and A_2. Repeating the operation for several points we get the form of the required graph, drawn heavy in Fig. 142. Points on (II) like A_2, B_2, C_2, where y has a maximum, zero, or minimum value are especially convenient to use in combining.

§ 284 *S*. **Harmonic Analysis.** By combining two or more sine or cosine curves, very odd graphs are obtainable.

E.g., if we plot

$$y = \sin x + \tfrac{1}{9}\sin 3x - \tfrac{1}{25}\sin 5x - \tfrac{1}{49}\sin 7x, \qquad (18)$$

the graph resembles Fig. 143, deviating only slightly from the three connected straight lines there shown. If to the right member of (18), we add four more such terms, viz.

$$\tfrac{1}{81}\sin 9x + \tfrac{1}{121}\sin 11x - \tfrac{1}{169}\sin 13x - \tfrac{1}{225}\sin 15x,$$

the deviations will be still less.

If, instead of the sum on the right side of (18), we took the *limit* of that sum as the number of terms is indefinitely increased, it can be proved that the graph would run exactly as in Fig. 143. When we wish to indicate briefly that we are considering such a limit of a sum — or as sometimes stated, such an infinite series of terms — it is customary to write several dots after the last term given (Cf. the caption of Fig. 143).

It was shown about 1820 by J. B. J. Fourier, a Frenchman,

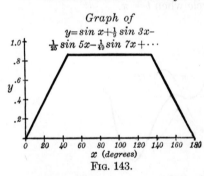

Graph of
$y = \sin x + \tfrac{1}{9}\sin 3x -$
$\tfrac{1}{25}\sin 5x - \tfrac{1}{49}\sin 7x + \cdots$

Fig. 143.

that if we have given any graph whatever, which has a definite height at every point and a limited number of discontinuities and maxima and minima, the function represented by it can be expressed as the "sum" of an infinite series of sines (or cosines, or both).

Such "Fourier series" are treated in detail in higher courses, being admirably adapted to the study of the vibrations of a string of a musical instrument, other types of wave motion, the flow of heat, etc.

The Fourier series for any given graph can be found as far as the first 80 terms by a machine, called an "harmonic analyzer," invented by Lord Kelvin and improved by A. A. Michelson. For instance, it will give an approximate equation for a human profile!

EXERCISES

1. Draw by inspection, the graphs of $y = 10 \sin t$, and $y = 2 \sin 2t$, over a common base line from $t = 0$ to $t = 2\pi$. By combining draw the graph of $y = 10 \sin t + 2 \sin 2t$.

2. Proceeding as in Ex. 1, draw the following graphs:

    (a) $y = 10 \sin t + 8 \sin 2 t$,   (b) $y = 10 \sin t + 2 \sin 3 t$,

    (c) $y = 10 \cos t + 3 \cos 2 t$,   (d) $y = 10 \cos t + 5 \cos 3 t$.

3. Make a table of values for $x = 0°, 30°, 60°$, etc., to $360°$, and plot:

    (a) $y = \sin x + \frac{1}{3} \sin 3 x + \frac{1}{5} \sin 5 x$;

    (b) $y = \sin x - \frac{1}{9} \sin 3 x + \frac{1}{25} \sin 5 x - \frac{1}{49} \sin 7 x$;

    (c) $y = \cos x - \frac{1}{3} \cos 3 x + \frac{1}{5} \cos 5 x - \frac{1}{7} \cos 7 x$;

    (d) $y = \cos x + \frac{1}{9} \cos 3 x + \frac{1}{25} \cos 5 x + \frac{1}{49} \cos 7 x$.

4. Plot $y = \sin \theta$, taking $\theta = 0, .5, 1$, to 3.5, and using 1 horizontal unit to represent $1^{(r)}$. Measure the slope at each calculated point, and plot the derived curve. (§ 72.) Does its form suggest anything as to the derivative of $\sin \theta$?

5. A variable y oscillates between 60 and $- 60$, has a graph of the sine type, and completes 20 cycles per sec. Write a formula for y after t sec., and calculate y when $t = .01$.

6. Like Ex. 5 for the following cases:

    (a) y varies between 50 and $- 50$, with 100 cycles per sec.;

    (b) y runs from 100 up to 140, down to 60, back to 100; and completes 10 such cycles per sec.;

    (c) As in (b), y varies between 250 and 150; 5 cycles per sec.

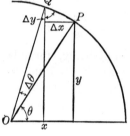

Fig. 144.

§ 285. Derivatives of sin θ and cos θ: Radian Measure. To differentiate $\sin \theta$ by the original process (§ 55), we first let θ increase by $\Delta\theta$ and see how much the sine increases.

By definition, $\sin \theta = y/r$, in which y and r may be taken for *any* point on the terminal line of θ. But by choosing that point P whose $r = 1$, we have simply

$$\sin \theta = y, \tag{19}$$

and the change in $\sin \theta$ due to any change in θ is simply Δy.

Now, when we increase θ, keeping $r = 1$, P must travel in a circle, and Δy is easily calculated from the small right triangle in Fig. 144. If we draw a line bisecting $\Delta\theta$, the angle $\theta + \frac{1}{2} \Delta\theta$ will have its sides perpendicular to those of $\angle Q$. (Verify.) Thus $\angle Q = \theta + \frac{1}{2} \Delta\theta$.

    $\therefore \ \Delta y = \text{chord } PQ \cdot \cos Q = \text{chord } PQ \cdot \cos (\theta + \frac{1}{2} \Delta\theta)$.

If $\Delta\theta$ is in radians, arc $PQ = r\,\Delta\theta$ (§ 270), $= \Delta\theta$ simply.

$$\therefore\ \ \frac{\Delta y}{\Delta\theta} = \frac{\text{chord } PQ}{\text{arc } PQ}\cdot\cos\left(\theta + \tfrac{1}{2}\,\Delta\theta\right). \tag{20}$$

Now as $\Delta\theta \to 0$, the ratio of the chord to the arc approaches 1. Hence, going to the *limit*:

$$\frac{dy}{d\theta} = \cos\theta, \quad\text{or}\quad \frac{d}{d\theta}\,(\sin\theta) = \cos\theta. \tag{21}$$

I.e., the derivative of $\sin\theta$ is $\cos\theta$, if the angle is in radians.

In like manner, noting that $x = \cos\theta$ in Fig. 144, and that the change in $\cos\theta$ due to $\Delta\theta$ is simply Δx, a negative quantity, we find

$$\frac{\Delta x}{\Delta\theta} = -\,\frac{\text{chord } PQ}{\text{arc } PQ}\cdot\sin\left(\theta + \tfrac{1}{2}\,\Delta\theta\right).$$

$$\therefore\ \ \frac{dx}{d\theta} = -\sin\theta, \quad\text{or}\quad \frac{d}{d\theta}\,(\cos\theta) = -\sin\theta. \tag{22}$$

Physically, formulas (21) and (22) mean that the rates at which $\sin\theta$ and $\cos\theta$ change, per radian increase in θ, are constantly equal to $\cos\theta$ and $-\sin\theta$, respectively.

Ex. I. Find the rate of change of $\sin\theta$, per radian, at $\theta = .5^{(r)}$.

Answer:
$$\frac{d}{d\theta}\,(\sin\theta) = \cos .5 = .87758.$$

Check. By tables, $\sin .49 = .47063$, $\sin .51 = .48818$. Thus $\sin\theta$ increases by $.01755$ while θ increases by $.02^{(r)}$ — or at an average rate of $.8775$ per radian for this interval.

§ 286 S. Modification for Degree Measure. If θ is in degrees instead of radians, then in Fig. 144, arc $PQ = .017453\,\Delta\theta$. (§ 270.) Hence dividing Δy by $\Delta\theta$ ($=$ arc $PQ/.017453$) gives instead of (20):

$$\frac{\Delta y}{\Delta\theta} = \frac{\text{chord } PQ}{\dfrac{\text{arc } PQ}{.017453}}\cos\left(\theta + \tfrac{1}{2}\,\Delta\theta\right). \tag{23}$$

$$\therefore\ \ \frac{dy}{d\theta} = .017453\cos\theta. \tag{24}$$

Likewise
$$\frac{dx}{d\theta} = -\,.017453\sin\theta. \tag{25}$$

That is, the rate of change of $\sin \theta$ and $\cos \theta$, per *degree* change in θ, is only a small fraction ($.017453 \ldots$) of the rate of change per *radian*, — which is evidently reasonable.

The great simplicity of (21) and (22) as compared with (24) and (25) is the reason for using radian measure in practically all problems requiring the differentiation of a sine or cosine.

§ 287. Sin u and cos u. If u is any function of θ, and

$$y = \sin u$$

then, by (21), p. 103,

$$\frac{dy}{d\theta} = \frac{dy}{du} \cdot \frac{du}{d\theta}, \tag{26}$$

or

$$\frac{dy}{d\theta} = \cos u \cdot \frac{du}{d\theta}. \tag{27}$$

In words: the derivative of the sine of any angle equals the cosine of that same angle times the derivative of the angle — expressed in radians.

Similarly for the derivative of a cosine.

Ex. I. Differentiate $i = \cos (100\, t)$.

Answer: $\dfrac{di}{dt} = -\sin (100\, t) \dfrac{d}{dt} (100\, t) = -100 \sin (100\, t). \tag{28}$

EXERCISES

1. Differentiate the following, the angles being in radians:

(a) $y = 35 \sin 4\, t$, (b) $x = 1.2 \cos 25\, t$,

(c) $z = 50 \cos \left(\dfrac{\pi}{2} t \right)$, (d) $w = 90 \sin \left(\dfrac{\pi}{18} t \right)$,

(e) $r = a \sin kt$, (f) $s = a \cos (3\, t + k)$.

2. Differentiate the following, the angles being in degrees:

(a) $x = 25 \cos (.8\, t + 50)$, (b) $y = 75 \sin (.04\, t - 30)$.

3. Find the instantaneous rate of increase of $\sin \theta$, per radian, at $\theta = .45^{(r)}$. Check by finding the average rate from $\theta = .4^{(r)}$ to $.5^{(r)}$.

4. The same as Ex. 3 for $\cos \theta$.

5. Find the instantaneous rate of increase of $\sin \theta$, per degree, at $\theta = 50°$. Check by comparing the actual increase from $49°$ to $51°$.

6. The same as Ex. 5 for $\cos \theta$.

7. An alternating current varied thus: $i = 250 \sin 400\,t$, where t is the number of seconds elapsed, and $400\,t$ the number of radians in "the phase-angle." Find i and di/dt when $t = .005$.

8. Like Ex. 7 for this case: $i = 80 \sin 120\,\pi t$.

9. The displacement (x mm.) of a point P in a vibrating musical string varied thus: $x = 2 \sin 256\,\pi t + .05 \sin 512\,\pi t - .01 \sin 1024\,\pi t$. Find the speed of P at $t = \frac{1}{800}$.

10. Similarly find the speed of an oscillating point P at $t = .05$ if its displacement varies thus:

(a) $x = .02 \sin 80\,t$,   (b) $x = .1 \cos 12\,t$,
(c) $x = .1 \cos 2\,\pi t + .03 \cos 4\,\pi t$,
(d) $x = .8 \sin 5\,\pi t + .1 \sin 15\,\pi t$.

11. The centrifugal acceleration of points on the earth's surface, due to the rotation, varies thus with the latitude ($L°$): $A = .1105 \cos L$, approximately. Find the rate at which A changes with L, per degree, at $L = 30$.

12. On p. 379 derive (12) from (9).

13. The angular displacement ($\theta^{(r)}$) of a pendulum varied thus: $\theta = .04 \sin 8\,\pi t$. Find its angular speed ($\omega^{(r)}/\text{sec.}$) at $t = .1$.

§ 288 S. Notation for an Angle.

The symbol $\sin^{-1}$ is commonly used to denote an *angle whose sine is* ... (whatever number follows).

Thus $\sin^{-1} .5$ denotes an angle whose sine is .5. This angle might be 30°, or 150°, or 390°, etc.

Likewise $\theta = \tan^{-1} 2.88$ means simply that θ is an angle whose tangent is 2.88, or $\tan \theta = 2.88$.

Observe that the -1 is not an exponent but simply a part of the new symbol for an angle. It does, however, have a significance somewhat analogous to that of a negative exponent, in this way: Looking up $\theta = \sin^{-1} .5$ is the *reverse* of the operation of looking up $\sin \theta$; just as multiplying by 10^{-1} is the reverse of multiplying by 10^1.

In problems of calculus, where radian measure is regularly used for differentiations and integrations, the meaning of the symbol $\sin^{-1} x$ is restricted to the *number of radians* in the numerically smallest angle whose sine is x. Somewhat similar agreements are made concerning the use of $\cos^{-1} x$, $\tan^{-1} x$, etc., in calculus formulas.* In all formulas radian measure is understood for these symbols.

* See *Higher Course*, §§ 36–37.

The symbol $\sin^{-1} x$ is also read "arcsine of x" and is frequently written arcsin x. Note also that

$$\text{if } y = \sin^{-1} x, \qquad \text{then } x = \sin y. \qquad (29)$$

This is another case of inverse functions. (§ 181.) In other words, the arcsine is the inverse of the *sine*. Similarly $\cos^{-1} x$, $\tan^{-1} x$, etc., are other inverse trigonometric functions.

§ 289. **Notation for Powers.** To indicate a power of a trigonometric function, it is customary to apply the exponent directly to the function, rather than to write it after the angle. Thus

$$\sin^2 \theta \quad \text{means} \quad (\sin \theta)^2,$$
$$\sec^3 \theta \quad \text{means} \quad (\sec \theta)^3,$$

etc., while $\sin \theta^2$ would mean the sine of an angle whose number of units is the square of the number in θ.

An exception occurs, however, in the case of the -1 power. We cannot write $(\sin u)^{-1}$ in the abbreviated form $\sin^{-1} u$, having adopted the latter symbol to denote an angle whose sine is u.

Ex. I. Differentiate $y = \sin^{10} \theta$.

Here y is not primarily a trigonometric function but rather a *power*, viz. $y = (\sin \theta)^{10}$. This is of the form $y = u^n$.

$$\therefore \frac{dy}{d\theta} = 10 (\sin \theta)^9 \cos \theta = 10 \sin^9 \theta \cos \theta.$$

[Where does the factor $\cos \theta$ come from? If in doubt, think how you would differentiate the form $y = (x^3 + 7)^{10}$. Note the $3 x^2$. (§ 77.)]

§ 290 *S.* **A Mnemonic Device.** Angles of $0°$, $30°$, $45°$, $60°$, $90°$, and related angles in other quadrants are much used. It is well to know the values of their principal functions without having to consult a table or derive them from a figure. The following way of writing the exact sine and cosine for these angles may be helpful to the memory.

θ	$0°$	$30°$	$45°$	$60°$	$90°$
$\sin \theta$	$\frac{1}{2}\sqrt{0}$	$\frac{1}{2}\sqrt{1}$	$\frac{1}{2}\sqrt{2}$	$\frac{1}{2}\sqrt{3}$	$\frac{1}{2}\sqrt{4}$
$\cos \theta$	$\cdots$ The same in reverse order $\cdots$				

E.g., for $30°$ this gives: $\sin 30° = \frac{1}{2}$, $\cos 30° = \frac{1}{2}\sqrt{3}$.

EXERCISES

1. Write the exact numerical values of these expressions:

(*a*) sin 30° sin 60°,   (*b*) sin 45° sin 90°,   (*c*) cos 30° cos 45°,
(*d*) sin 60° cos 0°,   (*e*) sin 60° cos 0°,   (*f*) sin 45° cos 60°.

Suggestion: First write out the table on p. 389, including cos θ.

2. Like Ex. 1 for the following:

(*a*) sin 240°,   (*b*) sin 210°,   (*c*) sin 315°,   (*d*) sin 330°,
(*e*) cos 135°,   (*f*) cos 300°,   (*g*) cos 240°,   (*h*) cos 150°.

3. Calculate $\sin^3 .8^{(r)}$ and $\cos^{-2}\left(\dfrac{\pi}{3}\right)$.

4. Using the table on p. 538 find the smallest positive angle denoted by: $\sin^{-1} .389$, $\cos^{-1} .765$, $\tan^{-1} .546$, $\cos^{-1}(-.801)$.

5. Using a table in degrees, and then converting to radians, find the angle nearest zero denoted by:

(*a*) $\sin^{-1} .2588$, (*b*) $\cos^{-1} .8660$, (*c*) $\tan^{-1} .7265$,   (*d*) $\sin^{-1}(-.8660)$,
(*e*) $\cos^{-1} .5878$, (*f*) $\tan^{-1} .5543$, (*g*) $\tan^{-1}(-.1228)$, (*h*) $\sin^{-1}(-.5299)$.

6. Find $\tan(\sin^{-1} .5446)$; also $\cos(\tan^{-1} .7002)$.

7. Without tables find the following (the angles being acute):

(*a*) $\sin(\tan^{-1}\frac{3}{4})$,   (*b*) $\cos(\sin^{-1}\frac{12}{13})$,   (*c*) $\tan(\cos^{-1}\frac{3}{5})$.

8. Like Ex. 7, the angles being in Quadrant II or IV:

(*a*) $\sin(\cos^{-1}\frac{5}{13})$,   (*b*) $\cos(\sin^{-1}-\frac{3}{5})$,   (*c*) $\tan(\cos^{-1}\frac{3}{5})$.

9. The volume of an unusual ring was calculated from the formula $V = 28\,\pi\left[y\sqrt{25 - y^2} + 25 \sin^{-1}(y/5)\right]$. Let $y = 3$ and find V.

10. Show that the area (S sq. ft.) of a segment cut from a circle of radius a ft. by a chord x ft. from the center is $S = a^2 \cos^{-1}(x/a) - x\sqrt{a^2 - x^2}$.

11. From the formula in Ex. 10 calculate S if $a = 10$ and $x = 8$.

12. Differentiate $y = 10 \sin^3 \theta$, the angle being in radians.

13. As in Ex. 12, differentiate these powers:

(*a*) $z = 2 \cos^4 \theta$,   (*b*) $w = 5 \sin^2(10\,t)$,   (*c*) $x = 8 \cos^5(2\,t)$.

14. Verify the following approximate equivalents:
$$1' = .0003^{(r)}, \qquad 1'' = .000\ 005^{(r)}.$$
[These are easily kept in mind if expressed in the form: "three zeros, three"; and "five zeros, five."]

[**15.**] The equation of a curve in polar coordinates is $r = 10 \sin 3\,\theta$. For what values of θ does r reach its maximum value of $+10$? Find r when $\theta = 90°$: where is the point?

§ 291. Curves in Polar Coordinates. As a point (r, θ) moves along any curve, r varies with θ in some definite way. That is, $r = f(\theta)$. Conversely, all the points whose polar coordinates satisfy a given equation lie along some definite curve.

Ex. I. Plot the curve

$$r = 10 \sin \theta. \tag{30}$$

Substituting values for θ gives the adjacent table. Plotting the positive values of r, we get the curve in Fig. 145.

θ	r
0	0
30	5
60	8.66
90	10
120	8.66
150	5
180	0
210	− 5
240	− 8.66
—	—

To plot the negative r's, we draw them from the pole or origin in a direction *opposite* to the terminal line of θ. (§ 266.) In the present example, the points so obtained merely retrace the curve found for positive r's.

This curve is a true circle. For $\sin \theta = y/r$, which gives in (30):

$$r^2 = 10 \, y,$$
$$i.e., \quad x^2 + y^2 = 10 \, y.$$

Transposing and completing the square:

$$x^2 + (y - 5)^2 = 25.$$

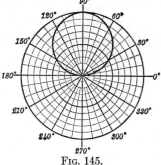

Fig. 145.

EXERCISES

1. In Ex. I, § 291, complete the table to $\theta = 360°$, plot the curve, and compare with Fig. 145.

2. Plot $r = 10 \cos \theta$ from $\theta = 0°$ to $\theta = 360°$. Compare Fig. 145.

3. Plot each following curve from $\theta = 0°$ to $\theta = 360°$:

(a) $r = 10 \, (1 - \cos \theta)$;   (b) $r = 5 + 10 \cos \theta$;

(c) $r = \dfrac{10}{1 + \cos \theta}$;   (d) $r = \dfrac{10}{2 - \cos \theta}$.

4. What sort of a curve is $r = k$? $r = \theta/3$? $r = k \, \theta$? $r \, \theta = 60$? (If in doubt make a table.)

5. Plot each following curve, taking θ at the intervals indicated. Then, by considering carefully how further values of θ must run, continue the curve to $\theta = 360°$. (Calculate further values of r if not sure.)

(a) $r = \sin 2\,\theta$,   taking $\theta = 0°, 15°, 30°, \cdots, 90°$.
(b) $r = \sin 3\,\theta$,   using $0°, 10°, 20°, \cdots, 60°$.
(c) $r = \cos 3\,\theta$,   taking $\theta = -30°, -20°, \cdots, +30°$.
(d) $r = \cos 2\,\theta$,   with $\theta = -45°, -30°, \cdots, +45°$.
(e) $r^2 = \sin 2\,\theta$,   using $\theta = 0°, 15°, 30°, \cdots, 90°$.

6. Draw roughly by inspection from $\theta = 0$ to $\theta = 2\,\pi$ (radians).

(a) $r = \tfrac{3}{2}\,\theta$,   (b) $r = \pi - \theta$,   (c) $r = e^{\frac{1}{2}\theta}$.

7. The equation of the path of Halley's Comet is $r = 1.158 \div (1 + .9673 \cos\theta)$. Calculate r when $\theta = 0°$ and when $\theta = 180°$. (Cf. Table 1, p. 368).

8. (a–d) In Ex. 3 (a–d) find the rate of change of r, per radian change in θ, at $\theta = \dfrac{\pi}{6}$.

9. (a–d) Likewise, in Ex. 3 (a–d) find the rate of change of r per degree change in θ, at $\theta = 30°$.

§ 292 S. The Conchoid. A famous curve studied by the ancient Greeks, and used by them to trisect any given angle, is the *conchoid*. This is defined as: the locus of a point P whose distance from a fixed line AB, measured on a line through a fixed point O, is some constant b. (Fig. 146.) There are two positions of P, marked P and P'.

Taking the pole at O with the polar axis along OA, and letting $OA = a$, we have $OB = a \sec\theta$. Hence for P and P':

$$r = a \sec\theta \pm b. \qquad (31)$$

This is the polar equation of the conchoid; and can be used to study its geometric properties. Or, since $\sec\theta = r/x$, and $r = \sqrt{x^2 + y^2}$, (31) can be transformed into the rectangular equation. (Ex. 18 below.) The result is

$$(x^2 + y^2)\,(x - a)^2 = b^2 x^2. \qquad (32)$$

To trisect any given angle AOB, erect a perpendicular AB, and construct a conchoid as in Fig. 146, taking twice OB as b. From B draw BQ parallel to OA, meeting the conchoid at Q. Draw OQ. Then $\angle AOQ = \tfrac{1}{3}\,\angle AOB$. For a simple proof, join B to the midpoint of the segment of

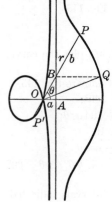

Fig. 146.

OQ included between Q and line AB, and consider the angles formed.

This is only one of many methods of trisecting an angle. But no Euclidean construction is possible for an arbitrarily given angle. (Ex. 9, p. 352.) Of course some angles can be trisected by Euclidean methods. (*E.g.*, how can you easily trisect a right angle?)

§ **293 S. Representation of the Functions by Lines.** Any existing trigonometric function of any angle θ can be represented by a *single directed line segment* which can be drawn by a simple geometrical construction. Fig. 147 illustrates this for $\theta = 125°$.

Place θ in trigonometric position at the center of a circle of unit radius. Choosing any point P on the terminal side of θ (or on that side reversed through O), and denoting the coordinates of P by (x, y), (r, θ), we have as always:

$$\sin \theta = \frac{y}{r}, \qquad \csc \theta = \frac{r}{y},$$

$$\cos \theta = \frac{x}{r}, \qquad \sec \theta = \frac{r}{x},$$

$$\tan \theta = \frac{y}{x}, \qquad \operatorname{ctn} \theta = \frac{x}{y}.$$

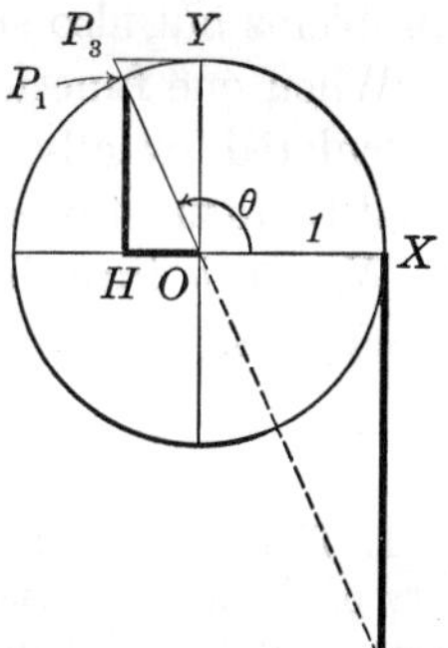

FIG. 147.

If we choose P_1 with $r = 1$, then

$$\sin \theta = y = \boldsymbol{HP_1}, \quad \cos \theta = x = \boldsymbol{OH}.$$

If we take P_2 with $x = 1$, then

$$\tan \theta = y = \boldsymbol{XP_2}, \quad \sec \theta = r = \boldsymbol{OP_2}.$$

Again, for P_3 with $y = 1$, we have

$$\operatorname{ctn} \theta = x = \boldsymbol{YP_3}, \quad \csc \theta = r = \boldsymbol{OP_3}.$$

Remarks. (I) These six directed line segments representing the functions show the *signs* as well as the values; here $+$ for HP_1, and for OP_3 (on the true terminal line of θ); but $-$ for OH, XP_2, YP_3, and for OP_2 (on the reversed terminal line).

(II) For any angle whatever, the line-segment representing the tangent is drawn from the same point X, in order to get a point P_2 having $x = 1$; that for the cotangent is drawn from Y, to make $y = 1$; and the sine and cosine segments are laid out with $r = 1$. The secant segment runs from O to the tangent line; and the cosecant runs to the cotangent.

(III) The above line representations indicate again why the trigonometric functions are often called "circular functions."

§ 294. **Summary of Chapter X.**   Polar coordinates are useful in locating points, plotting curves, studying motion, and defining the trigonometric functions.   In higher courses they are much used in studying curves analytically.

The trigonometric functions of large angles are chiefly useful in studying rotations and periodic oscillations.   Combinations of sines or cosines can approximate any type of variation as closely as may be desired.

The simplest unit angle in differentiations, and in motion problems generally, is the radian.   A circular arc simply equals its radius times the number of radians in its central angle. Very small angles, expressed in seconds, are useful in making close estimates which regard a small arc as equal to its chord.

The graphs of the functions not only are useful in scientific problems but also show how to look up any given function.

When one function of an angle is known, the others can be calculated exactly without tables.   This shows incidentally that there must be some definite relations between the functions.

We next turn to the consideration of such relations and their uses.

EXERCISES

1. The following table shows points (r, θ) and $r', \theta)$, on the boundary of the field of vision for a defective eye before and after an operation.   Draw each boundary.

$\theta°$	0	30	60	90	120	150	180	210	240	270	300	330
r	30	10	9	10	20	50	78	86	80	66	53	46
r'	57	58	53	53	57	74	83	86	81	69	51	47

2. Write formulas for the rectangular coordinates (x, y) of any point whose polar coordinates are (r, θ); and *vice versa*.

3. Find the rectangular coordinates of $(20, 325°)$, and the polar coordinates of $(-25, -60)$.

4. A surveyor in "running a traverse" recorded the following points, where each is referred to the one preceding as an origin or pole, with the polar axis always eastward: A $(0, 0°)$, B $(300, 40°)$, C $(200, 80°)$, D $(400, -25°)$, E $(100, -115°)$.   Map his course.   Suggest a way to calculate the position of E with respect to A.

5. Given ctn $A = -24/7$, find without tables the other five functions for both possible positive angles $< 360°$.

6. Find the values of the following in radians:

(a) $\sin^{-1}(-.5)$ and $\tan^{-1} 0$, between $-\dfrac{\pi}{2}$ and $\dfrac{\pi}{2}$;

(b) $\cos^{-1}(-1)$ and $\ctn^{-1} 1$, between 0 and π, inclusive.

7. Find the diameter of a sun spot in the center of the disc if it subtends at the earth, when 92,000,000 mi. away, an angle of $9''$.

8. About how far away is a mountain, if its elevation (6000 ft. above the observer) subtends an angle of $.04^{(r)}$?

9. A point moved in a circle of radius 10 in. so that after t min. $\theta = 30\,t^2 - t^3$ (radians). Find its maximum speed; also the distance traveled in reaching that speed.

10. When an object travels in a circle of radius r ft. with an angular speed of ω rad./sec., its centrifugal acceleration is $A = \omega^2 r$ (ft./sec.^{2}). Find A for points on the earth's equator, taking the radius as 3960 mi. Also show that for points in any latitude L: $A = .1105 \cos L$, approx. (Cf. Ex. 13, p. 371.)

11. Find the slope and flexion of the sine curve $y = \sin \theta$ at $\theta = 3^{(r)}$.

12. Show without plotting that the curves $r = 20\,e^{\theta}$ and $r = 6 \log \theta$ are spirals of some kind. In each find how fast r increases, per radian, at $\theta = .25$.

13. Solve Kepler's equation $\theta - e \sin \theta = M$ for θ when $e = .2$ and $M = .85$. (See § 260.)

[14.] Divide both members of the equation $x^2 + y^2 = r^2$ by r^2, and express the resulting equation in terms of trigonometric functions. The same, dividing by x^2; by y^2.

15. A variable y oscillates between the values 40 and -40, has a graph of the sine type, and completes 50 cycles per sec. Write the formula for y after t sec. Find y and dy/dt when $t = .002$.

16. Draw by inspection the graph of $y = 10 \sin t + 3 \sin 2\,t$.

17. In Fig. 146, take $a = 1$ and $b = 4$, construct several positions of P, and draw the conchoid approximately. Use this curve to trisect an angle of $60°$, giving a proof as suggested in § 292.

18. Derive equation (32) from (31), p. 392.

19. For each following *S.H.M.* find the maximum displacement and the length of a cycle (T sec.); also, the speed and acceleration when $t = \frac{1}{6}\,T$:

(a) $x = 20 \cos 4\pi t$;   (b) $x = 10 \sin .2\pi t$;   (c) $x = \cos\left(\pi t + \dfrac{\pi}{3}\right)$,

(d) $x = 2 \sin 6\pi t$.

CHAPTER XI

TRIGONOMETRIC ANALYSIS

FUNDAMENTAL RELATIONS AMONG THE FUNCTIONS

§ 295. The Basic Identities. The coordinates x, y, and r, used in defining the trigonometric functions (§ 272), always have this relation:

$$x^2 + y^2 = r^2. \tag{1}$$

Dividing by r^2 gives $(x/r)^2 + (y/r)^2 = 1$. That is,

$$(\cos \theta)^2 + (\sin \theta)^2 = 1,$$

or rearranging and using the notation of § 289:

$$\sin^2 \theta + \cos^2 \theta = 1. \tag{2}$$

Equation (2) is *true for every angle large or small*: for $300°$ or for $.02''$. For this reason $\sin^2 \theta + \cos^2 \theta$ is said to be *identically* equal to 1, and equation (2) is called an *Identity*.

By way of contrast, compare the equation $2 \cos \theta - 1 = 0$. This is only true when $\cos \theta = \frac{1}{2}$; that is, when θ has certain special values, $\pm 60° + n (360°)$.

Other identities result from dividing (1) by x^2 or y^2 (if $\neq 0$):

$$1 + \tan^2 \theta = \sec^2 \theta, \tag{3}$$
$$1 + \operatorname{ctn}^2 \theta = \csc^2 \theta. \tag{4}$$

Still others come from $\tan \theta = y/x$ and $\operatorname{ctn} \theta = x/y$ — provided these exist. Dividing numerator and denominator by r:

$$\tan \theta = \frac{y/r}{x/r} = \frac{\sin \theta}{\cos \theta}, \tag{5}$$

$$\operatorname{ctn} \theta = \frac{x/r}{y/r} = \frac{\cos \theta}{\sin \theta}. \tag{6}$$

These identities (2)–(6) and the reciprocal relations

$$\operatorname{ctn} \theta = \frac{1}{\tan \theta}, \qquad \sec \theta = \frac{1}{\cos \theta}, \qquad \csc \theta = \frac{1}{\sin \theta}, \tag{7}$$

will be used frequently, and should be memorized carefully.

Doing this thoroughly now will save much time and trouble. Practice writing the list (2)–(7) from memory. Then, if you get any wrong, study those especially. Notice the similarity of (3) and (4), and of (5) and (6); also that (3) involves no co-functions and (4) only co-functions.

§ 296. Some Applications. The foregoing identities are useful in solving equations, in simplifying complicated expressions before making numerical calculations or differentiating or integrating, and in many other ways. An identity can safely be used only when we know that *no denominator equals zero*.

Ex. I. Statisticians use what they call a "coefficient of correlation" r and a "coefficient of alienation" k, related thus: $r^2 + k^2 = 1$. When r is known, k has to be found. If r is considered as the sine of some angle θ, then k will be simply $\cos \theta$. Thus a table of sines and cosines can be used as a table relating r's and k's.

Ex. II. Simplify and differentiate $y = (\csc \theta - \sin \theta)/\operatorname{ctn} \theta$. By (6), (7):

$$y = \frac{\dfrac{1}{\sin \theta} - \sin \theta}{\dfrac{\cos \theta}{\sin \theta}}, \quad = \frac{1 - \sin^2 \theta}{\cos \theta}.$$

By (2) this reduces to $y = \cos^2 \theta / \cos \theta = \cos \theta$.

$$\therefore \frac{dy}{d\theta} = -\sin \theta.$$

N.B. It is usually best to express all the given functions in terms of the *sine* and *cosine*, as this can always be done without radicals. But it may be better to put $\operatorname{ctn} \theta = 1/\tan \theta$, if only these two functions appear; or to use (3) when only an even power of $\tan \theta$ appears with $\sec \theta$, or conversely; etc.

§ 297. Trigonometric Equations. In solving a trigonometric equation there are usually three steps: (*a*) expressing all the given functions in terms of a single function; (*b*) solving algebraically for the value of that function; and (*c*) finding all possible angles.

Ex. I.   Solve $5 \sin \theta - 10 \cos \theta + 11 = 0.$ (8)

Replacing $\cos \theta$ by $\pm \sqrt{1 - \sin^2 \theta}$, transposing, and squaring gives:

$$125 \sin^2 \theta + 110 \sin \theta + 21 = 0.$$

This is a quadratic equation for $\sin \theta$.   By formula (24), p. 343,

$$\sin \theta = \frac{-110 \pm \sqrt{110^2 - 4\,(125)\,(21)}}{250} = -\frac{7}{25}, \quad -\frac{3}{5}$$

$$\theta = \sin^{-1}\left(-\tfrac{7}{25}\right), \text{ or } \sin^{-1}\left(-\tfrac{3}{5}\right).$$

Substituting these values of $\sin \theta$ in (8) gives $\cos \theta = \tfrac{24}{25}$ or $\tfrac{4}{5}$.   Since θ has a negative sine and positive cosine, it lies in the fourth quadrant; and is found by subtracting from 360° (or $2\,\pi^{(r)}$) the acute angle whose sine is $\tfrac{7}{25}$ or $\tfrac{3}{5}$.

Ex. II.   When a block of weight W lb. rests on a plane of inclination θ, and with a "coefficient of friction" f, the pull up the plane necessary to prevent sliding is $P = W\,(\sin \theta - f \cos \theta)$.   If $f = .15$, what θ will just make $P = 0$?

Here $\sin \theta - .15 \cos \theta = 0$.   Dividing through by $\cos \theta$ gives $\tan \theta = .15$.   As only acute angles are to be considered, we have

$$\theta = 8°.5, \text{ approx.}$$

EXERCISES

1. Look up the sine, cosine, and tangent of 40°; and verify formulas (2) and (5) arithmetically for this angle.   Likewise for 220°.

2. Write a simpler expression for each following radical, giving the correct signs for Quadrant IV:

$$\sqrt{1 - \cos^2 \theta}, \qquad \sqrt{1 - \sin^2 \theta}, \qquad \sqrt{\sec^2 \theta - 1}, \qquad \sqrt{\csc^2 \theta - 1}.$$

3. Express each of the following in terms of $\sin \theta$ and $\cos \theta$ and simplify.   Then find the derivative of each (in radian measure).

(a) $\sin \theta \operatorname{ctn} \theta,$ (b) $\tan \theta / \sec \theta,$

(c) $\sec \theta - \tan \theta \sin \theta,$ (d) $\cos \theta \operatorname{ctn} \theta \tan^2 \theta,$

(e) $\dfrac{\sec \theta - \cos \theta}{\tan \theta},$ (f) $\dfrac{\sec^2 \theta - \tan^2 \theta}{\csc \theta},$

(g) $\dfrac{\sin \theta}{1 - \operatorname{ctn} \theta} - \dfrac{\cos \theta}{\tan \theta - 1},$ (h) $\cos \theta \sqrt{\sec^2 \theta - 1}, \quad [\theta < 90°].$

4. Establish each of the following identities by reducing the left member to the form on the right side:

(a) $\dfrac{\sin^2 \theta - \cos^2 \theta}{\tan \theta - \operatorname{ctn} \theta} = \sin \theta \cos \theta,$ (b) $\dfrac{\cos \theta}{1 + \sin \theta} + \dfrac{1 + \sin \theta}{\cos \theta} = 2 \sec \theta,$

(c) $\dfrac{\text{ctn } \theta \quad \cos \theta}{\text{ctn } \theta + \cos \theta} = \dfrac{\text{ctn } \theta - \cos \theta}{\text{ctn } \theta \cos \theta}$, (d) $\dfrac{\tan \theta + \sin \theta}{\text{ctn } \theta + \csc \theta} = \sin \theta \tan \theta$,

(e) $\dfrac{\text{ctn } \theta \sec \theta - \tan \theta \csc \theta}{\cos \theta - \sin \theta} = \sec \theta \csc \theta$,

(f) $\sqrt{\dfrac{1 + \cos \theta}{1 - \cos \theta}} = \csc \theta + \text{ctn } \theta, \quad \theta < 90°.$

Hint: Multiply numerator and denominator by $1 + \cos \theta$.

5. Reduce to simpler forms:

(a) $\sin^4 \theta \cos^2 \theta + \cos^4 \theta \sin^2 \theta$,   (b) $\sqrt{\dfrac{1 - \sin \theta}{1 + \sin \theta}}, \quad \theta < 90°$,

(c) $\text{ctn } \theta + \dfrac{\sin \theta}{1 + \cos \theta}$,   (d) $\dfrac{\tan^2 \theta}{\sec \theta + 1} + \dfrac{\text{ctn}^2 \theta}{\csc \theta - 1}$,

(e) In Ex. 3 (f), (h), simplify in part without changing to $\sin \theta$ and $\cos \theta$.

(f) Simplify and differentiate: $y = (\sqrt{1 + \cos \theta} + \sqrt{1 - \cos \theta})^2$.

6. Simplify and integrate each of the following expressions:

(a) $(\tan \theta + \text{ctn } \theta) \sin \theta \cos^2 \theta \, d\theta$,

(b) $(1 + \text{ctn } \theta + \csc \theta) (1 + \tan \theta - \sec \theta) \, d\theta$.

[7.] (a) Differentiate $y = \tan \theta$. Use (5), p. 396, and § 192.

(b) In similar fashion differentiate $y = \csc \theta$.

8. Solve for some function of θ, and look up each possible angle $> 0°$ and $< 360°$;

(a) $5 \tan \theta = 4 \sec \theta$,   (b) $\tan \theta + 5 \text{ctn } \theta = 6$,

(c) $\sin \theta - 2 \cos \theta = 0$.

9. The same as Ex. 8 for each angle, in radians, > 0 and $< 2\pi$, if:

(a) $5 \sec^2 \theta - 8 \tan^2 \theta = 4$,   (b) $2 \sin^2 \theta + 3 \cos \theta = 0$.

10. Solve $\sin \theta \cos \theta = .2$ by first eliminating $\cos \theta$.

11. Solve Ex. 10 also as follows: Add $2 \sin \theta \cos \theta$ to (2), p. 396, to get the square of $(\sin \theta + \cos \theta)$, and extract the square root. Likewise find $\sin \theta - \cos \theta$; and combine results to obtain $\sin \theta$.

12. Where does the curve $r = 20 \sin \theta \cos \theta$ cut the circle $r = 5$?

13. (a) In Ex. II, § 297, take $f = .2$ and solve. (b) Also, when $f = .2$, find θ for which $P = .4 \, W$.

14. Find for what inclination of a line of fixed length the sum of the horizontal and vertical projections will be greatest.

15. Two tangents to a circle are 20 in. long. The chord joining their points of tangency is 6 in. from the center. Find the angle between the tangents.

16. As in Ex. I, § 296, find the coefficient of alienation for each following coefficient of correlation: $r = .5$, $r = .71$, $r = .92$, $r = .98$.

17. To find at what angle θ a gun should be elevated to strike a distant object, ignoring air resistance, it was necessary to solve the equation $\sec^2 \theta - 10 \tan \theta + 2 = 0$. Find two possible acute angles.

§ 298 S. Further Derivatives. Differentiation formulas for the tangent, cotangent, etc., can be obtained by expressing these functions in term of the sine and cosine, and using the fraction formula (§ 192).

Ex. I. $\operatorname{ctn} \theta = \dfrac{\cos \theta}{\sin \theta}.$

The denominator ($\sin \theta$) times the derivative of the numerator ($- \sin \theta$) gives $- \sin^2 \theta$. From this we subtract the numerator ($\cos \theta$) times the derivative of the denominator ($\cos \theta$); and divide by the square of the denominator ($\sin^2 \theta$).

$$\therefore \frac{d}{d\theta}(\operatorname{ctn} \theta) = \frac{- \sin^2 \theta - \cos^2 \theta}{\sin^2 \theta} = - \frac{1}{\sin^2 \theta} = - \csc^2 \theta.$$

Ex. II. $\sec \theta = \dfrac{1}{\cos \theta} = (\cos \theta)^{-1}.$

We may use the fraction formula again or (22), p. 104.

$$\therefore \frac{d}{d\theta}(\sec \theta) = - 1 (\cos \theta)^{-2} \cdot \frac{d}{d\theta}(\cos \theta)$$

$$= + \frac{\sin \theta}{\cos^2 \theta} = \frac{1}{\cos \theta} \cdot \frac{\sin \theta}{\cos \theta} = \sec \theta \tan \theta.$$

N.B. For degree measure multiply by .017453 $\cdots$; and for derivatives with respect to t, multiply by $d\theta/dt$.

Tan θ and csc θ are differentiated similarly. All the formulas are listed in the Appendix, p. 527. They should be memorized if time permits their use at any length.

§ 299. Further Motion Problems. In Chapter VIII we saw how to study the motion of a point (x, y) when its equations of motion are known — *i.e.*, equations giving x and y in terms of t. (§§ 195–98.) Some further types of motion may now be considered, in whose equations trigonometric functions are involved.

EXERCISES

1. Using the formulas (E), p. 527, differentiate:

(a) $z = \tan 6\,t$,   (b) $y = \sin(2/t)$,   (c) $x = \sec 10\,t$,
(d) $w = \text{ctn}\, 2\,\theta$,   (e) $v = \cos(\theta/4)$,   (f) $u = \csc 5\,\theta$,
(g) $r = \log(\cos 2\,\theta)$,   (h) $q = \log(\sin 3\,\theta)$,   (i) $p = \log(\sec 4\,\theta)$

2. Differentiate the following powers and products:

(a) $l = \tan^4 \theta$,   (b) $m = \text{ctn}^2\, 3\,\theta$,   (c) $n = \csc^3 2\,\theta$,
(d) $p = e^{2t} \sin t$,   (e) $q = e^t \csc t$,   (f) $r = e^{-t} \tan t$.

3. Differentiate:

(a) $u = 3\,\theta - 3\tan\theta + \tan^3\theta$,   (b) $v = 4\,\theta + \text{ctn}\, 4\,\theta$,
(c) $w = \log(\sec\theta + \tan\theta)$,   (d) $r = \log(\csc\theta - \text{ctn}\,\theta)$,
(e) $x = \cos\theta + \theta\sin\theta$,   (f) $y = \sin\theta - \theta\cos\theta$.

4. Differentiate, after making any helpful simplifications:

(a) $y = \log\sqrt{\dfrac{1 - \cos x}{1 + \cos x}}$,   (b) $z = \dfrac{\tan^2\theta}{\sec\theta - 1}$,

(c) $w = \log\sqrt{\dfrac{\csc x + 1}{\csc x - 1}}$,   (d) $x = \tan\theta + \sec\theta\csc\theta\,(2\cos^2\theta - 1)$.

5. $(a\text{–}f)$ Differentiate the right members of Ex. 4 $(a\text{–}f)$, pp. 398–99.

6. What is the slope of the tangent curve (Fig. 139, p. 376) at $\theta = 0$? Of the curve $y = \text{ctn}\,\theta$ at $\theta = \pi/4$?

7. When a comet moves in a parabolic orbit, the equation of its path has the form $r = p\sec(\theta/2)$, p being the distance of nearest approach to the sun. If $p = .8$, find the rate at which r is changing, per radian, when $\theta = \pi/2$.

In Exs. 8–11, t denotes the number of radians in certain angles, and also the number of seconds of time elapsed.

8. A point (x, y) moved so that $x = 40\cos t$, $y = 40\sin t$. Plot the path, taking $t = 0$, .5, 1.0, $\cdots$, 6.0; $2\,\pi$ (p. 538). Could you have anticipated the result by combining the two equations so as to eliminate t? Explain.

9. In Ex. 8, find the speed at any time; also the distance traveled from $t = 0$ to $t = 2\,\pi$. (See §§ 196–98.)

10. A point moved so that $x = 10\cos t$, $y = 6\sin t$. Plot the path, $t = 0$ to $t = 2\,\pi$. What curve is this? What area has it?

11. Without plotting, determine the path if $P\,(x, y)$ moves thus:

(a) $x = 3\cos t$, $y = 2\sin t$;   (b) $x = 4\sec t$, $y = 5\cos t$;
(c) $x = 3\sec t$, $y = 2\tan t$;   (d) $x = 4\sin t$, $y = 5\cos t$.

12. Simplify, and find the numerical value when $\theta = 30°$:

(a) $(1 + \tan \theta + \sec \theta)(1 + \tan \theta - \sec \theta)$,   (b) $\sin^2 \theta/(1 + \cos \theta)$,

(c) $\dfrac{\cos \theta - \sin \theta}{\sec \theta \, \text{ctn} \, \theta - \csc \theta \tan \theta}$,   (d) $\dfrac{(\sec \theta - \csc \theta)^2}{\sec^2 \theta + \csc^2 \theta}$.

§ 300 *S*. Involutes. If a taut string is unwound from any given curve, the path of any point on the string is called an *involute* of that curve. The spiral in Fig. 148 is an involute of a circle. Arcs of this are used in designing gears, cams, etc., because of the excellent rolling contact obtainable. (See texts on machine design.)

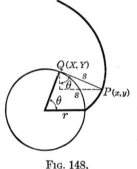

Fig. 148.

Ex. I. Derive equations for the involute in Fig. 148; in other words, equations showing the position of the free end P of the string at any time.

The sides of the right triangle in Fig. 148 are $(x - X)$ and $(Y - y)$. The hypotenuse is the length s unwound, $= a \theta$ by § 270.

$$\therefore \quad \frac{x - X}{a \theta} = \sin \theta, \qquad \frac{Y - y}{a \theta} = \cos \theta,$$

whence $x = X + a \theta \sin \theta, \quad = a (\cos \theta + \theta \sin \theta),$

$y = Y - a \theta \cos \theta, \quad = a (\sin \theta - \theta \cos \theta).$ (9)

If the string is unwound at a constant angular rate of k radians per sec., then $\theta = kt$. Substituting this in (9) gives the equations of motion for P.

§ 301 *S*. The Cycloid. When a circle rolls along a straight line without slipping, any point on it traces out some definite curve — a series of arches. This curve is called a *cycloid*.

To study it, choose axes through A where P starts up. Then

$$x = AQ - u, \qquad y = QC - v. \tag{10}$$

But AQ equals the arc PQ which rolled along it. That is, $AQ = a \theta$. Also $QC = a$, $u = a \sin \theta$, $v = a \cos \theta$. Hence (10) becomes

$$x = a (\theta - \sin \theta), \quad y = a (1 - \cos \theta). \tag{11}$$

If the circle rolls at a constant angular speed, k radians per sec., then $\theta = kt$, and substituting this in (11), we have the equations of motion.

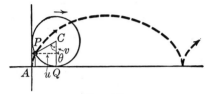

Fig. 149.

The cycloid has various interesting geometrical and physical properties, established in higher courses — of which the following may be mentioned here:

(1) The length of one arch is exactly four times the diameter of the rolling circle, and the area under the arch is exactly three times that of the circle.

(2) The curve down which a particle would *slide* from one given point to another *in the shortest possible time* is a cycloid — inverted. (3) The *time* of sliding to the lowest point is the same, no matter where the point starts on the cycloid. (4) The *involute* of a cycloid, starting to unwind at the middle of an arch, is an equal cycloid. Hence a pendulum swinging between two inverted cycloids, with its string unwinding alternately from each, travels along a cycloid. (5) The time of swing of such a "cycloidal pendulum" is strictly independent of the angle through which it swings. This is only approximately true of an ordinary pendulum.

EXERCISES

1. What are the equations of motion along a cycloid if the generating circle has a radius of 20 in. and an angular speed of .8 rad./sec.? What if $a = 30$ and $k = .5$?

2. In equations (11) find θ when P has its greatest height; half that height; one-fourth that height.

3. A taut string is unwound from a circle of radius 6, at an angular rate of $.5^{(r)}$ per sec. Write the equations of motion for the free end P.

4. In equations (9), when $\theta = \pi/2$, where is P? When $\theta = \pi$? When $\theta = 2\pi$?

5. A point P moves so that $x = 10\,(\cos t + t \sin t)$, $y = 10\,(\sin t - t \cos t)$. Plot the path from $t = 0$, to $t = 8$, taking t at intervals of $1^{(r)}$. Two figures in the value of each x or y will suffice.

6. In Ex. 5 show that the speed at any instant equals $10\,t$; and find the length of the path plotted. [Note the products $t\sin t$, etc. Cf. § 190.]

7. A point moves thus: $x = 10\,(t - \sin t)$, $y = 10\,(1 - \cos t)$. Plot the path, taking $t = 0$, 1, 2, to $8^{(r)}$. Exactly when does the first arch end?

8. In Ex. 7 find the speed at any instant.

9. A circle of radius 5 inches rolls along a straight line with an angular speed of .6 rad./sec. Find the speed of a point of the circumference when at half its greatest height, and also when highest. Compare this last with the speed of the center.

10. When a house is moved on rollers does it advance more rapidly than any roller? (Try rolling a book on pencils.) Explain the phenomenon.

11. A point P moves so that $x = 10\cos^3 t$; $y = 10\sin^3 t$. Plot the path from $t = 0$ to $t = 3.5$, at intervals of .5. For exactly what value of t is y greatest, and when is $y = 0$ again?

12. (a) In Ex. 11 find the speed at any time, and in particular, when P is nearest the origin. (b) Find the length of the path from $t = 0$ to $t = \pi/2$.

13. Simplify, and find the numerical value when $\theta = 60°$:

(a) $\dfrac{\sin^3\theta - \cos^3\theta}{\sin\theta - \cos\theta}$,   (b) $\dfrac{\sin\theta\,\sqrt{1 + \operatorname{ctn}^2\theta}}{\sqrt{\csc^2\theta - 1}}$.

14. Find the speed at any instant if a point moves thus:

(a) $x = 2\tan t$, $y = \sec^2 t$;   (b) $x = \sin^2 t$, $y = \sin t\cos t$.

15. In equations (9), estimate the value of θ at which the spiral will have completed one turn, with $y = 0$ and x positive. Calculate that θ by Newton's method, § 260.

§ 302 S. Damped Oscillations. The exponential curve (Fig. 92, p. 240) shows how a direct electric current will "die away" after the *E.M.F.* is cut off. But an *alternating* current continues to alternate while dying out, the intensity at an instant being given by some such equation as

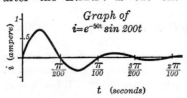

$$i = e^{-50t}\sin 200\,t. \qquad (12)$$

Fig. 150.

The "damping factor" e^{-50t} rapidly decreases, and makes the successive waves of the graph smaller and smaller. But, by (12), the waves all come

at the same intervals of time.   For $i = 0$ only when $\sin 200\,t = 0$
— *i.e.*, when $200\,t = 0$, π, $2\,\pi$, etc., or $t = 0$, .0157, .0314, etc.
   To locate the maxima, differentiate (as in § 190):

$$di/dt = e^{-50t} \cos 200\,t\,(200) + e^{-50t} \sin 200\,t\,(-50).$$

Putting $di/dt = 0$ gives, since e^{-50t} cannot be zero,

$$200 \cos (200\,t) - 50 \sin (200\,t) = 0. \tag{13}$$

To solve this equation easily, divide by $50 \cos 200\,t$:

$$\tan (200\,t) = 4.$$

In radians, the acute angle whose tangent is 4 is 1.33; the next
angle, in Quadrant III, is larger by π ($= 3.14$) radians; etc.

$$\therefore\ 200\,t = 1.33, \qquad 4.47,$$
$$\therefore\ t = .0066^+, \qquad .0223^+.$$

   The first of these values makes i a maximum, the next a minimum,
and so on.   (Verify by testing di/dt at $200\,t = 0$, $\pi/2$, π, etc.)

§ **303** *S.* **Trigonometric Integrals.***   In practical work it is
often necessary to integrate a trigonometric expression.

   In some cases this is merely a matter of reversing a standard
differentiation formula.   Thus

$$\int \cos\,\theta\,d\theta = \sin\,\theta + C,$$

$$\int \sec^2\,\theta\,d\theta = \tan\,\theta + C. \tag{14}$$

   Observe that the first of these results is *not* $-\sin\,\theta + C$.   We are
not differentiating $\cos\,\theta$, but are finding a function *which, when differentiated, will yield* $\cos\,\theta$.

   Some other forms are immediately reducible to known
derivatives.   For instance, $\tan^2\,\theta$ may be written $(\sec^2\,\theta - 1)$
and then integrated.   Thus

$$\int \tan^2\,\theta\,d\theta = \int (\sec^2\,\theta - 1)\,d\theta = \tan\,\theta - \theta + C. \tag{15}$$

   Observe that the integral of $\tan^2\,\theta$ is not $\tfrac{1}{3} \tan^3\,\theta$.   Differentiating
the latter would give $\tan^2\,\theta$ but *multiplied by the derivative of* $\tan\,\theta$,
viz. $\sec^2\,\theta$.

   Similarly the integral of $\sin^2\,\theta$ would not be $\tfrac{1}{3} \sin^3\,\theta$ (nor $\cos^2\,\theta$, etc.),
but a very different form, found later (Ex. I, p. 411).

   * If there is inadequate time for these, the integrations may be confined to
the sine and cosine.

By §§ 77, 101, a power of a quantity (whether a trigonometric function or something else) can be integrated, without
changing its form, only if we have present besides the power
the derivative of the quantity which is raised to the power.
Any power of *tan θ* can be integrated if it is multiplied by
$sec^2 θ \, dθ$; likewise any power of *sin θ* if multiplied by *cos θ dθ*.
And so on. [See Ex. II below.]

The systematic integration of trigonometric expressions
is treated in texts on Calculus.* Tables of integrals are available, covering many forms. (§ 316.)

Ex. I.   An alternating electric current varied thus: $i = 17 \sin 200\, t$.
Find the quantity of electricity transmitted in any time.

The intensity of the current is the rate of flow: $i = dq/dt$.

$$\therefore \; q = \int i \, dt = 17 \int \sin 200\, t \, dt = -\frac{17}{200} \cos 200\, t + C.$$

Since $q = 0$ when $t = 0$, $C = \frac{17}{200} \cos 0 = \frac{17}{200}.$

$$\therefore \; q = \frac{17}{200} (1 - \cos 200\, t). \tag{16}$$

Check this result by differentiating; also by substituting $t = 0$.

Ex. II.   Find $\int \sin^3 θ \cos θ \, dθ$.

Since *cos θ dθ* is the differential of *sin θ*, this is like having $u^3 \, du$ to
integrate, which would give $u^4/4$ — the *u* being sin θ.

$$\therefore \; \int \sin^3 θ \cos θ \, dθ = \tfrac{1}{4} \sin^4 θ + C. \qquad \text{(Check?)}$$

EXERCISES

1. Draw by inspection a graph for each of the following quantities,
showing a few waves, the value at $t = 0$, and the values of t where the
function is zero. Also find at what time the first maximum and minimum are reached.

(*a*) An alternating current died out thus: $i = 10 \, e^{-200t} \cos 600 \, t$;
(*b*) Another died out thus: $i = 30 \, e^{-60t} \sin 300 \, t$;
(*c*) The displacement of a pendulum thus: $θ = .2 \, e^{-.15t} \sin 2 \, \pi t$;
(*d*) The elevation of a wave in water thus: $y = 3 \, e^{-2t} \sin 5 \, t$;
(*e*) The displacement of a tuning-fork thus: $x = .08 \, e^{-t} \cos 840 \, \pi t$.

* See *Higher Course*, pp. 169–180.

2. Integrate: $\sin 15\, t\, dt$; $\cos 20\, t\, dt$; $8 \sin 10\, t\, dt$; $1.4 \cos .7\, t\, dt$. Check each result by differentiation.

3. Find the equation of a curve, if its slope at any point (x, y) is $20 \sin 4\, x$; and $y = 1$ at $x = 0$.

4. Find the area under the curve $y = \sin x$, from $x = 0$ to $x = \pi/3$.

5. Find the area from $x = 0$ to $x = \pi/2$ under a curve whose flexion at any point (x, y) is $80 \cos 2\, x$, if the slope and height at $x = 0$ are, respectively, 0 and 20.

6. The force moving an object varied thus: $F = 30 \cos t$. Find the momentum generated from $t = 0$ to $t = 3$.

7. An alternating current varied thus under steady conditions: $i = 10 \sin 500\, t$. Find i and di/dt when $t = .002$. Also find the quantity of electricity passed from $t = 0$ to $t = .002$.

8. The angular speed of a pendulum varied thus: $\omega = .2\, \pi \cos \pi t$. Find the angle swung through, from $t = 0$ to any time.

9. Show that the following integrals are special cases of $\int u^n\, du$, or $\int \dfrac{du}{u}$, and find each:

(a) $\displaystyle\int \sin^9 \theta \cos \theta\, d\theta$, (b) $\displaystyle\int \tan^3 \theta \sec^2 \theta\, d\theta$,

(c) $\displaystyle\int \frac{\cos \theta\, d\theta}{\sin^6 \theta}$, (d) $\displaystyle\int \frac{\csc^2 \theta\, d\theta}{\text{ctn}\, \theta}$.

10. Simplify and integrate:

(a) $\displaystyle\int \frac{(2 \sin \theta \cos \theta - \sin \theta)\, d\theta}{1 - \cos \theta - \sin^2 \theta + \cos^2 \theta}$, (b) $\displaystyle\int \left(\sqrt{1 + \sin \theta} + \sqrt{1 - \sin \theta} \right)^2 d\theta$.

11. (a)–(h) Integrate the expressions in Ex. 3 (a)–(h), p. 398.

§ 304. Addition Formulas. For various purposes we need to know how the sine of the sum of two angles $(A + B)$ is related to the functions of the two separate angles, A and B.

Fig. 151 illustrates the case where $(A + B)$ is an acute angle. From any point P on the terminal line of $(A + B)$, perpendiculars are dropped to the initial line and to the terminal line of $\angle A$; and,

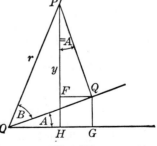

Fig. 151.

from Q, the foot of the latter, perpendiculars are dropped to the initial line and to the first perpendicular. Then, by definition,

$$\sin (A + B) = \frac{y}{r}. \tag{17}$$

The construction divides y or HP into two parts: $HF \ (= GQ)$ and FP. Also, it makes $\angle FPQ = \angle A$. (Why?) Solve $\triangle GQO$ for GQ, and $\triangle FPQ$ for FP — using the sine or cosine of A — and you will find that

$$GQ = OQ \sin A, \quad FP = PQ \cos A.$$

Substituting the sum of GQ and FP for y in (17) gives

$$\sin (A + B) = \frac{OQ \sin A + PQ \cos A}{r}$$

But $OQ/r = \cos B$, $PQ/r = \sin B$, whence

$$\sin (A + B) = \sin A \cos B + \cos A \sin B. \tag{18}$$

In words, *the sine of the sum of two angles equals the sine of the first times the cosine of the second, plus the cosine of the first times the sine of the second.*

E.g., $\sin (45° + 30°) = \sin 45° \cos 30° + \cos 45° \sin 30°$.
Thus $\sin 75°$ can be calculated from the functions of $45°$ and $30°$, which are known from simple right triangles.

In like manner, starting with $\cos (A + B) = OH/r$, and replacing OH by $OG - FQ$, we find

$$\cos (A + B) = \cos A \cos B - \sin A \sin B. \tag{19}$$

Verbal statements of (18) and (19) should be memorized very carefully.

Remark. So far (18) and (19) have been established only when $(A + B)$ is acute. But, by making suitable modifications in the constructions, they can be proved valid for any angles A and B whatever. Also, it is easily shown that

$$\sin (A - B) = \sin A \cos B - \cos A \sin B, \tag{20}$$
$$\cos (A - B) = \cos A \cos B + \sin A \sin B. \tag{21}$$

Observe that these formulas are just like (18) and (19) except for the sign in the middle on both sides. If we remember this fact, it will suffice to memorize (18) and (19) alone.

§ 305 *S.* **Multiple Angles.**   Expanding $\sin (\theta + \theta)$ and $\cos (\theta + \theta)$ by the Addition Formulas (18) and (19) we find

$$\sin 2\,\theta = 2 \sin \theta \cos \theta, \tag{22}$$
$$\cos 2\,\theta = \cos^2 \theta - \sin^2 \theta. \tag{23}$$

In like manner we can apply the Addition Formulas to reduce functions of any multiple of θ to functions of θ.

Such formulas are frequently used in scientific work, particularly (22) and (23).

Ex. I.   Ignoring air resistance, the range of a certain gun varies thus with the elevation θ:

$$R = 40000 \sin \theta \cos \theta.$$

What elevation gives a range of 10000 ft.?   The maximum range?
By (22) the formula may be rewritten
$$R = 20000 \sin 2\,\theta.$$
Hence to make $R = 10000$, we need merely make $\sin 2\,\theta = .5$;
i.e.,
$$2\,\theta = 30° \text{ or } 150°,$$
$$\therefore \ \theta = 15° \text{ or } 75°.$$

R will be greatest when $\sin 2\,\theta$ is greatest, *i.e.,* when the angle $2\,\theta$ is 90°, or $\theta = 45°$.   Then $R = 20000$.

EXERCISES

1. Expand the following, and substitute the known exact values of $\sin 30°$, $\cos 30°$, $\sin 90°$, etc.   (§ 290):

   (a) $\sin (A + 30°)$,   (b) $\cos (A + 30°)$,   (c) $\cos (A - 30°)$,
   (d) $\sin (90° - \theta)$,   (e) $\cos (90° - \theta)$,   (f) $\sin (180° + \theta)$,

   (g) $\cos (180° + \theta)$,   (h) $\sin \left(A + \dfrac{\pi}{4} \right)$,   (i) $\cos \left(A + \dfrac{\pi}{4} \right)$,

   (j) $\cos \left(\dfrac{3\,\pi}{2} - \theta \right)$,   (k) $\sin \left(A + \dfrac{\pi}{3} \right)$,   (l) $\cos \left(A + \dfrac{\pi}{3} \right)$.

2. Simplify each following combination:
(a) $\sin (A + B) - \sin (A - B)$;   (b) $\cos (A + B) - \cos (A - B)$;
(c) $\sin (A + B) \cos B - \cos (A + B) \sin B$;
(d) $\cos (A + B) \cos B + \sin (A + B) \sin B$.

3. By expanding the sine and cosine, and then forming the other four functions from them, express all six functions of $(90° + 3\,\theta)$ in terms of functions of $3\,\theta$.

4. Like Ex. 3 for the functions of these combinations:

(*a*) $(270° + 3\,θ)$, (*b*) $(270° - 4\,θ)$, (*c*) $(180° + 2\,θ)$, (*d*) $(360° - 5\,θ)$.

5. Knowing the exact values for 30° and 45°, find the sine and cosine of 75° and 15°. How could we find tan 75°?

6. (*a*) Carry out in detail all the steps of the derivations of (18) and (22) above. (*b*) Likewise for (19) and (23).

7. Using formulas (18) and (19) and the values of the sine and cosine of 1° and 2° as given in the tables, calculate sin 3° and cos 3°.

8. From the functions of $1^{(r)}$ calculate $\sin 2^{(r)}$ and $\cos 2^{(r)}$.

9. If $\tan A = 3$, find without tables all six functions of $2\,A$. (Hint: First find sin A and cos A.)

10. As in Ex. 9 find all the functions of $θ$ if $\tan \frac{1}{2}\,θ = u$.

11. Regarding $3\,θ$ as $(2\,θ + θ)$, and using (22), (23), derive the formula: $\sin 3\,θ = 3 \sin θ - 4 \sin^3 θ$. Verify it for $θ = 0°$, 30°, 90°.

12. Like Ex. 11 for $\cos 3\,θ = 4 \cos^3 θ - 3 \cos θ$; and $0°$, 60°, 90°.

13. Given $\sin A = \frac{4}{5}$, $\cos B = \frac{12}{13}$, A and B acute, find $\sin (A + B)$ and $\cos (A - B)$.

14. The same as Ex. 13, but with neither A nor B in Quadrant I.

15. If $\sin A = -\frac{5}{13}$, $\cos B = -\frac{3}{5}$, and A and B are in the same quadrant, find $\sin (A - B)$, $\cos (A + B)$.

16. Show that the area cut from a circle of radius r by a chord which subtends an angle $θ^{(r)}$ at the center is: $A = \frac{1}{2}\,r^2\,(θ - \sin θ)$.

[17.] By regarding $9\,θ$ as $(7\,θ + 2\,θ)$ and $5\,θ$ as $(7\,θ - 2\,θ)$, expand and simplify each of the following:

$$(a) \quad \frac{\sin 9\,θ + \sin 5\,θ}{\cos 9\,θ + \cos 5\,θ}, \qquad (b) \quad \frac{\sin 9\,θ - \sin 5\,θ}{\cos 9\,θ - \cos 5\,θ}.$$

§ 306 S. Some Applications.

The addition formulas (18)–(21), § 304, are useful in making simplifications, in solving equations, in studying simple harmonic motion, in calculating tables (§ 345) and in other ways.

Ex. I.   Expand $x = 10 \cos \left(kt - \dfrac{π}{3} \right)$.

By (21), $x = 10\,(\cos kt \cos π/3 + \sin kt \sin π/3)$.

But by tables: $\cos π/3 = .5$ and $\sin π/3 = .86603$.

∴ $x = 5 \cos kt + 8.6603 \sin kt$.

That is, the *S.H.M.*, $x = 10 \cos (kt - π/3)$, is equivalent to two *S.H.M.*'s, $x = 5 \cos kt$, and $x = 8.6603 \sin kt$, combined.

It is sometimes necessary to reverse the process of Ex. I,

and find a single *S.H.M.* equivalent to the combined effect of two others, of the same period. Also in solving equations, it is often helpful to convert a sine and cosine into a single function of a combination angle.

Ex. II.   Solve the equation $3 \sin \theta + 4 \cos \theta = 1.95$.
We first determine c and A such that

$$c \sin (\theta + A) = 3 \sin \theta + 4 \cos \theta, \qquad (24)$$

for all values of θ.   Expanding in (24), and comparing:

$$c \cos A = 3, \qquad c \sin A = 4.$$

Squaring and adding gives $c^2 = 3^2 + 4^2 = 25$: $c = 5$. Dividing gives $\tan A = \sin A / \cos A = \frac{4}{3}$: $A = \tan^{-1} \frac{4}{3} = 53°$, approx.
   Hence the given equation may be written:

$$5 \sin (\theta + 53°) = 1.95.$$

Hence $\sin (\theta + 53°) = .39$: $\theta + 53° = 23°$ (or $157°$) $\pm n (360°)$.

$$\therefore \quad \theta = -30° + n (360°), \qquad \text{or } \theta = 104° + n (360°).$$

§ 307 *S.* **Half-Angle Formulas.**   Combining (23) with the identity $1 = \cos^2 \theta + \sin^2 \theta$, we find

$$\begin{aligned} \sin^2 \theta &= \tfrac{1}{2}(1 - \cos 2\,\theta), \\ \cos^2 \theta &= \tfrac{1}{2}(1 + \cos 2\,\theta). \end{aligned} \qquad (25)$$

These two formulas are used in many calculations, reductions, and integrations.

Ex. I.   Integrate $\sin^2 \theta \, d\theta$.

$$\int \sin^2 \theta \, d\theta = \int (\tfrac{1}{2} - \tfrac{1}{2} \cos 2\,\theta) \, d\theta = \tfrac{1}{2}\,\theta - \tfrac{1}{4} \sin 2\,\theta + C.$$

Ex. II.   Knowing $\cos 30° = .86603$, calculate $\cos 15°$.

When $\theta = 15°$, formula (25) gives $\cos 15° = \sqrt{\tfrac{1}{2}(1 + \cos 30°)}$;

i.e., $\qquad \cos 15° = \sqrt{.93302} = .96593.$

The tables were originally calculated partly by this method. (How could it be continued?)

Formulas (25) give the sine and cosine for half of any known angle $2\,\theta$, and are called "Half-Angle Formulas." Often they are written

$$\sin^2 (\tfrac{1}{2}\,A) = \tfrac{1}{2}(1 - \cos A), \quad \cos^2 (\tfrac{1}{2}\,A) = \tfrac{1}{2}(1 + \cos A),$$

$$\text{or } \sin \tfrac{1}{2}\,A = \pm \sqrt{\frac{1 - \cos A}{2}}, \quad \cos \tfrac{1}{2}\,A = \pm \sqrt{\frac{1 + \cos A}{2}}. \quad (26)$$

In applied mathematics, the quantity $(1 - \cos A)$ is much used under the name, versine of A, written *vers A*. Likewise half this quantity is much used, and is called the "haversine of A," written *hav A*.

EXERCISES

1. From (26) derive the following formulas. (See Ex. 4 f, p. 399, if in doubt.)

(a) $\tan \frac{1}{2} A = \dfrac{\sin A}{1 + \cos A}$, (b) $\tan \frac{1}{2} A = \dfrac{1 - \cos A}{\sin A}$.

2. Obtain formulas for ctn $\frac{1}{2} A$, similar to those in Ex. 1.

3. If $\cos \theta = \frac{7}{25}$, and θ is in Quadrant IV, find all the functions of $\frac{1}{2} \theta$.

4. Like Ex. 3 if $\cos \theta = -\frac{7}{25}$, and θ is in Quadrant III.

5. Knowing $\cos 45° = \frac{1}{2} \sqrt{2}$, $= .70711$, calculate $\cos 22° 30'$ and $\cos 11° 15'$. Explain how you could also calculate $\cos 67° 30'$, and from it $\cos 33° 45'$.

6. In a right triangle one leg is $b = 999.95$ and the hypotenuse is 1000. Try to find $\angle A$ directly, but also solve by using the formula $\sin^2 (A/2) = \frac{1}{2} (1 - \cos A)$.

7. Resolve each of the following into two component *S.H.M*'s. What is the amplitude and period of each?

(a) $x = 40 \cos \left(5t - \dfrac{\pi}{3} \right)$, (b) $x = 8 \sqrt{2} \cos \left(8 \pi t - \dfrac{\pi}{4} \right)$.

8. For what values of c and A would $x = c \cos (10 t - A)$ give the expanded form $x = 5 \cos 10 t + 12 \sin 10 t$?

9. Combine into a standard *S.H.M.* form, $x = a \cos (kt - C)$; and give the amplitude, period, and angle of lag (C):

(a) $x = 3 \cos 2t + 4 \sin 2t$, (b) $x = 15 \cos 4 \pi t + 8 \sin 4 \pi t$,
(c) $x = 4 \cos 6t - 3 \sin 6t$, (d) $x = 24 \cos \pi t \ - 7 \sin \pi t$.

10. After expanding, solve each equation for $\tan \theta$ or ctn θ, and look up all positive values of $\theta < 360°$:

(a) $\cos (\theta - 60°) = 2 \cos \theta$, (b) $\sin (\theta - 30°) = -.8 \cos \theta$,
(c) $\cos (\theta + 30°) = .1 \sin \theta$, (d) $\sin (\theta - 45°) = \sqrt{2} \sin \theta$.

11. Two sides of a quadrangular farm are (in feet): $AB = 1200$, $AD = 1800$; three angles are $A = 80°$, $B = 90°$, $D = 90°$. Find the perimeter and area. (Hint: In the right triangles formed by the diagonal AC, show that $\cos (80° - \theta) = 1.5 \cos \theta$, where θ is $\angle BAC$. Expand and solve for $\tan \theta$; then proceed.)

[12.] Transform $\cos u + \cos v$ into $2 \cos \frac{1}{2} (u + v)$ $\cos \frac{1}{2} (u - v)$. (Hint: Let $u = A + B$ and $v = A - B$; expand $\cos u$ and $\cos v$, reduce, and substitute for A and B.)

13. Find the values of vers 20°, hav 20°; vers 120°, hav 120°.

14. (a) Show how to integrate $\cos^2 \theta$. (b) What would you suggest for $\cos^2 5\theta$? For $\sin^2 2\theta$?

§ 308 S. Sums, Differences, and Products.

It is often important to convert the sum or difference of two sines or cosines into a product form, or *vice versa*. For this purpose we derive the following formulas: *

$$\sin u + \sin v \ = 2 \sin \tfrac{1}{2} (u + v) \cos \tfrac{1}{2} (u - v); \qquad (27)$$

$$\sin u - \sin v \ = 2 \cos \tfrac{1}{2} (u + v) \sin \tfrac{1}{2} (u - v); \qquad (28)$$

$$\cos u + \cos v \ = 2 \cos \tfrac{1}{2} (u + v) \cos \tfrac{1}{2} (u - v); \qquad (29)$$

$$\cos u - \cos v = - 2 \sin \tfrac{1}{2} (u + v) \sin \tfrac{1}{2} (u - v). \qquad (30)$$

Proof of (27): Let

$$u = A + B, \qquad v = A - B. \qquad (31)$$

Then

$$\sin u = \sin A \cos B + \cos A \sin B,$$

$$\sin v = \sin A \cos B - \cos A \sin B.$$

Adding, and observing from (31) that $A = \frac{1}{2} (u + v)$ while $B = \frac{1}{2} (u - v)$, gives (27).

A method of going *from the product form to a sum or difference* is shown in Ex. III below.

Ex. I. Solve for x: $\sin 3x + \sin x = \sin 2x$.
By (27), $\sin 3x + \sin x = 2 \sin 2x \cos x$.

$$\therefore \ 2 \sin 2x \cos x = \sin 2x.$$

This gives $\cos x = .5$, or else $\sin 2x = 0$. (§ 64.)
Hence $x = 60°, 300°$, etc. Or else $2x = 0°, 180°$, etc.; *i.e.*, $x = 0, 90°, 180°$, etc.

Ex. II. Simplify $y = \dfrac{\sin 60° - \sin 10°}{\cos 60° + \cos 10°}$.

By (28) and (29): $\sin 60° - \sin 10° = 2 \cos 35° \sin 25°$; likewise $\cos 60° + \cos 10° = 2 \cos 35° \cos 25°$. Thus $y = \tan 25°$ simply.

---

* If you expect to work in higher mathematics or engineering, memorize statements of these formulas in words: "The sum of two sines equals *twice the sine of half the sum* (of the angles) *times the cosine of half the difference*." Etc. Note the $-$ sign in (30).

Ex. III.   Integrate $\cos 4x \cos x\, dx$.

We first change the product to a sum or difference.   The product $\cos 4x \cos x$ appears in the expansion of $\cos (4x + x)$, and in that of $\cos (4x - x)$.   [Write out these two expansions.]   Adding would eliminate the products in $\sin 4x \sin x$.   Thus

$$\cos 4x \cos x = \tfrac{1}{2} (\cos 5x + \cos 3x).$$

We can now integrate each term, getting

$$\tfrac{1}{2} [\tfrac{1}{5} \sin 5x + \tfrac{1}{3} \sin 3x] + C.$$

EXERCISES

1. Transform into products and simplify:

   (a) $\dfrac{\sin 7\,\theta - \sin 3\,\theta}{\cos 7\,\theta - \cos 3\,\theta}$,
       (b) $\dfrac{\sin 10\,\theta + \sin 4\,\theta}{\cos 10\,\theta + \cos 4\,\theta}$,

   (c) $\dfrac{\sin 70^\circ - \sin 10^\circ}{\sin 70^\circ + \sin 10^\circ}$,
       (d) $\dfrac{\cos 50^\circ + \cos 20^\circ}{\cos 50^\circ - \cos 20^\circ}$,

   (e) $\dfrac{\cos 65^\circ - \cos 25^\circ}{\sin 65^\circ + \sin 25^\circ}$,
       (f) $\dfrac{\cos 85^\circ + \cos 5^\circ}{\sin 85^\circ - \sin 5^\circ}$,

   (g) $\dfrac{\sin 50^\circ + \cos 80^\circ}{\cos 50^\circ + \cos 10^\circ}$,
       (h) $\dfrac{\cos 40^\circ - \cos 20^\circ}{\sin 40^\circ + \cos 70^\circ}$.

2. Derive formulas (28) and (30).

3. Transform into a sum or difference:

   (a) $\sin 8\,\theta \cos 4\,\theta$,
    (b) $\cos 10\,\theta \sin 6\,\theta$,
    (c) $\sin^2 7x$,

   (d) $\cos 5x \cos 3x$,
    (e) $\sin 9x \sin 2x$,
    (f) $\cos^2 8x$.

4. Find the numerical values of the following, after first transforming if advantageous:

   (a) $\cos 50^\circ \cos 10^\circ$,
    (b) $\sin 70^\circ \cos 20^\circ$,

   (c) $\sin 35^\circ \cos 5^\circ$,
    (d) $\sin 85^\circ \sin 5^\circ$.

5. Change sums entirely to products, or *vice versa*:

   (a) $\sin 16x + \sin 8x + \sin 6x - \sin 2x$,

   (b) $\cos 12x + \cos 6x + \cos 4x + \cos 2x$,

   (c) $16 \cos 10x \cos 8x \cos 4x$.

6. Show that $\displaystyle\int \cos 9\,\theta \cos 5\,\theta\, d\theta = \tfrac{1}{28} \sin 14\,\theta + \tfrac{1}{8} \sin 4\,\theta + C$.

7. As in Ex. I, § 308, solve for x:

   (a) $\sin 5x + \sin x = \sin 3x$;
    (b) $\sin 3x - \sin x = \cos 2x$;

   (c) $\cos 3x - \cos x = \tfrac{1}{2} \sin 2x$;
    (d) $\cos 3x + \cos x = 0$.

8. Solve for θ by any convenient method:

   (a) $\sin (2\,\theta + 30^\circ) = \tfrac{1}{4} \cos 2\,\theta$,
    (b) $\sin (2\,\theta + 30^\circ) = \cos 2\,\theta$,

   (c) $\cos (3\,\theta - 60^\circ) = \cos \theta$,
    (d) $\cos (3\,\theta - 30^\circ) = \sin \theta$.

§ 309 *S.* **Addition Formulas for Tangents.**   If we divide the expansion of $\sin(A + B)$ by that of $\cos(A + B)$, we obtain $\tan(A + B)$ in a form involving both sines and cosines. To get a more convenient form, we divide numerator and denominator by $\cos A \cos B$, as in Ex. 1 below, and obtain:

$$\tan(A + B) = \frac{\tan A + \tan B}{1 - \tan A \tan B}. \tag{32}$$

This expresses $\tan(A + B)$ in terms of tangents only.

For $(A - B)$, merely change the middle sign in both numerator and denominator of (32).

Similar formulas are obtainable for $\text{ctn}(A \pm B)$ by using $\cos(A \pm B)$, $\sin(A \pm B)$, expanding, and dividing numerator and denominator by $\sin A \sin B$.

§ 310 *S.* **Angle Between Two Curves.**   At any point of intersection, let two lines or curves have the direction angles θ_1 and θ_2, measured from the positive X-axis.   Then the angle from the first line to the second is $K = \theta_2 - \theta_1$.

$$\therefore \tan K = \tan(\theta_2 - \theta_1) = \frac{\tan \theta_2 - \tan \theta_1}{1 + \tan \theta_1 \tan \theta_2}.$$

Since each $\tan \theta$ is the slope l of a line (or curve), we can find the angle K directly from the two slopes:

$$\tan K = \frac{l_2 - l_1}{1 + l_2 l_1}. \tag{33}$$

§ 311 *S.* **Quadrant Rules.**   Let F denote any trigonometric function and CF the co-function.   Thus, if F is the sine, CF is the cosine, and *vice versa.**   Then, by using the addition formulas for the sine and cosine, and combining results, we can prove the following convenient rules:

$$F(180° \pm \theta) = \pm F(\theta), \quad F(360° \pm \theta) = \pm F(\theta), \quad (34)$$
$$F(90° \pm \theta) = \pm CF(\theta), \quad F(270° \pm \theta) = \pm CF(\theta). \tag{35}$$

The $+$ or $-$ sign on the right side is the same as the sign which the *left* member would have if θ were an acute angle.

---

* The cosine, cotangent, and cosecant are called the co-functions of the sine, tangent, and secant (§ 109); and *vice versa*.

416   TRIGONOMETRIC ANALYSIS

When θ is acute, formulas (34) simply restate our standard procedure for finding functions of large angles.   (§ 278.)

Ex. I. $\sec (270° + \theta) = \csc \theta$.
The secant, like the cosine, is positive in Quadrant IV.

Ex. II. $\operatorname{ctn} (90° + \theta) = - \tan \theta$.
The cotangent is negative in Quadrant II.

Ex. III. $\tan (180° - \theta) = - \tan \theta$, a familiar result.

EXERCISES

1. Derive formula (32), as outlined in § 309.

2. (*a*)–(*c*) Derive formulas for:
$$\tan (A - B); \qquad \operatorname{ctn} (A + B); \qquad \operatorname{ctn} (A - B).$$

3. Knowing $\tan 45°$ and $\tan 30°$ (§ 290) find the exact values of $\tan 75°$ and $\tan 15°$.

4. If $\tan A = \tfrac{1}{2}$ and $\tan B = \tfrac{1}{3}$, show that $A + B = \dfrac{\pi}{4}$.

5. The slopes of two lines are: $l_1 = 1$, $l_2 = \tfrac{2}{3}$.   Find the positive angle $< 180°$ which line 2 makes with line 1.   Check by drawing.

6. As in Ex. 5 find the positive angle in each case:

(*a*) $l_1 = 2$, $l_2 = 3$;   (*b*) $l_1 = - 1$, $l_2 = .5$;   (*c*) $l_1 = - 1$, $l_2 = 2$.

7. Find the positive acute angle between the lines:

(*a*) $2 x + 3 y = 6$, $x - y = 0$;   (*b*) $3 x - y = 6$, $x + y = 10$.

8. From (33) deduce the condition for perpendicular lines.

9. Where does $2 x - y = 5$ meet $xy = 12$, and at what angle do they cross each other?   Draw a rough figure by inspection.

10. Like Ex. 9 for $y = x^2$ and $y = 27 - 2 x^2$.

11. The same for $x^2 + y^2 = 25$, and $y = x - 1$.

12. (*a*) Verify formula (34) for $180° + \theta$, by expanding the sine and cosine of $(180° + \theta)$, and finding the other functions by division.

(*b*) Likewise verify (35) for $270° + \theta$.

13. By the Quadrant Rules express as functions of θ:
$$\sin (90° + \theta), \quad \cos (270° - \theta), \quad \tan (360° - \theta), \quad \operatorname{ctn} (180° + \theta),$$
$$\sec (90° + \theta), \quad \csc (270° - \theta).$$

14. Transform the equation
$$S = \cos 2\,\theta + \cos 4\,\theta + \cos 6\,\theta \cdots + \cos 80\,\theta, \tag{36}$$
into $S = \cos 41\,\theta \sin 40\,\vartheta \div \sin \theta$. [Hint: Multiply both sides of (36) by $2 \sin \theta$; change each product into the difference of two sines, the last being $\sin 81\,\theta - \sin 79\,\theta$; note the cancellations, and proceed.]

15. Similarly change the equation
$$S = \sin 2\,\theta + \sin 4\,\theta + \sin 6\,\theta \cdots + \sin 80\,\theta$$
into the form $S = \sin 41\,\theta \sin 40\,\theta \div \sin \theta$.

§ 312. Summary of Chapter XI. The basic formulas derived in this chapter may be classified as follows: (I) Formulas involving a single angle only. (II) Addition formulas. (III) Half-angle formulas. (IV) Conversion formulas for sums and products. (V) Differentiation formulas.

All of these should be carefully memorized if you expect to use mathematics extensively as a working tool. In any case it will pay to make a full list of the uses of each set of formulas, so far as shown. The integrals of the several functions, so far as obtained, need not be memorized; but the methods by which they were obtained should be familiar.

We shall next turn to a further study of the uses of integration, and methods of setting up integrals.

EXERCISES

1. Prove the identities:

(a) $\cos^2 \theta + \text{ctn}^2 \theta = \csc^2 \theta - \sin^2 \theta$,

(b) $\sin (\theta + 60°) - \sin \theta = \cos (\theta + 30°)$,

(c) $\dfrac{\sin 3\,\theta + \sin \theta}{\cos 3\,\theta + \cos \theta} = \tan 2\,\theta$, (d) $\dfrac{\tan 3\,\theta + \tan \theta}{\tan 3\,\theta - \tan \theta} = 2 \cos 2\,\theta$.

2. Prove that $\cos 4\,\theta = 8 \cos^4 \theta - 8 \cos^2 \theta + 1$.

3. Given $\csc A = \frac{13}{5}$ and $\sec B = -\frac{17}{8}$, with A and B in the same quadrant. Find all the functions of $A + B$.

4. Find all the functions of $\frac{1}{2}\,\theta$, if $\sin \theta = -\frac{4}{5}$, and $0° < \theta < 270°$.

5. Solve for θ, expressing the most general values:

(a) $\sin 5\,\theta - \sin 3\,\theta = .5 \cos 4\,\theta$, (b) $\sin 5\,\theta = \cos 4\,\theta$.

6. Find by inspection the maximum and minimum values of the following quantities, and the smallest positive θ which gives each:

(a) $8 + 4 \sin 2\,\theta$, (b) $2 \sin \theta \cos \theta$, (c) $\cos^2 \theta - \sin^2 \theta$.

7. A right triangle has a horizontal hypotenuse 30 ft. long. Show that its area is $A = 450 \sin \theta \cos \theta$, where θ is the inclination of either leg. For what θ will A be greatest? How large?

8. A pull of P lb. exerted horizontally on a pole by wires h ft. above ground is exactly balanced by a tension of T lb. in a guy wire l ft. long, inclined $\theta°$ and not reaching far up the pole. By § 129 show that $Ph = Tl \sin \theta \cos \theta$. What θ will make T least, l being constant?

9. When a plane surface, of inclination θ, is driven horizontally through the air at a fixed speed, the lifting power of air resistance is proportional to $Q = \sin^2 \theta \cos \theta$.   Find what θ will maximize Q.

10. The time required for a small force (F lb.) to raise a 200-pound weight 32 feet by pulling it up a smooth plane, of inclination θ, is $T = 20/\sqrt{D}$, where $D = \sin \theta \, (F - 200 \sin \theta)$.   What value of θ will make T a minimum?   (Hint: Simply make D a maximum.)

11. Two corridors 13.31 feet wide and 10 feet wide meet at right angles.   Find how long a pole can be carried from one into the other, while kept horizontal.   (Hint: Show that the contact distance across at the turn is expressible in the form $13.31 \csc \theta + 10 \sec \theta$.)

12. A "synmotor" plows a spiral furrow, being drawn steadily inward by a cable which winds up on a stationary cylindrical "drum." What kind of curve is this spiral, by definition?

13. A point moved in such a way that $x = 5 \cos t$, $y = 3 \sin t$.   Find the speed at any instant; also what kind of curve the path was.

14. Combine $x = 8 \sin 10 \, \pi t + 6 \cos 10 \, \pi t$ into a standard *S.H.M.* equation.   What is the amplitude?   Angle of lag?   Frequency?

15. Along the "great circle" from San Francisco to Manila, the latitude L varies with the longitude θ: $\tan L = .29 \sin \theta - .99 \cos \theta$, approximately.   Does the circle pass north or south of Honolulu ($\theta = 157° \, 50'$, $L = 21° \, 20'$)?   How fast does L change with θ, per degree, at $\theta = 150°$?   [Differentiate implicitly.   § 80.]

16. Where does the circle in Ex. 15 cross the equator?

17. Along every great circle of the earth the latitude (L) varies with the longitude (θ) according to the formula

$$\tan L = a \sin \theta + b \cos \theta,$$

where a and b depend on the course of the circle in question.   Find a and b if the circle is to pass through St. Johns, N.F. ($\theta = 52° \, 40'$, $L = 47° \, 34'$), and the Azores ($\theta = 29°$, $L = 38°$).   If an airplane is to fly over this course, what should its latitude be when in longitude $36°$?

18. The same as Ex. 17 for a great circle from St. Johns to Queenstown ($\theta = 8° \, 20'$, $L = 51° \, 50'$).

19. Find the angle between the curves $y = x^3$ and $y = 2 - x^2$ at any common point or points.

20. Like Ex. 19 for $y = x^3$ and $y = 7x - 6$.

21. If it were given that some constants c and k exist such that $\sin (A + \theta) = c \sin \theta + k \cos \theta$, show how (18) could be derived by substituting $\theta = 0$, here and after differentiating.

CHAPTER XII

DEFINITE INTEGRALS

THE SUMMATION OF MINUTE ELEMENTS

§ 313. Constant of Integration. We proceed now to note certain facts about integration which will enable us to apply it more easily to practical problems. And first we shall shorten somewhat the calculation of areas, volumes, etc., by observing that the constant of integration and the final result must always assume a certain *form*.

Consider for example the area under the curve $y = 1/x$ from $x = 2$ to $x = 7$.

$$A = \int y \, dx = \int \frac{1}{x} \, dx = \log x + C.$$

Since $A = 0$ when $x = 2$, we have $0 = \log 2 + C$, or

$$C = -\log 2. \tag{1}$$

Hence the area from $x = 2$ to any other value of x is

$$A = \log x - \log 2.$$

In particular, the area from $x = 2$ to $x = 7$ is

$$A = \log 7 - \log 2.$$

Similarly the area from $x = 3$ to $x = 11$ would be $\log 11 - \log 3$.

The final result is simply the *difference between the values of the integral function* at the beginning and end of the interval.

Clearly the same thing must be true for the area under any other graph. For the constant of integration must equal the value of the integral at the starting point — with the sign changed.

§ 314. Definite Integrals. The symbol

$$\int_a^b f(x) \, dx,$$

is used to denote the *difference of the values of the integral function* at $x = b$, and at $x = a$. It is called "the definite integral from a to b of $f(x)\,dx$"; and a, b are called the *limits of integration.**

This difference is also denoted by writing the symbol $\big]_a^b$ after the integral function. Thus

$$\int_a^b x^2\,dx = \tfrac{1}{3}\,x^3\,\Big]_a^b = \tfrac{1}{3}\,b^3 - \tfrac{1}{3}\,a^3.$$

$$\int_2^7 \frac{1}{x}\,dx = \log x\,\Big]_2^7 = \log 7 - \log 2.$$

§ 315. Calculations Abridged. By § 313 the area under a curve may be expressed in the form

$$A = \int_a^b y\,dx. \tag{2}$$

Similar reasoning shows that the volume of a solid, the work done by a varying force, etc., are simply:

$$V = \int_a^b A_s\,dx, \qquad W = \int_a^b f\,dx, \text{ etc.} \tag{3}$$

That is, in finding any such quantity we need not consider the constant of integration, but merely form the difference of two values of the integral.

Ex. I. Find the momentum generated from $t = 2$ to $t = 5$ by a force varying thus: $f = 100\,t - 12\,t^2$.

$$M = \int_2^5 f\,dt = \int_2^5 (100\,t - 12\,t^2)\,dt$$
$$= 50\,t^2 - 4\,t^3\,\Big]_2^5 = 750 - 168 = 582.$$

Remark. The constant of integration is present here in disguise, already determined, in the term -168. [Cf. (1), § 313.]

§ 316 S. Tables of Integrals. By various methods numerous integrals have been worked out and tabulated. Thus many integrals needed in practical work can be looked up in a table without working them out for ourselves.

There is a small table in the Appendix, pages 529–533. Larger ones are given in texts on Calculus; also separately.†

---

* An ordinary integral function involving an arbitrary constant is sometimes called an *indefinite* integral.

† Cf. H. B. Dwight, *Tables of Integrals and Other Mathematical Data.*

Ex. I. Find $\int \sec^3 x\, dx$.

This comes under (39), p. 531, with $n = 3$ and $a = 1$:

$$\therefore \int \sec^3 x\, dx = \tfrac{1}{2} \sin x \sec^2 x + \tfrac{1}{2} \int \sec x\, dx.$$

The latter integral is given in (9) of the table; viz. log (sec x + tan x). (Formulas like (39) are called *Reduction Formulas*.)

Ex. II. Find $\int \dfrac{x\, dx}{\sqrt{x^4 + 9}}$.

Clearly $x\, dx$ suggests x^2, as does also the *even* power, x^4. Putting $x^2 = t$, gives $x\, dx = \tfrac{1}{2}\, dt$, and

$$\int \frac{x\, dx}{\sqrt{x^4 + 9}} = \tfrac{1}{2} \int \frac{dt}{\sqrt{t^2 + 9}}.$$

This comes under (23), with $a = 3$.

$$\therefore \int \frac{x\, dx}{\sqrt{x^4 + 9}} = \tfrac{1}{2} \log (t + \sqrt{t^2 + 9}) = \tfrac{1}{2} \log (x^2 + \sqrt{x^4 + 9}).$$

Ex. III. Find $A = \displaystyle\int_4^5 \sqrt{25 - x^2}\, dx$.

This comes under (25) with $a = 5$.

$$\therefore A = \left[\frac{x}{2} \sqrt{25 - x^2} + \frac{25}{2} \sin^{-1} \frac{x}{5} \right]_4^5$$

$$= [0 + \tfrac{25}{2} \sin^{-1} 1] - [6 + \tfrac{25}{2} \sin^{-1} \tfrac{4}{5}].$$

In radian measure, $\sin^{-1} 1 = \pi/2 = 1.57080$ and $\sin^{-1} \tfrac{4}{5} = .92729$.

$$\therefore A = \tfrac{25}{2} (.64351) - 6 = 2.0439.$$

EXERCISES

Tables may be used wherever helpful.

1. Evaluate: $\displaystyle\int_1^3 9 x^2\, dx, \quad \int_{-2}^2 x^4\, dx, \quad \int_0^3 e^{2x}\, dx, \quad \int_0^{\frac{\pi}{3}} \sin x\, dx.$

2. Find the area bounded by the X-axis and the parabola $y = 16 - x^2$.

3. Like Ex. 2 for the X-axis and $y = 3 + 2\,x - x^2$.

4. Find the area under each following curve for the interval indicated:

(a) $y = 1/x^2$, $x = 2$ to 4; (b) $y = \sqrt{x}$, $x = 4$ to 16;
(c) $y = 1/\sqrt{x}$, $x = 1$ to 9; (d) $y = 10/x$, $x = 12$ to 36;
(e) $y = \cos x$, $x = 0$ to $\pi/6$; (f) $y = e^{3x}$, $x = 0$ to .5.

5. Find the work done by a gas in driving a piston from $x = 10$ to $x = 50$ if $F = 1000/x$ continually.

6. The force applied to a car varies thus: $F = 120\,t^2 - t^3$. Find the momentum generated between $t = 20$ and $t = 40$.

7. How much water must flow into a hemispherical cistern of radius 5 ft. to raise the depth (at the middle) from 2 ft. to 4 ft.?

8. Find from tables the integrals of the following:

(a) $\dfrac{dx}{\sqrt{9 - x^2}}$, (b) $\sqrt{x^2 - 16}\,dx$, (c) $\dfrac{dx}{(x^2 - 25)^{\frac{3}{2}}}$,

(d) $\sin^{\frac{7}{2}}\theta \cos\theta\,d\theta$, (e) $\operatorname{ctn}^4\theta\,d\theta$, (f) $\csc^3\theta\,d\theta$,

(g) $\cos 5\theta \cos\theta\,d\theta$, (h) $x^{10}\log x\,dx$, (i) $e^{-3t}\cos 4t\,dt$.

9. A cylindrical tank of radius 3 ft., lying horizontally, is half full of oil which weighs 50 lb. per cu. ft. Find the force of pressure against one end.

10. Find by integration the area of a quadrant of the ellipse: $16\,x^2 + 25\,y^2 = 400$. Check.

11. Find the area cut off from the ellipse in Ex. 10 by either latus rectum.

12. Find the volume generated by revolving about the X-axis the area under one arch of the sine curve. (Radian measure.)

13. A "conoid" has circular base of radius 6 in. Every section perpendicular to one diameter is an isosceles triangle, whose height is 10 in. Find the volume.

14. Plot the curve $y = x^2 + 1$ from $x = 0$ to $x = 2$, drawing the ordinates at $x = 0, .5, 1.0$, etc. Calculate the total area of the four rectangles inscribed under the curve in these strips. Likewise find the area for a similar set of 10 inscribed rectangles with bases $x = 0$ to .2, .2 to .4, etc. Compare the results with the area under the curve from $x = 0$ to 2, as found by integration.

§ 317. Fundamental Theorem. We proceed now to establish a theorem of the very greatest importance.

Let y be any quantity which varies continuously with x, and let $y_1, y_2, \cdots y_n$, be its values taken at equal intervals Δx from $x = a$ to $x = b$. Multiply each of these values by Δx, and consider the sum of the products:

$$y_1\,\Delta x + y_2\,\Delta x \cdots + y_n\,\Delta x.$$

If $\Delta x \to 0$, *this sum will approach a limit — that limit being the definite integral* $\int_a^b y\,dx$; i.e.,

$$\mathop{\mathrm{L}}_{\Delta x \to 0} (y_1\,\Delta x + y_2\,\Delta x \cdots + y_n\,\Delta x) = \int_a^b y\,dx. \qquad (4)$$

PROOF. The several products $y_1 \Delta x$, $y_2 \Delta x$, etc., are equal to the areas of rectangles inscribed in the graph of the varying quantity y (Fig. 152). And the limit of the sum of those rectangles as their number is indefinitely increased is precisely the area under the graph, or the definite integral in (4).

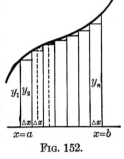

FIG. 152.

This theorem has been stated abstractly, but is of great practical importance, for it shows that

Any quantity whatever, which is expressible as the limit of a sum, of the type in (4), is therefore, without further argument, equal to a definite integral, as in (4).

By means of this "Fundamental Theorem" we can easily set up many integrals. Consider, for instance, the volume of a solid. If cut into n slices of thickness Δx by parallel planes, the volume of each slice will be approximately its face-area A times Δx, and the entire volume approximately

$$A_1 \Delta x + A_2 \Delta x \cdots + A_n \Delta x,$$

or, exactly, the *limit* of this sum as $\Delta x \to 0$. Hence without further proof:

$$V = \int A \, dx. \tag{5}$$

This integral can be set up still more quickly by reasoning freely as in § 99. But the present argument is logically sound and exact.

§ 318. Infinitesimal Analysis. Integration as defined in Chapter IV is the process of finding a quantity when given its derivative or rate of increase. This was in essence the conception of Newton, who first devised the process.

We have now seen that integration is also a method of calculating the *limit of a sum* of a certain type. This is almost the point of view of Leibnitz, who shares with Newton the honor of having invented the calculus, and who considered integration simply as a method of summing.

For instance, he regarded the area under a curve as composed of exceedingly many "infinitesimal" strips — so narrow that the height

y does not change within a strip (!). Calling the base of each strip dx and the area of each $y\,dx$, the whole area was the sum of all these areas:

$$A = \int_a^b y\,dx, \tag{6}$$

the sign $\int$ being simply an S, standing for "sum of."

We have already touched upon this conception (§ 99), and have seen that although logically defective it seems to work as a method of setting up integrals. We are now in a position to understand the matter more fully.

No matter how narrow a strip is, its height is not a fixed value y. Thus in Fig. 48, p. 135, $y\,dx$ is not the area of the strip, but of a rectangle inscribed in the strip.

The desired area is not the sum of the rectangles $y\,dx$, but the *limit* of that sum. *And the limit of the sum is the true integral* as we now define it. Thus Leibnitz set up a formula which is strictly correct in the sense in which we now use the sign.

Moreover, he obtained strictly correct results by a procedure which compensated for the inaccurate analysis in setting up the integral. Although he said that he was going to "sum up," actually he did not stop there, but took a step which gave him the *limit* of the sum — the thing really needed! In other words, he used rules for "summing" which were the same as our rules for integrating.

There is little doubt that both Newton and Leibnitz were thinking in terms of limit ideas; but the modern phraseology and sharp formulation were not current in their day. The brilliant achievement of these men in founding the calculus should not be lost sight of merely because their language was open to criticism.

The relation between Leibnitz' method of setting up integrals and the strictly logical procedure may become clearer if we refer again to the case of the volume of a solid.

By the old conception, as noted in § 99, the slices are regarded as so thin that the volume of each equals its face-area A times its thickness dx, making the whole volume the sum of these elements $A\,dx$:

$$V = \int A\,dx.$$

What we should say, reasoning exactly, as in § 317, is that the volumes of the slices are *approximately*

$$A_1\Delta x, \qquad A_2\Delta x, \qquad A_3\Delta x, \cdots;$$

that the entire volume V is approximately the sum of these, and *exactly* the *limit* of that sum, or by (4) the integral

$$V = \int A \, dx. \tag{7}$$

If the old method is regarded merely as a short way of stating the correct argument about the limit of a sum, and the person using it understands what he is doing, the old conception may properly be used in setting up integrals. Indeed it is the method regularly used by scientific men. The language, if not "rigorous," is at least "vigorous."

Of course the question arises as to when we can rely upon this older method to give a correct integral. The answer is simple: *Whenever the quantity under consideration is the limit of a sum of the type in* (4), *above.*

EXERCISES

1. By considering "infinitesimal elements," and also by an exact argument, set up the integral in each following case:

(a) The momentum generated by a variable force F;

(b) Radium decomposes at a variable rate R, say $R = f(t)$. Write an expression for the total amount lost from $t = t_1$ to $t = t_2$.

(c) A wound is healing at a variable rate, $= F(t)$. Express the total area healed in any time, $t = 0$ to $t = T$.

(d) The rate R at which the atmospheric pressure changes per foot varies with the elevation (x ft.). Express the total change in p from $x = 5000$ to 10000.

2. State how an exact argument in terms of limits and theorem (4) above would run in setting up these integrals:

(a) (21) in § 102;   (b) (B) in § 99;   (c) (C) in § 99.

3. The density of the earth (D lb. per cu. mi.) varies with the distance (x mi.) from the center: $D = F(x)$. Express the total weight of the earth from $x = 0$ to 3960. (Hint: Regard a spherical shell in the interior as "so thin that it is all the same distance x ft. from the center"!) Also give an exact argument.

4. Plot the parabola $y = x^2$ and the line $y = 2x + 3$, and measure the area bounded by them. Calculate the area by a single integral. (Hint: If the area be divided into "infinitesimal rectangles," running parallel to the Y-axis, what will be the length of any one in general?)

5. The same as Ex. 4 for the curves $y = x^2$ and $y = 2\,x - x^2$.

6. Find the total outflow from a reservoir in 24 hr., if the rate of flow of water (R tons per hr.) varies thus with the time (t hr.) after midnight: $R = 4000 \sin^2 (\pi t/24)$.

7. A beam 20 ft. long carries a load (L lb. per ft.) which varies thus with the distance (x ft.) from one end: $L = 120\,x - 6\,x^2$. Find the total load.

8. In Ex. 7 find the total moment of the load about the end mentioned. (§ 129.)

9. A horizontal semi-circular plate of radius 3 ft. weighs .06 lb. per sq. ft. What is the total moment of its weight about its straight side?

10. Find the total weight of a circular plate of radius 6 in., if the weight per sq. in. varies thus with the distance (x in.) from the center: $w = .2 - .03\,x$. (Consider a narrow ring x in. from the center.)

11. The kinetic energy of a particle of mass m traveling in a circle of radius x cm. with an angular speed of $\omega^{(r)}$/sec., is $\frac{1}{2}\,m\,\omega^2\,x^2$. Find the total kinetic energy of a circular plate of radius 10 cm. revolving about its center with $\omega = 5$, if the mass per sq. cm. is .36.

12. Find the total weight of a rectangular plate 30 in. long and 8 in. wide if the weight per sq. in. varies thus with the distance (x in.) from one end: $w = .4 + .003\,x$.

13. A hemispherical cistern of radius 4 ft. is full of water. Ignoring frictional losses, find the work required to pump the water to a level 3 ft. above the top. (Hint: Consider a thin sheet of water (x ft.) below the top. Water weighs 62.5 lb./ft.³ roughly.)

§ 319 S. **Length of a Curve.** If PQ is a chord joining any two points of a smooth curve (Fig. 153), then

$$\overline{PQ}^2 = \Delta x^2 + \Delta y^2 = \left[1 + \left(\frac{\Delta y}{\Delta x}\right)^2\right]\Delta x^2.$$

Fig. 153.

But $\Delta y/\Delta x$, the slope of PQ, must equal dy/dx, the slope of the tangent, at some point on the arc PQ.

$$\therefore \ PQ = \sqrt{1 + \left(\frac{dy}{dx}\right)^2}\ \Delta x. \qquad (8)$$

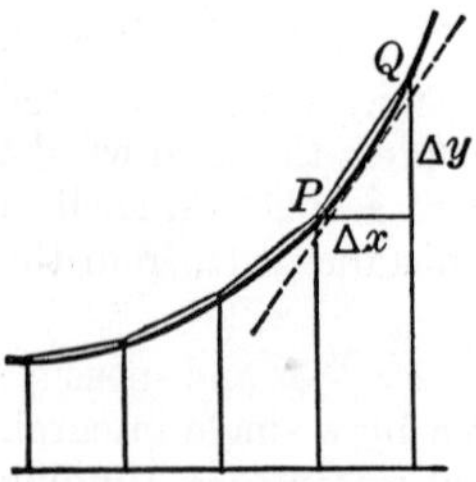

Now the length of the curve, s, is the *limit* of the sum of the lengths of its chords PQ, as each approaches zero (§ 42):

$$s = \mathop{\mathrm{L}}_{\Delta x \to 0} \left\{ \sqrt{1 + \left(\frac{dy}{dx}\right)_1^2} \, \Delta x + \sqrt{1 + \left(\frac{dy}{dx}\right)_2^2} \, \Delta x + \ldots \right\}$$

Hence, by (4) above, s equals the definite integral:

$$s = \int_a^b \sqrt{1 + \left(\frac{dy}{dx}\right)^2} \, dx. \qquad (9)$$

E.g., for the curve $y = x^3$, we have $dy/dx = 3\,x^2$,

$$\therefore \ s = \int \sqrt{1 + 9\,x^4} \, dx.$$

Remark. Using the brief "vigorous" method, we would consider any very short arc ds as straight, and as forming with dx and dy a right triangle. (Fig. 154.)

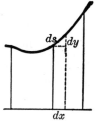

$$\therefore \ ds^2 = dx^2 + dy^2 = \left[1 + \left(\frac{dy}{dx}\right)^2\right] dx^2. \quad (10)$$

Hence as in (9) above the entire length of the curve is

FIG. 154.

$$s = \int_a^b \sqrt{1 + \left(\frac{dy}{dx}\right)^2} \, dx.$$

§ 320 S. Length in Polar Coordinates.

Let us also express the length of a curve whose equation is given in polar coordinates.

(I) *Using the short "vigorous method."* When $d\theta$ is infinitesimal, the circular arc PN (Fig. 155) is regarded as straight, and being perpendicular to its radius

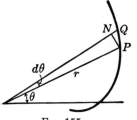

FIG. 155.

ON, it forms with PQ and NQ a right triangle (!), in which $PQ = ds$, $NQ = dr$, and $PN = r\,d\theta$, if θ is in radians. (§ 270.)

$$\therefore \ ds^2 = dr^2 + r^2\,d\theta^2, \qquad (11)$$

$$s = \int \sqrt{\left(\frac{dr}{d\theta}\right)^2 + r^2} \, d\theta. \qquad (12)$$

617

(II) *Using an exact method.* Formula (11) can also be set up by reasoning about limits. More simply, it can be rigorously deduced from (9) or the equivalent equation (10), as in Ex. 6 below.

§ 321 S. Surfaces of Revolution. When any curve $y = f(x)$ is revolved about the X-axis, it generates some curved

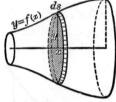

surface. Let us find the area S of this surface.

Using the short method, any tiny arc of the curve, ds, is regarded as generating a narrow band running around the surface — of length $2\pi y$ and width ds. The area of this tiny band of surface is then $2\pi y\,ds$.

FIG. 156.

Or, substituting for ds its value from (10), we have as the surface area:

$$S = \int 2\pi y \sqrt{1 + \left(\frac{dy}{dx}\right)^2}\, dx. \qquad (13)$$

This integral can also be set up by the "rigorous method" of limits; but far less simply.

To calculate the area of a general curved surface, which is not obtainable by revolving a plane curve, is a more difficult problem, which will not be treated in this course.

Ex. I. Find the area generated by revolving the parabola $y^2 = 4x$ about the X-axis, from $x = 0$ to $x = 8$.

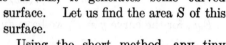

$$y = 2x^{\frac{1}{2}}, \qquad \therefore\ dy/dx = x^{-\frac{1}{2}} = 1/\sqrt{x}.$$

$$\therefore\ S = \int_0^8 4\pi x^{\frac{1}{2}} \sqrt{1 + \frac{1}{x}}\, dx = 4\pi \int_0^8 \sqrt{x+1}\, dx$$

$$= \frac{8}{3}\pi (x+1)^{\frac{3}{2}} \Big]_0^8 = \frac{208}{3}\pi.$$

EXERCISES

Use tables of integrals where helpful.

1. Find the length of each following curve in the interval given; and check (*b*) and (*d*):

    (*a*) $y = \frac{1}{2}x^2$, $x = 0$ to 3;   (*b*) $y = 2x + 3$, $x = 0$ to 10;

(c) $y = \log \cos x$, 0 to $\dfrac{\pi}{3}$; (d) Quarter circle, $r = 4$;

(e) $y = \frac{1}{2}(e^x + e^{-x})$, 0 to 1; (f) $y = \frac{2}{3}(x - 4)^{\frac{3}{2}}$, $x = 5$ to 8.

2. Find by integration the areas generated by revolving the following curves about the X-axis, checking (b) and (d):

(a) $y = \frac{1}{3}x^3$, $x = 0$ to 1; (b) $y = \frac{1}{3}x$, $x = 0$ to 6;

(c) $y^2 = 4x$, $x = 3$ to 15; (d) $x^2 + y^2 = 4$, 0 to 2;

(e) $y = \cos x$, 0 to $\dfrac{\pi}{2}$; (f) The arc in Ex. 1 (e).

3. Find the lengths of the following curves, each from $\theta = 0$ to $\theta = \pi^{(r)}$:

(a) $r = 2\theta$, (b) $r = e^{2\theta}$,

(c) $r = a\theta^2$, (d) $r = e^{-\theta}$,

(e) $r = 8\sin\theta$, (f) $r = 5\cos\theta$.

4. (a–f) Plot each curve in Ex. 3. Measure each desired length.

5. Express as an integral the area of the surface generated by revolving any given curve about:

(a) The Y-axis; (b) A line 4 units below the X-axis.

6. From the relations between rectangular and polar coordinates, $x = r\cos\theta$, $y = r\sin\theta$, obtain dx and dy in terms of dr and $d\theta$. Then show that (11) follows from (10).

7. Find the area of the spherical segment generated by revolving about the X-axis the circle $x^2 + y^2 = 100$ from $x = 6$ to $x = 10$.

8. Find the volume generated by revolving about the X-axis the area under the line $y = 4x$ from $x = 0$ to $x = 5$. Check.

9. A fine wire whose mass per unit length is 4 has the shape of the curve $y = .4x^{\frac{5}{2}}$ from $x = 0$ to $x = 4$. If it revolves about the Y-axis with an angular speed of $\omega^{(r)}$/sec., find its kinetic energy. (Cf. Ex. 11, p. 426.)

10. Like Ex. 13, p. 426, for a radius of 5 ft. and a level 1 ft. above the top.

§ 322. How to Plot a Surface.
To understand the calculation of volumes bounded by curved surfaces in general, we need to know how surfaces can be represented by equations.

Any plane curve (except a vertical straight line) is represented by some equation $y = f(x)$, which tells exactly how high the curve is above the X-axis at every point.

Similarly for a surface. We first select a horizontal reference plane, and in it choose X- and Y-axes. The height z

of the surface above this plane will vary from point to point in some definite way. The surface will be definitely described, if we tell by an equation $z = f(x, y)$ how high it is above every point (x, y) in the reference plane.

To plot a surface from its equation we proceed as in the following example.

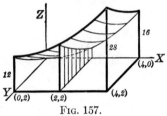

FIG. 157.

Ex. I. Draw that part of the surface

$$z = x^2 + y^2 + 4y \quad (14)$$

which stands directly above a rectangle in the XY-plane bounded by the axes $x = 0$ and $y = 0$, and the lines $x = 4$ and $y = 2$.

First draw the specified base in perspective. (Fig. 157.) Its corners are the points $(4, 2)$, $(0, 2)$, $(0, 0)$, $(4, 0)$.

Then calculate the height of the surface above each corner, and at various other points, using (14):

$$x = 4, \; y = 2, \quad \text{give} \quad z = 16 + 4 + 8 = 28,$$
$$x = 0, \; y = 2, \quad \text{give} \quad z = 0 + 4 + 8 = 12; \text{etc.}$$

Thus the height of the surface above the corners $A\,(4, 2)$ and $B\,(0, 2)$ is 28 units and 12 units, respectively. Similarly for the other values of z in the table.

Erect perpendiculars to represent the height of the surface above the base plane at these several points, and join the ends of the vertical lines by smooth curves. These are curves on the required surface, and show its general shape.

x	y	z
0	0	0
0	1	5
0	2	12
2	0	4
2	1	9
2	2	16
4	0	16
4	1	21
4	2	28

The surface forms a sort of tent-like roof over the space between it and the base plane.

Remarks. (I) In three-dimensional plotting it is customary to bring the Y-axis forward, as in Fig. 157, so that the region where x, y, and z are all positive will be nearest to the observer.

(II) The perspective is helped by choosing a short scale in the Y direction and drawing the Y-axis at such an angle as in Fig. 157; also by choosing the Z scale so as to let us see under the surface when feasible.

§ 323. Volumes by Double Integration. Let us find the volume of the solid drawn in Fig. 157.

Consider a section perpendicular to the X-axis at any distance x from the origin. If we can express its area (A_s) in terms of x, an integration will give the required volume. But as this section is not one of the figures of elementary geometry, we have no formula for its area, and must perform *a preliminary integration* to find its area.

Throughout this section, x has a constant value; but the height of the surface (z) varies with y. The element of area in this section is, then, $z\,dy$;* and

$$\therefore\; A_s = \int_0^2 z\,dy = \int_0^2 (x^2 + y^2 + 4\,y)\,dy. \tag{15}$$

Since x is a constant during this integration, we find

$$A_s = \left[\, x^2 y + \frac{1}{3} y^3 + 2\,y^2 \,\right]_{y=0}^{2} = 2\,x^2 + \frac{32}{3}. \tag{16}$$

We now have the sectional area in terms of x, and can find the volume as in earlier cases:

$$V = \int_0^4 A_s\,dx = \int_0^4 \left(2\,x^2 + \frac{32}{3} \right) dx = \left[\, \frac{2}{3} x^3 + \frac{32}{3}\,x \,\right]_0^4 = \frac{256}{3}.$$

This calculation would have been slightly modified, if the base of the solid, instead of being a rectangle, had been bounded, say, by the X-axis and the curve $y = x^3$, from $x = 0$ to $x = 2$.

As above, we first draw the part of the XY-plane which is to be the base of the solid. (Fig. 158.)

The curve $y = x^3$ need not be drawn accurately to scale for this purpose. But in calculating the height of the surface

$$z = x^2 + y^2 + 4\,y$$

above any point on this curve,

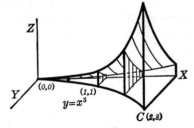

Fig. 158.

we must use the proper value of y as well as x at that point — the value of y being first found from the equation of the curve $y = x^3$. *E.g.*, at C (Fig. 158),

$$x = 2,\quad y = 8;\quad \therefore\; z = 100.$$

* If this is not clear, make a rough drawing showing how the section would appear, if seen at right angles, looking into the *end* of the required volume.

A_s is again found by integrating $z\, dy$; but the values between which y runs are not the same for all sections. The upper limit for y is a value depending upon the x of that section, viz. it is x^3. Hence *

$$A_s = \int_0^{x^3} z\, dy = \left[x^2\, y + \frac{1}{3}\, y^3 + 2\, y^2 \right]_{y=0}^{x^3} \tag{17}$$

$$= \tfrac{1}{3}\, x^9 + 2\, x^6 + x^5.$$

$$V = \int_0^2 A_s\, dx = \left[\frac{1}{30}\, x^{10} + \frac{2}{7}\, x^7 + \frac{1}{6}\, x^6 \right]_0^2 = 81\tfrac{13}{35}.$$

Remark. It is interesting to interpret this process from the standpoint of "infinitesimal elements." Consider a volume to be composed of tiny columns, of height z and bases $dy\, dx$. The whole volume is then the sum of these, or

$$V = \int\!\!\int z\, dy\, dx.$$

Summing first with respect to y all columns having the same x gives a slice $A\, dx$. Summing these slices, as to x, gives V.

EXERCISES

Draw that part of each of the following surfaces which stands over the specified portion of the XY-plane; and calculate the inclosed volume:

	Surface	Base	
1.	$z = x^2 + 12\, y,$	$y = 0$ to $2,$	$x = 0$ to $4.$
2.	$z = x^2 + 2\, y^2,$	$y = 0$ to $3,$	$x = 1$ to $4.$
3.	$z = x^2 + y^2,$	$y = 0$ to $y = x^2,$	$x = 0$ to $2.$
4.	$z = xy,$	$y = 0$ to $y = x,$	$x = 2$ to $6.$
5.	$z = xy,$	$y = 0$ to $y = \sqrt{x},$	$x = 0$ to $4.$
6.	$z = x^2 + 6\, y,$	$y = 0$ to $y = x^2,$	$x = 0$ to $3.$
7.	$z = 3\, x + y^2,$	$y = 1$ to $y = x,$	$x = 2$ to $x = 4.$
8.	$z = xy + y^2,$	$y = 1$ to $y = x,$	$x = 1$ to $x = 4.$
9.	$z = 6\, x + 10\, y,$	bounded by X-axis and $y = 4\, x - x^2.$	

§ 324. Special Plane Sections.

In studying the shape of a surface, it is helpful to know the nature of the cross-sections made by various planes. Sections perpendicular to an axis — in which x or y is constant — are the most easily studied.

---

* If it looks peculiar to have x^3 as a limit of integration, remember that *in this first integration x is a constant.*

Ex. I.   What sort of curve is cut from the surface
$$z = x^2 + y^4 + 10$$
by the plane $y = 2$?   What is its slope at any point?

Putting $y = 2$ makes $z = x^2 + 26$.   (Here z is the height of the curve and x the horizontal distance.)   The section is therefore a parabola, extending in the positive Z direction, and raised 26 units.   Differentiating gives $dz/dx = 2\,x$, the slope at any point.

This slope could be found directly from the equation of the surface by simply *treating y as constant* while differentiating.   Similarly, in any section perpendicular to the X-axis, x would be a constant; and the slope would be $dz/dy = 4\,y^3$.   (In such a section y would be the horizontal coordinate and z the vertical.)

§ 325.   Partial Derivatives.   Whenever, as in § 324, we differentiate a function $z = f(x, y)$, treating y as a constant, we are said to find the "partial derivative" of z with respect to x, written $\partial z/\partial x$.   Similarly for $\partial z/\partial y$.

Thus in the case $z = x^2 + y^4 + 10$ above,

$$\frac{\partial z}{\partial x} = 2\,x, \qquad\qquad \frac{\partial z}{\partial y} = 4\,y^3.$$

Similarly, if $z = x^6 + 5\,x^2y^3 + 8\,y^2$,

$$\frac{\partial z}{\partial x} = 6\,x^5 + 10\,xy^3, \quad \frac{\partial z}{\partial y} = 15\,x^2y^2 + 16\,y.$$

Geometrically interpreted: $\partial z/\partial x$ is the slope of a section of the surface $z = f(x, y)$ made by a plane $y = c$.   *Physically*, it is the rate at which z changes per unit change in x, if y remains constant.

In general, if z is a function of several variables x, y, u, v, $\ldots$, then $\partial z/\partial x$ will give the rate at which z will change with x, while y, u, v, $\ldots$, remain fixed — or, as we say in daily life: "Other things being equal."

§ 326.   Extreme Values.   It is sometimes necessary to find the maximum value of a function of two variables which can change independently of each other, say $z = f(x, y)$.

This amounts to finding the highest point on a surface, $z = f(x, y)$.   Such a point must be the highest on each of the two special sections ($x = c_1$, $y = c_2$) passing through it. Hence, unless the surface rises sharply to the point, the slope of each section must be zero:

$$\frac{\partial z}{\partial x} = 0, \qquad \frac{\partial z}{\partial y} = 0. \qquad (18)$$

And similarly for a minimum.

More generally, let z be a function of several variables, $z = f(x, y, u, \ldots)$. Its maximum value must be the greatest obtainable by varying x and keeping y, u, ... constant. Hence $\partial z/\partial x = 0$. Similarly, $\partial z/\partial y = 0$, etc.

Ex. I. Test $z = x^2 - 6x + y^2 - 4y + 30$.

$$\frac{\partial z}{\partial x} = 2x - 6 = 0, \qquad \frac{\partial z}{\partial y} = 2y - 4 = 0.$$

This gives $x = 3$, $y = 2$, whence $z = 17$.

Testing each derivative on both sides shows this point to be the lowest on each sectional curve. This suggests that it is the lowest point on the surface; but is not a sure test, since the surface might go lower somewhere between the sections. By completing the squares, however, we may write

$$z = (x - 3)^2 + (y - 2)^2 + 17.$$

This definitely shows 17 to be the minimum z, since $(x - 3)^2$ and $(y - 2)^2$ are positive when not zero. More general methods of making sure tests are discussed in advanced courses.

EXERCISES

1. Plot the surface $z = 4x + y^2$ from $y = 0$ to $y = x$ and from $x = 0$ to $x = 2$. What sort of section is made by the plane $x = 2$? By the plane $y = 1$? Find the slope of each at their intersection.

2. Find the volume under the plotted portion of the surface in Ex. 1.

3. What is the character of the sections of each of the following surfaces made by the specified planes, and what is the slope of each section at their common point?

Surface	Cutting Planes	
(a) $z = x^2 + 6y + 15$,	$x = 3$,	$y = 2$.
(b) $z = 100 - x^2 - y^2$,	$x = 6$,	$y = 5$.
(c) $z = xy$,	$x = 4$,	$y = 20$.
(d) $z = 5x - 2y$,	$x = 8$,	$y = 0$.

4. (*a*)–(*e*) The same as Ex. 3 for surfaces in Ex. 2, 4, 6, 8, 9, p. 432, and the cutting planes $x = 2$, $y = 1$.

5. Locate any possible maxima and minima for the following functions, and make a sure test if you can:

(*a*) $z = x^2 + 2\,y^2 - 8\,x + 8\,y + 25$,   (*b*) $z = 60 - x^6 - y^4$,

(*c*) $z = x^3 + 3\,y^2 - 12\,y + 30$,   (*d*) $z = 16\,x^2 + 20\,y^2 - x^4 - y^4$,

(*e*) $z = 100 + 6\,x + 8\,y - x^2 - y^2$,   (*f*) $z = 20 + 16\,x - x^2 - y^2$.

6. Prove that the greatest possible value of $z = e^{-x^2-y^2}$ is 1.

7. The temperature at any point (x, y) of a square metal plate varied thus: $T = x^2 + y^2 - 20\,x - 30\,y + 350$. Where was the coolest point?

8. Find the minimum value of $Q = x^2 + y^4 + z^2 - 8\,z + 200$.

9. What values of a and b will minimize the quantity

$$S = (a + 2\,b - 7)^2 + (a + 4\,b - 11)^2 + (a + 6\,b - 14)^2 ?$$

10. Like Ex. 9 for the quantity $S = (a - 9)^2 + (a + 3\,b - 15)^2 + (a + 6\,b - 20)^2$.

§ 327 S. The Mean-Value Problem Resumed.

The average force $\overline{F}$ used in moving an object any distance, say from $x = a$ to $x = b$, is by definition the total work done, divided by the distance; *i.e.*,

$$\overline{F} = \frac{\displaystyle\int_a^b F\,dx}{b - a}. \qquad (19)$$

Let us compare this definition of average force with the usual idea of an average of a number of distinct values.

Consider the actual average of n values of the force F selected at equal intervals of distance, Δx, from $x = a$ to $x = b$:

$$\text{av. of } n \text{ values} = \frac{F_1 + F_2 \cdots + F_n}{n}.$$

The larger we take n, the nearer this will come to what we would call the average of *all* the force-values between a and b.

To see what the limiting value is, which this approaches, multiply numerator and denominator by Δx:

$$\text{av. of } n \text{ values} = \frac{F_1\,\Delta x + F_2\,\Delta x \cdots + F_n\,\Delta x}{n\,\Delta x}.$$

Now as n becomes indefinitely great, $\Delta x \to 0$, and by the Fundamental Theorem of § 317, the limiting value of the numerator is $\int_a^b F\,dx$.   The denominator $n\,\Delta x$ is simply the whole distance from $x = a$ to $x = b$, *i.e.*, $(b - a)$.   Hence we consider the average of *all* the force-values between a and b to be

$$\overline{F} = \frac{\int_a^b F\,dx}{b - a}\,,$$

the same value as in (19).

Evidently the same argument would lead to the following definition of the average value of any continuously varying quantity $y = f(x)$ from $x = a$ to $x = b$:

$$\overline{y} = \frac{\int_a^b y\,dx}{b - a}\,. \tag{20}$$

Geometrically interpreted, the numerator of (20) is the area under the curve $y = f(x)$.   So that the average height $\overline{y}$ is simply the area divided by the length of base considered — agreeing with our definition of *mean ordinate* in § 10.

Ex. I.   If $y = x^2$, find the average value of y between $x = 1$ and $x = 5$.

Here
$$\overline{y} = \frac{\int_1^5 x^2\,dx}{5 - 1} = \frac{\frac{1}{3}[5^3 - 1^3]}{4} = \frac{31}{3}.$$

§ 328 S. **Simpson's Rule.**   Many quantities considered in the natural and social sciences are representable by the area under some graph, and can be approximated by measuring that area.   It is desirable, however, to be able to approximate such an area without plotting or integrating.

The problem is virtually to find the *average height* of the graph, which, multiplied by the base, would give the area.

The following rule, devised about 1750 by Thomas Simpson, an Englishman, gives excellent results for many curves: *To find the average height $\overline{y}$ from $x = a$ to $x = b$, add the heights at a and b to four times the height at the middle, and divide by 6:**

$$\overline{y} = (y_a + y_b + 4\,y_m) \div 6. \tag{21}$$

And the area under the graph is this $\overline{y}$ times the base $(b - a)$:

$$A = \tfrac{1}{6}(y_a + y_b + 4\,y_m) \cdot (b - a). \tag{22}$$

---

* In other words, form a "weighted" average of y_a, y_b, and y_m, counting y_m four times and each other y once.

Ex. I.   Find the area under the parabola $y = x^2$ from $x = 2$ to $x = 10$. The first height, at $x = 2$, is $y = 4$.   The final height, at $x = 10$, is $y = 100$.   The middle height, at $x = 6$, is $y = 36$.   Hence by (21):

$$\bar{y} = [4 + 100 + 4\,(36)] \div 6 = 41\tfrac{1}{3}.$$

Multiplying $\bar{y}$ by the base, from $x = 2$ to 10, gives the area: $A = 330\tfrac{2}{3}$.

Remarks.   (I) In this case we can check by integration:

$$A = \int y\,dx = \int_2^{10} x^2\,dx = \tfrac{1}{3}\,(992) = 330\tfrac{2}{3}.$$

But the rule is most useful when integration is impracticable.

(II) The rule gives exact results whenever the formula for the height of the graph is of the first, second, or third degree.   (This is proved in the Appendix, p. 525.)   Generally it gives only an approximation — but a close one if the interval is small.   A large interval may be split into smaller sub-intervals, and the rule applied to each.   In fact, Simpson's rule is usually stated in a more general form than (22), giving the total result for n intervals.

§ 329 S. General Applicability.

Any definite integral, whatever its original physical meaning, can be thought of as the area under some curve, and hence can be approximated by Simpson's Rule.

E.g., suppose the *work done by a force* was to be found from

$$W = \int_1^5 \sqrt{1 + x^2}\,dx.$$

This same integral would give the *area* under the curve $y = \sqrt{1 + x^2}$ from $x = 1$ to 5.   So to approximate the integral we would simply calculate the value of $\sqrt{1 + x^2}$ at 1, 3, and 5, average according to the rule, and multiply by the length of the interval, 4.

In general, we would proceed similarly with any function $f(x)$ to be integrated — getting its values at the beginning, middle, and end, etc. Thus, approximately,

$$\int_a^b f(x)\,dx = \tfrac{1}{6}[f(a) + f(b) + 4\,f(x_m)]\,(b - a), \qquad (23)$$

where x_m is the value of x midway between a and b.

EXERCISES

1. Find by Simpson's Rule the area under $y = x^3$ from $x = 3$ to 5. Check by integration.   What is the average height?

2. The same as Ex. 1 for the curve $y = x^2$ from $x = 2$ to 6.

3. Find the area under $y = 1/x$ from $x = 3$ to $x = 5$ by Simpson's Rule, without subdividing. What is the percentage of error?

4. What area problem would call for the calculation of the integral, $\int_1^9 \sqrt{x}\, dx$? How accurately does Simpson's Rule give this area?

5. Find the following integrals by Simpson's Rule and also by integration, determining the percentage of error in each case:

(a) $\displaystyle\int_1^3 x^4\, dx$, (b) $\displaystyle\int_0^4 (x^2 + 4\,x + 5)\, dx$, (c) $\displaystyle\int_0^2 e^x\, dx$,

(d) $\displaystyle\int_{10}^{20} x^{\frac{1}{2}}\, dx$, (e) $\displaystyle\int_0^1 \sqrt{1 - x^2}\, dx$, (f) $\displaystyle\int_{\frac{\pi}{6}}^{\frac{\pi}{2}} \sin x\, dx$.

6. Express as a definite integral, and then approximate by (23):

(a) The work done from $x = 2$ to $x = 6$ by a force varying thus· $F = .2\,x^2$. (Check.)

(b) The volume from $x = 0$ to $x = 3$ of a solid whose cross-section area varies thus: $A = \sqrt{x + 1}$.

7. Find the exact mean value of each of the following:

(a) Of x^6 from $x = 0$ to $x = 2$; (b) Of $\sqrt{x^3}$ from $x = 1$ to 8;

(c) Of $\sin^{-1} x$ from $x = 0$ to 1; (d) Of $\cos x$ from $x = 0$ to $\dfrac{\pi}{2}$.

8. For an electric current: $i = 10 \sin 200\, t$. Find the mean current flowing during a half-period.

9. For a pendulum: $\omega = .15 \cos \pi t$. Find the mean angular velocity, $\bar{\omega}$, during an upward swing.

10. A solid of height h has parallel bases of areas B and B', and a cross-section area M midway between bases. Show that the volume, according to Simpson's Rule, would be

$$V = \tfrac{1}{6} (B + B' + 4\, M)\, h. \qquad (24)$$

This is the celebrated "Prismoid Formula."

Use (24) to solve the following exercises.

11. A uniformly tapering timber 20 ft. long has ends 1 ft. square and 2 ft. square. Find its volume.

12. Find the approximate volume of a barrel 36 in. long with a radius of 10 in. at each end and 12 in. at the middle — inside dimensions.

13. An ellipsoid has three mutually perpendicular elliptic cross-sections, with semi-axes of 10 in., 8 in., and 6 in. Find its volume.

14. The frustum of a cone is 20 in. tall and has base radii of 4 in. and 6 in. Find its volume.

15. The base of a granite column is 5 ft. high, and has a radius of 2 ft. at the top, 2.5 ft. at the middle, and 4 ft. at the bottom. Find its approximate volume.

§ 330. Summary of Chapter XII. Any quantity expressible as the limit of a sum, of a certain form (§ 317), is equal to a certain definite integral, *i.e.*, the difference of two values of an indefinite integral.

E.g., the area under a curve $y = f(x)$ from $x = a$ to $x = b$ is

$$A = \underset{\Delta x \to 0}{L} \, [y_1 \Delta x + \cdots + y_n \Delta x] = \int_a^b y \, dx,$$

i.e., $A = F(b) - F(a),$

where F is the integral function, whose derivative equals y or $f(x)$. Further cases are listed in the Appendix, p. 527.

Originally, a definite integral was regarded as the sum of numerous infinitesimal elements. But the formulas then used in "summing" did not really give the sum. They were the same as our formulas for integrating, and thus gave the *limit* of the sum — the value required, in fact.

In finding the volume of a solid two successive integrations may be required: one to find the area of a cross-section, and the other to get the volume itself.

To show graphically how a quantity z varies with *two* other quantities x and y on which it depends, we must draw a *surface*. The variation of z with x or y alone is shown by a *section* of the surface perpendicular to the Y- or X-axis. The rate of change is then $\partial z / \partial x$ or $\partial z / \partial y$.

The mean value of a function is conveniently defined in terms of definite integrals. Its value may often be approximated by Simpson's Rule. Integrals in general can be approximated by measuring suitable graphical areas; or by using Simpson's Rule, applied to one or more intervals.

EXERCISES

Tables of integrals may be used when helpful.

1. Find the area bounded by the curve $y^2 = x^3$, the X-axis, and the positive ordinate at $x = 4$.

2. Find the length of the curved arc considered in Ex. 1.

3. Find the area bounded by the X-axis and the curve $y = 9 - x^2$. What kind of curve is this, and how located?)

4. Find the volume under the surface $z = xy$, above the part of the XY-plane from $y = 0$ to $y = x^2$ and from $x = 0$ to $x = 3$.   Plot.

5. Find the volume from $z = 0$ to $z = 3$ of a solid whose every horizontal section is an ellipse, with one of these equations:

$$(a) \ \frac{x^2}{25\,z} + \frac{y^2}{16\,z} = 1; \qquad (b) \ \frac{x^2}{25\,(1 + z^2)} + \frac{y^2}{9\,(1 + z^2)} = 1.$$

6. Find by Simpson's Rule the area under the curve $y = \sin x$ from 0 to $\pi/2$ — cutting this into three parts.   Compare the exact value.

7. The thickness (T in.) of certain pavement x ft. from the middle line is: $T = 4 + .006\, x^2$.   Find the average thickness, $x = 0$ to $x = 15$.

8. On a beam 200 in. long the loading (y lb. per in.) x in. from one end A is $y = .06\, x$.   Find the total load.

9. In Ex. 8 find the moment of the load about A.

10. A channel 9 ft. deep and 12 ft. wide at the top, with a parabolic cross-section, is full of water.   Find the force exerted against an end gate.

11. The capstone of a monument is 8 in. high and has square horizontal sections, whose vertices all lie on two vertical semi-circles of radius 10 in. with their common center in the base of the capstone. Find the volume of the cap.   (Hint: Show that the diagonal of the square top is 12 in., and of the base is 20 in.   How about the midsection?)

12. If a circle of radius 5 in. be revolved about a line in its plane 8 in. from its center, what sort of surface will be generated?   What sort of section will be made by any plane perpendicular to the axis of rotation?   Find the volume.

13. The base of a cylindrical can is a circle of radius 20 cm. with a hole of radius 1 cm. at the middle.   The base is covered uniformly with fine particles of dust, 20,000 per sq. cm.   If the dust is drawn off through the hole, each particle traveling straight toward the center, what is the aggregate distance traveled by all the particles in reaching the edge of the hole?

14. In a certain type of tank the weight of steel used in the wall varies thus with the diameter x and height y: $W = .01\, x^2\, y^2$.   Plot a surface showing this variation, from $x = 20$ to 60 and $y = 0$ to 10.

15. Like Ex. 13, p. 426, for oil weighing 50 lb./ft.^{3}, and a radius of 2 ft.

16. Evaluate: $\displaystyle\int_0^1 e^{-2x}\, dx.$

17. Likewise for $\displaystyle\int_0^{\frac{\pi}{6}} \cos x\, dx.$

CHAPTER XIII

PROGRESSIONS AND SERIES

INVESTMENT FORMULAS — CALCULATION OF FUNCTIONS

§ 331. Problems to be Considered. We have now defined and studied briefly the following kinds of functions: power, logarithmic, exponential, and trigonometric functions, derivatives and integrals. To round out our knowledge of these various functions — as far as practicable in an introductory course — we shall now consider a very general method of finding their values, by which we can calculate tables and discover relations among the different functions.

As a preliminary, however, we must recall certain formulas of elementary algebra. Incidentally we shall see how some fundamental problems of the Theory of Investment are solved.*

§ 332 S. Arithmetic Progressions. A series of numbers like

$$3, \quad 7, \quad 11, \quad 15, \quad 19, \quad \text{etc.,}$$

which have a constant difference is called an Arithmetic Progression — abbreviated as $A.P.$

If a denotes the first term and d the constant difference, any $A.P.$ may be written

$$a, \quad a+d, \quad a+2\,d, \quad a+3\,d, \quad \ldots$$

The fourth term is $a+3\,d$. What would the 10th be? The 17th?

If there are n terms in all, the last one is evidently

$$l = a + (n-1)\,d. \tag{1}$$

A formula for the *sum* of all the terms is easily found. Write the terms in the order above and also reversed:

$$S = a + (a+d) + (a+2\,d) \cdots + (l-d) + l,$$
$$S = l + (l-d) + (l-2\,d) \cdots + (a+d) + a.$$

*In business such problems are usually solved by merely consulting tables of interest, discount, annuities, etc. But our methods will handle cases not covered by the tables, and will show also how the standard tables were first obtained.

Add, and observe that each sum on the right reduces to $(a + l)$:

$$\therefore\ 2S = (a + l) + (a + l)\ \cdots + (a + l) = n\,(a + l).$$

$$\therefore\ S = \frac{n}{2}\,(a + l). \tag{2}$$

This formula has a simple interpretation which makes it easy to remember: The average value of the terms is $\frac{1}{2}\,(a + l)$, and the sum equals this average value multiplied by the number of terms.

Ex. I. Find the last term and sum of the A. P., 2, 5, 8, 11, ... to 20 terms.

Here $a = 2$, $d = 3$, $n = 20$.

$$\therefore\ l = 2 + 19(3) = 59, \qquad S = \tfrac{20}{2}\,(2 + 59) = 610.$$

Ex. II. A debt is to be paid off in 30 payments running as follows: $200, $195, $190, etc. Find the total amount to be paid.

The payments form an A. P. with $a = 200$, $d = -5$, $n = 30$. Hence the last term is $l = 200 + 29\,(-5) = 55$; and

$$S = \tfrac{30}{2}\,(200 + 55) = 3825.$$

§ 333. **Geometric Progressions.** A series of numbers such as

$$2, \qquad 6, \qquad 18, \qquad 54, \qquad 162, \qquad \text{etc.,}$$

each of which equals the preceding multiplied by some constant, is called a Geometric Progression — abbreviated G. P.

If a denotes the first term of a G. P., and r the constant multiplier or *ratio*, the progression may be written:

$$a, \qquad ar, \qquad ar^2, \qquad ar^3, \qquad \ldots$$

Here the 4th term is ar^3. What would the 10th term be? The 17th?

If there are n terms in all, the last one is evidently

$$l = ar^{n-1}. \tag{3}$$

A formula for the sum of all the terms,

$$S = a + ar + ar^2 + \cdots + ar^{n-1}$$

is easily found. If $r = 1$, clearly $S = na$. If $r \neq 1$, multiply S by r, and subtract S from rS:

$$rS = ar + ar^2 + \cdots + ar^{n-1} + ar^n.$$

$$\therefore\ rS - S = -a + ar^n.$$

Factoring both sides and solving for S, we have

$$S = \frac{a\,(r^n - 1)}{r - 1}, \qquad (r \neq 1). \tag{4}$$

Ex. I.   Find the last term and the sum of the $G.\ P.$, 2, 6, 18, etc., to 20 terms:

Here $a = 2$, $r = 3$, $n = 20$, whence $l = 2(3)^{19}$ and

$$S = \frac{2\,(3^{20} - 1)}{3 - 1} = 3^{20} - 1.$$

Approximate values of l and S can be found quickly by using logarithms.

Remark.   The amounts of a sum at compound interest at the ends of successive years form a $G.\ P.$, since the sum is multiplied by $(1 + r/k)$ during every interest period.

EXERCISES

1. 300 raffle tickets are sold, at all prices from 1¢ to $3.00. What are the total receipts?

2. What is the charge for 15 postage stamps, one of each denomination from 1¢ to 15¢? Check by addition.

3. Find the sum of the first 50 odd integers. Of the first 30 even integers. Of all even integers < 1001.

4. Find the sum of all integers between 100 and 600 which end in 7. Of all integers between 1 and 9999 which are divisible by 5.

5. On ten successive days of fruit picking, the quantities obtained ran thus: 840 lb., 775 lb., 710 lb., etc., decreasing regularly. Find the total amount.

6. In a contest there are to be 8 prizes: $250, $225, $200, etc. What will the total amount be? Check.

7. If we make 9 monthly deposits of $80 each, beginning now, and are allowed simple interest at 3% per annum, how much will there be to our credit one year hence?

8. In the $G.\ P.$, 16, 24, 36, ..., what are a and r? Express by a formula the 18th term; also the sum of 40 terms.

9. The same as Ex. 8 for the $G.\ P.$, 180, 120, 80, ...

10. In the $G.\ P.$, 3, 6, 12, ..., find by formula the 8th term and the sum of the first 7 terms. Check by direct calculation.

11. If the temperature (T°) of a nebula falls by 25% in any million-year period, and is now 10,000°, express T n million years hence. About when will $T = 1000$?

12. The widths of successive whirls in a spiral shell were 1.31, 1.12, .94, .80, .67, .57, .48, .41. Calculate a $G.\ P.$ having $a = 1.31$, $r = .8471$; and compare. (Four-place logarithms are handy for this: successively adding log .8471.)

13. In the $G.\,P.$, $100(1.05)^3$, $100(1.05)^4$, $\ldots$, $100(1.05)^{10}$, what are a, r, and n? Express the sum by formula.

14. Calculate the sum of the $G.\,P.$, $200(1.04)^5$, $200(1.04)^6$, $200(1.04)^7$ by using the formula; also by finding the separate terms.

15. If we make 5 annual deposits of $600 each, beginning now, and these draw interest at 3%, compounded annually, how much will there be to our credit 20 years hence? (Before trying to sum up, express the amount accumulated by the 1st deposit, 2d deposit, and last deposit. Note carefully when the last will be made.)

16. A present debt of $600 on a piano is to be paid in monthly installments of $30, plus accrued interest at 8%. How much will the first payment be, 1 month hence? The last? The total amount paid?

17. The same as Ex. 16 for a debt of $1200 on an automobile, to be paid off in monthly installments of $200 plus 9% interest.

18. A sewer assessment of $225 is payable $22.50 per year, beginning now, plus interest at 6%. How much will be paid in all?

19. The problem of dividing an octave into 12 equal half tones is mathematically the same as the problem of inserting 11 "geometric means" between 1 and 2 — *i.e.*, 1 and 2 are to be first and last terms of a $G.\,P.$ of 13 terms. Find the fourth and ninth terms.

20. Carry out in detail the derivation of formula (4), as given in § 333, in a special case, say $n = 5$, writing out all the terms. Then check by carrying out the division $(r^5 - 1) \div (r - 1)$ and getting the original $G.\,P.$

§ 334. Investment Problems: Accumulation.

In business it is often necessary to find how large a fund will be accumulated at a specified date by making certain deposits or payments at stated intervals. Or, conversely, how large the payments must be to yield a certain sum finally.

To solve such problems, simply express the amount accumulated on each payment at the end of the time, using the interest formula:

$$A = P\left(1 + \frac{r}{k}\right)^{kn}. \tag{5}$$

Then sum up. This is quickly done when the amounts form a $G.\,P.$

Ex. I. If we make 20 annual deposits of $100 beginning now, and are allowed 4% interest compounded annually, how much will there be to our credit 30 years hence?

1st deposit, with 30 yrs.' int. will amount to $100(1.04)^{30}$
2d deposit, with 29 yrs.' int. will amount to $100(1.04)^{29}$

. . . .

20th deposit, with 11 yrs.' int. will amount to $100(1.04)^{11}$

The 20th deposit, being made at the beginning of the 20th year, or 19 years hence, and running until 30 years from now, will be at interest for 11 years.

These amounts form a $G.\,P.$ For, starting from the bottom, if we multiply any of them by 1.04, we obtain the next above.

$$\therefore\ a = 100(1.04)^{11}, \quad r = 1.04, \quad n = 20.$$

The total amount to our credit 30 years hence will be the sum:

$$S = \frac{100(1.04)^{11}\,[(1.04)^{20} - 1]}{1.04 - 1},\ = 4584.20.* \tag{6}$$

Remarks. (I) In calculating S by logarithms, we must go from the logarithm of 1.04^{20} back to the number before subtracting the 1. The denominator, .04, divides easily.

(II) The amounts above also form a $G.\,P.$ starting from the top. But then the constant multiplier r is $\frac{1}{1.04}$, which is inconvenient.

(III) In the $G.\,P.$ formula n denotes the *number of items* to be added, *e.g.*, the number of *payments* — not some number of years. Also r denotes the *ratio for the G. P.* — not the interest rate.

Before trying to sum, always write out a few terms of the $G.\,P.$, to recognize a and r; and be especially careful as to the time that each payment draws interest. *The number of time-intervals elapsing between the first and last payments is one less than the number of payments.*

§ 335 *S.* **Special Tables.** The labor of calculating S in (6) is greatly reduced if interest tables are available. Sometimes one type of table is best, and sometimes another.

(I) *Table showing "Amount of 1 After n Years"*: $(1 + r)^n$. If, in (6), we multiply $(1.04)^{11}$ into the bracket, we get

$$S = 100\,[1.04^{31} - 1.04^{11}] \div .04.$$

The table shows in the 4% column opposite $n = 31$:†
$1.04^{31} = 3.3731\ 3341$; likewise, $1.04^{11} = 1.5394\ 5406$. Thus

$$S = 100\,[1.8336\ 7935] \div .04 = 4584.20.$$

* Five-place tables will not give this very accurately. A logarithm which is to be multiplied by a large exponent needs to be obtained with extra accuracy.

† For still larger tables, see F. C. Kent, *Tables of Compound Interest.*

(II) *Table showing "Amount of an Annuity."* Here the sum of the *G. P.* is shown: the total amount that would be accumulated *n* years hence, if we make *n* annual deposits of 1 unit each, *at the end of each year.* This table does not directly apply to *S* in (6); for there the number of years differed from the number of deposits.

We can, however, use the table as follows. If 11 more deposits were made — so as to complete the series and have the last deposit fall at the end of the last year — there would be in all an annuity of 31 deposits (whose period should be regarded as beginning a year ago, so that today's deposit falls at the end of the first year). The table shows the amount for the 31 deposits: 59.3283353; also, the amount for the supplied 11 deposits, 13.4863514. The difference, 45.8420, is the amount for the actual 20 deposits (of 1 unit each). As each deposit is $100, this gives again

$$S = 4584.20.$$

Even when special tables are used, it is generally best to write the formulas as in § 334 to serve as a guide. *E.g.*, when interest is at 4%, compounded semi-annually, 1.04 will not appear in the formula. Instead, higher powers of 1.02 will appear, which indicates that the 2% column would be needed in (I) above. The annuity table (II) will not fit if payments are annual and interest is compounded semi-annually.

EXERCISES

1. Express by formula as in (6) the sum of each following *G. P.*, and calculate it by logarithms or by a table of $(1 + r)^n$:

(a) 12 terms, $200(1.03)^{20}$, $200(1.03)^{19}$, ..., $200(1.03)^9$;

(b) 9 terms, $50(1.035)^{15}$, $50(1.035)^{14}$, ..., $50(1.035)^7$;

(c) 96 terms, $30(1.005)^{100}$, $30(1.005)^{99}$, ..., $30(1.005)^5$.

2. If we make 30 annual deposits beginning now, when will the last be made? How long will it be at interest if the date of final accumulation is 45 yrs. hence?

3. Like Ex. 2 for the following cases, beginning now:

(a) 40 semi-annual deposits, final date 23 yrs. hence;

(b) 60 quarterly deposits, final date 20 yrs. hence;

(c) 120 monthly deposits, final date 15 yrs. hence;

(d) 17 annual deposits, final date 16 yrs. hence.

4. Find the amount 35 yrs. hence at 4%, compounded annually, on 25 annual deposits of $500 each, beginning now. [Proceed as in Ex. I, §334.]

In Exs. 5–14, write the formulas involved; also calculate the required value by logarithms or special tables. Here, and in what follows, interest is to be compounded annually, unless otherwise specified.

5. Find the amount, at the time specified, on the following series of annual payments, each beginning now:

(a) 40 payments of $250 each, 3%, 50 yrs. hence;
(b) 9 payments of $50 each, $4\frac{1}{2}$%, 30 yrs. hence;
(c) 15 payments of $75 each, $3\frac{1}{2}$%, 40 yrs. hence.

6. When a boy was 1 year old, his father began depositing $50 a year in a bank which paid 4% interest. How much was available when the boy reached 18? (Include the final $50.)

7. What sum $P deposited annually 15 times, beginning now and drawing 6% interest, will amount to $10,000, 25 yrs. hence?

8. Like Ex. 7 for these cases:

(a) 20 deposits to produce $20,000, 30 yrs. hence, @ 5%;
(b) 8 deposits to yield $5000, 20 yrs. hence, @ 4%;
(c) 30 deposits to yield $2500, 29 yrs. hence, @ 3%.

9. Find the amount 30 yrs. hence of 50 semi-annual deposits of $200 each, beginning now and drawing 4% interest, compounded semi-annually.

10. (a), (b) Work Ex. 5 (a) and 7, respectively, if the payments are semi-annual, and the interest is compounded semi-annually, with the same final dates.

11. Find the amount 25 yrs. hence of 20 annual payments of $100 each, beginning now, with 5% interest compounded semi-annually.

12. How much should a firm set aside annually beginning one year hence and ending 20 years hence to replace a $100,000 building at the time of the last deposit if interest is at $3\frac{1}{2}$%?

13. A city has just issued bonds for $500,000 to construct an auditorium. What sum raised annually by taxation, beginning 1 year hence, and set aside at 6% interest, compounded semi-annually, will meet the face of the bonds when they mature 15 years hence?

14. In a certain society the annual dues are $5, payable in advance. A life membership costs $50. If a member lives slightly over 16 years after joining, which arrangement would have been the more economical, figuring interest at $5\frac{1}{2}$% on any dues paid in either way?

§ 336. Present Value. Money payable at some future date is not worth the same amount now. Its "present value" is only so much as would have to be invested now (at the prevailing rate of interest), to yield the specified payment at the time when due.

E.g., if money will now earn 6%, compounded annually, the present value of $1000 payable 10 years hence is only $558.40. For calculations show that $558.40 invested now at 6% would yield $1000 in 10 years.

A formula for the present value of any amount A, payable n years hence, is obtained immediately from the interest formula:

$$A = P \left(1 + \frac{r}{k} \right)^{kn}$$

$$\therefore \; P = \frac{A}{\left(1 + \dfrac{r}{k} \right)^{kn}}. \tag{7}$$

For the present value is simply the principal which will yield A. This "*P.V.*" formula is useful in many investment problems.

Observe that, the more remote the payment of a sum, the smaller its *P. V.* Thus the *P. V.* of $1000 after various intervals (n years) decreases approximately as in the adjacent table — if interest is at 6%, compounded annually.

n.	P.V.
0	1000
5	747
10	558
15	417
20	312

Special tables are available giving the *P. V.* of a single future payment, or of an annuity of n payments made at the end of each year; also, other useful items, explained in books on the mathematics of finance.

§ 337. Investment Problems: Disbursement. A very common problem in business is this: To determine how large a sum would have to be deposited now to provide for certain stipulated payments at specified future dates. Or, conversely, how much must be paid at stated intervals to use up a certain original sum, or pay off an original debt, in a certain length of time.

All such problems, where an original sum is to be *disbursed*, are conveniently solved by using the *P. V.* formula. For problems in which a final amount is to be *accumulated*, the interest formula is best.

Ex. I. How much must we deposit now to get back 20 annual installments of $600 each, beginning 15 years hence, if interest is at 4%, compounded semi-annually?

The last $600 is due 19 years after the first, or 34 years hence.

P. V. of first $600, due 15 years hence, is $\dfrac{600}{(1.02)^{30}}$.

P. V. of second $600, due 16 years hence, is $\dfrac{600}{(1.02)^{32}}$.

$\cdot \quad \cdot \quad \cdot \quad \cdot \quad \cdot \quad \cdot \quad \cdot \quad \cdot \quad \cdot \quad \cdot \quad \cdot \quad \cdot \quad \cdot \quad \cdot$

P. V. of last $600, due 34 years hence, is $\dfrac{600}{(1.02)^{68}}$.

The sum of these present values is the total amount we must deposit now to get back all 20 installments. In this $G. P.$,

$$a = \frac{600}{(1.02)^{68}}, \quad r = (1.02)^2, \quad n = 20.$$

$$\therefore \ S = \frac{600}{(1.02)^{68}} \ \frac{1.02^{40} - 1}{1.02^2 - 1}. \qquad \text{(Here } r^n = 1.02^{40}) \qquad (8)$$

By logarithms, or using tables of 1.02^n, $S = \$4667$, the total amount to be deposited now.

Setting aside the sum is called "capitalizing the annuity."

Ex. II. $2000 now due on a house is to be paid off with interest at 8% in 60 equal monthly installments beginning 3 months hence. How large must the installments be?

The last payment will be due 59 months after the first, or 62 months hence. The interest is figured monthly, making $k = 12$ and $r/k = .08/12 = .0066667$. If each payment is A, then

P. V. of 1st payment, due 3 months hence, is $\dfrac{A}{(1.0067)^3}$,

P. V. of last payment, due 62 months hence, is $\dfrac{A}{(1.0067)^{62}}$.

The sum is the total present value of all the payments and should equal the present debt, viz. $2000. Or since

$$a = \frac{A}{(1.0067)^{62}}, \quad r = 1.0067, \quad n = 60,$$

$$\therefore \ S = \frac{A}{(1.0067)^{62}} \ \frac{1.0067^{60} - 1}{.0066667} = 2000.$$

$$\therefore \ A = \frac{2000 \ (.0066667) \ (1.0067)^{62}}{1.0067^{60} - 1}. \qquad (9)$$

By logarithms, $A = 41.09$ — the monthly installment.

Observe that to round off the factor .0066667 as .0067 would produce a considerable error in A. But to round off 1.0066667 as 1.0067 does not.

Observe, too, that we have not credited against the *present debt* of $2000 the full amount ($$A$ each) of the coming payments, but only the *present values* of those payments. The total of the sixty installments is 60 A, or $2465.40; so that the debtor pays interest amounting in all to $465.40.

§ 338. *S*. Amortization Schedule. A rather tedious check on annuity calculations, often employed in business for reasons of bookkeeping, is to figure out a schedule of payments, showing how the debt or fund is *amortized*, or done away with. For Ex. II, § 337, the schedule would run as below.

```
Due now.................... $2000.00
Interest 3 mo. (compounded)...    40.26
Due at time of 1st payment ...  2040.26
        1st Payment...........    41.09
        ─────────────────────────────
            Balance.......... $1999.17
Int. 1 mo. @ ⅔% .............    13.33
Due at time of 2nd payment ...  2012.50
        2nd Payment..........    41.09
        ─────────────────────────────
            Balance.......... $1971.41
..........etc........................
```

The next month's interest would be ⅔% of 1971.41 (= 13.14); and so on. The 60th payment should leave a balance of nil.

Due to ignored fractions of a cent the final payment may have to be increased or decreased by a few cents.

EXERCISES

1. Find the present value of $25,000 payable 60 years hence, if interest is at 3%, compounded semi-annually.

2. Verify the second and the fourth values shown in the table of *P. V.*'s on page 448.

In Exs. 3–8 write the formulas, and find the required value by logarithms, or by special tables.

3. How much, deposited today, would provide for 10 annual payments of $600 beginning 15 years hence, if interest is at $3\frac{1}{2}$%?

4. The same as Ex. 3, for 30 annual installments of $600 beginning 10 yrs. hence, if interest is at 5%.

5. If we invest $5000 now at 6%, how much can we get back each year, 15 times, beginning 20 years hence?

6. A balance of $3000 now due on a house is to be paid off in 50 equal monthly installments beginning one month hence, including interest at 6%. Find the installment.

7. The same as Ex. 6, for a balance of $2500 to be paid in 40 monthly installments beginning 2 months hence, with interest at 8%.

8. How much deposited now would yield sixty quarterly install-ments of $200 each, beginning 15 years hence, if interest is at 4%, compounded quarterly?

9. Express by a formula the amount of the installment if:

(*a*) A balance of $600 on an auto is to be paid off in 10 monthly installments beginning one month hence, with interest at 1% per mo.

(*b*) A balance of $1500 on a house is to be paid off in 6 annual installments beginning one year hence, with interest at 9%.

(*c*) An Insurance Company which earns 4.8% is to make 80 quarterly payments beginning now, in lieu of paying $10,000 now.

10. (*a–c*) Calculate the values of the installments in Ex. 9 (*a–c*).

11. A debt of $1000 is to be paid in four annual installments of P each beginning 1 yr. hence, and including interest at 5%. Find P.

12. As a check, use the value of P in Ex. 11 to calculate an amortization schedule.

13. How expensive a house can be purchased by paying $500 down, plus 72 monthly installments of $50 each, if interest is at 6%, computed monthly?

14. A financing plan offers a loan of $600, at an interest charge of "5% deducted in advance," payable in 12 monthly installments of $50 each, beginning 1 mo. hence. The actual cost to the borrower is 9.6%, or .8% per mo. Verify this figure by using it to calculate an amortization schedule for the $570 which the borrower receives.

15. A bond calls for the payment of $1000 twenty years hence. If money is worth 5%, compounded semi-annually, what is the present value of the future payment?

§ **339** *S*. **Valuation of Bonds.** When a corporation or a government issues a bond, it promises to pay on a certain date the sum specified in the bond, and meanwhile to pay at stated intervals a certain amount of interest.

The *market value* of a bond, prior to the date of maturity, is usually different from the *face value* — due to the fact that the rate of interest prevailing in the money market rarely happens to be the same as the rate named in the bond.*

Normally, the market value of a bond is simply the sum of the present value of the principal payable at maturity, plus the present values of the several interest payments to be made on specified dates.

Ex. I. A $1000 municipal bond maturing 10 years hence

---

* The value is affected also by the nature of the security, privileges of con-version or tax-exemption, etc. — factors which cannot be discussed here.

carries interest at $4\frac{1}{4}\%$, payable semi-annually. Calculate its present value, assuming money now worth 5%, compounded semi-annually.

The municipality is to pay \$1000 ten years hence, and also pay \$21.25 interest every half-year, beginning 6 months hence, until maturity. The *P.V.*'s of the 20 interest payments, with money now at 5%, are

$$\frac{21.25}{(1.025)}, \quad \frac{21.25}{(1.025)^2}, \cdots \frac{21.25}{(1.025)^{20}},$$

or in all:

$$S = \frac{21.25}{(1.025)^{20}} \frac{(1.025^{20} - 1)}{.025} = 331.27. \tag{10}$$

The present value of the principal, \$1000, payable ten years hence, is

$$P = \frac{1000}{(1.025)^{20}} = 610.27. \tag{11}$$

The total $S + P = 941.54$, would be the present price of the bond, if "bought to yield 5%, convertible semi-annually."

N.B. The rate of interest named in the bond merely fixes the amount of the interest installments. All present values are determined by *the rate which money is now worth*; or, in other words, by the *yield rate*.

Observe, too, that the municipality will pay on the bond \$1000 + 20(21.25), or \$1425 in all, but the *P. V.* of these payments now is only \$941.54.

That the above bond will actually yield us $2\frac{1}{2}\%$ for every half-year if bought now for \$941.54 can be verified by calculating a schedule showing the gradual amortization of the purchase discount.

Due us now from bond.....	\$941.54
Interest $2\frac{1}{2}\%$, 6 mos............	23.54
Our investment 6 mos. hence....	\$965.08
1st coupon pays us	21.25
Balance due us	\$943.83
Interest $2\frac{1}{2}\%$..................	23.60
Our investment then	\$967.43
2nd coupon pays us........	21.25
Balance due us	\$946.18
And so on	

Each interest "coupon" pays less than the appropriate yield rate of $2\frac{1}{2}\%$. Thus we make a forced investment every 6 mos., until the total due us is \$1000, which is finally paid.

§ 340 S. Life Insurance.   One of the most important investment fields is that of life insurance and life annuities. The companies employ mathematical experts, called actuaries, who devise solutions for intricate problems relating to premiums, reserve funds, dividends, etc.   While we cannot go into detail as to actuarial mathematics, some important ideas will be explained in the next chapter.   (§ 368.)

EXERCISES

1. A $1000 bond maturing 30 yrs. hence carries $4\frac{1}{2}\%$ interest payable semi-annually. At what price should it be bought now to yield 5%, convertible semi-annually?

2. Express by formulas the present price of each following bond:

Description of Bond		Maturity	To Yield
(a) $1000	$5\frac{1}{2}\%$, semi.	15 yrs. hence	6%, semi.
(b) $500	$3\frac{1}{2}\%$, semi.	30 yrs. hence	3%, semi.
(c) $5000	5%, quart.	10 yrs. hence	4.8%, quart.
(d) $50	3%, semi.	20 yrs. hence	4%, semi.
(e) $10,000	4%, quart.	5 yrs. hence	3.6%, quart.

3. $(a–e)$ Calculate the values in Ex. 2 $(a–e)$.

4. A $1000 bond maturing 3 yrs. hence, with a $30 coupon each half-year, is bought to yield 5%, convertible semi-annually.   Find the price.   Check by calculating the schedule showing amortization of the premium.

5. A present debt of $3000 is to be amortized by 8 semi-annual payments of A each, including interest at 8% per annum.   Find A. Check by calculating the amortization schedule.

§ 341 S. Infinite Series.   It is sometimes necessary to deal with a $G.\ P.$ or other series of terms which runs on indefinitely — never ending.   Such an "infinite series" cannot in any literal sense be said to have a sum.   But we may need to find the sum of any number of terms, and see what happens as more and more terms are added on.

To illustrate, consider the simple series

$$1, \quad - x, \quad + x^2, \quad - x^3, \quad + x^4, \ldots \text{(unending)}.$$

The sum of the first n terms (a $G.\ P$, having $a = 1$, $r = - x$) is

$$S_n = \frac{1 \cdot [(- x)^n - 1]}{(- x) - 1} = \frac{1}{1 + x} [1 \pm x^n].$$

If x is numerically less than 1, then $x^n \to 0$ as $n \to \infty$. And the limit of S_n is simply $1/(1 + x)$.

This *limit* is called the *sum of the series to infinity*. We write simply

$$\frac{1}{1 + x} = 1 - x + x^2 - x^3 + \cdots. \qquad (12)$$

We do not mean by this that the fraction equals the sum of several terms, but that it is the *limit* approached by the sum as more and more terms are taken. The idea is the same as when we write

$$\tfrac{1}{9} = .1111 \cdots = \tfrac{1}{10} + \tfrac{1}{100} + \tfrac{1}{1000} + \tfrac{1}{10000} + \cdots.$$

The fact that the fraction is the limit approached, is also expressed by saying that the series "converges toward the value of the fraction." Remember, however, that it does so in the example above only when x is numerically less than 1.

§ 342 *S*. **An Application.** In more advanced courses it is proved legitimate to differentiate or integrate an infinite power series term by term: the resulting series will equal the derivative or integral of the function represented by the original series. Let us integrate both sides of (12) above:

$$\log (1 + x) = x - \frac{x^2}{2} + \frac{x^3}{3} - \frac{x^4}{4} \cdots + C. \qquad (13)$$

When $x = 0$, this gives $\log 1 = C$. $\therefore$ $C = 0$.

This equation is valid if x is numerically less than 1. *E.g.*, letting $x = .1$,

$$\log 1.1 = .1 - \frac{.01}{2} + \frac{.001}{3} \cdots = .1 - .005 + .0003 \cdots,$$

$\therefore$ $\log 1.1 = .0953$, approx. (Base e.)

In this way we can calculate the logarithms of numbers near 1. The logarithms of larger numbers are found by a combination of series.

Remark. In obtaining the differentiation formula for $\log u$ (§ 183) — used above in integrating (12) — we employed tables of logarithms of numbers near 1. But that formula can be obtained otherwise. Hence (13) could have been used to calculate the tables originally.

§ 343 *S*. **Maclaurin Series.** Equation (13) above expresses the function $\log (1 + x)$ as the "sum" of an infinite series of powers of x. This suggests that perhaps many other functions, such as sin x, e^x, etc., might be similarly expressed.

This is indeed the case; and it is easy to determine precisely what the series should be for any ordinary function. An example will make the process clear.

Ex. I.   Assuming that cos x equals *some* series of the form

$$\cos x = A + Bx + Cx^2 + Dx^3 + Ex^4 + \cdots, \qquad (14)$$

find what the coefficients A, B, C, etc., must be.

The method is simply to differentiate several times, and then substitute $x = 0$ in each of the resulting equations — and in the original equation.

Substituting $x = 0$ in (14) gives at once cos $0 = A$, or $A = 1$.

Differentiating (14) repeatedly:	Putting $x = 0$:
$-\sin x = B + 2\,Cx + 3\,Dx^2 + 4\,Ex^3 + \cdots$	$\therefore\ -\sin 0 = B,\quad = \quad 0$
$-\cos x = \quad 2\,C + 6\,Dx + 12\,Ex^2 + \cdots$	$\therefore\ -\cos 0 = 2\,C,\quad = -1$
$+\sin x = \qquad\quad 6\,D + 24\,Ex + \cdots$	$\therefore\ \sin 0 = 6\,D,\quad = \quad 0$
$+\cos x = \qquad\qquad\quad 24\,E + \cdots$	$\therefore\ \cos 0 = 24\,E, = \quad 1$

Continuing thus we have $A = 1$, $B = 0$, $C = -\frac{1}{2}$, $D = 0$, $E = \frac{1}{24}$, etc. Substituting these values in (14), that series becomes

$$\cos x = 1 + 0 \cdot x - \tfrac{1}{2}\,x^2 + 0 \cdot x^3 + \tfrac{1}{24}\,x^4 \cdots,$$

or simply

$$\cos x = 1 - \frac{x^2}{2} + \frac{x^4}{24} \cdots. \qquad (15)$$

That is, if cos x is the "sum" of any series of the form (14), this must be the series. It can also be proved that this series (15) does actually approach cos x as its limiting value, no matter how large x may be.

Remarks.   (I) In (15) x is necessarily the number of *radians* in the angle.   (Why so?)

(II) The possibility of expanding many functions into series of the form (14) was discovered by C. Maclaurin, a Scotchman, about 1740; and series of this type are called Maclaurin series. These are, however, only a special case of a more general type of power series expansion discovered by B. Taylor, an Englishman, about 1715.

(III) Maclaurin series are useful not only in calculating values of a function (§§ 342, 345), but also in performing integrations otherwise difficult or impossible. For instance, from (15) we could find:

$$\int \frac{1 - \cos x}{x}\, dx = \int \left(\frac{x}{2} - \frac{x^3}{24} \cdots \right) dx = \frac{x^2}{4} - \frac{x^4}{96} \cdots, \qquad (16)$$

an integral not otherwise obtainable by elementary methods.

§ 344. Factorial Notation. If n is a positive integer, the product of the integers from 1 up to n inclusive is called "*factorial n*," and is denoted by $n!$.

Thus $5! = 1 \cdot 2 \cdot 3 \cdot 4 \cdot 5 = 120$. And so on.

By means of this notation the series for $\cos x$ in (15) above can be written more conveniently. Thus the denominator 24, which arose as $4 \cdot 3 \cdot 2 \cdot 1$ in the repeated differentiations, is simply $4!$. Likewise the denominator 2 may be written $2!$, and series (15) becomes

$$\cos x = 1 - \frac{x^2}{2!} + \frac{x^4}{4!} \cdots. \qquad (17)$$

According to this beginning, how should the series continue? Can you tell from the derivation of (15) whether your inference is correct?

EXERCISES

1. Find Maclaurin's series for e^x as far as x^4. By inspection write three more terms. What would be the term containing x^{10}? x^n?

2. Substitute $x = 1$ in the series of Ex. 1, viz.

$$e^x = 1 + x + \frac{x^2}{2!} + \frac{x^3}{3!} + \frac{x^4}{4!} + \cdots; \qquad (18)$$

and thus calculate e approximately. (The calculation can quickly be carried to many decimals; for, dividing the third term by 3 gives the fourth, dividing this by 4 gives the fifth, and so on.)

3. Approximate $\displaystyle\int \frac{e^x - 1}{x}\, dx$ as far as x^4.

4. Differentiate the series for e^x and note the result carefully.

5. What does the series for e^x become if we replace x throughout by $-x^2$? Use the resulting series to find $\displaystyle\int_0^{.2} e^{-x^2}\, dx$ to 5 decimals.

6. Find $\displaystyle\int_0^{.1} e^x\, dx$ in two ways and compare.

7. Find Maclaurin's series for $\sin x$, as far as x^5. Write four more terms by inspection.

8. Obtain a series for $\cos x$, by differentiating the series for $\sin x$ in Ex. 7, viz.

$$\sin x = x - \frac{x^3}{3!} + \frac{x^5}{5!} - \cdots; \tag{19}$$

and compare (17) above.

9. Derive the cosine series also by integrating the sine series. Note the constant of integration.

10. Calculate $\sin .2^{(r)}$ and compare the tables.

11. Find $\sin 1°$ by substituting in (19) the radian equivalent of $1°$.

12. Similarly find $\cos 1°$.

13. (a) Find $\displaystyle\int_0^{.2} \frac{\sin x}{x}\, dx.$ (b) Find $\displaystyle\int_0^{\frac{1}{2}} \frac{1 - \cos x}{x^2}\, dx.$

14. Expand $(a + x)^5$ into a Maclaurin series as far as possible (a is constant.)

15. Expand $(a + x)^n$ as far as x^4.

§ 345 S. Calculation of Trigonometric Tables.

The sine and cosine of $1°$ are easily calculated as in Ex. 11–12 above. The Addition Formulas, § 304, then give the sine and cosine for $(1° + 1°)$ or $2°$; then for $3°$, $4°$, etc., to $45°$. Beyond $45°$ we need not go. (Why not?) Tangents can be found from the sines and cosines. (How?)

The Half-Angle Formulas, § 307, can be used for certain fractions of $1°$. Or $\sin 1'$ and $\cos 1'$ can be calculated from the series (19) and (17) by making a fresh start.

Still other methods were used in calculating the tables originally.

§ 346. Binomial Theorem.

The standard formula for expanding $(a + u)^n$ is obtainable by Maclaurin's method:

$$
\begin{array}{l|l}
(a+u)^n = A+Bu+Cu^2+Du^3+Eu^4\cdots & A=a^n \\
n(a+u)^{n-1} = B+2\,Cu+3\,Du^2+4\,Eu^3\cdots & B=na^{n-1} \\
n(n-1)\,(a+u)^{n-2} = 2\,C+6\,Du+12\,Eu^2\cdots\cdots & C = \dfrac{n(n-1)}{2\,!}\,a^{n-2}
\end{array}
$$

$$\cdots \cdots \cdots \cdots \cdots \cdots \cdots \cdots \cdots$$

$$\therefore \; (a + u)^n = a^n + na^{n-1}\,u + \frac{n(n-1)}{1\cdot 2}\,a^{n-2}u^2$$

$$+ \frac{n(n-1)\,(n-2)}{1\cdot 2\cdot 3}\,a^{n-3}u^3 + \cdots \tag{20}$$

This formula is called the *Binomial Theorem*. Notice how the terms run. The exponent of a is n at first and decreases by 1 at each step. The exponent of u increases simultaneously, keeping the sum of the two exponents always equal to n. In the coefficients, notice the factorial denominators; and also that each new factor in the numerator is less by 1 than the preceding. (Judging by the fourth term, what would the sixth be?)

From these facts we can see that the rth term will involve $(r-1)$! in the denominator, u^{r-1}, $a^{n-(r-1)}$, and factors from n down to $(n-\overline{r-2})$ in the numerator:

$$r\text{th term} = \frac{n(n-1)\,(n-2)\,\cdots\,(n-r+2)}{(r-1)\,!}\,a^{n-r+1}\,u^{r-1}. \quad (21)$$

If n is an integer, the series (20) will end presently. (When?)

If n is a fraction the series never ends; but, as is proved in higher algebra, the series converges, and the sum of r terms approaches the value of $(a+u)^n$, *provided $u < a$ numerically.*

Certain facts as to the Binomial Theorem were pointed out in obtaining the differentiation formula for x^n. (§ 57.) We have now gone farther, and have used that differentiation formula to get fuller information about the Binomial Theorem. An independent and purely algebraic proof of this theorem can also be given.

The Binomial Theorem has many uses, both in making numerical calculations and in integrating radical forms which will yield to no other treatment.

Ex. I. Find $\int_0^{.2} \sqrt{1-x^3}\,dx.$

The radical is a case of $(a+u)^n$, where $a=1$, $u=-x^3$, $n=\frac{1}{2}$. Clearly every power of "a" equals 1 here and need not be written. Thus:

$$(1-x^3)^{\frac{1}{2}} = 1 + \tfrac{1}{2}\,(-x^3)^1 + \frac{\tfrac{1}{2}\,(-\tfrac{1}{2})}{2\,!}\,(-x^3)^2$$

$$+ \frac{\tfrac{1}{2}\,(-\tfrac{1}{2})\,(-\tfrac{3}{2})}{3\,!}\,(-x^3)^3 + \cdots$$

$$= 1 - \tfrac{1}{2}\,x^3 - \tfrac{1}{8}\,x^6 - \tfrac{1}{16}\,x^9 - \cdots.$$

$$\therefore \int_0^{.2} \sqrt{1-x^3}\,dx = \left[\,x - \tfrac{1}{8}\,x^4 - \tfrac{1}{56}\,x^7 - \tfrac{1}{160}\,x^{10} - \cdots\,\right]_0^{.2}$$

$$= .2 - \tfrac{1}{8}\,(.0016) - \cdots = .1998.$$

This definite integral could be approximated by Simpson's Rule; but here we have found the indefinite integral also, valid if $x < 1$.

EXERCISES

1. Write the following expansions, and simplify the terms:

(a) $(a + x)^{12}$, as far as x^5, (b) $(a - x)^4$, complete,

(c) $(1 + x^4)^{10}$, as far as x^{12}, (d) $(2 + x^2)^5$, complete,

(e) $(1 - x^3)^{\frac{1}{3}}$, as far as x^9, (f) $(1 - x^2)^{-\frac{1}{2}}$, to x^4,

(g) $(1 - x)^{-1}$, as far as x^5, (h) $(5 + x^4)^{-2}$, to x^{12}.

2. Find $1/(1 - x)$ by division as far as x^5 and compare Ex. 1 (g). From this series find by integration a series for $\log (1 - x)$.

3. From the series in Ex. 2 for $\log (1 - x)$, viz.

$$\log (1 - x) = -x - \frac{x^2}{2} - \frac{x^3}{3} - \frac{x^4}{4} - \cdots, \qquad (22)$$

calculate:

(a) $\log .92$, (b) $\int_0^{.2} \log (1 - x)\, dx.$

4. Find the integral in Ex. 3 by Simpson's Rule.

5. Find approximately by expanding to four terms:

(a) $\int_0^{.4} \sqrt{1 + x^3}\, dx,$ (b) $\int_0^{.4} dx / \sqrt{1 - x^4}.$

6. (a)–(b) Find by Simpson's Rule the integrals in Ex. 5 (a)–(b).

7. Find $\sqrt[3]{1.06}$ approximately by regarding this as $(1 + .06)^{\frac{1}{3}}$ and expanding to four terms.

8. Like Ex. 7 for $\sqrt{.988}$ $\left[= (1 - .012)^{\frac{1}{2}} \right].$

9. Approximate by the Binomial Theorem:

(a) $\sqrt[3]{997}$, (b) $\sqrt{65}$, (c) $\sqrt[4]{630}$, (d) $\sqrt{101}$.

10. Let the series (18), p. 456, for imaginary values of x, *define* what shall be understood by an imaginary power of e. Substitute $x = \sqrt{-1}\, \theta$, and simplify. Collect separately the terms free from $\sqrt{-1}$ and those involving it. By comparing (17) and (19), show that

$$e^{\sqrt{-1}\theta} = \cos \theta + \sqrt{-1} \sin \theta. \qquad (23)$$

Here θ is the number of *radians* in the angle.

11. In (23) let $\theta = \pi$, 3π, or 5π; and reduce. Thus show that $\log (-1)$ can be regarded as $\pi\sqrt{-1}$, or $3\pi\sqrt{-1}$, etc.

12. By substituting $\theta = 2\pi$, etc., in (23), show that the number 1 may be regarded as having infinitely many imaginary logarithms, besides its single real logarithm.*

---

* The theory of imaginary logarithms, developed fully in higher courses, is basic for advanced studies in electrical engineering, and in some other fields.

13. Similarly substitute each following value for θ in (23) and interpret the result in terms of logarithms:

(a) $\theta = \pi/2$,   (b) $\theta = \pi/3$,   (c) $\theta = \pi/4$.

§ 347 S. Polynomial Laws. A quantity y sometimes varies according to some polynomial formula of the type

$$y = A + Bx + Cx^2 + \cdots. \tag{24}$$

Whenever this is the case, it is easy to discover the fact from a given table of values, and to find the proper values for the coefficients A, B, C, etc.

Suppose that the values of x in the table run at constant intervals, $\Delta x = k$. (If they do not, we can plot a graph and read off values which do.*)

Form the differences (Δy) between successive y values. If these vary, form *their* successive differences, and denote these "second-order differences" by $\Delta^2 y$, read "delta second y." If these also vary, form *their* differences ($\Delta^3 y$). And so on.

If the first-order differences (Δy) are constant, y increases at a constant rate, and the tabulated values satisfy a first-degree formula. More generally:

THEOREM. *If the differences ($\Delta^n y$) of order n are constant, the tabulated values of x and y satisfy a formula of degree n. And conversely.*

This theorem makes it possible to discover any Polynomial Law.

Ex. I. Discover the law for the following table:

	x	7	17	27	37	47	57
	y	60	136	192	228	244	240
1st Diffs.,	Δy		76	56	36	16	-4
2d Diffs.,	$\Delta^2 y$			-20	-20	-20	-20

These second-order differences being constant ($= -20$), the required formula is of the second degree:

$$y = A + Bx + Cx^2.$$

To find A, B, C, we substitute values of x and y from the table:

$$240 = A + 57\,B + 3249\,C$$
$$192 = A + 27\,B + 729\,C$$
$$60 = A + 7\,B + 49\,C$$

---

* More technical methods of handling irregular intervals are given in texts on finite differences or interpolation — as is also a proof of the Theorem stated here. Cf. Whittaker and Robinson, *The Calculus of Observations*, pp. 20–27.

Subtracting the third equation from each of the others gives two equations free from A. Solving these for B and C, and substituting back to get A, we obtain finally $A = -5.1$, $B = 10$, $C = -.1$. Hence the required formula is

$$y = -5.1 + 10\,x - .1\,x^2.$$

This is satisfied by all the tabulated values, as direct substitution would show.

Remark. If the differences never become exactly constant, but are very nearly so at some stage, we may obtain anyhow an approximate formula — a sort of Maclaurin series for the function. (See § 348.)

EXERCISES

1. From the formula $y = x^2 - 15\,x + 5$ calculate a table of values of y when $x = 0$, 10, 20, 30, 40, and 50. Verify that the second differences $\Delta^2 y$ are constant in your table.

2. Proceed as in Ex. 1 with the formula $y = .1x^3 + 3x + 20$, and show that your third differences $\Delta^3 y$ are constant.

3. Discover a formula satisfied by the values in each of the following tables:

(a)

x	0	2	4	6	8	10
y	1	17	45	85	137	201

(b)

x	0	5	10	15	20	25
y	-12	-2	28	78	147	237

(c)

x	10	20	30	40	50	60
y	-2	0	6	16	30	48

(d)

x	0	2	4	6	8	10
y	6	7	6	-3	-26	-69

(e)

x	1	2	3	4	5	6
y	3.10	3.76	4.15	3.97	2.92	0.70

4. The same as Ex. 3 for the following tables. (Observe that the intervals Δx are unequal; and plot as suggested in § 347.)

(a)

x	0	24	62	110	218	290
y	125	113	94	70	16	-20

(b)

x	0	5	8	13	16	20
y	0	75	96	91	64	0

5. The speed of a moving object (v ft./min.) varied with the time elapsed (t min.) as in the following table. Discover the formula, and calculate the distance traveled from $t = 0$ to $t = 10$; also the acceleration at $t = 5$.

t	0	2	4	6	8	10	12
v	0	40	128	216	256	200	0

6. By inspection of Table I below show that y varies as the square of $(x - 3)$ and so obtain the formula. Check by the polynomial method.

[7.] Plot the reciprocals of the values of x, y in Table II, and discover the formula.

(I)

x	3	5	7	9	11
y	0	8	32	72	128

(II)

x	.1	.2	.3	$-.4$	$-.6$
y	.1	.25	.5	$-.2$	$-.25$

§ 348 S. Approximate Formulas. Often the values (x, y) in a table almost meet the test for a certain type of formula, but not exactly. The discrepancies may be due to errors in the table. Or, the table may be accurate, but may fit some more involved law, which the tested formula approximates closely. In any event, we ask what values the constants in the formula should have, in order to "fit the table as well as possible."

A commonly used criterion for "goodness of fit," based on considerations explained in the next chapter, is this: The best values of the constants are those for which *the sum of the squares of the errors* in the values of the function y is a *minimum*. Based on this idea we have the following method of "curve fitting."

§ 349 S. Method of Least Squares. Assuming a particular type of formula, we express the value of y for each tabulated x, subtract the tabulated y to obtain the error E, and then proceed to minimize the sum of the squares of all the E's.

Ex. I. The force (y lb.) required to stretch a wire x thousandths of an inch varied as in the adjacent table. Theoretically these values should satisfy an equation of the form

x	y
3	20
5	33
11	73

$$y = mx \qquad (25)$$

whose graph is a straight line through $(0, 0)$. But there are discrepancies due to errors of measurement. Find the value of m which gives the best fit.

When $\quad x = 3, \qquad 5, \qquad 11;$
the formula gives: $\quad y = 3\,m, \qquad 5\,m, \qquad 11\,m.$

The discrepancies or errors in the values of y are therefore:

$$E = 3\,m - 20, \qquad 5\,m - 33, \qquad 11\,m - 73.$$

The best value of m minimizes the sum of the squares,

$$S = (3\,m - 20)^2 + (5\,m - 33)^2 + (11\,m - 73)^2.$$

Differentiating and equating dS/dm to zero gives:

$$\frac{dS}{dm} = 2\,(3\,m - 20)\,(3) + 2\,(5\,m - 33)\,(5) + 2\,(11\,m - 73)\,(11) = 0.$$

$$\therefore\ 155\,m = 1028, \qquad m = 6.632.$$

And the most probable values of y for $x = 3, 5, 11$, are by (25):

$$y = 3\,m = 19.90, \qquad y = 5\,m = 33.16, \qquad y = 11\,m = 72.95.$$

§ 350 S. **Several Coefficients.** In trying to find the most probable "Polynomial Law" (of some specified degree) for a given table, say

$$y = a + bx + cx^2 + \cdots kx^n, \tag{26}$$

the sum of the squares of the errors, S, is a function of several unknown coefficients, a, b, etc.   For a minimum of S we set each of its partial derivatives equal to zero (§ 326):

$$\frac{\partial S}{\partial a} = 0, \qquad \frac{\partial S}{\partial b} = 0, \text{ etc.}$$

x	y
10	1.6
20	4.2
30	6.6

Ex. I. Find the most probable linear formula $y = a + bx$ for the adjacent table.

For each pair of tabulated values, $a + bx$ should equal y. Any difference is an error.   That is, the errors here are:

$$a + 10\,b - 1.6, \qquad a + 20\,b - 4.2, \text{ etc.}$$

The sum of the squares of the errors is, then,

$$S = (a + 10\,b - 1.6)^2 + (a + 20\,b - 4.2)^2 + (a + 30\,b - 6.6)^2.$$

$$\frac{\partial S}{\partial a} = 2\,(a + 10\,b - 1.6) + 2\,(a + 20\,b - 4.2) + 2\,(a + 30\,b - 6.6).$$

$$\frac{\partial S}{\partial b} = 20\,(a + 10\,b - 1.6) + 40\,(a + 20\,b - 4.2) + 60\,(a + 30\,b - 6.6).$$

Equating these to zero, canceling 2 or 20, and collecting:

$$3\,a + 60\,b - 12.4 = 0$$
$$6\,a + 140\,b - 29.8 = 0.$$

Solving these equations gives $a = -\frac{13}{15}$, $b = \frac{1}{4}$.
Hence the most probable law is

$$y = -\tfrac{13}{15} + \tfrac{1}{4}\,x.$$

Remark.   In applying the method of least squares to the *C.I.L.*, Power Law, etc., it is customary first to simplify the equation by taking logarithms, and then minimizing the sum of the squares of the errors in log y. This involves a little different assumption as to the "best fit" for the given table; but it saves much labor, and gives very similar results.

EXERCISES

1. Find the value of m in the formula $y = mx$ which best fits each following table:

(a)
x	10	20	50
y	4	8	21

,

(b)
x	1	3	5
y	4.5	13.4	22.8

.

2. The following elongations of a rod should, if strictly accurate, vary with the stretching force according to the formula $e = kF$.

F	5000	10000	15000
e	.161	.324	.481

(a) Find the most probable value of k.

(b) Using your value of k, calculate e from the formula when $F = 5000$, etc., and compare the table.

3. Find the most probable values for a and b in the formula $y = ax + b$ for each of these tables:

(a)
x	20	30	40
y	5.1	6.9	9.1

,

(b)
x	2	5	10
y	-0.41	2.01	6.00

.

4. The weight of common salt which dissolves in 100 gm. of water at various temperatures is shown in the following table. Find the most probable linear formula, $W = aT + b$.

T	0	10	30	50	100
W	35.6	35.7	36.0	36.7	39.1

5. Find the formula $y = a + bx + cx^2$ which best fits the table:

x	0	1	3	5
y	0	2.4	4.8	6.1

6. Find the most probable formula $y = a \sin .1 \pi x$ for the table in Ex. 5.

7. Find the most probable *C.I.L.* for the adjacent table:

x	1	2	5
y	14	18	45

§ 351. Discovery of Laws Summarized.

Let us now list the methods we have used to discover formulas for given tables.

Plotting tests are used in four cases (§§ 30, 180, 282):

I *Linear Law*, $y = ax + b$: Ordinary graph straight;

II *Power Law*, $y = kx^n$: Logarithmic graph straight;

III *C.I.L.*, $y = Pe^{rx}$: Semi-logarithmic graph straight;

IV *Harmonic Oscillations*, such as $y = a \sin kt$ or $y = a \cos kt$.

In IV the graph is seen to resemble a sine or cosine curve; the constants a and k are fitted by inspection, and the formula is checked against the table.

Successive differences are used (§ 347) to test for

V *Polynomial Laws*, $y = A_0 + A_1 x \cdots + A_n x^n$: $\Delta^{(n)} y$ constant.

Another graphical test, illustrated in Ex. 7, p. 462, plots the reciprocals of x and y to test for laws of the form

VI $xy + Ax + By = 0$: linear in $\dfrac{1}{x}$ and $\dfrac{1}{y}$.

If, in VI, there is also a constant term, we can take any point (x_1, y_1) in the table as a new origin, and form a new table by subtracting x_1 from every x and y_1 from every y. Then the form VI, whose locus passes through $(0, 0)$, holds for the new table.

To fit an approximate formula to a table when some of these tests are nearly fulfilled, we use the method of Least Squares. Numerous other methods are used in discovering formulas, both exact and approximate.* Among these is the use of an harmonic analyzer (§ 284) to approximate a function by a series of sines and cosines.

§ 352. Summary of Chapter XIII. Formulas relating to *A.P.*'s and *G.P.*'s can be used to solve problems on investments for which no tables would serve. Also they may be used to calculate further tables.

Many functions can be expressed as the "sum" of an infinite series of powers of x, *i.e.*, a Maclaurin series. By the "sum" of such a series in general is meant the *limit* approached by the sum of n terms as $n \to \infty$. If no limit is approached, we cannot speak of the "sum" of the series.

As noted in § 284, a function can also be expressed as the "sum" of an infinite Fourier series of sines and cosines.

* See T. R. Running, *Empirical Formulas.*

Various useful approximations are obtained by taking the first few terms of a series. Logarithmic and trigonometric tables may be so calculated. Many indefinite integrals can be obtained as infinite series, and in no simpler form.

Functions of *imaginary* variables are often defined by means of series which are valid when the variables are real. In this way we can give meaning to imaginary logarithms, and can obtain logarithms for negative numbers. (Cf. Ex. 10–13, pp. 459–60.)

Methods have been found for discovering further types of empirical formulas to fit a given table — including Polynomial Laws.

We shall next consider some further topics of algebra, closely related to series and the binomial theorem, which are basic in the scientific study of statistics.

EXERCISES

1. Express by a formula the amount accumulated 25 yrs. hence by 40 semi-annual deposits of $200 each, beginning now and drawing interest at 4%, compounded semi-annually. Calculate this amount, by logarithms or a special table.

2. Express by a formula the answer to each question:

(a) What sum set aside annually, 12 times, beginning 1 year hence, would provide a sinking fund amounting to $30,000 forty years hence, if interest is at 6%, compounded quarterly?

(b) What sum set aside now would provide an accident indemnity of $600 a year for 25 years, beginning 1 year hence, if interest is at 5%?

(c) How much should an insurance company pay annually for 15 years, beginning now, in lieu of paying $20,000 now, if it earns $4\frac{1}{2}\%$?

(d) What is the present value of a $1000 bond bearing $3\frac{1}{2}\%$ interest payable semi-annually, and maturing 25 years hence, if money is now worth 4%, compounded semi-annually?

3. (a–d) Calculate each answer in Ex. 2 (a–d).

4. Approximate $\sqrt[3]{1.008}$ by the Binomial Theorem.

5. As in Ex. 4 find an approximate formula for $\sqrt[n]{1 \pm x}$ when x is very small. Use your formula to find $\sqrt{1.0006}$, $\sqrt[4]{1.0012}$, $\sqrt[5]{.9995}$.

6. In finding the ratio of the lever arms of a fine balance, it was necessary to approximate $\sqrt{1.000\ 000\ 023}$. Do this by inspection.

7. Calculate in two ways: $\displaystyle\int_0^{.2} \sqrt{1 + x^4}\, dx.$

8. A circle used in structural engineering has the equation $x^2 + (y + R - h)^2 = R^2$. To calculate y accurately for a small x, the equation was solved for y and the binomial theorem was then used. Show thus that $y = h - \dfrac{x^2}{2\,R}\left(1 + \dfrac{x^2}{4\,R^2} + \cdots\right)$.

9. In Ex. 8 take $h = .25$, $x = 10$, $R = 5000$, and find y both from the original and from the modified equation.

10. Find Maclaurin's series for $\log(1 + x)$ as far as x^4. Use it to calculate $\log 1.2$, and compare the table, p. 536.

11. Discover a formula satisfied by the values in this table:

x	0	2	4	6	8	10	12	14
A	0	4.8	16	28.8	38.4	40	28.8	0

12. In Ex. 11, A sq. cm. is the area of a horizontal cross-section of a solid x cm. above the lowest point. Calculate the volume.

13. A debt of $900 is to be paid off, beginning now, by paying $100 monthly on the principal, plus interest at 6%. How much will be paid in all?

14. A loan of $2,500,000 is made today to finance the construction of an office building. What sum set aside from the rentals, monthly, 300 times, beginning 8 months hence, will just amortize the debt including interest at 6% per annum due monthly?

15. A $1000 bond maturing 20 yrs. hence with a $30 coupon each half-year, is bought for $1070. Approximately what annual yield does the purchaser realize, convertible semi-annually? (Hint: We first make a rough estimate by noting that the bond would yield 6% if bought at par; but that we suffer a reduction of $70 in principal — which amounts to reducing the interest during the 20 yrs. Cf. Ex. 11, p. 358.)

[16.] How many different "chords" could be sounded by striking three of the four keys, A, C, E, G? Write out the combinations.

[17.] How many code "words" could be spelled by using any three of the four letters A, C, E, G?

CHAPTER XIV

COMBINATIONS, PROBABILITY, AND STATISTICAL METHOD

§ 353. The Problem of Arrangements. It is sometimes useful to know in how many different orders a given set of objects can be arranged — using all or a part of the set at a time. Such questions may be reasoned out as follows:

EXAMPLE. Three flags are to be placed in a vertical row as a signal. If we have seven different flags, how many signals are possible?

The top place can be filled by any one of the seven flags — that is, in 7 ways. The middle place can then be filled in 6 ways; and the lowest place in 5 ways. For *each* way of filling the first place, there are 6 ways of filling the second: hence 7×6 ways of filling the first two places. Similarly there are $7 \times 6 \times 5$ ways of filling the three places. *I.e.,* there are $7 \times 6 \times 5$ possible signals.

§ 354. Formula. The foregoing example shows that the number of possible orders of 7 objects taken 3 at a time is $7 \times 6 \times 5$. Can you see from this how many orders are possible for 9 objects taken 4 at a time? For 13 objects taken 6 at a time?

An order, or arrangement in sequence, is also called a "permutation." The number of permutations of n objects taken r at a time is denoted by $P_{n,\,r}$. Thus the result in the example above may be written

$$P_{7,\,3} = 7 \times 6 \times 5. \qquad \text{(3 factors, from 7 down.)}$$

This suggests that $P_{n,\,r}$ is the product of r factors, viz.

$$P_{n,\,r} = n\,(n-1)\,(n-2) \cdots (n-r+1). \qquad (1)$$

To prove this, simply reason as in the example above.

Ex. I. How many line-ups are possible for a basketball team of five to be selected at random from 12 men?

Ans. $P_{12,\,5} = 12 \cdot 11 \cdot 10 \cdot 9 \cdot 8 = 95\,040.$

If all n objects are used every time, $r = n$; and hence

$$P_{n,\,n} = n\,(n-1)\,(n-2)\,\cdots 1.$$

Or, in factorial notation (§ 344), we may write

$$P_{n,\,n} = n\,!. \tag{2}$$

§ 355 S. Restricted Arrangements. Whenever an arrangement is to be made, subject to some restriction, it is important to consider the restricted groups first.

Ex. I. On each side of a car are 30 seats. In how many ways can 60 persons be seated, 20 of whom insist upon sitting on the sunny side?

We first take 20 of the 30 sunny seats and assign them to the 20 restricted persons in some order. This can be done in $P_{30,\,20}\,[=30\cdot29\cdot28\cdots11]$ ways. The other 40 persons may sit anywhere in the remaining 40 seats, in $P_{40,\,40}\,[=40\,!]$ ways.

For *each* seating of the 20 persons, there are 40 ! seatings of the company as a whole. Hence, in all

$$P_{30,\,20} \times P_{40,\,40} \qquad \text{or} \qquad 40\,!\,[30\cdot29\cdot28\cdots11]$$

is the total number of arrangements possible.

This value is easily calculated by logarithms. (Some tables give on the first page the logarithms of the integers from 1 to 100, including the characteristics. The needed logarithms can be added without copying them off.)

§ 356 S. Circular Orders. In seating n persons around a circular table, we may be interested only in their order relative to one another, and not in their absolute positions with respect to the table. The number of such circular orders is $(n-1)\,!.$

Proof: For any one circular order there are n possible shifts around the table. Hence the number of circular orders is one-nth of the number of possible arrangements in the n seats; or, $n\,! \div n$, which equals $(n-1)\,!.$

§ 357 S. Some Objects Alike. The number of distinguishable arrangements of n objects, p of which are alike of one kind, q of another, and r of another is

$$P_{n(p,\,q,\,r)} = \frac{n\,!}{p\,!\;q\,!\;r\,!}. \tag{3}$$

Proof: Starting with any one arrangement, and interchanging like objects among themselves in all ways, we get $p\,!\;q\,!\;r\,!$

arrangements all appearing to be the same as the original. Thus, the total number of arrangements of the n objects, $n!$, must be $p! \, q! \, r!$ times the number of *distinguishable* arrangements. Hence, the latter number is $n! \div (p! \ q! \ r!)$.

EXERCISES

1. How many different numbers can be formed, using any three of the digits, 1, 2, 3, 4, 5, 6, 7, without repetition in any one number?

2. How many code "words" are possible, using any four letters of the alphabet without duplication?

3. Nine men compete in a race in which the first three places score. In how many ways may the scoring turn out, barring ties?

4. Four persons enter a car in which 7 seats are vacant. In how many ways can they be seated?

5. In how many numbers between 1000 and 10000 is there neither a repeated digit nor a zero?

6. How many numbers can be formed from 1, 2, 3, and 4, using all the digits each time? Three each time? In all possible ways?

7. How many six-place numbers can be formed from the digits 1, 2, 3, 4, 5, and 6, if 2 and 5 are always to occupy the middle two places?

8. In how many ways may a basketball team line up if two of the men can play only as guards?

9. How many batting orders are possible for a baseball nine, if the three fielders bat before the other players, and the catcher and pitcher bat after the others?

10. In how many orders can 8 children arrange themselves in a circle for a game?

11. In how many circular orders may 4 men and 4 women sit, if men and women are to alternate?

12. Given five colors of ribbons and five other colors of flowers, express the number of patterns that could be formed by placing flowers and ribbons alternately on the 10 spokes of a wheel.

13. How many code "words" of 7 letters each can be formed from the letters of *college*?

14. Express the number of "words" that are possible using all the letters of *interdependent*.

15. How many patterns are possible by flying on a pole 3 identical *U.S.* flags, 2 Canadian, 1 Mexican, and 1 Panaman?

16. Like Ex. 15 if the flags are to be flown in a horizontal circle.

§ 358. The Problem of Combinations. It is often important to know how many different *sets* of r objects can be chosen from n objects. This is not a question of the number of orders or permutations, but rather the number of *groups* or *combinations*. A set, however, is regarded as different if even a single individual is replaced.

EXAMPLE. How many triangles can be drawn with vertices chosen from among five points A, B, C, D, E, no three of which are in the same straight line?

There will be as many triangles as there are sets of three letters.

Each set of 3 letters could be arranged in 3 ! (= 6) different orders. Hence the number of sets is only one sixth as large as the total number of possible orders — which is $P_{5,\,3}$. Hence the number of sets, or triangles, is

$$\frac{P_{5,\,3}}{3\,!} = \frac{5\cdot4\cdot3}{1\cdot2\cdot3} = 10.$$

§ 359. Formula. The number of sets or combinations of r objects that can be chosen from n objects is denoted by $C_{n,\,r}$.

Evidently

$$C_{n,\,r} = \frac{P_{n,\,r}}{r\,!}. \tag{4}$$

For each *set* of r objects has r ! possible orders; and hence the total number of orders must be r ! times the number of sets.

Or the number of sets $= \dfrac{1}{r\,!} \times$ the number of orders.

Thus, by (1),

$$C_{n,\,r} = \frac{n\,(n-1)\,(n-2)\cdots(n-r+1)}{r\,!}. \tag{5}$$

If we multiply numerator and denominator by $(n-r)$! we shall have in the numerator the product of all integers from n down to 1.

$$\therefore\ C_{n,\,r} = \frac{n\,!}{r\,!\,(n-r)\,!}. \tag{6}$$

This expression is useful in formula work, though in actual calculations (4) or (5) is generally used.

Ex. I. How many selections of three out of 21 different flags are possible?

$$Ans. \quad C_{21,\,3} = \frac{21\,!}{3\,!\,\,18\,!} = \frac{21 \cdot 20 \cdot 19}{1 \cdot 2 \cdot 3} = 1330.$$

(Cancelling 18 ! into 21 ! leaves the three factors $21 \cdot 20 \cdot 19$, as shown.)

Ex. II. A pack of 52 cards contains "spades," "clubs," "diamonds," and "hearts" in equal numbers. In how many ways can a hand of 12 cards be drawn, so as to contain precisely 5 spades?

Any 5 of the 13 spades might be drawn, which can be done in $C_{13,\,5}$ ways. By hypothesis, the other 7 cards may be any 7 of the 39 clubs, diamonds, and hearts. These can be drawn in $C_{39,\,7}$ ways. Each set of 5 spades can go with *any* set of the 7 other cards. The total number of hands possible is then

$$C_{13,\,5} \times C_{39,\,7} = \frac{13\,!}{5\,!\,\,8\,!} \times \frac{39\,!}{7\,!\,\,32\,!}.$$

§ 360. Zero Factorial. In the case of $C_{9,\,9}$, (6) reads

$$C_{9,\,9} = \frac{9\,!}{9\,!\,\,0\,!} = \frac{1}{0\,!}. \tag{7}$$

Now 0 ! has not yet been defined. The definition given for n ! is not applicable: we cannot speak of the product of the integers starting at 1 and running up to zero. But if we arbitrarily assign the value 1 to 0 ! (just as we assigned the value 1 to x^0 in § 32) equation (7) will then give $C_{9,\,9} = 1$; which is clearly correct.

This is another instance of generalizing the meaning of a symbol to make it cover an otherwise exceptional case.

§ 361 S. Selecting and Arranging. When a problem involves both the selection and arrangement of objects, with a limitation upon either, it is best to consider the two steps separately. That is, ask (a) In how many ways can *a suitable set of objects be chosen*, and (b) In how many ways may *each chosen set be arranged*.

Ex. I. How many line-ups are possible, choosing a football eleven of 6 seniors and 5 juniors, from a squad containing 10 seniors and 15 juniors?

(a) The 6 seniors may be chosen in $C_{10,\,6}$ ways, the 5 juniors in $C_{15,\,5}$ ways. Hence the *set* of players may be chosen in $C_{10,\,6} \times C_{15,\,5}$ ways.

(b) Any one set of 11 men can line up in 11 ! ways. Hence the total number of possible line-ups is

$$C_{10,\,6} \times C_{15,\,5} \times 11\,! \;=\; \frac{10\,!}{6\,!\;4\,!} \times \frac{15\,!}{5\,!\;10\,!} \times 11\,!.$$

[Would it be correct here to reason that the number of orders for the seniors would be $P_{10,\,6}$, and for the juniors $P_{15,\,5}$; and hence, in all, $P_{10,\,6} \times P_{15,\,5}$? No, for this allows only for shifts of the seniors and juniors among themselves and not of seniors with juniors.]

§ 362. $C_{n,\,r}$ in the Binomial Theorem. The general term in the expansion of $(a + u)^n$ is by § 346:

$$\frac{n\,(n-1)\,\cdots\,(n-r+1)}{r\,!}\,a^{n-r}\,u^r.$$

If n is a positive integer, this is the same thing as $C_{n,\,r}\,a^{n-r}\,u^r$. Hence the binomial theorem may be rewritten:

$$(a + u)^n = a^n + C_{n,\,1}\,a^{n-1}\,u + C_{n,\,2}\,a^{n-2}u^2 + \cdots. \qquad (8)$$

In fact, another proof of the theorem for positive integral values of n is easily given from the standpoint of combinations.

To illustrate the idea, think of $(a + u)^{10}$ as

$$(a + u)^{10} = (a + u)\,(a + u)\,\cdots\,(a + u),\; 10 \text{ factors.}$$

Multiplying the a's in three factors and the u's in the other seven would give $a^3\,u^7$. This particular term will arise as many times as there are *sets* of 3 factors — i.e., $C_{10,\,3}$ times. Hence the expansion will contain $C_{10,\,3}\,a^3\,u^7$.

You may see from this illustration how the proof would run that the coefficient of $a^r\,u^{n-r}$ in $(a + u)^n$ must be $C_{n,\,r}$. Likewise for $a^{n-r}\,u^r$.

EXERCISES

1. Calculate: $C_{25,\,4}$; $C_{10,\,3}$; $C_{7,\,3}$; $C_{16,\,8}$; $C_{8,\,8}$; $C_{5,\,5}$.

2. Write the expansions of the following binomials, expressing their coefficients in the $C_{n,\,r}$ notation:

(a) $(a + x)^6$;   (b) $(a^2 - y^2)^{20}$, to four terms.

(c) $(1 + 1)^5$. Note the expression thus obtained for 2^5.

3. In how many ways could:

(a) A bodyguard of four be chosen from 12 secret service men?

(b) A bowling team of five be chosen from a club of 20 men?

(c) A president, a secretary, and a treasurer be elected from a club membership of 50?

(d) A committee of 3 seniors and 2 juniors be chosen from a club consisting of 15 seniors and 10 juniors?

(e) An arbitration board consisting of 3 employers, 3 laborers, and 1 outsider be chosen from 10 employers, 30 laborers, and 8 outsiders?

(f) A combination of three tones be selected from the chromatic scale of 13 tones?

(g) A "word" be formed using three out of 12 given consonants and two of five given vowels?

(h) Three flavors be selected for an ice cream "brick" out of thirty listed flavors?

4. How many straight lines are determined by 10 points located on a circle? How many triangles have three of those points as vertices?

5. How many (separate or overlapping) rectangles are formed by 7 horizontal and 4 vertical lines?

6. How many private telephone lines are needed to connect each of 6 officials with every other one?

7. A town has 12 streets running east-west, and 8 running north-south. To walk from the NW corner to the SE corner of the town, without covering unnecessary distance, how many routes are available? (Hint: Thinking of the 18 successive blocks to be walked, what must we decide in choosing a route?)

8. If we draw 8 cards from a pile containing 12 "spades" and 9 "hearts," in how many ways may we get 3 spades and 5 hearts?

9. If we draw 5 balls at random from a bag containing 11 red and 6 white balls, in how many ways may we get 3 red and 2 white?

10. Drawing 6 names from a list of 20 men and 15 women, in how many ways may we get 4 men and 2 women?

11. From 9 seniors and 7 juniors how many basketball teams can be chosen, if each includes 3 seniors and 2 juniors? How many "line-ups" are obtainable thus?

12. How many football line-ups are obtainable from a squad of 25, if only 4 can play as ends and only 6 as backs, and these 10 men can play nowhere else?

13. In how many ways can 15 books be shelved in a row, without separating one set of 6 volumes or another of 3 volumes?

14. How many four-figure numbers can be formed from the digits 1 to 9 allowing repetition?

15. To open a locker three dials must be turned until certain letters are at the top. If each dial bears 15 letters, how many lockers can there be without duplicating any "combination"?

16. For a key to open a certain lock, it must push the five tumbler pins to certain positions. If each pin can have 10 positions, how many different keys are needed for all possible locks of that design?

Solve Exs. 17–21 by using the hints in Exs. 17–18.

17. In how many ways may a boy make a selection of one or more flags from 7 flags, all different? (Hint: As to each flag, he simply takes or omits it. But he cannot omit all.)

18. Like Ex. 17 if there are 3 identical *U.S.* flags, 2 Canadian, one Mexican and one Panaman. (Hint: As to *U.S.* flags he has four options, viz. to take 3, 2, 1 or none; etc.)

19. How many different assortments of one or more pieces of fruit can we make from 6 oranges, 4 bananas, 2 peaches, 1 pear, 1 plum, and 1 apple?

20. How many different sums can be formed with a dollar, a quarter, a dime, and a nickel?

21. Like Ex. 20, with a British farthing, $\frac{1}{2}d.$, $1d.$, $3d.$, $6d.$, shilling, and half-crown?

A. PROBABILITY

§ 363. The Idea of Chance. The theory of chance is fundamental in many lines of scientific work — *e.g.*, in statistical studies of physical, biological, and social phenomena, in the theory of errors of measurement, etc. The basic ideas of chance underlying these studies are familiar to everyone, as the following illustrations will show.

(1) If we toss up a coin, we say that the chance of its falling "heads" is 1/2. We mean that it may fall in either of two ways, which are regarded as equally probable. In several thousand trials we should expect "heads" just about half the time, and "tails" about half.*

(2) If we are to name a future date at random, the chance that it will be a Tuesday (assuming our present calendar to be continued) is 1/7. We judge that we are no more likely or less likely to hit upon Tuesday than upon any other day of the week.

(3) If we draw a ball at random from a bag containing 3

---

* When we speak of the turn of a coin as a "chance event," we do not mean to imply that there is nothing which determines how it will fall. But the determining factors are so complex — and so far beyond our knowledge when the coin is honestly flipped — that we are quite unable to predict the fall. And we sum all this up in calling the turn of the coin a "chance event."

red and **7** black balls, the chance or probability that it will
be red is $3/10$.

§ 364. Probability Defined. If an event can occur in x
ways, and can fail in y ways, all equally likely, we say that
the probability of success (p) and the probability of failure
(q) are respectively:

$$p = \frac{x}{x + y}, \qquad q = \frac{y}{x + y}. \tag{9}$$

That is, the probability of an event equals *the number of ways
it can occur, divided by the total number of ways it can occur or
fail, when the ways are equally likely.*[*]

Observe that $p + q = 1$. That is, the chance of success
+ the chance of failure equals 1. If an event is sure to occur,

$$y = 0.$$
$$\therefore \; p = 1.$$

Thus, in questions of chance, certainty is denoted by 1, and
impossibility by 0.

In problems of a more advanced sort, however, involving an unlimited number of alternatives, a zero probability is not inconsistent
with actual occurrence.

Ex. I.　If 5 balls are drawn at random from a bag containing 7 red
and 8 black balls, what is the chance for precisely 3 red balls?

Any three of the 7 red balls might be drawn: this could happen in
$C_{7,3}$ ways.　The other two balls must be black.　These could be
drawn in $C_{8,2}$ ways; and hence the required combination can be obtained in $C_{7,3} \times C_{8,2}$ ways.　But the total number of ways of drawing
some 5 balls is $C_{15,5}$.　Hence the probability of succeeding is

$$p = \frac{C_{7,3} \times C_{8,2}}{C_{15,5}} = \frac{\dfrac{7!}{3!\,4!} \times \dfrac{8!}{2!\,6!}}{\dfrac{15!}{5!\,10!}} = \frac{140}{429}.$$

There is approximately "one chance in 3."

§ 365. Compound Probability. What is the probability
that two events, *independent of one another*, will both occur?

---

* For a discussion of what constitutes a suitable basis for judging that various
"ways" are in reality "equally likely," see the treatises on Probability by
J. L. Coolidge, Arne Fisher, and T. C. Fry; also a paper by T. C. Fry in *The
American Mathematical Monthly*, 1934, pp. 207–19.

Suppose the first can occur in x_1 ways and fail in y_1 ways; and that the second can occur in x_2 ways and fail in y_2 ways. Any one result for the first event might be associated with any result for the second. Hence the two events can both occur in $x_1 x_2$ ways; and can occur or fail in $(x_1 + y_1) \cdot (x_2 + y_2)$ ways. Thus the chance that *both* will occur is

$$p = \frac{x_1 x_2}{(x_1 + y_1)(x_2 + y_2)} = \frac{x_1}{x_1 + y_1} \cdot \frac{x_2}{x_2 + y_2} = p_1 p_2, \quad (10)$$

where p_1 and p_2 are the probabilities of the two events, considered separately.

Ex. I. If a ball is drawn from a bag containing 3 red balls and 7 black ones, and a card is drawn from a pack, what is the probability that the ball will be red and the card a spade?

The chance for a red ball is $p_1 = 3/10$. The chance for a spade is $p_2 = 13/52 = 1/4$. Hence the required chance is

$$p_1 p_2 = \tfrac{3}{10} \cdot \tfrac{1}{4} = \tfrac{3}{40}.$$

That is, in the long run, a red ball would be drawn in three tenths of all the trials; and, in one fourth of these cases, a "spade" also would be drawn.

Ex. II. If three dice are fairly cast, what is the chance that everyone will fall a "five"?

The chance for a "five" on any one die is obviously 1/6. Hence for three throws:

$$p = \left(\tfrac{1}{6}\right)\left(\tfrac{1}{6}\right)\left(\tfrac{1}{6}\right) = \tfrac{1}{216}.$$

[Why would it be incorrect to argue similarly that the chance of drawing a "spade" from a pack is 1/4; and hence the chance that two cards drawn in succession will both be spades is $p = (1/4)^2$? Would this argument be correct if the first card were replaced before drawing the second?]

EXERCISES

1. What is the probability: (a) of throwing a "six," when rolling a single die; (b) of getting an ace when drawing one card from a "pack," without the joker; (c) of hitting upon a Sunday, when naming a date at random; (d) of choosing a man, when selecting one person by lot from a group of 30 men and 20 women?

2. Of 800 students taking a certain course in recent years 40 have failed. What is the probability that a member of the class, picked at random, will pass?

3. In recent years a professional examination has been passed by 388 out of 4220 who tried it. If a candidate's paper is picked out of the pile at random, what is the probability of its being a "pass"?

4. Of the 150 men in a college club, 18 are over 6 ft. tall. If a girl makes a "blind date" for a club party by drawing lots from the entire membership, what is the probability that her escort will be over 6 ft. tall?

5. In round numbers the 1930 U.S. population was 123 million, of whom 14 million were foreign born, and 50 million were members of churches. If a name were taken at random from the entire list, what would be the probability for drawing: (*a*) a native; (*b*) a church member?

6. Out of 2220 June days recorded in a certain city, 1558 were fair. What is the chance that a June day, selected at random, will be fair?

7. If 5 chocolates are taken at random from a box in which there are 9 chocolates with cream centers and 6 with nut centers, what is the probability of getting: (*a*) precisely 3 cream centers; (*b*) all cream?

8. A freshman class includes 61 Iowa men and 140 from other states. If an Iowan draws two other men at random to share a dormitory suite, what is the probability that both men drawn will be Iowans? That one will be? That neither will be?

9. Drawing 6 cards out of a pack, what is the chance: (*a*) that all will be hearts? (*b*) that 4 will be hearts and 2 diamonds? (*c*) that 4 will be hearts and the other two anything else?

10. Naming a date at random, and simultaneously drawing 3 cards from a pack, what is the chance of getting a Friday and 3 clubs?

11. Taking 3 chocolates from the box in Ex. 7, and simultaneously throwing a die, what is the chance of getting precisely two cream centers, and an "ace" on the die?

12. (*a*) If 4 coins are tossed, what is the chance that all will fall "tails"? (*b*) The same question for 10 coins.

13. If in the long run 90% of July days are clear, and if three successive days are selected in advance, what is the probability: (*a*) that all will be clear? (*b*) that the first two will be clear and the third not?

14. If 3 dates are named at random what is the chance: (*a*) that all will be Sundays? (*b*) that the first will be a Sunday, and the other two something else?

[15.] A mortality table indicates that, out of 100,000 persons at age 10, there will be 69,804 living at 50; and 847 at 90. What is the chance that the average person 10 yrs. old will: (*a*) live to 90? (*b*) die before reaching 50?

16. The probability for a man to be surviving 20 yrs. hence is $\frac{1}{4}$; for his wife, $\frac{1}{3}$. What is the probability for both to be living then?

§ 366. An Illustrative Problem.

If five dice are thrown at random, what is the chance that *some* pair will fall "aces" (*i.e.*, one-spots) and the other three dice fall in some other way?

First consider the probability that a *certain* pair will fall aces, etc.

For each ace the chance is $1/6$; for the pair it is $(1/6)^2$. For any other die to fall in some *other* way than ace, the probability is $5/6$; for all three dice to do so it is $(5/6)^3$. Hence the chance that a *certain* pair will face aces, and the others not aces is $(1/6)^2 (5/6)^3$.

The chance for *some* pair to fall aces, etc., is much larger, for there are $C_{5,2}$ $(= 10)$ possible pairs, and any one of these might be the pair to fall aces. Hence the total chance, as required in the question above, is

$$P = C_{5,2} \left(\tfrac{1}{6}\right)^2 \left(\tfrac{5}{6}\right)^3. \tag{11}$$

This is also the chance that a single die, thrown 5 times, would fall an ace twice and only twice.

§ 367. r Successes in n Trials.

The result in (11) merely illustrates the following theorem: If p is the chance of success in one trial, and q $(= 1 - p)$ is the chance of failure, then the probability that the event will occur precisely r times in n independent trials is

$$p_r = C_{n,r}\, p^r q^{n-r}. \tag{12}$$

Proof: The probability that a *certain* r trials will all succeed is p^r; the probability that all the others will fail is q^{n-r}; and the r successful trials could be selected from n trials in $C_{n,r}$ ways.

Ex. I. If 20 dates are named at random, what is the chance that precisely 5 will be week-ends (Saturdays or Sundays)?

The chance that a single date would be a week-end is $2/7$. Thus $p = 2/7$, $q = 5/7$; and hence

$$p_5 = C_{20,5}\left(\tfrac{2}{7}\right)^5 \left(\tfrac{5}{7}\right)^{15} = .1897, \text{ approx.}$$

Ex. II. If 20 cards are drawn from a pack, what is the probability that precisely 5 will be spades?

The only short method here is the earlier method. (Cf. Ex. I, § 364.)

Ans. $C_{13,5} \cdot C_{39,15} \div C_{52,20} = .2568.$

§ **368** S. **Life Probabilities.** The American Experience Mortality Table, based on vital records of some decades ago, purports to show the number of survivors at any age (x years) out of an original group of 100,000 typical persons aged 10. Though mortality is now much lower in youth and middle life than the table indicates, the table is still used by most American life insurance companies as a basis for their rates.

The companies, by charging rates sufficient to provide for the "expected mortality" in the table, have a wide margin of security. In most companies the policy holders receive annual dividends as a return of excess charges.

Age	Survivors
10	100,000
20	92,637
21	91,914
22	91,192
30	85,441
40	78,106
50	69,804
60	57,917
70	38,569
80	14,474
90	847

Some sample figures from the table are shown here. These will be used for the following illustrative points, and in our exercises.

(I) Of the 30-yr. group, 78,106 survive at age 40; hence 7335 die during the ten years. For a typical person aged 30, the probability of dying within 10 yrs. is, therefore, $7335 \div 85{,}441$, or .08585. The probability of surviving 10 yrs. is .91415.

The probability that eight typical persons aged 30 will all survive 10 yrs. is $(.91415)^8 = .4877$ — not quite an "even chance."

(II) A company agrees to pay a 30-year old person $1000 ten years hence, if he survives. Omitting administrative expense, and ignoring interest, what should be the net charge for this contract? If there were 85,441 such contracts, the company would have to pay $1000 in each of 78,106 cases and nothing in the others. The charge per contract sold would be $78,106,000 \div 85441$, or $914.15. We see that this is simply the probability of survival (.91415) times the $1000 face of the contract.

If the company earns interest at 4% convertible annually the net charge for this contract, if paid in advance, would be $914.15 $\div$ 1.04^{10} = $617.57. Of course, expense must be added.

(III) Ignoring interest, what should be the net charge for a one-year term insurance policy for $1000 on the life of a typical person aged 20? Of the 92,637 persons in the 20-yr. group, 723 die within the year. The necessary net charge is, then, $723,000 ÷ 92,637, or $7.80.

Suppose a $1000 two-year term policy were issued to 92,637 persons at age 20, for a net annual premium of P each, payable at the beginning of each year by all then surviving. The company would receive the first year 92,637 premiums, and the second year 91,914 premiums, a total of 184,551 P dollars. The death losses for the two years would be $723,000 + $722,000, totalling $1,445,000. Without interest we should have $P = 1,445,000 ÷ 184,551 = 7.83$. The slightly larger premium of $7.83 per year in this case is due to the fact that some persons do not live to pay the second time. On long-term policies — e.g., "whole life" policies — the increase in mortality in later years is also a potent factor in raising rates.

This illustration shows the essence of the method used in calculating "whole life" net premiums, except that the effect of interest has to be included. Net premiums for "endowment" policies can be calculated by a combination of the methods of (II) and (III) above, while taking account of interest.

EXERCISES

1. What is the probability of getting precisely:

    (a) Two heads, in flipping 6 coins?

    (b) Three aces, in throwing 12 dice?

    (c) Four Sundays, in naming 20 dates at random?

2. If 75 out of 100 graduates of a college have later won honors in a certain professional school, what is the probability that three other typical graduates will all win similar honors? That just one of the three will do so?

3. In a large community where 10% of the people are illiterate, what is the probability that 3 persons chosen by lot will all be able to read and write? That only one will?

4. If 70% of ten-year-old boys live to be 50, what is the probability that five typical boys of age 10 will all survive to 50? That just three of the five will so survive?

5. Of the electric lamps made by a factory, 80% give 750 hours of service or better. What is the probability that four lamps picked at random will all fail in less than 750 hrs.? That just two will so fail?

6. Averaged over many years, 30% of April days are too rainy for golf, in a certain locality. What is the chance that precisely 2 of four Saturdays will be too rainy?

7. On the average a certain electric clock stops once in 100 days, 'and is as likely to stop on one day as on another. What is the probability that it will stop just twice in a sequence of 30 Sundays?

8. If 10 dates are named at random, and 7 coins are tossed, what is the probability that precisely 3 dates will be week-ends (Saturday or Sunday) and 4 coins fall "heads"?

9. If 6 cards are drawn from a pack and 4 dice are thrown, what is the probability for just 3 aces in the cards and also on the dice?

10. By the abridged mortality Table, p. 480, what is the probability that a person aged 20 will live to be 80? That a person aged 80 will live to be 90?

11. A man of age 30 marries a woman of 20. Ignoring the possibility of divorce, what is the probability of their celebrating their Golden Wedding?

12. In Ex. 11, what is the probability, if 15 out of 100 marriages end in divorce within 50 yrs.?

13. An insurance company insures a man of 30 for $10000 for a ten-year term. What is the probability that it will have to pay a death loss? If no interest were earned, what net charge, payable in a lump sum, would the company have to make for such a policy — in addition to a charge for expenses?

14. (*a*) As in Ex. 13 find the net charge in advance that would be necessary for another contract, in which the company agrees to pay the man $10000 at age 70 if he survives. (*b*) What net charge, if the company investments earn $4\frac{1}{2}\%$ interest, convertible annually?

[15.] If 5 coins are tossed, what is the probability of five heads? Of four heads? (And so on, to no heads.) Represent these several probabilities graphically by ordinates, equally spaced.

[16.] Show that the probability in Ex. 1 (*c*) equals one term in the expansion of the binomial $(\frac{1}{7} + \frac{6}{7})^{20}$.

§ 369. Normal Binomial Distribution. If we toss up 10 coins, there are 11 possible results: 10 heads, 9 heads, $\cdots$, 1 head, no heads. The chances for these several results are represented by the heights — or preferably we may say by the *areas* — of the several rectangles in Fig. 159. In other words, this "staircase"

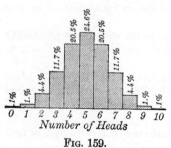

Number of Heads

Fig. 159.

shows the relative *frequency* with which the various numbers of heads would occur in a very large number of trials, tossing 10 coins each time. Fig. 160, below, shows the same thing for 100 coins. Observe how slight the chances are for more than 65 heads or fewer than 35.)

The probability of r heads when tossing n coins once is

$$p_r = C_{n,\,r} \left(\tfrac{1}{2}\right)^r \left(\tfrac{1}{2}\right)^{n-r}, \quad = C_{n,\,r} \left(\tfrac{1}{2}\right)^n. \tag{13}$$

Since the factor $(1/2)^n$ occurs in every p_r, the several probabilities p_r are proportional to the coefficients $C_{n,\,r}$ in the expansion of $(p + q)^n$. For this reason a distribution of frequencies like that in Fig. 159 is called a *Normal Binomial Distribution*.* Such distributions are common in statistical studies. Some illustrations follow.

(I) The staircase in Fig. 4, p. 4, which shows the relative commonness of various chest measures among a number of soldiers, resembles one for a Normal Binomial Distribution. So would a similar chart for *statures*, and many other biological measurements.

(II) A series of rectangles similarly drawn to show the relative frequency of *marriages* at various *ages* also resembles the normal binomial staircase. Likewise for the relative commonness of life insurance policies taken out at various ages; etc.

370. Normal Probability Curve. If instead of 10 coins we toss up 10,000, and draw a "staircase" representing the chances for no head, 1 head, 2 heads, etc., to 10,000 heads, making the bases of the rectangles much smaller, the staircase will ascend by such tiny steps as to be practically a smooth curve. (Cf. Fig. 160 for 100 coins.) Indeed, if the number of steps is indefinitely increased, and if the bases of the rectangles are decreased in

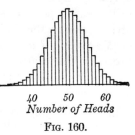

40   50   60
Number of Heads

FIG. 160.

such a way as to keep the middle height some constant a, while holding the total area equal to 1 (to represent 100%),

---

* The distribution of frequencies for the various possible numbers of "aces" when throwing n dice is a different type of Normal Binomial Distribution, not symmetrical with respect to vertical center line — p and q being unequal in this case, $\tfrac{1}{6}$ and $\tfrac{5}{6}$. If, however, n is large and we consider only occurrences near the most common, the distribution is nearly symmetrical in that limited region.

the limiting form approached by the staircase can be proved to be the curve whose equation is

$$y = a\,e^{-\pi a^2 x^2}. \tag{14}$$

This is called the Normal Probability Curve.

A preferable form of equation for some later purposes is obtained by putting $\pi a^2 = h^2$ or $a = h/\sqrt{\pi}$. Thus

$$y = \frac{h}{\sqrt{\pi}}\,e^{-h^2 x^2}. \tag{15}$$

The curve does not apply with exactness to the tossing of any actual group of coins, for there we have a finite number of discrete events. But, as will be explained shortly, it is useful in studying probabilities relating to variables that can change *continuously*, like statures, etc. It is, moreover, often adequate, to a desired degree of approximation, for problems of tossed coins, etc., when n, the number of trials, is large.

§ 371. **Form of the Normal Curve.** Changing the sign of x in (14) does not affect y. Thus the curve is symmetrical with respect to the Y-axis. It has its maximum height, $y = a$, at $x = 0$. This may be large or small. As $x \to \pm \infty$, $y \to 0$. Thus the curve recedes to infinity, to the right and left, with the X-axis as an asymptote.

If a is very large, the curve must fall rapidly and be narrow in its central portion, since the total area is 1. (By the total area is meant the limit of the area from $x = -X$ to $x = X$ as $X \to \infty$.) If a is small the curve falls slowly and appears broad in the central part. Normal curves may thus differ in appearance; but they all share an important area property, stated below.

In fact that property will hold even if we plot a Normal Curve on a different scale, multiplying every ordinate by some constant N, and making the area N instead of 1.

In Fig. 161 suppose the points $x = E$ and $x = -E$ to be chosen in such a way that half the entire area lies between the ordinates erected there — *i.e.*, with 25% from the middle to each. Then other ordinates at $x = 2\,E$, $3\,E$, etc., will terminate other definite percentages of the entire area. These percentages, the same for all Normal Curves, are approximately 16% and 7%, leaving about 2% of the area beyond $x = 3\,E$. (More precise figures are given on p. 533; but the foregoing round numbers are commonly used.)

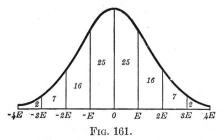

FIG. 161.

§ 372. **Applications.** The statures of all the men in the country cluster somewhat around an average value. Small deviations from the average are common; large deviations, comparatively rare. A graph showing the relative frequencies of different statures would resemble the Normal Curve. In fact, the percentage of statures falling between the average and any other height is given closely by a corresponding area in the Normal Curve. There is a "probable deviation," E in., such that just 25% of the statures deviate upward from the average by less than E in., and likewise 25% downward; and, between deviations of E in. and $2\,E$ in., there fall 16% of the statures, etc.

Similarly for many other variables, whose values we shall say distribute themselves "according to the Normal Curve." An important illustration from business follows.

Ex. I. Tests of samples show that the electric lamps made by a factory vary in length of "life" approximately in accordance with the Normal Curve, with the middle 50% between 800 and 1000 hours. About what percentage last: (a) between 700 and 800 hr.; (b) over 1000 hr.; (c) less than 600 hr.?

The average life is 900 hr.; and the probable deviation E is 100 hr. We re-label the base of Fig. 161 accordingly. Thus, at the zero point we write 900; at $x = E$, 1000; at $2\,E$, 1100; at $-E$, 800; etc. We then see at a glance that the answers to our questions are:

  (a) 16%,   (b) 25%,   (c) 2%.

Remarks. (I) If the factory guarantees replacement of all lamps which fail in less than 600 hr., and all such lamps are redeemed, the cost of the guarantee will be about 2%.

(II) To find the probability that a lamp will last between 900 and 950 hr., we could estimate the area from 0 to $\frac{1}{2} E$ in Fig. 161. More accurately, we read from the small table on p. 533: $p = .132$ or 13.2%.

EXERCISES

In Exs. 1–5 re-draw Fig. 161 freely, re-labeling the base line with numbers which fit the problem.

1. Suppose that the distribution of male statures in a nation follows the Normal Curve, with the middle half of all the statures between 66 in. and 70 in. If a man's height is 72 in., what percentage of his compatriots are taller? What if his height is 64 in.? 62 in.?

2. The scores made by numerous students on a psychological test are distributed approximately according to the Normal Curve, with the middle half running from 180 to 220 points. If a student scored 240, what portion of the group did he excel? If he scored 140?

3. The "lives" of electric lamps of a certain make are distributed nearly according to the Normal Curve, with the middle half falling between 680 and 820 hr. What percentage fail in less than 540 hr.? In less than 890 hr.?

4. In Ex. 3 what is the probability that three lamps chosen at random will all fail in less than 680 hr.? That only one will so fail?

5. If the "lives" of certain tires are distributed in accordance with the Normal Curve, and if the middle half run from 10000 mi. to 12000 mi., what percentage last longer than 13000 mi.? Than 10500 mi.? Than 12500 mi.? (See p. 533).

6. In Ex. 5 what is the probability that four tires, bought from general stock will all run more than 13000 mi.?

7. In a certain forest the diameters of trees are distributed approximately according to the Normal Curve, with the middle half between 12.6 and 19.8 in. What percentage exceed 27 in.? 21.6 in.? 14.4 in.?

8. In Ex. 7 if there are 200 000 trees per sq. mi., about how many should be expected to have diameters of 16.2 to 18 in.?

9. From (15), p. 484, show that the Normal Curve has its points of inflection at $x = \pm 1/(h\sqrt{2})$.

Remark. The foregoing uses of the Normal Probability Curve assume it known that the values of the variables are distributed according to that curve. But how is such a fact

determined in the first place, based on original observations?
This brings us to the consideration of the

(B) Statistical Treatment of Tabulated Data

§ 373 *S.* **Frequency Distributions.**   Although distributions
of values are often "normal" or nearly so, they are more commonly asymmetric and somewhat irregular.

Illustration.   The adjacent table shows in round numbers
the distribution of the gross incomes of
5640 physicians in the United States in
1928.*   Here the incomes are divided into
nine groups or "classes."   The first runs
up to, but does not include, $2000; the
second runs from $2000 to $4000, not
including the latter figure; etc.   The
number of incomes in each class is the
class frequency.

Income ($1000 ×)	No. of Persons
0– 2	210
2– 4	830
4– 6	1320
6– 8	1070
8–10	800
10–12	570
12–14	370
14–16	300
16–18	170

The tabulated distribution can be por-
trayed by a set of rectangles, whose heights or areas represent

Fig. 162.

the class frequencies.   In Fig. 162 the area idea is used as the
basis in labeling the heights.   *E.g.*, the height .415 multiplied by the base 2000 gives 830, the class frequency in that
interval.

* Based on figures given in the *Journal* of the American Medical Association,
May 16, 1931.   There were 688 larger incomes scattered along up to $160,000:
but to save many figures we confine our illustration to the group reported here.

Such a staircase, consisting of the upper bases of the rectangles and the vertical segments connecting them, is called in statistical work a "histogram," but is usually labeled so that the *height* represents the class frequency.

Fig. 162 also shows a "frequency curve" based on this table and drawn by a method to be explained shortly. (§ 378.) The area under this curve in any class interval represents the corresponding class frequency. The ordinate at any point represents the number of incomes or persons involved *per dollar interval of income* — which is called simply "the frequency." The mean ordinates for class intervals, equal to the heights of the histogram, represent the average number of incomes per dollar range, in those intervals.

This curve would show more humps if available figures for $1000 classes had been used. Possibly it would smooth out if a larger number of physicians had been included in the sample. Great precautions are needed in drawing any conclusions about probabilities from a curve supposed to show a frequency distribution that would be encountered in the long run.

Remark. Any ordinate of the Normal Curve represents the expected percentage of cases per unit range in the variable (x), at the value in question. (The idea involves the limit of an average percentage in a shrinking interval of width Δx.) Any mean ordinate, multiplied by the corresponding base, gives the area, which represents the total percentage of cases in the interval. Areas in the Normal Curve can also represent class frequencies in a normal distribution of a large number of values (N) — by changing the scale or multiplying every ordinate by N. The equation of the curve is often written with such a multiplier included for this purpose.

§ 374 S. Averages. We often indicate whether the items in a group are large or small by saying something about an "average." The word is loosely used to denote several different measures. Let us illustrate these by referring again to the incomes covered in the table of § 373.

(1) *The Mean* income is found by adding all the incomes, taking each the number of times it occurs, and then dividing by the total number of incomes. *E.g.*, treating the incomes

$6000 to $8000 as if all were $7000, the total income for that class of 1070 persons would be $7,490,000. Dealing likewise with the other classes gives the total of $42,460,000 for the entire group of 5640. Dividing shows the arithmetical average or mean to be about $7530.

This figure might be affected if we knew how incomes are distributed within each class.

(2) *The Mode* is the most common income: $4000 to $6000 by our table, since more physicians (1320) had incomes in this class than in any other.

According to Fig. 162 the mode, based on very small intervals, would be about $5000, where the curve is highest.

(3) *The Median* is the middle income for the entire list: half of the 5640 physicians receive more, and half receive less. We estimate it by running down our table until 2820 incomes have been included. The three lowest groups together include 2360 incomes: we must take in 460 more — *i.e.*, must go into the next group 460/1070 of its whole extent ($2000), or an amount of $860, approx. The median is, then, about $6860.

Remarks. (I) Still other types of averages — the "geometric mean," the "harmonic mean," etc. — are used for some purposes: but would not be useful in our income illustration.*

(II) The economic status of the physicians considered above is better described by giving all three figures than by any one alone:

mean = $7530, mode = $4000 to $6000, median = $6860. Further light is shed by giving the curve or histogram to show the frequency distribution, or by otherwise indicating the amount of scattering. (§ 377.)

(III) If the larger incomes, scattered along up to $160,000 as reported by 688 other physicians, were included, the median would be raised somewhat, viz. to $7500. The mode would not be affected by including the higher incomes. The mean would be raised greatly, viz. to $9760, as the scattered high incomes add largely to the total.

* For these, and for fuller discussion of the significance of the concepts mentioned in §§ 373–81, see anv text on statistics.

§ 375 S. Quartiles, Deciles, and Percentiles.   In studying distributions and in describing the position of an individual relative to the whole group, it is customary to divide the group into four, ten, or one hundred equal parts.   The values of the variable — in our example, the incomes — which serve as the division points are called respectively *quartiles*, *deciles*, and *percentiles*.   They are numbered from the smallest to the greatest.

Thus, the first quartile Q_1 is a value which separates the lowest 25% of the cases from the rest.   The second quartile is the median; and the third quartile Q_3 cuts off the highest 25%.

In a "normal" distribution, represented by Fig. 161, Q_1 would fall at the $-E$ point of the base line, and Q_3 at the $+E$ point.   For tabulated distributions we find Q_1 and Q_3 by counting along, as when locating the median.   Similar steps are taken to find any decile or percentile.

In the table of § 373 counting 1410 incomes from the lowest takes us 370 incomes into the third group.   Hence $Q_1 = 4000 + \frac{370}{1320}$ (2000) = 4560 (dollars).   Similarly, counting 1410 incomes down from the highest tabulated, we arrive exactly at the bottom of the group $12000–$14000.   Hence Q_3 is barely under $12000.

Thus, the middle half of the incomes lie between $4560 and $12000. They are not, however, symmetrically distributed about the median. Q_3 exceeds $6860 by $5140; Q_1 falls below by $2300.

EXERCISES

For each following case find (a) the median, mode, and mean; (b) the quartiles and the fourth and sixth deciles.   (Keep the values of the means and quartiles, for use in the next set of exercises.)

1. Table I shows the distribution of the grades of 40 students in a test.   Each grade class includes the lower boundary but not the upper.

2. Table II shows a hypothetical distribution of the weights (w oz.) of 800 ears of corn.   Each class interval includes the upper but not the lower boundary.

3. Table III shows a hypothetical distribution of 300 incomes (in thousands of dollars) in a residential suburb.   Upper boundaries only are included in the class intervals.

4. Table IV shows the distribution of incomes in Oregon for 1933, received by those who filed Income Tax Returns.   The amounts are in thousands; and upper boundaries only are included in the class intervals. The total of the ten incomes "above 40,000" is $495,559.

TABLE I		TABLE II		TABLE III		TABLE IV	
Grade	No., f.	Wt.	No., f.	Income	No., f.	Income	No., f.
30– 40	1	0– 2	5	0–1	25	1– 2	12743
40– 50	0	2– 4	41	1–2	130	2– 5	15033
50– 60	1	4– 6	106	2–3	70	5–10	1110
60– 70	4	6– 8	127	3–4	40	10–15	168
70– 80	8	8–10	144	4–5	20	15–20	84
80– 90	18	10–12	183	5–6	10	20–25	17
90–100	8	12–14	132	6–8	0	25–30	16
100	0	14–16	53	8–9	4	30–40	16
		16–18	9	48.5	1	Above 40	10

§ 376 S. Measures of Dispersion.

The amount of scattering or variability in a distribution is usually described by one of four measures. The last one mentioned below is by far the most important.

(1) *Quartile Deviation, Q.* This is defined as half of the interquartile range: $Q = \frac{1}{2}(Q_3 - Q_1)$. In "normal" distributions, represented by Fig. 161, $Q = E$.

In our example: $Q = \frac{1}{2}(\$12000 - \$4560) = \$3720$.

(2) *Probable Deviation:* This is the theoretical deviation from the *mean*, which, in the long run, is exceeded by exactly half of all such deviations, taken as positive. It is the important "E" in a "normal distribution"; but is not particularly useful for asymmetric distributions.

This may differ from the median of a set of deviations of tabulated values from the mean, taken positively.

(3) *Mean or Average Deviation, M.D. or A.D.:* This is simply the arithmetic average of all (positively taken) deviations from the mean — or from the median when preferred. The calculation in our income example runs as below, taking deviations from the mean.

We use x to denote the "class mark" or income at the middle of each interval; and let $\bar{x}$ denote the mean income, which, in thousands of dollars, is approximately 7.53 (§ 374). We also use $|d|$ to de-

note the positive or numerical value of the deviation $d, = x - \bar{x}$
The last column is for later use.

Income Class	Class Mark, x	Class Freq., f	Deviation $d = x - \bar{x}$	$f|d|$	fd^2
0– 2	1	210	− 6.53	1371	8955
2– 4	3	830	− 4.53	3760	17032
4– 6	5	1320	− 2.53	3340	8449
6– 8	7	1070	− 0.53	567	301
8–10	9	800	1.47	1176	1729
10–12	11	570	3.47	1978	6863
12–14	13	370	5.47	2024	11071
14–16	15	300	7.47	2241	16740
16–18	17	170	9.47	1610	15246
		$n = 5640$		18067	86386

Taking each deviation positively, the number of times it occurs, the
sum is 18067.   Divided by the total frequency or number of cases,
$n = 5640$, this gives 3.22.

$$M.D. = 3.22 \text{ (thousand dollars).*}$$

The calculation of the mean, as outlined in § 374, consists
of forming the sum of the products $f \cdot x$, and dividing by the
total frequency 5640.

(4) *Standard Deviation, S.D.* or σ (Greek letter *sigma*):
This is the square root of the mean of the squared deviations,
each taken the number of times it occurs.

Thus, in the tabulation above, multiplying $(- 6.53)^2$ by 210 gives
8955; etc.   The sum of all the fd^2 items is 86386.   Dividing by 5640
gives as the mean of the squared deviations:

$$\frac{86386}{5640} = 15.32.$$

Extracting the square root gives $\sigma = 3.91$ (thousand dollars).

Remark.   If by integration we calculate the standard deviation for a large theoretical group whose frequency distribution is represented by the Normal Curve

$$y = \frac{h}{\sqrt{\pi}} e^{-h^2 x^2}, \tag{16}$$

* The $M.D.$, $\bar{x}$, and σ would all be modified if, instead of each class mark, we
could use the actual incomes within the class.

It turns out to be

$$\sigma = \frac{1}{h\sqrt{2}}. \tag{17}$$

Hence $h = 1/(\sigma\sqrt{2})$, and equation (16) may be written *

$$y = \frac{1}{\sigma\sqrt{2\pi}}\, e^{-\frac{x^2}{2\sigma^2}}. \tag{18}$$

By Ex. 9, p. 486, the curve has its points of inflection at $x = \pm\,\sigma$.

The tables most used by statisticians are based on this new form of equation. They show for a "normal" distribution the percentage of cases falling between $x = 0$ and $x = $ any number of σ's, say $x = .01\,\sigma$, $x = .02\,\sigma$, $\ldots$, $x = 4.00\,\sigma$. The tables show the "probable deviation," E, to be related thus to σ:

$$E = .6745\,\sigma, \qquad\qquad \sigma = 1.4826\,E. \tag{19}$$

Between $x = 0$ and $x = \sigma$, there fall 34.13% of the cases; between $x = -3\,\sigma$ and $x = 3\,\sigma$, 99.74%. One use for σ in studying tabulated data is to see how far the distribution in successive intervals differs from that found in a Normal Curve.

In our income example the value, $\sigma = 3.91$, indicates that about 34% of the incomes would fall within $3910 of the mean ($7530) on each side, if the distribution were "normal."

§ 377 S. Coefficient of Variability. This is the quotient C obtained by dividing the standard deviation by the mean:

$$C = \frac{\sigma}{\bar{x}}. \tag{20}$$

Thus, if a distribution has $\sigma = 50$ and $\bar{x} = 200$, the coefficient is .25 or 25%.

This is a high degree of variability: a range of $3\,\sigma$ each side of $\bar{x}$ covers values of x from 50 to 350. But $\sigma = 50$ with $\bar{x} = 2000$ would mean low variability, $2\frac{1}{2}$%.

§ 378 S. Frequency Polygon and Curve. To represent graphically the class frequencies in a table we may erect

---

* This theoretical σ, differing slightly from the σ for a tabulated sample, is calculated from the table in the same way, except that the sum of the products d^2 is divided by $(n-1)$ instead of n.

ordinates at the middle of the intervals. Joining the ends of successive ordinates by straight lines gives a graph called the *frequency polygon*. (Drawing a horizontal line through the top of each ordinate, and connecting these lines vertically, would give the histogram, already mentioned.)

Instead of the polygon we may prefer a smooth *frequency curve, F*, like the curve in Fig. 162. One good method of construction will be described in the case of that income curve.[*]

The total area, $\int y\, dx$, from $x = 0$ to the end of any interval, is to represent the cumulative frequency for that range of x. Adding frequencies in the table of § 373 gives the adjacent table. (*E.g.*, the number of incomes under \$4000 is $210 + 830 = 1040$.) Now plot a "cumulative curve," C, with the cumulative frequencies as ordinates, assuming that other frequencies would fit in smoothly with the table if we had intermediate information. The ordinate Y of curve C is $\int y\, dx$ for the curve F. Hence $y = dY/dx$. In other words, the *required frequency curve F is the derived curve for C*, and can be constructed by measuring slopes along C. (§ 72; p. 145, Exs. 21–25.)

INCOME BELOW	CUMULA- TIVE f.
0	0
2	210
4	1040
6	2360
8	3430
10	4230
12	4800
14	5170
16	5470
18	5640

A check is to note that the mean ordinates of F, multiplied by the length of interval (2000), should equal the original class frequencies (p. 487).

EXERCISES

1-4. In Ex. 1–4, p. 490, find (*a*) the quartile deviation; (*b*) the mean deviation from the mean; (*c*) σ; (*d*) the coefficient of variability.

5-8. In the same exercises draw (*a*) the histogram for each table; and (*b*) the frequency polygon.

9. (*a*) From Table II, p. 491, make a table of cumulative frequencies for weights from 0 to 2, 4, 6, $\cdots$, 18; and plot the cumulative graph. (*b*) Measure slopes at several points, and use them to show the general shape of the derived graph, or frequency curve. Check mean ordinates of the latter by Table II.

[*] Rougher methods are more commonly employed.

§ 379 S. **Theory of Errors.** If we measure the length of a room many times, say with a yardstick, our results will disagree by small fractions of an inch. But the values will tend to cluster closely around their mean — which, in the absence of further information, we regard as the true value. Errors in general tend to distribute themselves like a chance event; and the frequency curve for their distribution will in the long run approximate the Normal Probability Curve as closely as we please.* In fact the latter curve is often called Gauss's Normal Curve of Error.

Ultimately, half of all the errors will numerically exceed and half be less than a certain amount called the "probable error," *P.E.* This is the useful *"E"* in a Normal Curve. (§ 371.)

In dealing with a set of measurements, we find E from the *theoretical* σ by (19), after getting this σ as described in the footnote, p. 493.

The constant h in the equation of the Normal Curve (16) is called the "index of precision." Since $\sigma = 1 / (h\sqrt{2})$ a large h gives a small σ, the measurements deviate little from their mean, and have good precision.

§ 380 S. **Propagation of Errors.** When we calculate any quantity y from a measurement x on which it depends, any small error Δx in the value of x produces some error Δy in y. By § 63,

$$\Delta y = \frac{dy}{dx} \Delta x, \text{ approx.} \tag{21}$$

Exs. 9–11, p. 86, illustrate this idea.

Usually, the absolute errors Δy and Δx are less important than the *relative errors, i.e.*, the ratios of the errors to the quantities themselves:

$$\frac{\Delta y}{y}, \text{ and } \frac{\Delta x}{x}.$$

These ratios are often stated in the form of percentage errors. They can be compared readily by using (21).

---

* The method of least squares in curve fitting is based on this theory. See § 349; Ex. 1–7, p. 464.

Ex. 1. If $y = kx^n$, then $dy/dx = knx^{n-1}$; and (21) gives

$$\frac{\Delta y}{y} = \frac{knx^{n-1}\,\Delta x}{kx^n} = n\,\frac{\Delta x}{x}, \quad \text{approx.}$$

That is, for very small errors, the relative error in y is n times that in x.

E.g., letting $y = x^2$, the relative error in x^2 is twice as large as that in x; that in $\sqrt{x}$ is half as large; that in $\frac{4}{3}\pi x^3$ is three times as large; etc.

Ex. II. If $y = uv$, then by § 190, $dy = u\,dv + v\,du$.

$$\therefore\;\frac{dy}{y} = \frac{dv}{v} + \frac{du}{u}\cdot$$

Interpreting dy, dv, du, as approximations for Δy, Δv, Δu (§ 84): the relative error in a product equals the algebraic sum of the relative errors in the factors. (Either du or dv may be negative.) Cf. Fig. 98, p. 266.

§ 381 S. The Idea of Correlation.

Suppose we have two tabulated variables x and y. And, suppose that numerous values of y have been found associated with any one value of x. We cannot simply write $y = f(x)$. But the *mean*, $\bar{y}$, of the y values associated with any x, may vary with x in a fairly definite manner. Then, although individual predictions as to the y value to be expected with a given x will be subject to considerable uncertainty, we can determine whether, on the average, large or small values of y tend to go with large values of x. We can, in fact, make individual predictions with smaller average errors than if we guessed at random. The idea is expressed by saying that there is some "correlation" between x and y. This is a concept of far-reaching importance, and is developed at length in texts on Statistics.

EXERCISES

1. In 60 measurements the deviations (d mm.) from the mean were distributed with the following frequencies f:

d	-3	-2	-1	0	1	2	3
f	2	7	12	25	9	4	1

Find σ for this table; also, the theoretical σ and the probable error, *P.E.*

2. Some measurements of a certain period of time (t sec.) ran as in the following table. Find the *P.E.*

t	5.0–5.2	5.2–5.4	5.4–5.6	5.6–5.8	5.8–6.0
f	5	20	49	22	4

3. In the long run a measurement has a *P.E.* of .04 cm. Approximately what percentage of the measurements will be too small by more than .08 cm.? What is the chance that another measurement will err by less than .12 cm.? (Cf. §§ 371–72.)

4. At a certain range a certain gun has a *P.E.* of 10 yd. What is the probability that three successive shots will all be "overs" by less than 20 yd.? "Shorts" by more than 20 yd.?

5. What will be the percentage errors in the calculated

(*a*) Volume and area of a cube if the measured edge is erroneous by .04%?

(*b*) Radius and area of a sphere if the measured volume is erroneous by $\frac{1}{2}$%?

(*c*) Circumference of a circular sheet of metal if the area, determined by weighing, is erroneous by .08%?

(*d*) Area of a rectangle if the measured base and height are both too large by 1%?

(*e*) Like (*d*) if one is too large and one too small by 1%?

6. The "coefficient of correlation" r of certain variables x and y, is obtainable by using the formula

$$r^2 = (d\bar{y}/dx) \cdot (d\bar{x}/dy), \tag{22}$$

with the two equations: $\bar{y} = 1.23 + .402\,x$, $\bar{x} = .67 + .591\,y$. Find r.

7. Discriminating as closely as possible, the probability of an error of x mm. in certain measurements is proportional to e^{-x^2}. How does the chance for an error of 1 mm. compare numerically with the chance for an error of .5 mm. or .2 mm.?

8. In Ex. 7 what is the probability that two successive measurements will have errors of .5 mm. and .2 mm., as compared with the chance for 1 mm. each time?

9. If the chances for errors of x_1, x_2, $\cdots$, x_r, in r successive measurements are individually proportional to

$$e^{-nx_1^2}, \qquad e^{-nx_2^2}, \qquad \cdots, \qquad e^{-nx_r^2},$$

express the probability of the *set* of these r errors as a group, and show that *the most probable set is that for which the sum of the squares of the errors is least.* (Cf. § 349.)

10. The height of a desk was measured, with the same care each time, as 20.0 in., 20.2 in., 20.1 in., and 19.9 in. Show that, according to the conclusion in Ex. 9, the most probable height (x in.) is the arithmetical average of the four measurements.

§ 382. **Summary of Chapter XIV.** The formula for the number of combinations of n things taken r at a time is derived from the formula for the number of arrangements. Besides its more important uses, it enables us to write the binomial theorem for integral exponents in a new way.

The foregoing problems in permutations and combinations are confined to the simplest cases. Also, we have had only a glimpse of probabilities and statistical method. But even this glimpse may serve as an introduction, and provide some orientation for any who later pursue these topics further. Perhaps the most important idea in the chapter is that of the Normal Probability Curve in connection with distributions of a continuous variable which resemble the limiting distribution for certain chance events.

To round out our knowledge of the number system of algebra, and of the use of "imaginaries" in studying certain kinds of variation, we shall conclude the course with a brief study of "Complex Numbers."

EXERCISES

1. How many baseball batting-orders are obtainable in choosing a nine from 12 sailors and 15 soldiers so as to include 4 sailors and 5 soldiers, if the sailors are to bat before the soldiers?

2. If 8 cards are drawn at random from a pack, what is the chance for precisely 2 spades?

3. If in the long run, male and female mice are born in equal numbers, what is the probability that a litter of 10 would contain 7 males and 3 females, on the basis of pure chance? About how many times should this be expected in 1000 litters of 10 each?

4. Like Ex. 3 for 5 males and 5 females, in 100 litters of 10 each.

5. If boys and girls are born in the ratio of 104 : 100, what is the probability, on the basis of chance determination, that four children will all be boys?

6. In throwing three dice what is the probability for 3 aces? Precisely 2 aces? 1 ace? No ace? On the average, how many times should each outcome be expected in 216 trials?

7. In Ex. 6 suppose that a player is charged $1 a throw; and that a prize of $25 is given for 3 aces, $5 for 2 aces, or $1 for one ace. In 216 throws should a player expect to win or lose, on the average; and how much?

8. In measuring a rod 80 times various lengths (l mm.) were obtained, with the frequencies shown in the following table:

l	99.7	99.8	99.9	100.0	100.1	100.2	100.3
f	3	9	17	22	17	9	3

Draw the frequency polygon showing this distribution.

9. In Ex. 8 find the median, mode, mean, quartiles, and σ.

10. Make a cumulative table showing the percentage of the area of the Normal Probability Curve from $x = -4E$ to $x = -3E$, $-2E$, $-E$, etc. Plot A as a function of x from $-4E$ to $4E$. [This curve, with a suitable horizontal scale, is the "phi-gamma curve" of Psychophysics.]

11. Find the mean and σ for the following table in which the class intervals do not include the upper boundaries:

x	0–2	2–4	4–6	6–8	8–10	10–12
f	3	8	18	20	9	2

12. In Ex. 11 draw the histogram and the frequency polygon.

13. In studying the relation of a firm's advertising expenditure and volume of business, it was necessary to find the most probable linear formulas for $\bar{y}$ and $\bar{x}$ in these tables:

x	2	4	6	8
$\bar{y}$	60	68	75	84

y	60	80	100	120
$\bar{x}$	2	3.6	5.3	6.8

The index of correlation is $r = \sqrt{(d\bar{y}/dx) \cdot (d\bar{x}/dy)}$. Find this.

14. In a psychological test the middle 50% of the students in "X" College scored between 200 and 240. In a large group of colleges the middle 50% scored between 175 and 225. If both distributions were "normal," what percentage of the scores in each case were above 200? Above 250? Below 150? Draw the two overlapping curves.

CHAPTER XV

COMPLEX NUMBERS

OPERATIONS WITH DIRECTED QUANTITIES

§ 383. The Real Number System. Elementary arithmetic deals only with positive numbers — running from zero upward. In algebra we invent another set of numbers — "negative numbers" — running from zero downward.

In arithmetic it is impossible to subtract 7 from 5, or 9 from 0, or any other number from a smaller one. In algebra this is possible: $5 - 7$ gives simply -2; etc. The introduction of negative numbers makes subtraction possible in all cases.

Still more important, the complete set of positive and negative numbers is adapted to the study of *opposite quantities*, such as temperatures above and below zero, elevations above and below sea-level, latitudes north and south, gains and losses, forces upward and downward, etc.

The complete set of positive and negative numbers is called the Real Number System.

The positive numbers can be represented by the points of a line in one direction from a chosen point or origin; the complete set of positive and negative numbers by all the points of a line, in both directions from the origin or zero point.

Students just beginning algebra sometimes wonder how negative numbers are possible. Can there be any number lower than zero? Not if we are thinking of numbers as in arithmetic. But this is just the point: In algebra we are talking about a *new kind* of number. But are not such numbers purely fictitious or abstract? Yes, until we exhibit some concrete interpretation for them — some definite set of objects to which they can be applied, such as temperatures below zero, accelerations downward, etc.

To deal with negative numbers, certain rules of operation are agreed upon, such as $(-a) \times (-b) = (+ab)$, etc. These, while arbitrary, are justified by the useful way in which the rules work. The same will be true of what we shall say about "imaginary numbers."

(In inventing any new kind of number, we have a right to prescribe the rules of combination — just as the inventor of any game, such as chess, had the right to specify how the "pieces" should move. But of course the only rules of combination widely adopted are those which for esthetic or other reasons are found, upon trial, to be suitable.)

§ 384. "Imaginary" Numbers.

In elementary algebra, as long as we know only the real number system, it is impossible to solve the equation $x^2 = -4$. For the square of any real number, positive or negative, is positive, and hence never -4.

But we can solve this and similar equations by inventing a still different set of numbers, commonly called *imaginary* numbers. We may do this as follows:

Let i denote a number whose square is -1, that is,

$$i^2 = -1, \text{ or } i = \sqrt{-1}. \tag{1}$$

And let $-i$ denote the result of subtracting i from zero; that is, $(-i) = 0 - (i)$. Squaring shows that $(-i)^2 = i^2 = -1$. Thus there are two numbers, i and $-i$, whose square equals -1. So -1 has two square roots, i and $-i$. We shall denote either by $\sqrt{-1}$.

Observe that i and $-i$ are not "real" numbers; and are not to be regarded as positive or negative, greater or less than zero. They are, however, opposites.

With the introduction of the "imaginary unit" i, and multiples of i, we can extract the square root of any negative number. *E.g.*,

$$\sqrt{-4} = \sqrt{4}\sqrt{-1}, \quad = 2i, \text{ or } -2i.$$
$$\sqrt{-13} = \sqrt{13}\sqrt{-1}, \quad = \sqrt{13}\,i, \text{ or } -\sqrt{13}\,i.$$

In fact, by using combinations of real and imaginary units, such as $3 + 2i$, etc., called *complex* numbers, we can extract the square root, or any other root, of any real or complex number.

For instance: $\sqrt{7 - 24\,i} = 4 - 3\,i$ or $-4 + 3\,i$. This may be verified by squaring either result.

Indeed, the number system composed of all possible combinations, such as $a + bi$, where a and b are any real numbers, suffices for all the purposes of ordinary algebra.

§ 385. Operations. We agree that complex numbers shall be combined according to the usual rules of algebra, multiplying sums term by term, adding like terms, etc.

For instance:

$$(2 + 3\,i) + (5 + 8\,i) = 7 + 11\,i$$
$$(2 + 3\,i)\,(5 + 8\,i) = 10 + 15\,i + 16\,i + 24\,i^2$$

Since $i^2 = -1$, this last reduces to $-14 + 31\,i$.

To perform a division, we first indicate the result as a fraction, and then rationalize the denominator. If the denominator is $a + bi$ we have simply to multiply above and below by $a - bi$.

For instance:

$$(2 + 3\,i) \div (5 + 8\,i) = \frac{2 + 3\,i}{5 + 8\,i} = \frac{(2 + 3\,i)\,(5 - 8\,i)}{(5 + 8\,i)\,(5 - 8\,i)}$$

$$= \frac{34 - i}{5^2 - (8\,i)^2} = \frac{34}{89} - \frac{1}{89}\,i.$$

In this way, the quotient of any two complex numbers is reducible to the standard form of a complex number, $c + di$. (How could any division be checked?)

THEOREM. *Two complex numbers can be equal only if their real parts are equal, and also their imaginary parts.*

For instance, if $x + yi = 3 + 4\,i$, then $x = 3$ and $y = 4$. For $x - 3 = (4 - y)i$, and if both sides were not zero, we should on squaring have a positive number equal to a negative.

To extract a square root, denote the required root by $a + bi$. Then square, and compare with the given number.

For instance, let us find $\sqrt{7 - 24\,i}$, $= a + bi$, say.
Squaring: $7 - 24\,i = a^2 + 2\,abi + b^2i^2$. Equating real parts, and also imaginary parts: $a^2 - b^2 = 7$, $2\,ab = -24$. Solving gives $a = \pm 4$, $b = \mp 3$.

$$\therefore \ \sqrt{7 - 24\,i} = 4 - 3\,i, \text{ or } -4 + 3\,i.$$

EXERCISES

1. Perform these additions and subtractions, and simplify:

  (a) $(3 + 5\,i) + (7 + 2\,i)$,   (b) $(14 + 10\,i) - (6 + i)$,
  (c) $(-5 - 3\,i) + (2 - 10\,i)$,   (d) $(-4 + 3\,i) - (-7 - 9\,i)$.

2. Perform the multiplications and divisions, in each case reducing the result to the standard form $x + yi$:

(a) $(6 + 3\,i)\,(10 - 2\,i)$,   (b) $(7 - 2\,i) \div (3 - i)$,
(c) $(-2 + 11\,i) \div i$,   (d) $(-2 + 11\,i)\,i$,
(e) $(2 - 7\,i)\,(i^4 - i^3)$,   (f) $5 \div (7 + 3\,i)$,
(g) $(1 - i)^4$,   (h) $i \div (8\,i - 3)$.

3. Find two square roots for each of the following:

(a) $5 + 12\,i$,   (b) $5 - 12\,i$,   (c) $-5 - 12\,i$,   (d) $-12 + 5\,i$,
(e) $8 - 15\,i$,   (f) $-15 - 8\,i$,   (g) $24 + 7\,i$,   (h) $21 - 20\,i$,
(i) $63 + 16\,i$,   (j) $11 - 60\,i$,   (k) $-9 + 40\,i$,   (l) $-91 - 60\,i$.

§ 386. Geometrical Representation of Complex Numbers. In any given plane let a pair of rectangular coordinate axes OX and OY be selected. And *let any complex number $x + yi$ be represented by the directed line-segment, or "vector," OP* drawn from the origin O to the point P whose coordinates are x and y.

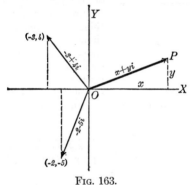

FIG. 163.

E.g., the number $-3 + 4\,i$ is represented by the vector from O to the point $(-3, 4)$. Observe that it is not the *length* of the vector (viz. 5) which represents the complex number, but rather the *vector itself* — *i.e.*, the directed line-segment.

The length of the vector OP, written $|x + yi|$, is called the absolute value or numerical value of the number $x + yi$:

$$Num.\ value\ of\ x + yi = |\,x + yi\,| = \sqrt{x^2 + y^2}. \qquad (2)$$

Observe that when we say that the numerical value of $-3 + 4\,i$ is $\sqrt{(3)^2 + (4)^2} = 5$, we are not saying that $-3 + 4\,i = 5$. The numerical value of -10 is 10: but -10 does not equal 10.

With this representation of a complex number, let us see what will represent the *sum* of two such numbers. We have agreed that

$$(x + yi) + (x' + y'i) = (x + x') + (y' + y)\,i. \qquad (3)$$

Hence the vector representing the sum should run from O to the point whose coordinates are $(x + x',\, y + y')$.

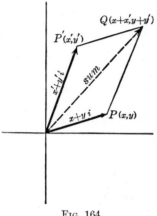

In other words, to add two complex numbers graphically, proceed just as in finding the combined effect of two forces which act from a common point. Make a parallelogram.

Remark. Such vectors, combined in this way, have all the properties of complex numbers. Hence to picture to yourself what sort of thing an "imaginary" number is, simply think of these directed lines. Thus a complex number is not something vague and impossible of existence in a real world. It is simply a more general kind of number than the "real" numbers whose vectors all lie along the X-axis.

Fig. 164.

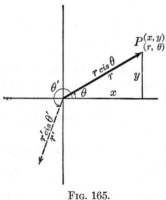

Fig. 165.

§ 387. **Polar Form of a Complex Number.** In the form $x + yi$, a complex number is expressed in terms of the rectangular coordinates x and y of the end of its vector. For many purposes it is better expressed in terms of the polar coordinates (r, θ) of that point. (Fig. 165.)

Clearly we have $x = r \cos \theta$, and $y = r \sin \theta$; hence

$$x + yi = r\,(\cos \theta + i \sin \theta). \qquad (4)$$

This latter is called the "polar form" of the complex number.

while $x + yi$ is called the rectangular form of expression.
As before, r is called the *absolute value* of the number; θ is called the *argument* or simply the angle.

Cos $\theta + i$ sin θ is often abbreviated cis θ. Thus

$$x + yi = r \operatorname{cis} \theta. \qquad (5)$$

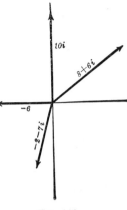

To change easily from the rectangular to the polar form, or *vice versa*, simply draw the vector; and calculate the required values of (r, θ) or (x, y) from the figure. Such changes are exceedingly important and should be practiced freely.

Fig. 166.

Ex. I. Find the polar forms for $8 + 6\,i$; $-2 - 7\,i$; -6; $10\,i$. Fig. 166 shows the vectors representing these numbers.

(1) Here $r = \sqrt{8^2 + 6^2} = 10$; $\tan \theta = \frac{3}{4}$, $\theta = 36°\,52'$.

$\therefore\ 8 + 6\,i = 10\,(\cos 36°\,52' + i \sin 36°\,52') = 10 \operatorname{cis} 36°\,52'$.

(2) Here $r = \sqrt{(-2)^2 + (-7)^2} = \sqrt{53}$, $\tan \theta = \frac{-7}{-2}$, $\theta = 180° + 74°\,3'$.

$\therefore\ -2 - 7\,i = \sqrt{53} \operatorname{cis} 254°\,3'$.

(3) Here, by inspection, $r = 6$; $\theta = 180°$.

$\therefore\ -6 = 6\,(\cos 180° + i \sin 180°) = 6 \operatorname{cis} 180°$.

(4) Here, by inspection, $r = 10$; $\theta = 90°$.

$\therefore\ 10\,i = 10\,(\cos 90° + i \sin 90°) = 10 \operatorname{cis} 90°$.

EXERCISES

1. Mark the points and draw the vectors representing these numbers:

$-6\,i$,	$7 + 2\,i$,	$-4 - 3\,i$,	-8,
$8.5\,i$,	$3 - 7\,i$,	$-2 + i$,	3.

2. Perform the following additions algebraically, and also geometrically by means of the vectors representing the given numbers:

(a) $(2 + 5\,i) + (4 + 6\,i)$,   (b) $(3 + 4\,i) + (2 - 7\,i)$,
(c) $(4 + i) + (-6 + 3\,i)$,   (d) $(2 + 9\,i) + (-2 - 3\,i)$,
(e) $(10 - 4\,i) + (7\,i)$,   (f) $(-18) + (-5\,i)$.

3. Draw the vector representing each of the following numbers, find its r and θ, and re-write the number in polar form:

(a) $4 + 3\,i$,   (b) $3 - 3\,i$,   (c) $- 4\,i$,

(d) $3 - 4\,i$,   (e) $- 5\sqrt{3} + 5\,i$,   (f) $-11\,i$,

(g) 7,   (h) $- 5\sqrt{3} - 5\,i$,   (i) -10.

What are some of the different values of θ which can be chosen in c, f, g, i if we do not limit the size of θ?

4. Draw the vector for each of the following, find the x and y belonging to the number, and re-write the number in the form $x + yi$:

(a) 3 cis $60°$,   (b) 2 cis $310°$,   (c) $.4$ cis $270°$,   (d) $.6$ cis $720°$,

(e) $.3$ cis $495°$,   (f) 10 cis $240°$,   (g) 5 cis $180°$,   (h) 8 cis $0°$.

5. Plot, and find the standard polar form for these numbers:

(a) $\cos 50° - i \sin 50°$,   (b) $- 5$ cis $70°$,   (c) $- 10\,(\cos 60° + i \sin 30°)$.

§ 388. Multiplication and Division, in Polar Form.   Any two complex numbers can be expressed in the form:

$$r\,(\cos \theta + i \sin \theta), \qquad r'\,(\cos \theta' + i \sin \theta').$$

Multiplying these together will give

$$rr'\,[(\cos \theta \, \cos \theta' - \sin \theta \, \sin \theta') + i \,(\sin \theta \, \cos \theta' + \cos \theta \, \sin \theta')].$$

But by the Addition Formulas of Trigonometry (§ 304), the first parenthesis is $\cos (\theta + \theta')$, and the second is $\sin (\theta + \theta')$. Hence the product above reduces to

$$rr'\,[\cos (\theta + \theta') + i \sin (\theta + \theta')].$$

$$r \text{ cis } \theta \cdot r' \text{ cis } \theta' = rr' \text{ cis } (\theta + \theta'). \tag{6}$$

That is, to multiply two complex numbers, *multiply their absolute values and add their angles.*   To divide, simply reverse this process.   (If the numbers are given in the form of $x + yi$, first put them into the polar form.)

Ex. I.   Multiplying 5 cis $300°$ by 7 cis $40°$ gives 35 cis $340°$, *i.e.*, $(35 \cos 340°) + (35 \sin 340°)\,i$, or $11.97 - 32.89\,i$.

Ex. II.   Find $x = (2 \text{ cis } 15°)^{10}$.

For this repeated multiplication, we keep on multiplying the r's and adding the θ's, until we finally get

$$x = 2^{10} \text{ cis } 150° = 1024\,(- .866 + .500\,i) = - 887 + 512\,i.$$

Remark.   By (23), p. 459, $\cos \theta + i \sin \theta = e^{i\theta}$,   ($\theta$ in radians).
Hence equation (6) above may be written:

$$re^{i\theta} \cdot r'e^{i\theta'} = rr' \cdot e^{i(\theta + \theta')}.$$

In other words, this shows that the usual law for exponents in multiplying holds good even when the exponents are pure imaginaries, $i\theta$ and $i\theta'$.

§ **389. Powers and Roots.** From (6) it follows that for any positive integral value of n:

$$(r \operatorname{cis} \theta)^n = r^n \operatorname{cis} n\theta.$$

Thus we can very quickly find any high power of a complex number which is given in the polar form.

This same idea furnishes a means of *extracting any root* of a complex number.

ILLUSTRATION.   Find $x = \sqrt[3]{7 \operatorname{cis} 300°}$.

Let us denote any possible value of x by $r \operatorname{cis} \theta$:

$$r \operatorname{cis} \theta = \sqrt[3]{7 \operatorname{cis} 300°}.$$

Cubing: $r^3 \operatorname{cis} 3\,\theta = 7 \operatorname{cis} 300°.$

This equation is satisfied by $r = \sqrt[3]{7}$ and $\theta = 100°$.

∴ $\sqrt[3]{7 \operatorname{cis} 300} = \sqrt[3]{7} \operatorname{cis} 100° = -.332 + 1.884\,i$, approximately.

This, however, is not the only possible cube root of the given number. For adding any multiple of 360° to the given angle would not change the value of its sine or cosine; and thus the given number could be written in any of the forms:

$$7 \operatorname{cis} 300°, \ 7 \operatorname{cis} 660°, \ 7 \operatorname{cis} 1020°, \ 7 \operatorname{cis} 1380°, \ldots$$

The cube roots obtained from these would be

$$\sqrt[3]{7} \operatorname{cis} 100°, \ \sqrt[3]{7} \operatorname{cis} 220°, \ \sqrt[3]{7} \operatorname{cis} 340°, \ \sqrt[3]{7} \operatorname{cis} 460°, \ldots$$

The last of these equals the first, however. And further forms would only repeat some of the first three.

Thus, $7 \operatorname{cis} 300°$ has three cube roots which are distinct — and no more.

In getting r there is no ambiguity. For r is real, and 7 has only one *real* cube root.

In general there are n distinct nth roots of any number, real or imaginary — except zero. They can be found by expressing the given number in the several polar forms:

$$r \operatorname{cis} \theta, \ \ r \operatorname{cis} (\theta + 360°), \ \ r \operatorname{cis} (\theta + 720°), \ldots,$$

extracting the nth root of r, and dividing each angle by n. Further illustrations follow.

Ex. I.   Find the fourth roots of $z = 81$ cis $20°$.
The given number z may also be written:

$$z = 81 \text{ cis } 380°, \quad 81 \text{ cis } 740°, \quad 81 \text{ cis } 1100°, \ldots .$$

$$\therefore \sqrt[4]{z} = 3 \text{ cis } 5°, \quad 3 \text{ cis } 95°, \quad 3 \text{ cis } 185°, \quad 3 \text{ cis } 275°.$$

Ex. II.   Find the square roots of i.
Proceeding as in § 387, we express i in the form

$$i = \text{cis } 90°, \qquad \text{or cis } 450°, \ldots .$$

$$\therefore \sqrt{i} = \text{cis } 45°, \qquad \text{or cis } 225°, \ldots .$$

That is, since sin $45°$ and cos $45°$ are both $\frac{1}{2}\sqrt{2}$ (by geometry),

$$\therefore \sqrt{i} = \frac{\sqrt{2}}{2}(1 + i), \qquad \text{or} -\frac{\sqrt{2}}{2}(1 + i). \quad \text{(Check?)}$$

EXERCISES

1. Find the following products and quotients, expressing the results in both the polar and rectangular forms, and drawing the various vectors involved:

(a) $7 \text{ cis } 50° \times 2 \text{ cis } 10°$,   (b) $7 \text{ cis } 50° \div 2 \text{ cis } 10°$,
(c) $4 \text{ cis } 70° \times 6 \text{ cis } 110°$,   (d) $.4 \text{ cis } 130° \div .01 \text{ cis } 250°$,
(e) $(3 \text{ cis } 80°)^2$,   (f) $-i \div 3 \text{ cis } 120°$,
(g) $(4 \text{ cis } 25°)^3 \times 3 i$,   (h) $(5 \text{ cis } 30°)^0 \div (2 \text{ cis } 54°)^5$.

2. Calculate $x = 3 (\cos 160° - i \sin 160°) \div 4 \text{ cis } 110°$.   (The dividend is not in standard form: consider its vector.)

3. Calculate $x = 35 \div 7 \text{ cis } 80°$.   (The vector for 35 has $\theta = 0$ or $360°$, etc.   Which is best here?)

4. Verify that squaring either answer to Ex. II, § 389, will give i.

5. Find the following roots (all values of each):

(a) $\sqrt[5]{32 \text{ cis } 100°}$,   (b) $\sqrt[4]{81 \text{ cis } (-80°)}$,   (c) $\sqrt[8]{625 \text{ cis } 320°}$,

(d) $\sqrt[3]{-27 i}$,   (e) $\sqrt{64 (\cos 60° - i \sin 60°)}$,   (f) $\sqrt{\cos 20° - i \sin 20°}$.

6. Find the five fifth-roots of -1; and express numerically in the $x + yi$ form by trigonometric tables.   (Hint: What is the polar form for -1?)

7. Find the three cube roots of $+1$, and plot roughly the points representing them.   Where do those points lie?

8. The same as Ex. 7 for the four fourth-roots of $+1$.

§ 390. nth Roots of Unity.   The nth roots of the number $+1$ are interesting, and, in Higher Algebra, very important. Let us consider first the *sixth* roots.

Expressed in the polar form,

$$1 = \operatorname{cis} 0°, \quad \operatorname{cis} 360°, \quad \operatorname{cis} 720°, \quad \operatorname{cis} 1080°, \quad \text{etc.,}$$

$$\therefore \sqrt[6]{1} = \operatorname{cis} 0°, \quad \operatorname{cis} 60°, \quad \operatorname{cis} 120°, \quad \operatorname{cis} 180°, \quad \text{etc.}$$

The vectors representing these sixth roots all have $r = 1$, and their successive angles differ by 60°. Hence their ends lie *on a circle of unit radius,* and are *vertices of a regular inscribed hexagon.*

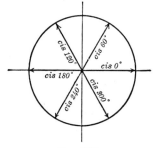

Similarly the nth roots of $+ 1$ are represented by vectors drawn to the vertices of a regular inscribed n-gon.

The nth roots of any number other than 1 would be represented by vectors to the vertices of a regular n-gon inscribed in

FIG. 167.

some circle perhaps of a different radius, and the first vertex being perhaps at some point off the real axis.

§ 391. Summary of Chapter XV. The number system of elementary arithmetic consists solely of real positive numbers, representable by points on a line in one direction from a chosen origin. The complete number system of algebra consists of: (I) All real numbers, representable by all the points along a line or all vectors drawn from the "origin" to those points. (II) All pure imaginaries, representable by vectors to all points on another line perpendicular to the first. (III) All complex numbers (combinations of reals and pure imaginaries) and representable by vectors to all points in the plane.*

The so-called "imaginary" numbers are susceptible of concrete interpretation, and become very useful in electrical engineering and elsewhere.

The rectangular form $x + yi$ is best for addition and subtraction; the polar form $r (\cos \theta + i \sin \theta)$ for finding powers and roots, also for most simple multiplications and divisions.

There are n distinct nth roots of any number, except zero.

* Strictly speaking, (III) includes (I) and (II).

The two square roots (+ or −) as found in elementary algebra are merely a special case of this.

EXERCISES

1. Find the following nth roots and mark the n points representing them in each case:

(a) $\sqrt[8]{1}$,   (b) $\sqrt[4]{-1}$,   (c) $\sqrt[12]{1}$,

(d) $\sqrt[9]{i}$,   (e) $\sqrt[10]{1}$,   (f) $\sqrt[3]{-1}$,

(g) $\sqrt[6]{-1}$,   (h) $\sqrt[3]{-i}$,   (i) $\sqrt[4]{i}$.

2. The same as Ex. 1 for the following

(a) $\sqrt[3]{27 \text{ cis } 30°}$,   (b) $\sqrt[4]{9 \text{ cis } 240°}$,   (c) $\sqrt{4 \text{ cis } 300°}$.

3. In Ex. 1 (a), (b), show graphically and also by calculation that the sum of all the n roots is zero.

4. In what further parts of Ex. 1–2 is the sum of the roots zero?

5. Carry out these calculations, marking the points and getting the results in both polar and rectangular form:

(a) $(8 + 3\,i) + (6 - 5\,i)$,   (b) $(6 + 8\,i) \div (3 - 4\,i)$,

(c) $9 \text{ cis } 30° \times 3 \text{ cis } 90°$,   (d) $18 \text{ cis } 130° \div 8 \text{ cis } 40°$,

(e) $(7 \text{ cis } 22°)^3$,   (f) $\sqrt[4]{16 \text{ cis } 280°}$.

6. Draw the vector 10 cis 90°. Let this represent the maximum strength of an alternating current which varies thus: $y = 10 \sin kt$. Draw the circle having this vector as a diameter, and use it to read off y when kt (or θ) $= \dfrac{\pi}{6},\ \dfrac{5\,\pi}{6},\ \dfrac{3\,\pi}{2},\ \dfrac{11\,\pi}{6}$. (Cf. Fig. 145, p. 391.)

Retrospect and Prospect

We have now considered some of the more important problems relating to variation and the mutual dependence of quantities; and have developed methods of dealing with these problems, at least in the simpler cases.

Most of the mathematical processes covered here and in more elementary courses originated in the effort to solve certain practical problems. For instance, geometry developed out of problems of mensuration, trigonometry from problems of surveying, and algebra from the attempt to systematize certain kinds of calculations. The basic problem of differential calculus is to find the rate at which some quantity will vary with some other quantity on which it depends. Integral calculus seeks to determine how large a varying quantity will be at any time, knowing its present size and its rate of increase at all times. Or, what amounts to the same thing, to find the sum of all infinitesimal elements of a quantity, knowing how each element that we add will vary in size. It would be hard to think of any problem of science or business which is more common or more important than these. Moreover, the calculus methods of analysis — once they are thoroughly understood and have become a habit of thought — are invaluable in analyzing new problems on variation or summation.

As yet, however, we are only on the threshold of Mathematics. We have considered only the most elementary functions — trigonometric, logarithmic, exponential, and power functions, and simple combinations of these. There are many other types of functions, relating to important kinds of variation, not discussed in this course. The study of their differentiation, integration, and application makes calculus a vastly larger subject than the very brief introduction given in this course might suggest.*

Analytic geometry also is an exceedingly extensive subject. Besides rectangular and polar coordinates, numerous other systems of coordinates have been invented, especially for studying geometry upon various kinds of surfaces. There is scarcely any limit to the variety of curves and surfaces whose geometrical properties have been, and are being, investigated analytically. Then, too, there are the *non-euclidean* geometries, and the geometry of *hyperspace* or n dimensions. And in modern times new methods of investigation, of a purely geometrical character ("projective" methods), have led to many beautiful theorems concerning triangles, circles, and other figures.

Algebra, too, has many higher branches — dealing with number relations, the solution of equations, the simplification of expressions by algebraic substitutions, infinite series, etc. Further kinds of numbers, which combine according to laws

* There is in fact no limit to the possible variety of functions, for a quantity may vary with another in any manner whatever.

different even from those for the "imaginary numbers," have also been invented and studied.

In fact, Mathematics has in modern times grown to such vast proportions that no one can now hope to have a detailed knowledge of, let us say, even a tenth of the whole field. Moreover, it is still growing, and more rapidly than ever. Hundreds of research papers are published each year developing new processes and announcing theorems previously unknown.

Much of this higher mathematics is very abstract. But it is not therefore valueless, even from the standpoint of applications. Several subjects which originally developed in a theoretical way with no thought of a practical application have later been taken over bodily by some practical science, *e.g.*, electrical engineering, crystallography, etc. Several others have contributed powerful methods to the solution of particular problems. The theoretical mathematics of today may be practical mathematics tomorrow.

But this is only one aspect of the matter. The intellectual values obtainable from a contemplation of the power, elegance, and absolute precision of mathematical reasoning, and of the perfect harmony existing among the various branches, are very great indeed. Abstract mathematics is a work of invention — *a free creation of the human spirit*, as truly a work of art as the Moonlight Sonata or the Sistine Madonna, but on a much vaster scale than the entire library of great symphonies, the whole gallery of famous paintings, or, indeed, the total assemblage of celebrated cathedrals. In elementary courses — such as this, and those immediately following — which are designed for all classes of students, the practical aspects of the subject deserve particular emphasis. But men and women who have time to get an understanding of the more advanced branches find nothing finer and more inspiring than the wonderfully abstruse investigations of pure mathematics — achievements of the reason which far transcend the realms of physical sense, and time and space.

EXERCISES FOR REVIEW *

1. Calculate to five significant figures:

$$x = \sqrt[3]{\frac{(72.844)^2 \, (.05487)}{1689300}}.$$

2. Two forces, of 24 tons and 11 tons respectively, are applied to an object at a common point, with an included angle of 60°. Find by measurement and also by calculation their resultant and the angle which it makes with the 24-ton force.

3. Differentiate: $y = 6 \sqrt[3]{x^8} + 5 \, (16 - x^2)^{10}$.

4. Find the third derivative of
$$y = x^5 + \tfrac{1}{12} \, x^4 - 10 \, x + 25 + (3/x).$$

5. Find the integrals:

$(a) \displaystyle\int x^3 \, (6 + x)^2 \, dx;$ $(b) \displaystyle\int (\sqrt{x} + 4/x^2) \, dx.$

6. A stone is thrown straight down from an airplane 490 ft. high with an initial speed of 48 ft./sec. Find its angle of elevation as seen 3 sec. later at a point on the level ground 500 ft. away from the point where the stone will strike.

7. The slope of a certain curve at any point is $18 \, x - 3 \, x^2$, and the height at $x = 1$ is 10 units. (a) Calculate the area under the curve from $x = 2$ to $x = 6$. (b) Find the maximum slope of the curve. (c) Plot the curve and check your answers graphically.

8. The force moving an object varied thus: $F = 60 \, t^2 - 4 \, t^3$. Find the momentum imparted from the start until the force reached its maximum value.

9. The height of a certain curve at $x = 0$ is 10. The slope varies with x as shown by the following table:

x	0	1	2	3	4
slope	2	8	14	20	26

Find a formula for the slope and calculate the area under the curve from $x = 0$ to $x = 3$.

10. A boy is pulling his sled along level ground, his pull on the rope being 12 lbs. What are the vertical and horizontal components of the force if the rope makes an angle of 21° with the ground?

11. A partially filled cylindrical cup of diameter 6 in. is gradually tilted up. When the water in it wets just half the base, the inclination of the base is 55°. Find the volume of water, also the area of the level surface of water at that instant.

* See also pp. 227–232.

12. The population of a city on Jan. 1, 1920, was 400,000. It has grown at a rate (R persons per yr.), which has varied as the time (t yr.) elapsed since that date, and which was $R = 2400$ at $t = 2$. What was the population on July 1, 1935?

13. Differentiate:

(a) $z = \log (x^4 + 7\,x)$,   (b) $y = 12\,e^{-5x^2}$,   (c) $Q = 20 \cos 300\,t$.

14. A quantity Q, originally equal to 600, grew at a constant percentage rate of 4 per cent. Write a formula for Q at any time, and show it correct both as to the original value and the rate.

15. Discover the formula for the adjacent table, given that the graph on logarithmic paper would be straight.

16. The values in the following table give a straight graph on semi-logarithmic paper. Find the formula.

x	y
1	600
4	150
12	50
15	40
20	30

x	0	10	20	30	40	50
y	60	98.94	163.10	268.92	443.34	730.92

17. The adjacent table shows the sum total of savings accounts ($\$S$) in a bank t yr. after a certain date. (a) What important curve does the graph resemble? (b) How could you ascertain whether S increased at a constant percentage rate? (c) Find how fast S was increasing at $t = 7$. (d) Find the average sum on deposit from $t = 2$ to $t = 6$.

18. Draw by inspection the curves:

(a) $(x - 3)^2 + (y + 8)^2 = 25$;   (b) $\dfrac{x^2}{100} - \dfrac{y^2}{64} = 1$.

t	S
0	10,000
2	13,500
4	18,220
6	24,600
8	33,200
10	44,820
12	60,500

19. Is the line which joins (1, 4) to the point midway between (7, 2) and (9, 14) perpendicular to the line whose equation is $10\,x + 3\,y = 6$? Show your test.

20. From one end of the minor axis of the curve $\dfrac{x^2}{225} + \dfrac{y^2}{144} = 1$ straight lines are drawn to the two foci. What is the angle between these lines?

21. The arched ceiling of a hall 80 feet wide is parabolic, 8 feet lower at either side than in the middle. Find the slope and inclination of the parabola 30 feet either side of the middle.

22. The arch of a bridge is a semi-ellipse. Its horizontal span is 100 feet and its height at the middle is 30 feet. How high is it 40 feet from the middle?

23. The slope of a certain curve at any point (x, y) is $6x$; and the height at $x = 2$ is 15. Find the equation of the curve. State what kind of curve it is, and draw it roughly.

24. (a) Plot from $x = -4$ to $x = 5$ the graph of $y = 1/x$. What kind of curve is it? (b) Find the area under this curve from $x = 1$ to $x = 5$ graphically and by calculation. (c) Find by calculation the value of x at which an ordinate should be erected to bisect the area in (b).

25. Draw the curve $\dfrac{x^2}{25} - \dfrac{y^2}{9} = 1$. Also find the angle between the asymptotes.

26. How could you lay out an elliptical playground 200 feet long and 120 feet wide? What area would it have? Approximately what perimeter? How wide would it be, measured through either focus?

27. The focus and vertex of the curve $y^2 = 8x$ are both joined to the point on the curve at which $y = 8$. Find the angle between the joining lines.

28. A batted ball traveled thus: $x = 40t$, $y = 4 + 62t - 16t^2$. Draw a figure showing its position at $t = 1$; also its speed and direction of motion then. When was it highest?

29. A parabola has the point $(0, 0)$ as its focus and the line $y = 4$ as its directrix. Find its equation (by inspection, if you can). Also find the area bounded by the parabola and the X-axis.

30. Calculate the angle between lines joining the foci of the ellipse $9x^2 + 25y^2 = 900$ to a point P on the curve if P is 9 in. from one focus.

31. The flexion of a certain curve at any point (x, y) is -2; the slope and height at $x = 0$ are respectively 9 and 0. Find the area under the curve from $x = 0$ to $x = 6$. Also find the maximum height. What kind of curve is it?

32. A point moves so that the square of its distance from $(0, 4)$ always equals the sum of the squares of its distances from $(0, 0)$ and $(2, 0)$. Determine the path. Check by finding a point where the path crosses the X-axis, and testing its distances from the given points.

33. At what point on the curve $x^2 = 20y$ is the tangent line parallel to the line which joins the focus to the point on the curve where $x = 20$?

34. Find all the roots and rational factors of
(a) $3x^4 + 20x^3 + 29x^2 - 4 = 0$,   (b) $2x^4 + 7x^3 - 8x + 3 = 0$.

35. The speed of a moving point after t min. was $v = 20t + 2t^3 - t^4$. Find the distance traveled from the start to the time when the speed was greatest.

36. If the equation $925\,x^{31} - 960\,x^{30} - 1000\,x + 1035 = 0$, has a root near $x = 1.04$, what steps could you take to approximate the root more closely?

37. Find approximately the root of $x^3 - 100\,x - 4 = 0$ which lies near $x = 10$.

38. (*a*) Find all positive angles θ less than $360°$ for which ctn $\theta = -4.3315$. (*b*) Express the following angles in degrees: $\frac{3}{5}\,\pi^{(r)}$, $2.107^{(r)}$.

39. An electric current varied thus: $i = 5\sin 1000\,t$. (The time t is in seconds, and the angle $1000\,t$ in radians.) Find i and the rate at which i was changing at $t = .002$. How many complete cycles per second? What maximum value for i?

40. An alternating electric current follows a formula of the type $i = a\sin kt$. It has a maximum intensity of 10 units and makes 100 complete cycles per second. Find how fast i is changing at $t = .002$.

41. For what inclination of a line 20 in. long will the sum of its horizontal projection and twice its vertical projection be a maximum?

42. An electric current died out thus:

$$i = 10\,e^{-15t}\sin 100\,t.$$

How fast was i changing at $t = .01$?

43. If $y = 10\,e^{-6t}\cos 20\,t$, find the smallest positive value of t at which y reaches a maximum.

44. The number of extra workers needed in a health resort at various times t months after Jan. 1 are shown in the table:

t	0	1	2	3	4	5	6
N	0	100	173	200	173	100	0

(*a*) Plot, regarding months as equal. Find how rapidly the extra workers are being added or laid off, on Feb. 1; likewise on May 1. (*b*) Find a sine formula which should fit the table, at least approximately. Check by calculating two or three values of N from your formula. Also check each rate asked for in (*a*).

45. Given $\sin A = -\frac{3}{5}$ and $\tan B = -\frac{12}{5}$, each angle being less than $270°$: find exact fractional values for $\sin (A + B)$, $\cos (A + B)$, and $\tan (A + B)$.

46. Differentiate:

(*a*) $y = \dfrac{1 - \sin^2 \theta}{\cos \theta}$,   (*b*) $y = \dfrac{\sin^2 \theta}{1 - \cos \theta}$.

47. Simplify and then differentiate:

$$y = \sin^2 x\,(\tan x + \text{ctn } x).$$

48. Find the volume under the surface $z = 4x + y^2$ above the rectangle in the XY-plane bounded by $y = 0$, $y = 2$, $x = 0$, $x = 3$. What sort of curve is cut from this surface by the plane $x = 2$?

49. A hemispherical cistern of radius 10 feet is full of water. Find the work required to pump the water to a level 2 feet above the top, assuming no work to be lost in friction, etc.

50. A hemispherical cistern of radius 6 ft. is partly filled with water, 5 ft. deep at the center. Find the volume of water. Also find for what depth of water the cistern would be half full.

51. The interest rate R that a certain bond will yield depends upon the purchase price (P) and upon the time (T yr.) yet to run. State a possible method for showing graphically how R varies with both P and T, assuming tabulated values available.

52. A balance of $2000 now due on a house is to be paid off in three equal annual installments including interest at 10% per annum, beginning one year hence. Find the size of the installment. Check by calculating the amortization schedule.

53. In each of the following cases express by a formula the value of the item asked for:

(*a*) A $10,000 bond maturing 15 yr. hence carries interest at $5\frac{1}{2}\%$ payable semi-annually. What is its price if bought to yield 6%, compounded semi-annually?

(*b*) A balance of $3000 now due on a house is to be paid, with interest at 6%, in 40 equal monthly installments, beginning 6 months hence. Find the amount of each installment.

(*c*) To rebuild a $100,000 bridge 30 years hence a city is to set aside a fixed sum annually, beginning now and making the last payment 25 years hence. If interest is at 5%, compounded annually, how much must the annual deposit be?

54. Find the numerical answer to each part of Ex. 53, using whatever tables you prefer.

55. A $1000 6% bond (with annual interest coupons) maturing 10 years hence is purchased today for $1030. Describe in detail a method by which you could proceed to find very closely what rate of interest r, convertible annually, the bond will yield the purchaser.

56. If 5 cards are drawn at random from a pack which includes the joker, and simultaneously 5 dice are thrown, what is the probability that precisely 2 aces will be drawn and precisely 2 aces turn up on the dice?

57. Suppose that the statures of women in a nation are distributed according to the Normal Probability Curve with the middle half falling between 62 in. and 65 in. What percentage of all the women are taller than 68 in.? Shorter than 60.5 in.?

EXERCISES FOR REVIEW

58. The ages of pupils entering the sixth grade are distributed approximately according to the Normal Probability Curve, with the middle half of the pupils between 11.5 and 12.5 years. What percentage are under 11 years? Over 13.5 years?

59. Find the most probable linear formula for the adjacent table.

60. The heart weight (W gm.) and the normal pulse frequency (F beats per minute) are apparently related thus: $F = 316/W^{.26}$. Show the general form of the graph, calculating points for $W = 200$ and $W = 300$.

x	y
1	3.1
2	7.9
3	12.9
4	18.1

61. By considering concentric shells of "infinitesimal" thickness express the volume of a sphere of radius 10 in. as a definite integral. Work out and check.

62. Because of the accidental death of a workman, the state is to pay his widow 200 monthly installments of \$30 for herself and 100 monthly installments of \$5 for a minor child, beginning 1 mo. hence. What sum set aside today and drawing 6% interest, compounded monthly, would suffice to meet these payments?

63. The speed V of a chemical reaction is 24 units at a temperature of 20°, and doubles with every rise of 10°. Obtain a formula for the speed at any temperature $T°$. Find V when $T = 35$.

64. Find all non-negative values of $\theta < 360°$ for which

$$\sin \theta \, (2 \cos \theta + 1) \, (\sin \theta - \cos \theta) = 0.$$

65. The same as Ex. 64 for $27 \csc^2 \theta - 54 \operatorname{ctn} \theta - 35 \tan \theta + 9 = 0$.

66. A hemispherical cistern of radius 6 ft. is full of water. Calculate the volume of water by elementary geometry, and by integration.

67. (a) Calculate the wet area of the cistern in Ex. 66 by integration, and check. (b) Knowing that the pressure x ft. below the surface is $62.5 \, x$ lb. per sq. ft., find the total force with which the water presses against the cistern.

68. Differentiate and simplify:

(a) $\log (x + 2) + \dfrac{4x + 7}{2 (x + 2)^2}$,

(b) $\dfrac{\tan \theta + \operatorname{ctn} \theta}{\sec \theta}$,

(c) $\dfrac{\sin x}{\cos x \tan^2 x}$,

(d) $\dfrac{1 - \cos x}{x^2}$.

69. Integrate, using tables if necessary:

(a) $\sec^3 t \tan t \, dt$,

(b) $\sqrt{x^2 - 16} \, x \, dx$,

(c) $\dfrac{dx}{(400 - x^2)^{\frac{3}{2}}}$,

(d) $\dfrac{dx}{x^3 \sqrt{x^2 - 100}}$,

(e) $26 \, e^{-3t} \sin 2 t \, dt$,

(f) $80 \cos 300 \, t \, dt$.

70. A man bought a piece of property for $1000, and ten years later bought another for $2000. After five years more, he sold the two for $5000. The income had meantime just paid for taxes and repairs. To what rate of interest, compounded annually, would this profit be equivalent? (Give the answer correct to the nearest tenth of 1%.)

71. If a ball nine containing 2 seniors, 4 juniors, 3 sophomores draw batting positions at random, what is the chance that the seniors will bat before all others and the juniors after all others?

72. If the chance for a certain event to occur twice in three independent trials is .25, what is the chance, p, that it will occur in a single trial? (Find p correct to 2 decimals.)

73. On a certain day two planets had the positions U (19.8, 303° 14′) and N (30, 114° 34′). Find their distance apart and their rectangular coordinates, at that time.

74. Write by inspection the product of the two complex numbers $7 (\cos 80° + i \sin 80°)$ and $2 (\cos 5° + i \sin 5°)$. Verify your result by multiplying out and comparing.

75. The "hyperbolic sine" and "hyperbolic cosine" of x are two higher functions defined as follows:

$$\sinh x = \tfrac{1}{2} (e^x - e^{-x}), \quad \cosh x = \tfrac{1}{2} (e^x + e^{-x}).$$

Find the value of each when $x = 0$ and when $x = 1$. What is the derivative of each? Find Maclaurin's series for $\sinh x$ as far as x^3.

76. A flywheel of radius 5 ft. was turning with an angular speed of 16 rad./min. when the power was cut off, after which (until the wheel stopped) the acceleration was $d^2 \theta/dt^2 = 12 t^2 - 24 t$. Find how far a point on the rim traveled while the wheel was coming to rest.

77. Write in determinant form the equation of the circle through $(2, 1)$, $(1, -2)$, $(0, 3)$. Simplify and check.

78. Find the equation of a line with slope 3, which is tangent to $y^2 = 10 x - 20$.

79. For what values of l and b will the line $y = lx + b$ be tangent to the curve $y = x^4 - 2 x^2 + x + 3$ at *two* points? Plot and check. [Hint: After eliminating y choose l and b, by inspection so that the quartic equation will have two pairs of equal roots.]

80. The vertices of a triangle are $(2, 5)$ $(10, 9)$ $(14, -3)$. Prove analytically that a line joining the midpoints of two sides is parallel to the third side and equal to half of it.

81. A parabola has the X-axis as directrix and the point $(0, 4)$ as focus. Find to 2 decimal places the value of x at which an ordinate if erected would bisect the area under the parabola from $x = 0$ to $x = 6$.

82. The curve of a loaded beam is such that the derivative of the flexion x feet from one end is $.12\,x - .34$. At $x = 0$ the flexion is .38, the slope is $-.15$, and the height is 10. Find the equation of the curve. Also find the value of x (to two decimal places) at which the maximum and minimum heights occur.

83. A particle oscillated along a straight line in such a way that its distance (x in.) from the starting point after t seconds was: $x = 20 \sin 3\,t$, the angle $3\,t$ being in radians. Find the speed, the acceleration, and the rate at which the acceleration was changing, at $t = .2$. How long a time was consumed in one complete oscillation?

84. The energy (E ergs) needed per sq. mm. to kill $x\%$ of exposed bacteria with ultraviolet light varied as in the following table. Plot the semi-logarithmic graph.

x	30	40	50	60	70	80	90	100
E	2000	2500	3150	3900	4900	6250	8300	10,500

85. The strength of a telephonic current after traveling x mi. in a certain cable is $S = Pe^{-.018x}$. What percentage of the initial strength remains after 25 mi.?

86. The theoretical coefficient of correlation for blended inheritance of a child and parent is .3; child and grandparent, .15; child and great-grandparent, .075. Continuing this progression ten more generations back, what would the coefficient be?

87. A formula of statistical biology is $R = 2\,\sigma\,\sqrt{2 \log\,[n/(\sigma\sqrt{2\,\pi})]}$. Calculate R if $\sigma = 2.3775$ and $n = 1000$.

88. The "life" of a violin string varies in accordance with the Normal Probability Curve. If the middle half run from 900 hours to 1000 hours, what percentage of strings last less than 700 hours? Less than 1200 hours?

89. The weight of silver nitrate which will dissolve in 100 gm. of water at various temperatures is shown here. Find the most probable linear formula.

T	0	20	50	80
W	122	222	455	669

90. By Weber's law in psychology we should have in the adjacent table: $\Delta i = mi$. Here Δi is the smallest increase in the intensity i of a light which a certain observer could detect. Find the most probable value of m.

i	25	60	120	300
Δi	0.2	0.5	0.8	2.5

91. The following tables relate to the statures of a certain group of fathers and sons. Find the most probable linear formulas for $\bar{y}$ and $\bar{x}$; also the index of correlation. (See Ex. 13, p. 499).

x	64	66	68	70
$\bar{y}$	66.7	67.6	69.0	69.7

y	65	67	69	71
$\bar{x}$	65.4	66.5	67.9	69

92. A man says he is thinking of a type of motion in which the speed varies as the square of the elapsed time, while the acceleration varies as the cube of the time. Is this possible? Would it be possible if the two statements were reversed? Explain. Also show that, if the speed varied according to a C. I. L., the acceleration would necessarily vary similarly, and that the acceleration might in fact be always numerically equal to the speed.

93. The rate (R persons per year) at which a city's population grew, has varied thus with the time (t yr.) since Jan. 1, 1900: $R = 2000 + 600\,t - 15\,t^2$. What was the maximum rate of growth and when did it occur? What was the total increase in population in the three decades ending Jan. 1, 1930? Explain how this latter result could be checked graphically.

94. Plot by inspection: $y = 10 \sin x + 4 \sin 2\,x$. Calculate the true height and slope of the graph at $x = \dfrac{\pi}{6}$. Mention some particular field of study in which the addition of sine terms is useful.

95. An arch is a semi-ellipse with a horizontal span of 40 ft., and a height of 16 ft. What is the area of the opening under the arch? How high is the arch where it passes over either focus? What is the angle between two lines drawn from the foci to the highest point of the arch?

96. Write in determinant form the equation of the straight line through $(2, 3)$ and $(5, 4)$. Simplify, and check the equation.

97. Draw by inspection the curves: $y = x^2$, and $(x - 1)^2 + (y - 5)^2 = 20$. Also find all their intersections exactly.

98. A quantity varied thus: $Q = 20 \sin t + 4 \sin 3\,t$. Obtain its graph by inspection, combining two graphs.

99. The frequency f of various numbers of rays (N) on the dorsal fins of 703 flounders was found by C. G. Petersen to be as follows:

N	47	48	49	50	51	52	53	54	55	56	57	58	59	60	61
f	5	2	13	23	58	96	134	127	111	74	37	16	4	2	1

(a) Draw the frequency polygon. (b) Calculate $\overline{N}$. (c) Find σ.

100. Referred to certain axes the coordinates, x ft. and y ft., of certain points on the downstream central profile of the Boulder Dam are shown in the following table. Draw the curve.

x	0	43	113	202	297.5	386.5	459	495
y	727	600	500	400	300	200	100	5

101. In testing the rate of compression R of a substance for specimens of different heights (h in.), the values of h and R were found to give a straight logarithmic graph. When $\log h = 1.5$, $\log R = -2.05$; when $\log h = 1.9$, $\log R = .05$. Show that $R \approx kh^{\frac{21}{4}}$, where k is some constant.

102. In the final equation of Ex. 101, replace R by dh/dt; and derive the relation $h^{-\frac{17}{4}} + \frac{17}{4} kt = C$, some constant.

103. If $y = \log (x + 2 + \sqrt{x^2 + 4x + 1})$, find dy/dx.

104. If $x^2 + 6xy - y^2 = 20$, find dy/dx. Also show that

$$(y - 3x)\left(1 + 3\frac{dy}{dx}\right) - (x + 3y)\left(\frac{dy}{dx} - 3\right) = -\frac{200}{y - 3x}.$$

105. Find values of A, B, C such that adding the fractions

$$\frac{A}{x + 4} + \frac{Bx + C}{x^2 + 1} \text{ will give } \frac{6x^2 - 11}{(x + 4)(x^2 + 1)}.$$

106. If we put $x = 2 \sin t$, show that

$$\frac{\sqrt{4 - x^2}}{x^2}\frac{dx}{dt} = \csc^2 t - 1.$$

107. If $Q = 6 - 5x - x^2$, reduce Q to the difference of a constant and the square of a binomial.

108. In Ex. 107, let $\sqrt{Q} = (6 + x)t$, and find both x and $\sqrt{Q}$ as functions of t alone..

109. Let $\sqrt{6 - 5x + x^2} = t - x$, and express x and dx/dt as functions of t alone.

110. Find the length of a straight line segment joining two points A and B on the surface of a sphere of radius 10 in., if AB makes an angle of 20° with the diameter through A.

111. How many intersections would you ordinarily expect for the line $y = lx + b$ and $x^3 + y^3 + 2xy = 0$? Find them if $l = 5$ and $b = 4$. What if $l = -1$ and $b = \frac{2}{3}$?

APPENDIX

SOME PROOFS

A. Instantaneous Speed and Direction of Motion

$$v = \sqrt{v_x^2 + v_y^2}, \tag{1}$$

$$\tan A = v_y/v_x. \tag{2}$$

Proof of (1): Let Δs be the length of arc PQ traveled during a short time Δt, just following the instant. Then the required speed v is the limit of the average speed $\Delta s/\Delta t$.

There is no simple relation between Δs, Δx, and Δy. But

$$\text{chord } PQ^2 = \Delta x^2 + \Delta y^2,$$

$$\left(\frac{\Delta s}{\Delta t}\right)^2 \left(\frac{\text{chord } PQ}{\Delta s}\right)^2 = \left(\frac{\Delta x}{\Delta t}\right)^2 + \left(\frac{\Delta y}{\Delta t}\right)^2. \tag{3}$$

Let $\Delta t \to 0$. Then $(\Delta s/\Delta t) \to v$, $(\Delta x/\Delta t) \to v_x$, $(\Delta y/\Delta t) \to v_y$. Also the ratio of chord PQ to arc Δs approaches 1 as the arc becomes more nearly straight. Taking limits in (3) we have (1).

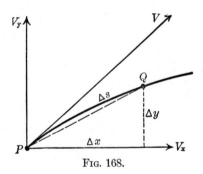

Fig. 168.

Proof of (2): The direction of motion is the direction of the **tangent** line.

$$\tan A = \frac{dy}{dx}.$$

Dividing numerator and denominator by dt, we have (2).

Remark. Equations like (1) and (2) hold also for the total acceleration a and its direction angle A':

$$a = \sqrt{a_x^2 + a_y^2}, \qquad \tan A' = a_y/a_x.$$

The tangential acceleration, however, is dv/dt.

B. Area of a Triangle.   (Cf. § 157)

$$S = \sqrt{h\,(h-a)\,(h-b)\,(h-c)}.$$

Proof: Let p be the altitude of the triangle drawn to the base b — cutting b into segments x and $b-x$.   (Draw a figure.)

Then $\qquad\qquad p^2 = a^2 - x^2 = c^2 - (b-x)^2,$

whence $\qquad\qquad x = (a^2 + b^2 - c^2) \div 2\,b.$

Substituting this in $p^2 = (a+x)\,(a-x)$:

$$p^2 = \left[a + \frac{a^2+b^2-c^2}{2\,b}\right] \cdot \left[a - \frac{a^2+b^2-c^2}{2\,b}\right]$$
$$= [(a+b)^2 - c^2]\,[c^2 - (a-b)^2] \div 4\,b^2$$
$$\therefore 4\,b^2\,p^2 = (a+b+c)\,(a+b-c)\,(c+a-b)\,(c-a+b).$$

Now the quantities in these parentheses are $2\,h$, $(2\,h - 2\,c)$, $(2\,h - 2\,b)$, $(2\,h - 2\,a)$.

$$\therefore 2\,b\,p = \sqrt{16\,h\,(h-a)\,(h-b)\,(h-c)}.$$

The area of the triangle is $\tfrac{1}{2}\,bp$, which gives the formula.

Remark.   For an equilateral triangle with sides a, a, a, the formula gives $S = \sqrt{\tfrac{3}{2}\,a \cdot \tfrac{1}{2}\,a \cdot \tfrac{1}{2}\,a \cdot \tfrac{1}{2}\,a}$; or $a^2\sqrt{3}/4$, evidently correct.

C. Simpson's Rule

Theorem: Simpson's rule gives the exact value of the integral from a to b of any cubic function: $y = k + lx + mx^2 + nx^3$.*

Proof: $\qquad$ At $x = a$, $\quad y_1 = k + la + ma^2 + na^3,$
$\qquad\qquad$ at $x = b$, $\quad y_2 = k + lb + mb^2 + nb^3,$

and midway between, at $x = (a+b)/2$,

$$y_m = k + l\frac{a+b}{2} + m\left(\frac{a+b}{2}\right)^2 + n\left(\frac{a+b}{2}\right)^3.$$

Multiplied out and used in the rule, this gives

$$\tfrac{1}{6}(y_1 + y_2 + 4y_m)(b-a) = k(b-a) + \frac{l}{2}(b^2-a^2) + \frac{m}{3}(b^3-a^3) + \frac{n}{4}(b^4-a^4).$$

But this is precisely the value of the integral:

$$\int_a^b y\,dx. \qquad\qquad Q.\,E.\,D.$$

*For $n = 0$ this covers also quadratics.   And so on.

SOME STANDARD FORMULAS

A. Mensuration.   (Cf. § 62)

Circle: $C = 2\,\pi r,$ $A = \pi r^2.$

Sphere: $S = 4\,\pi r^2,$ $V = \frac{4}{3}\,\pi r^3.$

Cylinder: $S = 2\,\pi rh,$ $V = \pi r^2 h.$

Cone: $S = \pi rs,$ $V = \frac{1}{3}\,\pi r^2 h.$

Frustum: $S = \pi\,(R + r)\,s,$ $V = \frac{1}{3}\,\pi h\,(R^2 + Rr + r^2).$

Segment, of height h, cut from sphere of radius r:

$$S = 2\pi rh, \qquad\qquad V = \frac{1}{3}\,\pi h^2\,(3\,r - h).$$

Segment of circle, central angle θ: $A = \frac{1}{2}\,r^2\,(\theta - \sin\theta).$

Ellipse: $C = 2\,\pi a\,(1 - \frac{1}{4}\,e^2 - \frac{3}{64}\,e^4 - \frac{5}{256}\,e^6 - \cdots),\quad e = c/a.$

B. Algebra and Series

Roots of Quadratic, $ax^2 + bx + c = 0$: $x = \dfrac{-b \pm \sqrt{b^2 - 4\,ac}}{2\,a}.$

Interest: $A = P(1 + r/k)^{kn},\ \ P = A \div (1 + r/k)^{kn}.$

Geom. Progression: $l = ar^{n-1},$ $S = a\,(r^n - 1) \div (r - 1).$

Arith.   ''   : $l = a + (n - 1)d,\ \ S = \frac{n}{2}\,(a + l).$

Relation of base e to base 10: $\log_e N = 2.30259\,\log_{10} N.$

$$C_{n,\,r} = \frac{n\,!}{r\,!\,(n-r)\,!}, \qquad P_{n,\,r} = \frac{n\,!}{(n-r)\,!}. \qquad [0! = 1\,.]$$

Maclaurin series for e^x, $\sin x$, $\cos x$, $\log(1+x)$: see pp. 455–57.

$$\tan x = x + \tfrac{1}{3}\,x^3 + \tfrac{2}{15}\,x^5 + \tfrac{17}{315}\,x^7 + \cdots. \qquad [x^2 < \pi^2/4.]$$

$$\log_e \frac{1+x}{1-x} = 2\,x + \tfrac{2}{3}\,x^3 + \tfrac{2}{5}\,x^5 + \tfrac{2}{7}\,x^7 + \cdots. \qquad [x^2 < 1.]$$

$$(a + x)^n = a^n + \frac{n}{1}\,a^{n-1}\,x + \frac{n\,(n-1)}{1.2}\,a^{n-2}\,x^2 + \cdots. \qquad \begin{bmatrix} \text{any } n, \\ x^2 < 1. \end{bmatrix}$$

$$(1 + x)^{-1} = 1 - x + x^2 - x^3 + \cdots. \qquad [x^2 < 1.]$$

$$(1 + x)^{-2} = 1 - 2\,x + 3\,x^2 - 4\,x^3 + \cdots. \qquad [x^2 < 1.]$$

$$(a + b + c)^2 = a^2 + b^2 + c^2\ + 2\,(ab + bc + ca).$$

$$a^4 + a^2 b^2 + b^4 = (a^2 + ab + b^2)\,(a^2 - ab + b^2).$$

$$a^4 + b^4 = (a^2 + ab\sqrt{2} + b^2)\,(a^2 - ab\sqrt{2} + b^2).$$

$$1 + 2 + 3 + 4 + \cdots + n\ = \tfrac{1}{2}\,n\,(n + 1).$$

$$1^2 + 2^2 + 3^2 + \cdots\ + n^2 = \tfrac{1}{6}\,n\,(n + 1)\,(2\,n + 1).$$

$$1^3 + 2^3 + 3^3 + \cdots\ + n^3 = [\tfrac{1}{2}\,n\,(n + 1)]^2.$$

C. Trigonometry

Definitions:

$\sin \theta = y/r$, (= ordinate ÷ radius vector), etc.   [§ 272.]

Basic Identities:

$\sin^2 \theta + \cos^2 \theta = 1$, $\tan \theta = \sin \theta / \cos \theta$, etc.   [§ 295.]

Addition Formulas:

$\sin (A + B) = \sin A \cos B + \cos A \sin B$, etc.   [§ 304.]

Double-Angles:

$\sin 2\theta = 2 \sin \theta \cos \theta$, $\cos 2\theta = \cos^2 \theta - \sin^2 \theta$.

Half-Angles:

$\sin (\tfrac{1}{2} \theta) = \pm \sqrt{\tfrac{1}{2} (1 - \cos \theta)}$, $\cos (\tfrac{1}{2} \theta) = \pm \sqrt{\tfrac{1}{2} (1 + \cos \theta)}$.

Triangle Laws: Sines,   Cosines, Tangents, Half-Angles,
                     Area: see text references in Index.

Projections: $p = s \cos C$.   [§ 115.]

D. Analytic Geometry

Distance: $d = \sqrt{(x_2 - x_1)^2 + (y_2 - y_1)^2}$.

Midpoint: $\bar{x} = \tfrac{1}{2} (x_1 + x_2), \bar{y} = \tfrac{1}{2} (y_1 + y_2)$.

Slope: $l = (y_2 - y_1) \div (x_2 - x_1)$.

Inclination: $\theta = \tan^{-1} l$.

Angle between lines: $\tan A = (l_2 - l_1) \div (1 + l_1 l_2)$.

Perpendiculars: $l_1 l_2 = -1$, or $l_2 = -1/l_1$.

For equations of lines and curves, see Index under name of that curve.

E. Derivatives

$y =$	$dy/dx =$
u^n	$nu^{n-1}\, du/dx$
x^n	nx^{n-1}
* $\log u$	$\dfrac{1}{u} du/dx$
$\log x$	$\dfrac{1}{x}$
e^u	$e^u\, du/dx$
e^x	e^x
a^u	$a^u \log_e a\, du/dx$

$y =$	$dy/dx =$
† $\sin u$	$\cos u\, du/dx$
$\cos u$	$- \sin u\, du/dx$
$\tan u$	$\sec^2 u\, du/dx$
$\operatorname{ctn} u$	$- \csc^2 u\, du/dx$
$\sec u$	$\sec u \tan u\, du/dx$
$\csc u$	$- \csc u \operatorname{ctn} u\, du/dx$
uv	$u\, dv/dx + v\, du/dx$
$\dfrac{u}{v}$	$\dfrac{v\, du/dx - u\, dv/dx}{v^2}$

*Base e.   † Radian measure.

THE IDEA OF "INFINITY"

ILLUSTRATION. If $y = 60/(2 - x)$, then

(a) There is no possible value for y when $x = 2$;

(b) As x *approaches* 2, y exists and *increases without limit*.

These facts are often stated briefly by saying that

"y approaches infinity $(y \rightarrow \infty)$ as $x \rightarrow 2$,"

or "$y =$ infinity $(y = \infty)$, when $x = 2$."

These statements, however, must not be misunderstood as saying that there is some enormous number (∞) which y equals when $x = 2$. They are to be used only in a technical sense, as a brief way of stating the two facts (a) and (b) above.

USE OF A PROTRACTOR

(I) Fig. 169 illustrates the measurement of a given angle ABC ($= 73°$). The radiating lines on the protractor should meet at the vertex B and the $0°$ line fall directly along BC. If AB tends to cross any radial line, the protractor is not placed correctly as to the vertex.

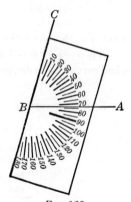

FIG. 169.

(II) In drawing an angle of $73°$, we would first draw AB to serve as one side. Then, placing the protractor so that its $73°$ line falls directly over AB, we would draw BC along the $0°$ line of the protractor. (In allowing for the width of the pencil point, the protractor is slid along in such a way as to keep its $73°$ line *pointing directly along AB*.)

TABLE OF INTEGRALS

GENERAL HINTS

I. *Sums* of several terms: integrate term by term.

II. *Products* or *powers:* multiply out if necessary and feasible.

III. *Fractions:* often simplified by dividing out, or by writing as negative powers.

IV. *Radicals:* may be regarded as fractional powers.

V. *High powers:* use reduction formulas (32)–(44).

VI. *Quadratic expressions* like $ax^2 + bx + c$ can be reduced to binomial forms like $a(t^2 + k)$ by *completing the square:*

$$ax^2 + bx + c = a\left[\left(x^2 + \frac{b}{a}x + \frac{b^2}{4\,a^2}\right) + \left(\frac{c}{a} - \frac{b^2}{4\,a^2}\right)\right]; \text{ let } \left(x + \frac{b}{2\,a}\right) = t.$$

VII. A *constant* should be added to each integral below.

INTEGRALS

1. $\displaystyle\int u^n\,du = \frac{1}{n+1}\,u^{n+1}$ $\qquad\qquad (n \neq -1).$

Here n may have any positive or negative value except -1. *E.g.,*

$$\int x^{\frac{1}{2}}\,dx = \tfrac{2}{3}\,x^{\frac{3}{2}}; \quad \int x^{-1.73}\,dx = -\tfrac{1}{.73}\,x^{-.73}.$$

(2)–(4) *are special cases of* (1).

2. $\displaystyle\int (ax^m + b)^n x^{m-1}\,dx = \frac{1}{n+1}\cdot\frac{1}{ma}\cdot(ax^m + b)^{n+1}.$

This includes forms like $\sqrt{x^4+25}\,x^3\,dx$, $\sqrt{4-x^2}\,x\,dx$, $(3\,x^2+7)^{10}\,x\,dx$, $x\,dx/(x^2-16)^{\frac{5}{2}}$, etc. Simply use in (2) the values of a, b, m, n, which appear in each of these forms.

3. $\displaystyle\int \sin^n x \cos x\,dx = \frac{1}{n+1}\sin^{n+1} x,$ $\qquad (n \neq -1).$

4. $\displaystyle\int \cos^n x \sin x\,dx = -\frac{1}{n+1}\cos^{n+1} x,$ $\qquad (n \neq -1).$

These include forms like $\sin^5 x \cos x\,dx$, $\sin x\,dx/\cos^2 x$, etc.

5. $\displaystyle\int \frac{du}{u} = \log u.$

(6)–(10) *are special cases of* (5).

6. $\displaystyle\int \frac{x^{m-1}\,dx}{ax^m + b} = \frac{1}{ma}\log (ax^m + b).$

This includes forms like $x^3\,ax/(2\,x^4 - 5)$, $\sqrt{x}\,dx/(7\,x^{\frac{3}{2}} + 9)$, etc.

7. $\displaystyle\int \text{ctn } ax \, dx = \int \frac{\cos ax}{\sin ax} \, dx = \frac{1}{a} \log \sin ax.$

8. $\displaystyle\int \tan ax \, dx = -\frac{1}{a} \log \cos ax, = \frac{1}{a} \log \sec ax.$

9. $\displaystyle\int \sec ax \, dx = \int \frac{(\sec^2 ax + \sec ax \tan ax)dx}{\sec ax + \tan ax} = \frac{1}{a} \log (\sec ax + \tan ax).$

10. $\displaystyle\int \csc ax \, dx = -\frac{1}{a} \log (\csc ax + \text{ctn } ax).$

11. $\displaystyle\int \sin ax \, dx = -\frac{1}{a} \cos ax; \qquad \int \cos ax \, dx = \frac{1}{a} \sin ax.$

12. $\displaystyle\int \frac{dx}{a \sin x + b \cos x} = \frac{1}{\sqrt{a^2 + b^2}} \log \tan \frac{x + k}{2},$ where $k = \tan^{-1} b/a.$

13. $\displaystyle\int e^u \, du = e^u; \qquad \int e^{kx} \, dx = \frac{1}{k} e^{kx}.$

14. $\displaystyle\int e^{kx} \sin ax \, dx = \frac{e^{kx}}{k^2 + a^2} (k \sin ax - a \cos ax).$

15. $\displaystyle\int e^{kx} \cos ax \, dx = \frac{e^{kx}}{k^2 + a^2} (k \cos ax + a \sin ax)$

16. $\displaystyle\int \cos ax \cos bx \, dx = \frac{\sin (a - b) x}{2 (a - b)} + \frac{\sin (a + b) x}{2 (a + b)}.$ $\left.\begin{array}{l} \\ \\ \\ \\ \\ \end{array}\right\}$ $a \neq b.$

17. $\displaystyle\int \sin ax \sin bx \, dx = \frac{\sin (a - b) x}{2 (a - b)} - \frac{\sin (a + b) x}{2 (a + b)}.$

18. $\displaystyle\int \sin ax \cos bx \, dx = -\frac{\cos (a - b) x}{2 (a - b)} - \frac{\cos (a + b) x}{2 (a + b)}.$

19. $\displaystyle\int \cos^2 ax \, dx = \frac{1}{2 a} [ax + \tfrac{1}{2} \sin 2 ax].$

20. $\displaystyle\int \sin^2 ax \, dx = \frac{1}{2 a} [ax - \tfrac{1}{2} \sin 2 ax].$

21. $\displaystyle\int \frac{du}{u^2 - a^2} = \frac{1}{2 a} \log \frac{u - a}{u + a}.$

22. $\displaystyle\int \frac{du}{u^2 + a^2} = \frac{1}{a} \tan^{-1} \frac{u}{a}, = \frac{-1}{a} \text{ctn}^{-1} \frac{u}{a}.$

23. $\displaystyle\int \frac{du}{\sqrt{u^2 \pm a^2}} = \log (u + \sqrt{u^2 \pm a^2}).$

24. $\displaystyle\int \frac{du}{\sqrt{a^2 - u^2}} = \sin^{-1} \frac{u}{a}, = -\cos^{-1} \frac{u}{a}.$

25. $\int \sqrt{a^2 - u^2}\, du = \dfrac{u}{2} \sqrt{a^2 - u^2} + \dfrac{a^2}{2} \sin^{-1}\dfrac{u}{a};$

26. $\int \sqrt{u^2 \pm a^2}\, du = \dfrac{u}{2} \sqrt{u^2 \pm a^2} \pm \dfrac{a^2}{2} \log\left(u + \sqrt{u^2 \pm a^2}\right).$

27. $\int \dfrac{du}{u\, \sqrt{u^2 - a^2}} = \dfrac{1}{a} \sec^{-1}\dfrac{u}{a} = \dfrac{1}{a} \cos^{-1}\dfrac{a}{u}.$

$du / (u\sqrt{au + b}) = 2\, dr / (r^2 - b)$, where $r = \sqrt{au + b}$. Use (21) or (22).

28. $\int \dfrac{du}{(u^2 \pm a^2)^{\frac{3}{2}}} = \dfrac{\pm u}{a^2\, \sqrt{u^2 \pm a^2}};$ $\int \dfrac{du}{(a^2 - u^2)^{\frac{3}{2}}} = \dfrac{u}{a^2\, \sqrt{a^2 - u^2}}.$

29. $\int \sin^{-1} x\, dx = x \sin^{-1} x + \sqrt{1 - x^2}.$

30. $\int \tan^{-1} x\, dx = x \tan^{-1} x - \tfrac{1}{2} \log(1 + x^2).$

31. $\int x^n \log x\, dx = x^{n+1}\left[(n + 1) \log x - 1\right] \div (n + 1)^2.$

REDUCTION FORMULAS

32. $\int x^n e^{kx}\, dx = \dfrac{1}{k} x^n e^{kx} - \dfrac{n}{k}\int x^{n-1} e^{kx}\, dx.$ Leads to (13).

33. $\int x^n \cos ax\, dx = \dfrac{x^n}{a} \sin ax - \dfrac{n}{a}\int x^{n-1} \sin ax\, dx.$ ⎫

34. $\int x^n \sin ax\, dx = -\dfrac{x^n}{a} \cos ax + \dfrac{n}{a}\int x^{n-1} \cos ax\, dx.$ ⎬ Lead to (11).

35. $\int \sin^n ax\, dx = -\dfrac{\sin^{n-1} ax \cos ax}{na} + \dfrac{n-1}{n}\int \sin^{n-2} ax\, dx.$ (11),

(19),

36. $\int \cos^n ax\, dx = \dfrac{\cos^{n-1} ax \sin ax}{na} + \dfrac{n-1}{n}\int \cos^{n-2} ax\, dx.$ or

(20).

37. $\int \tan^n ax\, dx = \dfrac{\tan^{n-1} ax}{(n-1)\, a} - \int \tan^{n-2} ax\, dx.$

38. $\int \operatorname{ctn}^n ax\, dx = -\dfrac{\operatorname{ctn}^{n-1} ax}{(n-1)\, a} - \int \operatorname{ctn}^{n-2} ax\, dx.$

39. $\int \sec^n ax\, dx = \dfrac{1}{(n-1)\, a} \sin ax \sec^{n-1} ax + \dfrac{n-2}{n-1}\int \sec^{n-2} ax\, dx.$

40. $\int \csc^n ax\, dx = \dfrac{-1}{(n-1)\, a} \cos ax \csc^{n-1} ax + \dfrac{n-2}{n-1}\int \csc^{n-2} ax\, dx.$

in (41)–(44) below, u denotes $ax^n + b$, and each formula is valid as long as its denominator is not zero. When a denominator is zero, the expression is integrable by some other formula, such as (2), (6), (21), etc., or by substituting $ax^n + b = t$ or $x^n\, t$.

41. $\displaystyle \int x^m\, (ax^n + b)^p\, dx = \frac{1}{m + np + 1}\left(x^{m+1}u^p + npb \int x^m\, u^{p-1}\, dx\right).$

42. $\displaystyle \int x^m\, (ax^n + b)^p\, dx = \frac{1}{bn\,(p+1)}\Big(-x^{m+1}\, u^{p+1}$
$$+ (m + n + np + 1)\int x^m\, u^{p+1}\, dx\Big).$$

43. $\displaystyle \int x^m\, (ax^n + b)^p\, dx = \frac{1}{(m+1)\,b}\Big(x^{m+1}\, u^{p+1}$
$$- a\,(m + n + np + 1)\int x^{m+n}\, u^p\, dx\Big).$$

44. $\displaystyle \int x^m\, (ax^n + b)^p\, dx = \frac{1}{a\,(m + np + 1)}\Big(x^{m-n+1}\, u^{p+1}$
$$- (m - n + 1)\, b \int x^{m-n}\, u^p\, dx\Big)$$

N.B. By (41)–(44) the power of the binomial can be raised or lowered by one unit at each step, or the power outside be increased or decreased by the power inside the parentheses.

These formulas cover such types as:

$$\int \frac{dx}{(x^2 + 16)^3},\ [m = 0,\ p = -3.\ \text{Use (42) twice, then (22)}];$$

$$\int \frac{x\, dx}{\sqrt{ax + b}},\ [m = n = 1,\ p = \tfrac{1}{2}.\ \text{Use (44) once, then (2)}].$$

APPLICATIONS

45. Area under a curve $y = f(x)$, $\qquad A = \displaystyle\int y\, dx.$

46. Volume of a solid, sectional area A_s, $\quad V = \displaystyle\int A_s\, dx.$

47. Length of curve, $y = f(x)$, $\qquad s = \displaystyle\int \sqrt{1 + (dy/dx)^2}\, dx.$

48. Surface of revolution about X-axis, $\quad S = \displaystyle\int 2\pi\, y\, ds.$

49. Length of curve, $r = f(\theta)$, $\qquad s = \displaystyle\int \sqrt{r^2 + (dr/d\theta)^2}\, d\theta.$

50. Work of a force, $\qquad\qquad\qquad W = \displaystyle\int F\, dx.$

51. Momentum generated, $M = \int F\, dt.$

52. Force of water pressure, $F = \int 62.5\, xw\, dx.$

53. Total attraction of rod, $F = \int G\, mk\, dx/x^2.$

54. Quantity of electricity flowing, $Q = \int i\, dt.$

SOME IMPORTANT CONSTANTS

$\pi = 3.14159265,$ $\log_{10} \pi = .49714987.$

$e = 2.71828183,$ $\log_{10} e = .43429448.$

$$\log_e 10 = \frac{1}{\log_{10} e} = 2.30258509.$$

$1^{(r)} = 57°.2957795$	$1° = .01745329^{(r)}$
$1^{(r)} = 206264''.806$	$1'' = 4.848137^{(r)} \times 10^{-6}$
1 ft. = 30.48 cm.	1 cm. = .0328 ft.
1 cu. ft. = 28317 cc.	1 cc. = .0000353 cu. ft.
1 lb. = .4536 kg.	1 kg. = 2.2046 lb.
1 gal. = 231 cu. in.	1 watt = .738 ft.-lb./sec.
1 acre = 10 sq. chains	1 chain = 66 ft.

THE EARTH'S RADIUS

Equatorial, 3963.4 mi.	Polar, 3950.0 mi.

GRAVITATIONAL ACCELERATION (sea-level, lat. 45°)

$g = 980.60$ cm./sec.^{2} $g = 32.172$ ft./sec.^{2}

For any other latitude $L°$ multiply by $(1 - .0026 \cos 2\,L)$.

DISTRIBUTION OF DEVIATIONS IN NORMAL CASE

(E = Probable deviation)

Zero to....	$\frac{1}{4}E$	$\frac{1}{2}E$	$\frac{3}{4}E$	E	$\frac{5}{4}E$	$\frac{3}{2}E$	$\frac{7}{4}E$	$2\,E$	$3\,E$	$4\,E$
Percentage	6.7	13.2	19.4	25.0	30.0	34.4	38.1	41.1	47.8	49.7

The *standard deviation* σ (or square root of the mean of the squares of all the deviations of N values from their average) should in the long run approach $1.4826\,E$; or $E = .6745\,\sigma$.

SQUARES AND SQ. ROOTS — CUBES AND CUBE ROOTS

N	N²	√N̄	√10 N		N³	∛N̄	∛10 N	∛100N
1.0	1.00	1.0000	3.1623		1.000	1.0000	2.1544	4.6416
1.1	1.21	1.0488	3.3166		1.331	1.0323	2.2240	4.7914
1.2	1.44	1.0954	3.4641		1.728	1.0627	2.2894	4.9324
1.3	1.69	1.1402	3.6056		2.197	1.0914	2.3513	5.0658
1.4	1.96	1.1832	3.7417		2.744	1.1187	2.4101	5.1925
1.5	2.25	1.2247	3.8730		3.375	1.1447	2.4662	5.3133
1.6	2.56	1.2649	4.0000		4.096	1.1696	2.5198	5.4288
1.7	2.89	1.3038	4.1231		4.913	1.1935	2.5713	5.5397
1.8	3.24	1.3416	4.2426		5.832	1.2164	2.6207	5.6462
1.9	3.61	1.3784	4.3589		6.859	1.2386	2.6684	5.7489
2.0	4.00	1.4142	4.4721		8.000	1.2599	2.7144	5.8480
2.1	4.41	1.4491	4.5826		9.261	1.2806	2.7589	5.9439
2.2	4.84	1.4832	4.6904		10.648	1.3006	2.8020	6.0368
2.3	5.29	1.5166	4.7958		12.167	1.3200	2.8439	6.1269
2.4	5.76	1.5492	4.8990		13.824	1.3389	2.8845	6.2145
2.5	6.25	1.5811	5.0000		15.625	1.3572	2.9240	6.2996
2.6	6.76	1.6125	5.0990		17.576	1.3751	2.9625	6.3825
2.7	7.29	1.6432	5.1962		19.683	1.3925	3.0000	6.4633
2.8	7.84	1.6733	5.2915		21.952	1.4095	3.0366	6.5421
2.9	8.41	1.7029	5.3852		24.389	1.4260	3.0723	6.6191
3.0	9.00	1.7321	5.4772		27.000	1.4422	3.1072	6.6943
3.1	9.61	1.7607	5.5678		29.791	1.4581	3.1414	6.7679
3.2	10.24	1.7889	5.6569		32.768	1.4736	3.1748	6.8399
3.3	10.89	1.8166	5.7446		35.937	1.4888	3.2075	6.9104
3.4	11.56	1.8439	5.8310		39.304	1.5037	3.2396	6.9795
3.5	12.25	1.8708	5.9161		42.875	1.5183	3.2711	7.0473
3.6	12.96	1.8974	6.0000		46.656	1.5326	3.3019	7.1138
3.7	13.69	1.9235	6.0828		50.653	1.5467	3.3322	7.1791
3.8	14.44	1.9494	6.1644		54.872	1.5605	3.3620	7.2432
3.9	15.21	1.9748	6.2450		59.319	1.5741	3.3912	7.3061
4.0	16.00	2.0000	6.3246		64.000	1.5874	3.4200	7.3681
4.1	16.81	2.0248	6.4031		68.921	1.6005	3.4482	7.4290
4.2	17.64	2.0494	6.4807		74.088	1.6134	3.4760	7.4889
4.3	18.49	2.0736	6.5574		79.507	1.6261	3.5034	7.5478
4.4	19.36	2.0976	6.6332		85.184	1.6386	3.5303	7.6059
4.5	20.25	2.1213	6.7082		91.125	1.6510	3.5569	7.6631
4.6	21.16	2.1448	6.7823		97.336	1.6631	3.5830	7.7194
4.7	22.09	2.1679	6.8557		103.823	1.6751	3.6088	7.7750
4.8	23.04	2.1909	6.9282		110.592	1.6869	3.6342	7.8297
4.9	24.01	2.2136	7.0000		117.649	1.6985	3.6593	7.8837
5.0	25.00	2.2361	7.0711		125.000	1.7100	3.6840	7.9370
5.1	26.01	2.2583	7.1414		132.651	1.7213	3.7084	7.9896
5.2	27.04	2.2804	7.2111		140.608	1.7325	3.7325	8.0415
5.3	28.09	2.3022	7.2801		148.877	1.7435	3.7563	8.0927
5.4	29.16	2.3238	7.3485		157.464	1.7544	3.7798	8.1433
5.5	30.25	2.3452	7.4162		166.375	1.7658	3.8030	8.1932
5.6	31.36	2.3664	7.4833		175.616	1.7752	3.8259	8.2426
5.7	32.49	2.3875	7.5498		185.193	1.7863	3.8485	8.2913
5.8	33.64	2.4083	7.6158		195.112	1.7967	3.8709	8.3396
5.9	34.81	2.4290	7.6811		205.379	1.8070	3.8930	8.3872
6.0	36.00	2.4495	7.7460		216.000	1.8171	3.9149	8.4343

SQUARES AND SQ. ROOTS — CUBES AND CUBE ROOTS

N	N²	$\sqrt{N}$	$\sqrt{10\,N}$	N³	$\sqrt[3]{N}$	$\sqrt[3]{10\,N}$	$\sqrt[3]{100\,N}$
6.0	36.00	2.4495	7.7460	216.000	1.8171	3.9149	8.4343
6.1	37.21	2.4698	7.8102	226.981	1.8272	3.9365	8.4809
6.2	38.44	2.4900	7.8740	238.328	1.8371	3.9579	8.5270
6.3	39.69	2.5100	7.9373	250.047	1.8469	3.9791	8.5726
6.4	40.96	2.5298	8.0000	262.144	1.8566	4.0000	8.6177
6.5	42.25	2.5495	8.0623	274.625	1.8663	4.0207	8.6624
6.6	43.56	2.5690	8.1240	287.496	1.8758	4.0412	8.7066
6.7	44.89	2.5884	8.1854	300.763	1.8852	4.0615	8.7503
6.8	46.24	2.6077	8.2462	314.432	1.8945	4.0817	8.7937
6.9	47.61	2.6268	8.3066	328.509	1.9038	4.1016	8.8366
7.0	49.00	2.6458	8.3666	343.000	1.9129	4.1213	8.8790
7.1	50.41	2.6646	8.4261	357.911	1.9220	4.1408	8.9211
7.2	51.84	2.6833	8.4853	373.248	1.9310	4.1602	8.9628
7.3	53.29	2.7019	8.5440	389.017	1.9399	4.1793	9.0041
7.4	54.76	2.7203	8.6023	405.224	1.9487	4.1983	9.0450
7.5	56.25	2.7386	8.6603	421.875	1.9574	4.2172	9.0856
7.6	57.76	2.7568	8.7178	438.976	1.9661	4.2358	9.1258
7.7	59.29	2.7749	8.7750	456.533	1.9747	4.2543	9.1657
7.8	60.84	2.7928	8.8318	474.552	1.9832	4.2727	9.2052
7.9	62.41	2.8107	8.8882	493.039	1.9916	4.2908	9.2443
8.0	64.00	2.8284	8.9443	512.000	2.0000	4.3089	9.2832
8.1	65.61	2.8460	9.0000	531.441	2.0083	4.3267	9.3217
8.2	67.24	2.8636	9.0554	551.368	2.0165	4.3445	9.3599
8.3	68.89	2.8810	9.1104	571.787	2.0247	4.3621	9.3978
8.4	70.56	2.8983	9.1652	592.704	2.0328	4.3795	9.4354
8.5	72.25	2.9155	9.2195	614.125	2.0408	4.3968	9.4727
8.6	73.96	2.9326	9.2736	636.056	2.0488	4.4140	9.5097
8.7	75.69	2.9496	9.3274	658.503	2.0567	4.4310	9.5464
8.8	77.44	2.9665	9.3808	681.472	2.0646	4.4480	9.5828
8.9	79.21	2.9833	9.4340	704.969	2.0724	4.4647	9.6190
9.0	81.00	3.0000	9.4868	729.000	2.0801	4.4814	9.6549
9.1	82.81	3.0166	9.5394	753.571	2.0878	4.4979	9.6905
9.2	84.64	3.0332	9.5917	778.688	2.0954	4.5144	9.7259
9.3	86.49	3.0496	9.6437	804.357	2.1029	4.5307	9.7610
9.4	88.36	3.0659	9.6954	830.584	2.1105	4.5468	9.7959
9.5	90.25	3.0822	9.7468	857.375	2.1179	4.5629	9.8305
9.6	92.16	3.0984	9.7980	884.736	2.1253	4.5789	9.8648
9.7	94.09	3.1145	9.8489	912.673	2.1327	4.5947	9.8990
9.8	96.04	3.1305	9.8995	941.192	2.1400	4.6104	9.9329
9.9	98.01	3.1464	9.9499	970.299	2.1472	4.6261	9.9666
10.0	100.00	3.1623	10.0000	1000.000	2.1544	4.6416	10.0000

Notes: (I) To determine in which column to find a required root, use the pointing-off method, as in § 14. Thus

$\sqrt{.0076}$ $= \sqrt{\cdot 00 \cdot 76 \cdot}$;   starts with 08; hence .087178.

$\sqrt[3]{.076}$ $= \sqrt[3]{\cdot 076 \cdot 000 \cdot}$; starts with 4; hence .42358.

$\sqrt[3]{7600000} = \sqrt[3]{7 \cdot 600 \cdot 000 \cdot}$; starts with 1; hence 196.61.

(II) For any third figure f in N, add f tenths of the difference between tabulated values; *e.g.*, $\sqrt[3]{7.64} = 1.9661 + \tfrac{4}{10}\,(1.9747 - 1.9661) = 1.9695$.

NATURAL LOGARITHMS (Base e) $\qquad$ e^x

N	0	1	2	3	4	5	6	7	8	9
1.0	0.0 000	10J	198	296	392	488	583	677	770	862
1.1	953	*044	*133	*222	*310	*398	*484	*570	*655	*740
1.2	0.1 823	906	989	*070	*151	*231	*311	*390	*469	*546
1.3	0.2 624	700	776	852	927	*001	*075	*148	*221	*293
1.4	0.3 365	436	507	577	646	716	784	853	920	988
1.5	0.4 055	121	187	253	318	383	447	511	574	637
1.6	700	762	824	886	947	*008	*068	*128	*188	*247
1.7	0.5 306	365	423	481	539	596	653	710	766	822
1.8	878	933	988	*043	*098	*152	*206	*259	*313	*366
1.9	0.6 419	471	523	575	627	678	729	780	831	881
2.0	931	981	*031	*080	*129	*178	*227	*275	*324	*372
2.1	0.7 419	467	514	561	608	655	701	747	793	839
2.2	885	930	975	*020	*065	*109	*154	*198	*242	*286
2.3	0.8 329	372	416	459	502	544	587	629	671	713
2.4	755	796	838	879	920	961	*002	*042	*083	*123
2.5	0.9 163	203	243	282	322	361	400	439	478	517
2.6	555	594	632	670	708	746	783	821	858	895
2.7	933	969	*006	*043	*080	*116	*152	*188	*225	*260
2.8	1.0 296	332	367	403	438	473	508	543	578	613
2.9	647	682	716	750	784	818	852	886	919	953
3.0	986	*019	*053	*086	*119	*151	*184	*217	*249	*282
3.1	1.1 314	346	378	410	442	474	506	537	569	600
3.2	632	663	694	725	756	787	817	848	**878**	909
3.3	939	969	*000	*030	*060	*090	*119	*149	*179	*208
3.4	1.2 238	267	296	326	355	384	413	442	470	499
3.5	528	556	585	613	641	669	698	726	754	782
3.6	809	837	865	892	920	947	975	*002	*029	*056
3.7	1.3 083	110	137	164	191	218	244	271	297	324
3.8	350	376	403	429	455	481	507	533	558	584
3.9	**610**	635	**661**	686	712	737	762	788	813	838
4.0	863	888	913	938	962	987	*012	*036	*061	*085
4.1	1.4 110	134	159	183	207	231	255	279	303	327
4.2	351	375	398	422	446	469	493	516	540	563
4.3	586	609	633	656	679	702	725	748	770	793
4.4	816	839	861	884	907	929	951	974	996	*019
4.5	1.5 041	063	085	107	129	151	173	195	217	239
4.6	261	282	304	326	347	369	390	412	433	454
4.7	476	497	518	539	560	581	602	623	644	665
4.8	686	707	728	748	769	790	810	831	851	872
4.9	892	913	933	953	974	994	*014	*034	*054	*074
5.0	1.6 094	114	134	154	174	194	214	233	253	273

x	e^x
.05	1.051
.10	1.105
.15	1.162
.20	1.221
.25	1.284
.30	1.350
.35	1.419
.40	1.492
.45	1.568
.50	1.649
.6	1.822
.7	2.014
.8	2.226
.9	2.460
1.0	2.718
1.1	3.004
1.2	3.320
1.3	3.669
1.4	4.055
1.5	4.482
1.6	4.953
1.7	5.474
1.8	6.050
1.9	6.686
2.0	7.389
2.1	8.166
2.2	9.025
2.3	9.974
2.4	11.023
2.5	12.182
3.0	20.086
3.5	33.115
4.0	54.598
4.5	90.017
5.0	148.413
5.5	244.692
6.0	403.429
6.5	665.14
7.0	1096.6
7.5	1808.0
8.0	2981.0

Notes: When given a larger or smaller value of **N**, express it in Scientific Notation (§172).

Thus $1720 = 1.72 \times 10^3$. $\therefore \log 1720 = \log 1.72 + 3 \log 10$.

When given a logarithm outside the table, reverse this operation.

Note: Don't interpolate in this small table. Locate further values of x among *logs* in the main table, and read e^x from N-column.

MULTIPLES OF Log_e 10

$\log 10 = 2.3026$	$4 \log 10 = 9.2103$	$- \log 10 = .6974 - 3$
$2 \log 10 = 4.6052$	$5 \log 10 = 11.5129$	$- 2 \log 10 = .3948 - 5$
$3 \log 10 = 6.9078$	$6 \log 10 = 13.8155$	$- 3 \log 10 = .0922 - 7$

NATURAL LOGARITHMS (Base e)

N	0	1	2	3	4	5	6	7	8	9
5.0	1.6 094	114	134	154	174	194	214	233	253	273
5.1	292	312	332	351	371	390	409	429	448	467
5.2	487	506	525	544	563	582	601	620	639	658
5.3	677	696	715	734	752	771	790	808	827	845
5.4	864	882	901	919	938	956	974	993	*011	*029
5.5	1.7 047	066	084	102	120	138	156	174	192	210
5.6	228	246	263	281	299	317	334	352	370	387
5.7	405	422	440	457	475	492	509	527	544	561
5.8	579	596	613	630	647	664	681	699	716	733
5.9	750	766	783	800	817	834	851	867	884	901
6.0	918	934	951	967	984	*001	*017	*034	*050	*066
6.1	1.8 083	099	116	132	148	165	181	197	213	229
6.2	245	262	278	294	310	326	342	358	374	390
6.3	405	421	437	453	469	485	500	516	532	547
6.4	563	579	594	610	625	641	656	672	687	703
6.5	718	733	749	764	779	795	810	825	840	856
6.6	871	886	901	916	931	946	961	976	991	*006
6.7	1.9 021	036	051	066	081	095	110	125	140	155
6.8	169	184	199	213	228	242	257	272	286	301
6.9	315	330	344	359	373	387	402	416	430	445
7.0	459	473	488	502	516	530	544	559	573	587
7.1	601	615	629	643	657	671	685	699	713	727
7.2	741	755	769	782	796	810	824	838	851	865
7.3	879	892	906	920	933	947	961	974	988	*001
7.4	2.0 015	028	042	055	069	082	096	109	122	136
7.5	149	162	176	189	202	215	229	242	255	268
7.6	281	295	308	321	334	347	360	373	386	399
7.7	412	425	438	451	464	477	490	503	516	528
7.8	541	554	567	580	592	605	618	631	643	656
7.9	669	681	694	707	719	732	744	757	769	782
8.0	794	807	819	832	844	857	869	882	894	906
8.1	919	931	943	956	968	980	992	*005	*017	*029
8.2	2.1 041	054	066	078	090	102	114	126	138	150
8.3	163	175	187	199	211	223	235	247	258	270
8.4	282	294	306	318	330	342	353	365	377	389
8.5	401	412	424	436	448	459	471	483	494	506
8.6	518	529	541	552	564	576	587	599	610	622
8.7	633	645	656	668	679	691	702	713	725	736
8.8	748	759	770	782	793	804	815	827	838	849
8.9	861	872	883	894	905	917	928	939	950	961
9.0	972	983	994	*006	*017	*028	*039	*050	*061	*072
9.1	2.2 083	094	105	116	127	138	148	159	170	181
9.2	192	203	214	225	235	246	257	268	279	289
9.3	300	311	322	332	343	354	364	375	386	396
9.4	407	418	428	439	450	460	471	481	492	502
9.5	513	523	534	544	555	565	576	586	597	607
9.6	618	628	638	649	659	670	680	690	701	711
9.7	721	732	742	752	762	773	783	793	803	814
9.8	824	834	844	854	865	875	885	895	905	915
9.9	925	935	946	956	966	976	986	996	*006	*016
10.0	2.3 026	036	046	056	066	076	086	096	106	115

e^{-x}

x	e^{-x}
.05	.951
.10	.905
.15	.861
.20	.819
.25	.779
.30	.741
.35	.705
.40	.670
.45	.638
.50	.607
.6	.549
.7	.497
.8	.449
.9	.407
1.0	.368
1.1	.333
1.2	.301
1.3	.273
1.4	.247
1.5	.223
1.6	.202
1.7	.183
1.8	.165
1.9	.150
2.0	.135
2.1	.122
2.2	.111
2.3	.100
2.4	.091
2.5	.082
3.0	.050
3.5	.030
4.0	.018
4.5	.011
5.0	.0067
5.5	.0041
6.0	.0025
6.5	.0015
7.0	.0009
7.5	.0006
8.0	.0003

Note: Further values: $e^{-x} = \dfrac{1}{e^{x}}$. See **N** column for e^{x} values, x being in body of **Table.**

Trigonometric Functions (Radian Measure)

$\theta^{(r)}$	$\sin \theta$	$\cos \theta$	$\tan \theta$	$\theta^{(r)}$	$\sin \theta$	$\cos \theta$	$\tan \theta$
.00	.000	1.000	.000	1.0	.841	.540	1.557
.05	.050	.999	.050	1.5	.997	.071	14.101
.10	.100	.995	.100	2.0	.909	− .416	− 2.185
.15	.149	.989	.151	2.5	.598	− .801	− .747
.20	.199	.980	.203	3.0	.141	− .990	− .143
.25	.247	.969	.255	3.5	− .351	− .936	.375
.30	.296	.955	.309	4.0	− .757	− .654	1.158
.35	.343	.939	.365	4.5	− .978	− .211	4.637
.40	.389	.921	.423	5.0	− .959	.284	− 3.379
.45	.435	.900	.483	5.5	− .706	.709	− .996
.50	.479	.878	.546	6.0	− .279	.960	− .291
.60	.565	.825	.684	7.0	.657	.754	.871
.70	.644	.765	.842	8.0	.989	− .145	− 6.800
.80	.717	.697	1.030	9.0	.412	− .911	− .452
.90	.783	.622	1.260	10.	− .544	− .839	.648

Radians to Degrees $(1^{(r)} = 57° \; 17' \; 44''.806)$

	Radians			Tenths			Hundredths			Thousandths			Ten-Thousandths		Hundred-Thousandths
	°	′	″	°	′	″	°	′	″	°	′	″	′	″	″
1	57	17	45	5	43	46	0	34	23	0	3	26	0	21	2
2	114	35	30	11	27	33	1	8	45	0	6	53	0	41	4
3	171	53	14	17	11	19	1	43	08	0	10	19	1	02	6
4	229	10	59	22	55	06	2	17	31	0	13	45	1	23	8
5	286	28	44	28	38	52	2	51	53	0	17	11	1	43	10
6	343	46	29	34	22	39	3	26	16	0	20	39	2	04	12
7	401	4	14	40	6	25	4	0	38	0	24	04	2	24	14
8	458	21	58	45	50	12	4	35	01	0	27	30	2	45	16
9	515	39	43	51	33	58	5	9	24	0	30	56	3	06	19

Degrees to Radians $(1° = .017453293^{(r)})$

1°	.01745$^{(r)}$	10°	.17453	1′	.00029	10′	.00291$^{(r)}$	1″	.000005
2°	.03491	20°	.34907	2′	.00058	15′	.00436	2″	.000010
3°	.05236	30°	.52360	3′	.00087	20′	.00582	3″	.000015
4°	.06981	40°	.69813	4′	.00116	25′	.00727	4″	.000019
5°	.08727	50°	.87266	5′	.00145	30′	.00873	5″	.000024
6°	.10472	60°	1.04720	6′	.00175	35′	.01018	6″	.000029
7°	.12217	70°	1.22173	7′	.00204	40′	.01164	7″	.000034
8°	.13963	80°	1.39626	8′	.00233	45′	.01309	8″	.000039
9°	.15708	90°	1.57080	9′	.00262	50′	.01454	9″	.000044

TRIGONOMETRIC FUNCTIONS
and their common logarithms

An-gle	SINE Value	log	TANGENT Value	log	COTANGENT Value	log	COSINE Value	log	
0°	.0000	......	.0000	......	......	......	1.0000	0.0000	90°
1°	.0175	8.2419	.0175	8.2419	57.290	1.7581	.9998	9.9999	89°
2°	.0349	8.5428	.0349	8.5431	28.636	1.4569	.9994	9.9997	88°
3°	.0523	8.7188	.0524	8.7194	19.081	1.2806	.9986	9.9994	87°
4°	.0698	8.8436	.0699	8.8446	14.301	1.1554	.9976	9.9989	86°
5°	.0872	8.9403	.0875	8.9420	11.430	1.0580	.9962	9.9983	85°
6°	.1045	9.0192	.1051	9.0216	9.5144	0.9784	.9945	9.9976	84°
7°	.1219	9.0859	.1228	9.0891	8.1443	0.9109	.9925	9.9968	83°
8°	.1392	9.1436	.1405	9.1478	7.1154	0.8522	.9903	9.9958	82°
9°	.1564	9.1943	.1584	9.1997	6.3138	0.8003	.9877	9.9946	81°
10°	.1736	9.2397	.1763	9.2463	5.6713	0.7537	.9848	9.9934	80°
11°	.1908	9.2806	.1944	9.2887	5.1446	0.7113	.9816	9.9919	79°
12°	.2079	9.3179	.2126	9.3275	4.7046	0.6725	.9781	9.9904	78°
13°	.2250	9.3521	.2309	9.3634	4.3315	0.6366	.9744	9.9887	77°
14°	.2419	9.3837	.2493	9.3968	4.0108	0.6032	.9703	9.9869	76°
15°	.2588	9.4130	.2679	9.4281	3.7321	0.5719	.9659	9.9849	75°
16°	.2756	9.4403	.2867	9.4575	3.4874	0.5425	.9613	9.9828	74°
17°	.2924	9.4659	.3057	9.4853	3.2709	0.5147	.9563	9.9806	73°
18°	.3090	9.4900	.3249	9.5118	3.0777	0.4882	.9511	9.9782	72°
19°	.3256	9.5126	.3443	9.5370	2.9042	0.4630	.9455	9.9757	71°
20°	.3420	9.5341	.3640	9.5611	2.7475	0.4389	.9397	9.9730	70°
21°	.3584	9.5543	.3839	9.5842	2.6051	0.4158	.9336	9.9702	69°
22°	.3746	9.5736	.4040	9.6064	2.4751	0.3936	.9272	9.9672	68°
23°	.3907	9.5919	.4245	9.6279	2.3559	0.3721	.9205	9.9640	67°
24°	.4067	9.6093	.4452	9.6486	2.2460	0.3514	.9135	9.9607	66°
25°	.4226	9.6259	.4663	9.6687	2.1445	0.3313	.9063	9.9573	65°
26°	.4384	9.6418	.4877	9.6882	2.0503	0.3118	.8988	9.9537	64°
27°	.4540	9.6570	.5095	9.7072	1.9626	0.2928	.8910	9.9499	63°
28°	.4695	9.6716	.5317	9.7257	1.8807	0.2743	.8829	9.9459	62°
29°	.4848	9.6856	.5543	9.7438	1.8040	0.2562	.8746	9.9418	61°
30°	.5000	9.6990	.5774	9.7614	1.7321	0.2386	.8660	9.9375	60°
31°	.5150	9.7118	.6009	9.7788	1.6643	0.2212	.8572	9.9331	59°
32°	.5299	9.7242	.6249	9.7958	1.6003	0.2042	.8480	9.9284	58°
33°	.5446	9.7361	.6494	9.8125	1.5399	0.1875	.8387	9.9236	57°
34°	.5592	9.7476	.6745	9.8290	1.4826	0.1710	.8290	9.9186	56°
35°	.5736	9.7586	.7002	9.8452	1.4281	0.1548	.8192	9.9134	55°
36°	.5878	9.7692	.7265	9.8613	1.3764	0.1387	.8090	9.9080	54°
37°	.6018	9.7795	.7536	9.8771	1.3270	0.1229	.7986	9.9023	53°
38°	.6157	9.7893	.7813	9.8928	1.2799	0.1072	.7880	9.8965	52°
39°	.6293	9.7989	.8098	9.9084	1.2349	0.0916	.7771	9.8905	51°
40°	.6428	9.8081	.8391	9.9238	1.1918	0.0762	.7660	9.8843	50°
41°	.6561	9.8169	.8693	9.9392	1.1504	0.0608	.7547	9.8778	49°
42°	.6691	9.8255	.9004	9.9544	1.1106	0.0456	.7431	9.8711	48°
43°	.6820	9.8338	.9325	9.9697	1.0724	0.0303	.7314	9.8641	47°
44°	.6947	9.8418	.9657	9.9848	1.0355	0.0152	.7193	9.8569	46°
45°	.7071	9.8495	1.0000	0.0000	1.0000	0.0000	.7071	9.8495	45°
	Value	log	Value	log	Value	log	Value	log	An-gle
	Cosine		Cotangent		Tangent		Sine		

Note: log sec $x = -$ log cos x,   log csc $x = -$ log sin x.

COMMON LOGARITHMS (Base 10)

N	0	1	2	3	4	5	6	7	8	9	u. d.
10	0000	0043	0086	0128	0170	0212	0253	0294	0334	0374	4.2
11	0414	0453	0492	0531	0569	0607	0645	0682	0719	0755	3.8
12	0792	0828	0864	0899	0934	0969	1004	1038	1072	1106	3.5
13	1139	1173	1206	1239	1271	1303	1335	1367	1399	1430	3.2
14	1461	1492	1523	1553	1584	1614	1644	1673	1703	1732	3.0
15	1761	1790	1818	1847	1875	1903	1931	1959	1987	2014	2.8
16	2041	2068	2095	2122	2148	2175	2201	2227	2253	2279	2.6
17	2304	2330	2355	2380	2405	2430	2455	2480	2504	2529	2.5
18	2553	2577	2601	2625	2648	2672	2695	2718	2742	2765	2.4
19	2788	2810	2833	2856	2878	2900	2923	2945	2967	2989	2.2
20	3010	3032	3054	3075	3096	3118	3139	3160	3181	3201	2.1
21	3222	3243	3263	3284	3304	3324	3345	3365	3385	3404	2.0
22	3424	3444	3464	3483	3502	3522	3541	3560	3579	3598	1.9
23	3617	3636	3655	3674	3692	3711	3729	3747	3766	3784	1.8
24	3802	3820	3838	3856	3874	3892	3909	3927	3945	3962	1.8
25	3979	3997	4014	4031	4048	4065	4082	4099	4116	4133	1.7
26	4150	4166	4183	4200	4216	4232	4249	4265	4281	4298	1.6
27	4314	4330	4346	4362	4378	4393	4409	4425	4440	4456	1.6
28	4472	4487	4502	4518	4533	4548	4564	4579	4594	4609	1.5
29	4624	4639	4654	4669	4683	4698	4713	4728	4742	4757	1.5
30	4771	4786	4800	4814	4829	4843	4857	4871	4886	4900	1.4
31	4914	4928	4942	4955	4969	4983	4997	5011	5024	5038	1.4
32	5051	5065	5079	5092	5105	5119	5132	5145	5159	5172	1.3
33	5185	5198	5211	5224	5237	5250	5263	5276	5289	5302	1.3
34	5315	5328	5340	5353	5366	5378	5391	5403	5416	5428	1.3
35	5441	5453	5465	5478	5490	5502	5514	5527	5539	5551	1.2
36	5563	5575	5587	5599	5611	5623	5635	5647	5658	5670	1.2
37	5682	5694	5705	5717	5729	5740	5752	5763	5775	5786	1.2
38	5798	5809	5821	5832	5843	5855	5866	5877	5888	5899	1.1
39	5911	5922	5933	5944	5955	5966	5977	5988	5999	6010	1.1
40	6021	6031	6042	6053	6064	6075	6085	6096	6107	6117	1.1
41	6128	6138	6149	6160	6170	6180	6191	6201	6212	6222	1.0
42	6232	6243	6253	6263	6274	6284	6294	6304	6314	6325	1.0
43	6335	6345	6355	6365	6375	6385	6395	6405	6415	6425	1.0
44	6435	6444	6454	6464	6474	6484	6493	6503	6513	6522	1.0
45	6532	6542	6551	6561	6571	6580	6590	6599	6609	6618	1.0
46	6628	6637	6646	6656	6665	6675	6684	6693	6702	6712	.9
47	6721	6730	6739	6749	6758	6767	6776	6785	6794	6803	.9
48	6812	6821	6830	6839	6848	6857	6866	6875	6884	6893	.9
49	6902	6911	6920	6928	6937	6946	6955	6964	6972	6981	.9
50	6990	6998	7007	7016	7024	7033	7042	7050	7059	7067	.9
51	7076	7084	7093	7101	7110	7118	7126	7135	7143	7152	.8
52	7160	7168	7177	7185	7193	7202	7210	7218	7226	7235	.8
53	7243	7251	7259	7267	7275	7284	7292	7300	7308	7316	.8
54	7324	7332	7340	7348	7356	7364	7372	7380	7388	7396	.8

Note: The column u. d. (=unit difference) may be used in interpolating. Multiply the *u. d.* value by figure in 4th place of given number and add to logarithm read from table for first 3 figures of number.

COMMON LOGARITHMS

N	0	1	2	3	4	5	6	7	8	9	u. d.
55	7404	7412	7419	7427	7435	7443	7451	7459	7466	7474	.8
56	7482	7490	7497	7505	7513	7520	7528	7536	7543	7551	.8
57	7559	7566	7574	7582	7589	7597	7604	7612	7619	7627	.8
58	7634	7642	7649	7657	7664	7672	7679	7686	7694	7701	.7
59	7709	7716	7723	7731	7738	7745	7752	7760	7767	7774	.7
60	7782	7789	7796	7803	7810	7818	7825	7832	7839	7846	.7
61	7853	7860	7868	7875	7882	7889	7896	7903	7910	7917	.7
62	7924	7931	7938	7945	7952	7959	7966	7973	7980	7987	.7
63	7993	8000	8007	8014	8021	8028	8035	8041	8048	8055	.7
64	8062	8069	8075	8082	8089	8096	8102	8109	8116	8122	.7
65	8129	8136	8142	8149	8156	8162	8169	8176	8182	8189	.7
66	8195	8202	8209	8215	8222	8228	8235	8241	8248	8254	.7
67	8261	8267	8274	8280	8287	8293	8299	8306	8312	8319	.6
68	8325	8331	8338	8344	8351	8357	8363	8370	8376	8382	.6
69	8388	8395	8401	8407	8414	8420	8426	8432	8439	8445	.6
70	8451	8457	8463	8470	8476	8482	8488	8494	8500	8506	.6
71	8513	8519	8525	8531	8537	8543	8549	8555	8561	8567	.6
72	8573	8579	8585	8591	8597	8603	8609	8615	8621	8627	.6
73	8633	8639	8645	8651	8657	8663	8669	8675	8681	8686	.6
74	8692	8698	8704	8710	8716	8722	8727	8733	8739	8745	.6
75	8751	8756	8762	8768	8774	8779	8785	8791	8797	8802	.6
76	8808	8814	8820	8825	8831	8837	8842	8848	8854	8859	.6
77	8865	8871	8876	8882	8887	8893	8899	8904	8910	8915	.6
78	8921	8927	8932	8938	8943	8949	8954	8960	8965	8971	.6
79	8976	8982	8987	8993	8998	9004	9009	9015	9020	9025	.5
80	9031	9036	9042	9047	9053	9058	9063	9069	9074	9079	.5
81	9085	9090	9096	9101	9106	9112	9117	9122	9128	9133	.5
82	9138	9143	9149	9154	9159	9165	9170	9175	9180	9186	.5
83	9191	9196	9201	9206	9212	9217	9222	9227	9232	9238	.5
84	9243	9248	9253	9258	9263	9269	9274	9279	9284	9289	.5
85	9294	9299	9304	9309	9315	9320	9325	9330	9335	9340	.5
86	9345	9350	9355	9360	9365	9370	9375	9380	9385	9390	.5
87	9395	9400	9405	9410	9415	9420	9425	9430	9435	9440	.5
88	9445	9450	9455	9460	9465	9469	9474	9479	9484	9489	.5
89	9494	9499	9504	9509	9513	9518	9523	9528	9533	9538	.5
90	9542	9547	9552	9557	9562	9566	9571	9576	9581	9586	.5
91	9590	9595	9600	9605	9609	9614	9619	9624	9628	9633	.5
92	9638	9643	9647	9652	9657	9661	9666	9671	9675	9680	.5
93	9685	9689	9694	9699	9703	9708	9713	9717	9722	9727	.5
94	9731	9736	9741	9745	9750	9754	9759	9763	9768	9773	.5
95	9777	9782	9786	9791	9795	9800	9805	9809	9814	9818	.5
96	9823	9827	9832	9836	9841	9845	9850	9854	9859	9863	.5
97	9868	9872	9877	9881	9886	9890	9894	9899	9903	9908	.4
98	9912	9917	9921	9926	9930	9934	9939	9943	9948	9952	.4
99	9956	9961	9965	9969	9974	9978	9983	9987	9991	9996	.4

ABBREVIATIONS AND SYMBOLS

A., amount, area, attraction.

A. P., arithmetical progression.

C. I. L., compound interest law.

E., or **P. E.**, probable error.

G. P., geometrical progression.

M., mass, moment, momentum.

P., pressure, principal, probability, present value (or *P. V.*).

R. P. M., revolutions per minute.

S. H. M., simple harmonic motion.

V., value, volume, speed.

$\dfrac{d}{dx}$, derivative (as to x).

$\dfrac{\partial}{\partial x}$, partial derivative.

$\log_b$, logarithm of $\cdots$, base b.

ln, logarithm to the base e.

sin, cos, sine, cosine.

tan, ctn, tangent, cotangent.

sec, csc, secant, cosecant.

$\mathbf{C}_{n,\,r}$, $\mathbf{P}_{n,\,r}$. (See §§ 354, 359.)

cis, cosine + i sine. (See § 387.)

$\triangle$, triangle.

Δ (delta), increment.

$| \,|$, Δ, determinant.

$\Delta_v{}^{(n}y$, nth difference in y.

θ (theta), polar angle.

ω (omega), angular speed.

$n!$, factorial n, $= 1 \cdot 2 \cdot 3 \cdots n$.

$\mathbf{1}^{(r)}$, radian.

i, imaginary unit $(\sqrt{-1})$.

σ, standard deviation

$\bar{y}$, mean value of y.

$\displaystyle\int$, integral.

$\rightarrow$, approaches the limit $\cdots$.

L, limit of $\cdots$, as $\Delta x \rightarrow 0$.
$\scriptstyle \Delta x \rightarrow 0.$

∞, infinity.

$\rightarrow \infty$, increases without limit.

$<$, is less than (algebraically).

$>$, is greater than (algebraically).

$\neq$, is not equal to.

$|\cdots|$, absolute value of $\cdots$.

INDEX